# THE
# NEW ENGLAND-ACADIAN
# SHORELINE

# THE
# NEW ENGLAND-ACADIAN
# SHORELINE

BY

## DOUGLAS JOHNSON

*Professor of Physiography in Columbia University*

AWARDED THE
A. CRESSY MORRISON PRIZE OF THE NEW YORK ACADEMY OF SCIENCES
FOR 1924

*(Facsimile of the Edition of 1925)*

HAFNER PUBLISHING CO.
NEW YORK and LONDON
1967

*Printed and published by*
HAFNER PUBLISHING COMPANY, INC.
31 East 10th Street
New York, N.Y. 10003

Library of Congress Catalog Card Number: 66-29970

*Printed in U.S.A. by*
NOBLE OFFSET PRINTERS, INC.
NEW YORK 3, N. Y.

# CONTENTS

## PART I

### INITIAL FORM OF THE NEW ENGLAND-ACADIAN SHORELINE

## PART II

### SEQUENTIAL FORMS OF THE NEW ENGLAND-ACADIAN SHORELINE

# INTRODUCTION

A few years ago the writer set forth, in a volume entitled "Shore Processes and Shoreline Development," the fundamental principles of shoreline evolution, and promised that in a later work he would apply those principles to the study of certain features of the Atlantic Coast of North America. The present volume represents the partial fulfillment of that promise. It is based on field investigations and other researches prosecuted at intervals during a period of more than fifteen years, and is believed to be the first work in which the genetic method of treating landforms is systematically employed in an attempt to explain somewhat fully the origin and evolution of an extended strip of complicated shoreline.

**The Problem of Changes of Level.** — The reader of the earlier volume will have discovered that throughout its pages there appeared from time to time the thread of a discussion of possible changes of level, one of the most fascinating problems connected with any study of the meeting place of land and sea. He will have no difficulty in picking up that thread in the pages of the present treatise, and in finding that it leads him toward a third volume in which the discussion of changes of level will be concluded. For the author has had in view, among other objects, the following: (1st) to present in the volume on "Shore Processes and Shoreline Development" those principles which should enable one to differentiate stable, recently rising, and recently subsiding coasts; (2nd) to set before the reader, in the present volume on "The New England-Acadian Shoreline," evidence showing that the Atlantic Coast of North America has suffered a geologically recent subsidence which culminated only a few thousand years ago; and (3rd) to consider in a future volume on "The Coastal Plain Shoreline" evidence which seems to prove essential coastal stability during the last few thousand years. It should be understood that the evidences discovered along the New England-Acadian shoreline and along the Coastal Plain shoreline conduct one to the same conclusions regarding the reality of a *geologically recent subsidence,* and the absence of appreciable *subsidence in historic time;* but the former is more easily demonstrable along the New England-Acadian shoreline, while the question of historic subsidence can better be studied in connection with the wholly different Coastal Plain shoreline.

**Scope of the Present Work.** — The reader will appreciate, however, that while the thread of the subsidence problem is readily traceable throughout the three volumes in question, giving to them, perhaps, a certain measure of unity, the main fabric of the text is usually woven of other stuff. In the present work the primary object has been to treat in systematic fashion the origin and evolution of that great stretch of shoreline extending from the mouth of the Hudson River to the Gulf of St. Lawrence. This New England-Acadian shoreline is first classified as a " shoreline of submergence," the salient characteristics of which are due to a sinking of the land or to a rise of sealevel. Three distinct subdivisions of the shoreline are recognized: (1) the shoreline bordering the upland; (2) the shoreline bordering the weak-rock lowlands; and (3) the shoreline bordering unconsolidated débris (mainly glacial deposits). The initial forms characterizing each of these three subdivisions or shoreline types are first described, and the effects of minor oscillations of level upon such initial forms are considered. Incidentally the rectilinear segments of shoreline bordering certain portions of the resistant upland receive special treatment becauses of the important problems they present to the student of shore forms.

There follows an extended analysis of the evolution of the three shoreline types, involving in each case a study of: (*a*) the forms produced by wave erosion upon the coast; (*b*) the forms produced by the constructive action of the waves; and (*c*) the hidden submarine forms adjacent to the coast. Data for the latter study have been secured through an elaborate series of profiles obtained by projecting upon vertical planes all of the soundings charted for selected belts of the seabottom, according to a method fully described in Chapter VIII. Finally, the rôle of the tides in shoreline development is considered; the tidal marshes of the region under investigation are classified and described, and their origin explained; and the subordinate rôle of shore ice in the development of this shoreline is discussed. The treatment is not wholly limited to the New England-Acadian area, for where comparison with other regions will serve to clarify problems presented by the particular shoreline under investigation, excursions into such regions are made. Thus profile studies in the St. Lawrence embayment, in the Great Lakes, and off the Atlantic Coastal Plain are made to throw light on the evolution of the New England-Acadian shoreline.

**Special Problems.** — Any systematic treatment of a complicated portion of the earth's surface is apt to encounter a certain number of special problems possessing more than ordinary interest for students of land forms. Our study of the New England-Acadian shoreline is no exception to this rule; and it may aid the reader in his perusal of the text if we here record some of the problems to which particular attention will be given. These problems can most conveniently be stated in the form of conclusions, which it is believed the evidence and arguments presented in the text will adequately support:

The eastern coast of North America has suffered differential warping or tilting, involving a submergence which is progressively greater toward the northeast and which in the Maine region amounts to more than 1200 feet at the minimum. The downward tilting of the continent toward the northeast is responsible for the striking contrast in the two major shoreline provinces of our eastern coast, the one extending northeastward, the other southwestward, from the vicinity of New York.

Minor oscillations of level, involving both emergence and submergence, were superimposed upon the major differential submergence described above. The latest movement was one of gradual progressive submergence, which culminated only a few thousand (perhaps between 3000 and 5000) years ago. The theory that the last oscillation of the coast was a slight emergence is apparently disproved by the character of the tidal marsh deposits. Incidental evidence is adduced in support of the belief that during the last few thousand years there has been no appreciable change in the relative positions of land and sea; but, as already noted in another connection, the full treatment of this question is reserved for a later volume.

The fishing " Banks," or submarine plateaus extending from Cape Cod to Newfoundland, the origin of which has long been disputed, are found to represent a submerged upland or cuesta of the Atlantic coastal plain, with typical steep scarp facing the crystalline oldland, and gentle backslope descending to the edge of the continental shelf.

The Gulf of Maine is the drowned " inner lowland " between

the Banks cuesta and the crystalline oldland of New England. The topography and geology of the floor of the Gulf are roughly mapped on the basis of an analysis of the submarine forms.

A submarine escarpment, sometimes divided into two or more branches and bordering one of the major fault fractures of North America, is discovered under the waters of the Gulf of Maine and traced to its connection with topographic features bordering the northwestern side of the Bay of Fundy. The escarpment is recognized from the head of the latter bay to a point off the Massachusetts coast, a distance of some 350 miles.

The remarkable migration of the Pine Barrens and Coastal Plain flora of New Jersey northeastward to Nova Scotia and Newfoundland, described by Hollick and Fernald, finds an explanation in a physiographic history of the New England-Acadian coast which seems better to account for the phenomena in question than do other theories previously advanced.

The broad and shallow submerged platforms bordering the Gaspé Peninsula and the shores of the St. Lawrence embayment, heretofore interpreted as due to extensive wave erosion, appear to be normal subaërial features, formed above sealevel, then submerged and very slightly modified by marine agencies.

Collateral studies of the Great Lakes shores indicate that instead of the single subaqueous terrace reported to border these shores 60 feet below lake level, and widely accepted as proof that wave action on the Lakes ceases to be effective at a depth of 60 feet, there are terraces at various depths; that the most important ones are distinctly warped, varying from less than 40 to more than 100 feet below the lake surface; that these presumably are of subaërial origin rather than products of wave action; and that none of the forms in question has any value as a criterion of the depth of wave base on the Lakes.

The edge of the continental shelf bordering the North American continent on the east is found to be wholly unrelated to the traditional depth of about 100 fathoms popularly supposed to delimit the margins of such shelves. It is found at progressively greater depths from southwest to northeast, and apparently was not in any degree developed with reference to the present sealevel, but rather has been warped or tilted out of its initial position.

The so-called " fjords " of the Maine and Nova Scotian coasts appear to be, for the most part, drowned normal river valleys unrelated to true fjords. An occasional embayment of the coast

of Mount Desert Island, and the drowned gorge of the Hudson in
the Highlands of New York, alone seem to be in some degree
worthy of the name of fjord.

Rectilinear shorelines, most frequently attributed both in this
country and abroad to fracturing or faulting of the earth's crust,
are due to a variety of causes among which faulting is one of the
rarest. Nearly all of the rectilinear shorelines of New England
and Acadia heretofore explained by fracturing seem to be due
to other causes; but fault-controlled shorelines are recognized,
including some not previously described.

**Matter Addressed to a Wider Range of Readers.** — The evidence submitted in support of the conclusions stated above
will for the most part interest primarily the specialist in geology and geography. For teachers of these subjects the author
has attempted to make available numerous examples of the application of physiographic principles to the interpretation of various
shore features, and to render easily accessible a carefully selected
portion of that great wealth of illustrative material provided by
Coast Survey and Hydrographic charts, not otherwise to be
secured by those denied access to an extensive collection of these
valuable documents. Students of shoreline phenomena may find
the bibliographies at the ends of the chapters of some service in
their labors.

But it has been the author's ambition to make this volume of
service to others than fellow teachers and students in the two related earth sciences. Thus it is hoped that the botanist may find
in the discussion of the submarine physiography of the Gulf of
Maine and of the Banks, and in its possible application to problems of late Tertiary or early Pleistocene plant migrations, as well
as in the chapters on the structure and evolution of the salt
marshes bordering the New England and Acadian shores, something worthy of his consideration.

To the engineer and others interested in coast protection and
marsh reclamation there are offered illustrations of variable shore
forms found along different types of coasts, with some account of
the rapid changes which take place in spits and bars so commonly
associated with harbors; figures for the rates of coastal erosion
under dissimilar physical conditions; a discussion of the rôle of
the tides along the North Atlantic Coast; and descriptions of
the wild and reclaimed marshes built up in greater or lesser degree
from tidal deposits.

The lawyer knows that not a few legal complications, involving the value of coastal lands and even the title to such lands, may be solved through the study of past changes in the shore, its present peculiarities, and its probable future development. He will find in the following pages brief accounts of actual cases in which such studies have proven of decisive weight in legal controversies, together with suggestions regarding errors to be avoided when investigating shore problems based on cliff erosion, beach and inlet migration, the location of high water mark or marsh boundaries, and other unstable shore features.

The theory of a gradually sinking continent, and the phenomena of old shorelines now raised high above the sea, appeal strongly to every one interested in the curious behavior of our restless earth. The scenic features of the coast, — its ragged scarps, its ever-changing beaches and bars, its silent marshes with their mysterious past, — all excite the imagination, and tempt the wanderer by the shore to seek an explanation for these manifestations of Nature's handiwork. To such lovers of Nature the author would recommend a judicious " skipping " of those passages in the text, sometimes long and rather technical, in which it is sought to demonstrate, by analysis of evidence and arguments, the truth or falsity of certain supposed events in the past history of the coast. Such a process of selection will not be found difficult, for the " Advance Summary " at the beginning of each chapter, the " Résumé " at the end, and the section headings throughout the text, will enable the reader to follow easily the general argument of any portion of the work, without accompanying the author in all the details of his discussions. If those who are not geographers or geologists, botanists, engineers, or lawyers, but who love the sea and the forms it fashions along the margins of the land, find in these pages some answers to questions they have frequently asked about our coastal scenery, the author will feel doubly repaid for his labors.

**Acknowledgments.** — The studies upon which the present work is based were begun in connection with the author's service as consulting geologist in a legal controversy involving title to valuable lands fronting on Boston Harbor. Their prosecution was enormously facilitated in 1911 by a grant of two thousand dollars from the Shaler Memorial Fund of Harvard University, which made possible the study of typical portions of the American coast from Prince Edward Island to the Florida Keys, and visits to critical points on the coasts of England, Holland, Germany, and Sweden for the purpose of checking conclusions reached on the western shores of the Atlantic. Later these observations were supplemented by studies in France, Cape Breton, the Gaspé Peninsula, and elsewhere; and while the foreign investigations concerned mainly the problem of modern coastal subsidence, to be treated fully in a later volume, the observations of shore forms made in all these localities offered important support for many of the conclusions stated in the following pages.

The author's indebtedness to the authorities of Harvard University is not limited to the financial encouragement of his researches which they provided from the Shaler Memorial Fund; he must here acknowledge with sincere gratitude the generosity of spirit with which they have awaited the publication of results delayed by the expansion of the problem far beyond the limits originally conceived, by the necessity of establishing in an earlier volume the fundamental principles upon which the present discussion had to rest, as well as by enterprises incident to the War and the Peace Conference unforeseen by all concerned. If the patience of his Harvard colleagues has been tried by this delay, they have given him no sign of that fact; and it is a pleasure to acknowledge not only this friendly attitude on their part, but other courtesies which have placed the author profoundly in their debt.

The reader will understand from what has just been written how eminently appropriate it is that the present volume should be included in the Shaler Memorial Series of Harvard University. But there exists an even stronger reason for connecting the name of Nathaniel Southgate Shaler with any treatise which aspires to discuss the origin and evolution of the Atlantic shoreline. Every student of this coast will quickly discover that in his investigations no name so often confronts him as does that of the distinguished geologist of Cambridge, who for many years devoted no small share of his energies to the elucidation of our coastal phenomena. His contributions to different aspects of this subject provide a wealth of valuable information; and if the student finds that many theories entertained in earlier days of our science must be revised in the light of fuller knowledge now at our command, he will at the same time be constrained to acknowledge the heavy debt we owe to the fertile and suggestive imagination of one whose name is forever associated with man's attempt to decipher the physical history of the Atlantic seaboard.

The author finds himself much embarrassed when he confronts the well-nigh impossible task of expressing his appreciation of the aid rendered by individuals and organizations during the progress of studies which have occupied him intermittently for nearly a score of years. At best he can record his debt to but a few of the many who have so generously assisted him in that portion of his investigations covered by the present volume. First let him name the three assistants who shared his labors from the rocky shores of Cape Breton to the coral reefs of Florida, — Dr. Donald C. Barton, Dr. John K. Wright, and Dr. Guilford B. Reed, to whose capable services in the field the writer owes much, and to whom further acknowledgments are made in the text. Dr. Reed was under the direction of the United States Bureau of Mines, and special thanks are due that Bureau for its coöperation on a basis which enabled our party to profit not only by the marsh studies prosecuted by Dr. Reed, but also by the presence in the field of the Bureau's eminent authority on salt marsh deposits, Dr. Charles A. Davis. It is a source of keen disappointment to the author that Dr. Davis did not live to see the conclusion of this work; and he wishes to express in these lines his sense of deep obligation both for the material aid contributed by Dr. Davis in the field and later in the study of marsh samples, and for the profit derived from his frequent discussions of problems in which he and the writer mutually were interested.

Special acknowledgments are also due Mr. Myron L. Fuller, who provided facilities for studying in detail many parts of the New England coast, and whose company on these excursions was not only a source of practical aid and personal pleasure, but equally a source of profit through critical discussion of the problems under investigation. Mr. George B. Dorr, Superintendent of Lafayette National Park, extended exceptional opportunities for seeing parts of the Maine coast by land and by sea, and contributed many excellent photographs (acknowledged in the text) made under his direction by that most skillful portrayer of America's scenic features, Mr. Herbert W. Gleason. Mr. Dorr's staff at the Lafayette National Park headquarters, by means of countless courtesies, facilitated the work in hand and made the visit to Mount Desert and adjacent regions doubly delightful. Among the many others who offered special facilities for studying selected portions of the New England and Acadian coasts there should be named Mr. H. J. McCann and Mr. F. W. Gray of the Dominion

Coal Company at Sydney, Cape Breton, who accompanied the author to points of interest on the Cape Breton coast, and placed at his disposal the results of careful studies of shoreline changes conducted by them; Mr. F. O. Condon of Moncton, New Brunswick, who rendered similar services on a visit to the shores of Northumberland Strait; and Mr. George F. Matthew of St. John, New Brunswick, whose knowledge of geological conditions about the Bay of Fundy was especially serviceable during an early visit to that region. Dr. John M. Clarke, whose intimate acquaintance with the geology and scenery of the Gaspé coast is a source of profit and pleasure to all who traverse that picturesque region, gave the author freely of his counsel, prepared for him in advance a friendly reception on the occasion of his visit there, and contributed helpful criticisms of that part of the manuscript dealing with the shore forms of Gaspé.

Professor R. A. Daly of Harvard University, Dr. Arthur Hollick of the New York Botanical Garden, Professor R. A. Harper of Columbia University, Professor Florence Bascom of Bryn Mawr College, and Professor W. H. Hobbs of the University of Michigan have read portions of the manuscript and rendered other courtesies which it is a pleasure to acknowledge. The volume has benefited largely from their criticisms and suggestions. Professor W. O. Crosby of the Massachusetts Institute of Technology aided materially in furnishing important data concerning the Boston Harbor region. Mr. Norman Taylor of the Brooklyn Botanic Garden generously identified the plant remains in certain samples of salt marsh peat, and criticised portions of the manuscript.

The investigations of coastal physiography recorded in the following pages have involved extensive map studies, and it is a pleasant duty to acknowledge the invariable courtesy with which every facility for this work has been extended by officers of the United States Coast and Geodetic Survey and of the United States Hydrographic Office. Commander R. S. Patton, Chief of the Division of Charts of the Coast Survey, deserves special thanks for the generous manner in which he contributed his time and his expert knowledge in securing material for profile studies of the seafloor and in other phases of the work. The American Geographical Society made long-time loans of numerous maps and charts invaluable for the study of parts of the Canadian shores, and in other ways contributed to the success of the investigation. To the Geological Survey of Canada acknowledgment is due for an opportunity to visit a portion of the Micmac Terrace in company with Professor J. W. Goldthwait; for permission to use a number of photographs made under the Survey's direction; for the loan of the manuscript mentioned in the following paragraph; and for data supplied on a number of points in response to the author's request. Similarly the Director of the United States Geological Survey, and several members of his staff, including Mr. N. H. Darton and Dr. Laurence LaForge, have furnished important data, photographs, or valuable criticisms. The discussions of the shoreline of Prince Edward Island adjacent to Cascumpeque Harbor, and of the development of Nantasket Beach near Boston, appeared some years ago in slightly different form in the Geographical Journal (London) and the Journal of Geology (Chicago) respectively.

The author's obligations to Professor J. W. Goldthwait and to Professor J. E. Hyde are especially heavy. Their intimate knowledge of the geological history of important sections of Acadia and their observations of shoreline phenomena along these coasts have been most generously placed at his disposal. In the text will be found frequent references to these two authorities; but the reader should know that the volume has profited from their knowledge more extensively than it is possible to indicate by specific citations. The indebtedness to Professor Goldthwait is due to many discussions of shoreline problems in personal conversation and by letter, to his companionship in the field on more than one occasion, to his courtesy in making available the unpublished manuscript of his volume on the Physiography of Nova Scotia and certain of his photographs, and to valuable criticisms offered by him on parts of the present work. Professor Hyde not only prepared an extended statement of the geology and physiography of portions of the Acadian shoreline illustrated by sketches and photographs, a communication frequently cited in later pages, but in further communications discussed some of the more difficult problems of this coast, offered pertinent criticisms on the manuscript, and contributed some of the photographs which illustrate the present text. It is an especial pleasure to record here the debt of gratitude owed these two colleagues for their generous aid.

Greatest of all is the author's indebtedness to his associates in Columbia University. Most of this volume has been written at Columbia, under conditions made peculiarly favorable by the cordial support of Departmental colleagues and University authorities. Their interest in his labors has not only assured the writer time for many of the lines of research herein recorded, but in addition the very substantial aid of a research assistant whose energies have been devoted to advancing the investigations upon which are based many of the conclusions set forth in the present volume, and to seeing the manuscript through the press. The author gladly acknowledges his great obligation to Miss Harriet G. Bray, Research Assistant in Physiography at Columbia University, who has performed these heavy labors with fidelity and marked ability. A large majority of the profiles were plotted by Miss Bray, and most of the block diagrams and other illustrations were drawn by her on the basis of rough sketches or other data furnished for the purpose. The services of the University's library staff have been invaluable in securing from many sources maps and reports essential to some of the studies here recorded; and to Miss Amy L. Hepburn, in particular, thanks are due for the efficient aid rendered by her in connection with this part of the work. Nor can the author omit to mention the loyal coöperation of many of his students in different phases of his shoreline investigations. How much he owes to them the reader may judge from citations in the text of such names as Wright, Reed, Roorbach, Barton, Bond, Stolfus, Moon, Nichols, and others, who in the course of work under the writer's direction have contributed materially to our knowledge of shore forms. He would also express his appreciation of the sympathetic support accorded his investigations by Professor Frederick J. E. Woodbridge, Dean of the Faculty of Pure Science at Columbia University, whose encouragement of scientific research and whose friendly counsel have been, for many besides the author, sources of real inspiration.

Finally, it is a pleasure to acknowledge the assistance rendered by the publishers, John Wiley and Sons, who have manifested such a friendly interest in the investigations as has transformed what might have been a formal business relationship into what has become for the writer a most delightful association.

It remains only to apologize for the frequency with which the writer's former work on " Shore Processes and Shoreline Development " has been cited in the text and in the bibliographies at the ends of chapters. This has been done to spare the reader full discussion in the present book of problems sufficiently set forth in the earlier volume; and it is hoped the reader will make due allowance for the fact that in a series of three more or less related volumes, it was necessary to choose between two evils: that of frequently citing the earlier work, and that of burdening the later texts with unnecessary repetitions.

DOUGLAS JOHNSON.

COLUMBIA UNIVERSITY, *December* 1, 1924.

# PART I

**INITIAL FORM OF THE NEW ENGLAND-
ACADIAN SHORELINE**

# NEW ENGLAND-ACADIAN SHORELINE

## CHAPTER I

### GENESIS OF THE SHORELINE:
### INITIAL FORM BORDERING RESISTANT UPLANDS

**Advance Summary.** — In the present chapter we shall briefly trace those events in the physiographic history of the New England-Acadian province which are primarily responsible for the initial character of the shoreline now bordering the province on the southeast. The rôles played by a geologically recent change in the relative levels of land and sea, and by the geological structure of the landmass involved, will appear in the course of the discussion. For the most part, our attention will largely be directed to a consideration of the shorelines bordering upland areas of comparatively resistant rock, since these uplands constitute by far the most important element in the physiography of the region under investigation. In a later chapter the shorelines bordering weak-rock lowlands, here claiming only incidental attention, will receive a fuller treatment.

**Unity of the Shoreline.** — From the Gaspé peninsula on the north to the shores of Connecticut and Manhattan on the south, the rocky upland of Acadia and New England slopes southeastward into the waters of the Atlantic. Intricate in pattern and wonderfully varied in details of form, this great sweep of shoreline is nevertheless a single and simple geographic unit. To treat it in connection with the shoreline bordering the low, sandy plains of Long Island, New Jersey, and the country to the south would be to confuse two strikingly different physiographic types. To subdivide it into fractions would be to lose sight of its most significant characteristics. A unit in origin and in history of development, the New England-Acadian shoreline must be treated as a whole.

3

**Method of Treatment.** — Geologic and geographic literature contains a large number of shoreline studies in which the forms of the shore are in considerable measure described empirically, with only subordinate consideration of the origin of the shoreline, and little if any attention to its systematic evolution. Excellent examples of this method of treating the Atlantic Coast will be found in Meinhold's " Die Küste der Mittleren Atlantischen Staaten Nordamerikas "[1] and Weidemüller's " Die Schwemmlandküsten der Vereinigten Staaten von Nordamerika."[2] The present work is based on the premise that it is impossible properly to understand a shoreline, unless one first understands the form of the landmass which it borders. As was first pointed out by Davis, and later developed more fully by Gulliver, the initial character of any shoreline depends upon the character of the land surface against which the sea comes to rest; its sequential forms depend upon the stage of development under marine erosion attained at any given period of its orderly evolution. The principles of shoreline classification and description, according to this genetic method of treatment, I have set forth at some length in a volume on " Shore Processes and Shoreline Development." I now propose to apply these principles in a discussion of the physiography of the shoreline bordering the New England-Acadian province.

**Physiographic History of the New England-Acadian Province.** — In order that we may understand the remarkable significance of the present New England-Acadian shoreline, let us go backward in time some millions of years, and sketch briefly the changes wrought by the forces of nature upon that part of the earth's crust lying between the St. Lawrence River and the Atlantic Ocean.* The rocks of this region were long ago compressed into a series of approximately parallel folds, having the prevailing northeast-southwest trend characteristic of the whole Appalachian province, of which New England and Acadia form the northeastern section. As the process of folding was not limited to a single period, but was several times repeated at long intervals,

* A good, brief account of the major surface forms of New England will be found in W. M. Davis' essay on "The Physical Geography of Southern New England."[3] The best general account of the Acadian region is R. A. Daly's paper on "The Physiography of Acadia."[4] An excellent short account is J. W. Goldthwait's "Physiography of Eastern Quebec and the Maritime Provinces,"[5] while the same author's monograph on the physiography of Nova Scotia, soon to appear, presents the most recent and complete description of this particular province.

the older rocks, suffering compression in all of the mountain-making epochs, were much more profoundly wrinkled than the later ones. Furthermore, the older rocks, having been subjected to greater and longer continued pressure, heat, and other meta-morphic processes, and including a greater proportion of igneous intrusions, are as a rule more crystalline and more resistant to erosion than the later formations.

For the purposes of the present study, we may recognize three principal groups of rocks as making up the system of northeast-southwest trending belts so noticeable on any geological map of the New England-Acadian region:

(1) Very complexly folded slates, quartzites, schists, gneisses, granites, and other crystalline rocks, most of them resistant to erosion, but including in some places non-crystalline sandstones, shales, and limestones. (For the greater part these constitute the Precambrian and older Paleozoic formations of the geologists, and certain huge masses of intruded igneous rocks.)

(2) A less strongly folded series of red and grey sandstones, conglomerates, shales, limestones and gypsum, most of them only moderately resistant to erosion. (These are mainly the Carboniferous beds which receive so much attention in geological reports on the New Brunswick, Nova Scotia, Boston, and Narragansett regions, but include also some Devonian and Permian; and they rest unconformably upon the older series described above.)

(3) Very slightly folded, — usually only moderately warped or tilted, — red and grey sandstones and shales, which are very easily eroded. (These are the red beds, commonly referred to as the Triassic or Newark series, which rest unconformably on either or both of the two older series. While these red beds themselves yield readily to erosion, they include sheets of lava which are extremely resistant.)

The general relations of these three rock groups to each other are shown diagrammatically in Fig. 1. It should be realized that the diagram is simpler than the conditions found in nature, and that it does not accurately represent specific features observed in an actual cross-section of the New England-Acadian region. But it correctly portrays the essential geological relations of the three rock groups important to students of the shoreline of this region, and will help us in tracing the chief events in the long history responsible for the shore forms.

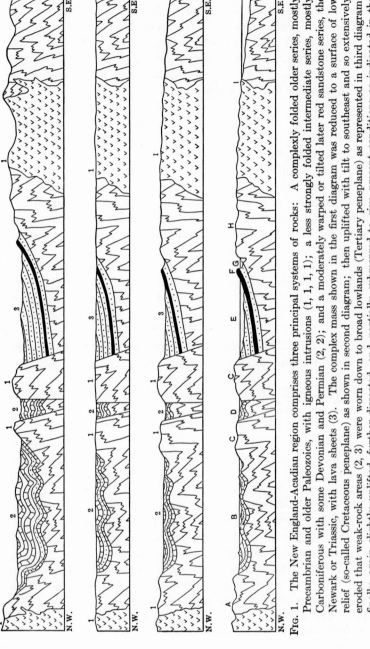

Fig. 1. The New England-Acadian region comprises three principal systems of rocks: A complexly folded older series, mostly Precambrian and older Paleozoics, with igneous intrusions (1, 1, 1, 1); a less strongly folded intermediate series, mostly Carboniferous with some Devonian and Permian (2, 2); and a moderately warped or tilted later red sandstone series, the Newark or Triassic, with lava sheets (3). The complex mass shown in the first diagram was reduced to a surface of low relief (so-called Cretaceous peneplane) as shown in second diagram; then uplifted with tilt to southeast and so extensively eroded that weak-rock areas (2, 3) were worn down to broad lowlands (Tertiary peneplane) as represented in third diagram; finally again slightly uplifted, further dissected, and partially submerged to give present conditions as indicated in the fourth diagram.

After the rocks had been folded and warped, with varying degrees of intensity, along axes trending northeast-southwest, to give such conditions as those represented in Fig. 1, long-continued erosion reduced a large part of the region to near sealevel. Whether subaërial or marine forces were the more effective erosive agents, and whether the landmass was reduced to a surface slightly above or slightly below sealevel, need not now concern us. The important fact is that a vast stretch of country in the New England-Acadian region was reduced to a low-lying surface of erosion which truncated the geological structures, bevelling across resistant and non-resistant formations alike. (Fig. 1, second diagram.) As this great work of denudation was long believed to have approached completion about the close of the Cretaceous geological period, the almost-plane erosion surface is widely known as the " Cretaceous peneplane," although there is accumulating evidence that it is really of later date.

Part, at least, of the low erosion plane was for a time submerged beneath the sea and covered with marine deposits. But the next event of primary concern to us was a broad upheaval which raised the eroded surface of the country well above sealevel, with a marked tilt toward the southeast. The higher parts of the tilted plane, toward the northwest, were now two thousand feet or more above sealevel; while still greater heights were attained by those scattered mountains or mountain groups which, because they were composed of exceptionally resistant rock or were located far from the main drainage lines, were not worn down to the peneplane level. We may ignore these exceptional areas, and note that the plateau-like upland, one or two thousand feet high toward the northwest, sloped gradually downward to disappear southeastward beneath the waters of the Atlantic. To the uplifted remnants of this surface still preserved in New England and Acadia, Goldthwait[6] applies the name " Atlantic Upland."

There now began a new period of erosion, sufficiently long to reduce the larger weak-rock areas to broad lowlands near sealevel, although in resistant rocks the rivers had time to do little more than excavate narrow valleys for themselves. Thus was formed the so-called " Tertiary peneplane " in the districts where limestones, shales, and other weak beds (especially the Carboniferous) were exposed, and where the weak sandstones of the red beds (Triassic) formed the surface (Fig. 1, third diagram); and coincidentally were carved the narrower valleys now observed in the slates, schists, gneisses, granites, and other crystalline rocks of the older series.  Because of the northeast-southwest trend of the rock structure, even in the crystalline areas, streams developing in this direction, and searching out the weaker members of the generally resistant series, enjoyed a marked advantage over those streams flowing southeastward down the slope of the upland directly to the Atlantic, and therefore compelled repeatedly to cross belts of the most resistant rocks.  As a result, there is a general tendency for streams trending with the structure to have long and moderately open parallel valleys, while the valleys of transverse streams are as a rule shorter, often narrower, and of more irregular pattern.

A later moderate uplift permitted streams flowing across the lowlands to entrench themselves slightly beneath the surface of the lowland peneplane (Tertiary?), while the narrower valleys trenching the upland peneplane (so-called Cretaceous peneplane) were still further deepened.  Near the sea, the lower courses of the principal valleys, even most of those developed in crystalline areas, ultimately became rather broadly open; for here the land was least uplifted, the streams most quickly cut down to base-level, and their energies were soonest concentrated on the work of valley-widening.

**Genesis of the Shoreline.** — We are now prepared to see how each event in the physiographic history of the region described above is reflected in the form of the shoreline of today.  Imagine the region described, and represented roughly in the third diagram, to be slightly depressed.  The sea would invade the lower parts of the valleys to give bays or estuaries, often with branch bays extending up the side valleys (Fig. 1, fourth diagram).  These are the " drowned valleys," or " rias," so common along many coasts of the world.  Low divides would be submerged, leaving the higher parts of ridges projecting as islands; or where divides were not quite drowned, narrow isthmuses would connect peninsulas with the mainland.  The whole would give an extremely irregular shoreline characterized by interlocking bays and peninsulas, and fringed by numerous islands.  A glance at any good map shows that this description corresponds to the form of the New England-Acadian shoreline.

**Character of the Initial Shoreline Bordering Resistant Uplands.** — Where the shoreline was, in general, parallel to the northeast-southwest trend of the rock belts, and the valleys draining to the sea were therefore those of the shorter, irregular, transverse streams flowing across the structure, the type of shoreline produced was that characteristic of the main Atlantic shoreline of Nova Scotia, with its prevailingly short, irregular bays (Fig. 2). In striking contrast are certain parts of the shoreline cutting across the rock structure, where the sea spread far up the long, parallel valleys eroded on weaker rock belts, leaving intervening resistant ridges as parallel peninsulas or as groups of elongated islands having a fairly uniform trend. Such, for example, are the Boothbay (Fig. 3), Casco Bay (Fig. 5), and other sections of the Maine shoreline. The pattern of the island fringe will appear very different in the two cases, for where the shore is, in general, parallel to the structure the islands will " march with the shoreline " (Fig. 4), whereas if the shore truncates the structure the islands will extend directly or obliquely from the shore, boldly out to sea (Fig. 5). Where the crystallines are so massive that little encouragement was offered to streams to develop parallel to the structure (because of the absence of weaker rock belts), the shoreline more closely resembles the Nova Scotian type of Fig. 2. This seems to be the case with much of the Connecticut shoreline, and also with parts of the Massachusetts shoreline where the sea cuts across the rock belts which curve strongly eastward in the vicinity of Cape Ann. Both these types of shoreline give coastal scenery of great beauty, especially where the islands, peninsulas, and the shores of the branching bays are wooded, and their dark green slopes, usually with a fringe of bare rock at the water's edge, descend into the blue waters of the sea.

If the rocks were all resistant enough to prevent the development of longitudinal valleys parallel to the structure, but the seaward slope was sufficiently pronounced to cause the formation of long consequent rivers flowing down the slope to the sea, long narrow embayments without important branches would result from submergence. The narrow bays transverse to the rock structure which are found occasionally on the southeast coast of Nova Scotia, associated with the shorter, wider, irregular bays already described, appear to be in part of this origin.

It might be supposed that occasionally the sea would invade a cross valley connecting with one or more parallel longitudinal valleys developed on weak-rock belts farther inland, drowning both the cross valley and extensive portions of longitudinal valleys.

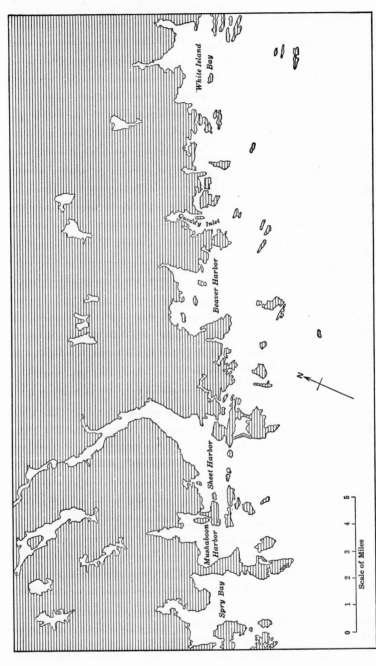

FIG. 2. Young shoreline of submergence bordering the southeastern coast of Nova Scotia, where relatively short valleys transverse to the rock structure are drowned to give bays which as a rule are comparatively short and broad. The rocks are mainly metamorphosed sediments (slates and quartzites) trending parallel with the general direction of the

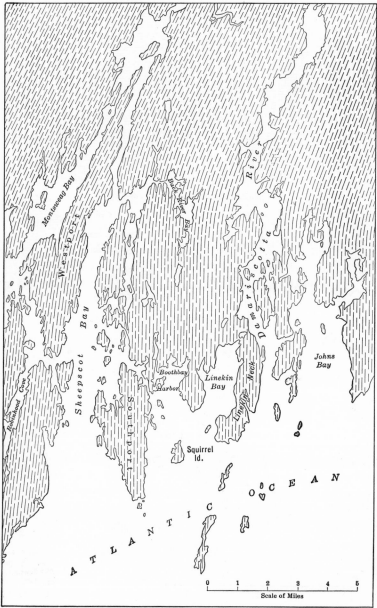

Fig. 3.  Young shoreline of submergence of southern Maine, where longitudinal valleys parallel to the rock structure are drowned to give long,
comparatively narrow bays, some of which penetrate scores of miles inland.
The rocks are mainly metamorphosed sediments (schists), striking northeast in the northern part of the map, and north-south in the southern
part where the structure makes nearly a right angle with the outer
shoreline.  Compare with Fig. 2.                                    (11)

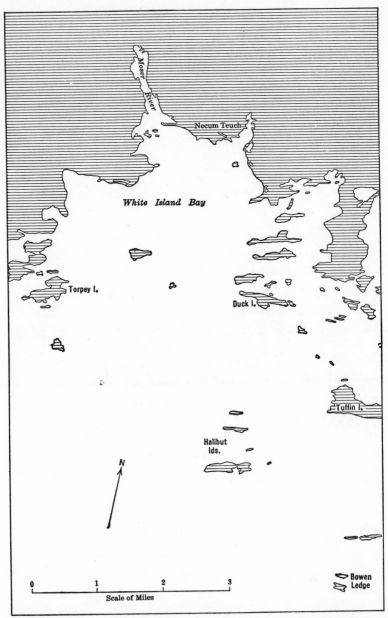

FIG. 4. Young shoreline of submergence bordering the southeast coast of Nova Scotia, showing fringe of islands parallel to shore where the general trend of the shoreline coincides in direction with the rock structure. The rocks are mainly metamorphosed sediments (Cambrian (?) slates and quartzites) striking nearly east and west. Compare with Fig. 5.

(12)

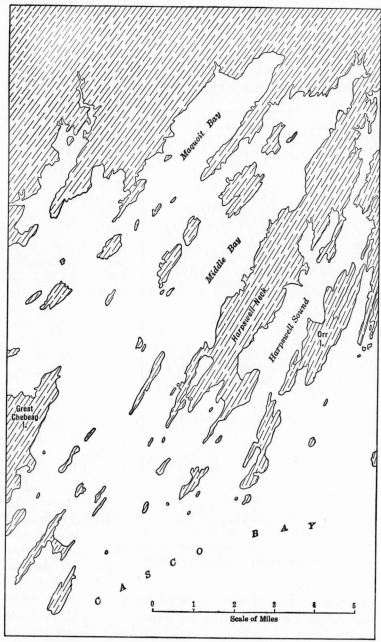

Maquoit Bay

Middle Bay

Harpswell Neck

Harpswell Sound

Orr I.

Great Chebeag I.

C A S C O   B A Y

0        1        2        3        4        5
Scale of Miles

Fig. 5.  Young shoreline of submergence in the Casco Bay region, Maine, showing fringe of islands projecting seaward where the shoreline cuts obliquely across the rock structure.  The rocks are mainly schists consisting of folded metamorphosed sediments striking northeast-southwest, more or less completely concealed in places by glacial deposits.  Compare with Fig. 4.                                                                (13)

A beautiful example of this condition is afforded by the shoreline in the vicinity of St. John, New Brunswick (Fig. 10), where several long parallel bays are connected with each other and with the ocean by transverse straits. Similar examples on a smaller scale are found along the Maine coast in the Cobscook Bay region (Fig. 7; see also Eastport topographic quadrangle), Gouldsboro Harbor region (Bar Harbor quadrangle), and the Harraseeket River region (Freeport quadrangle). Even more like the St. John case is the series of parallel bays and transverse straits east of Wiscasset, Maine (Fig. 6), except that here the short stream or streams carving the transverse valleys appear to have flowed westward. In this latter class belong the Back River region near the center of the Boothbay topographic quadrangle, and the North Harbor region near the center of the Vinalhaven quadrangle. One of these drowned transverse valleys which cuts obliquely across the structure is shown on the U. S. Coast Survey Chart No. 315a, representing the inside passage between Bath and Boothbay Harbors.

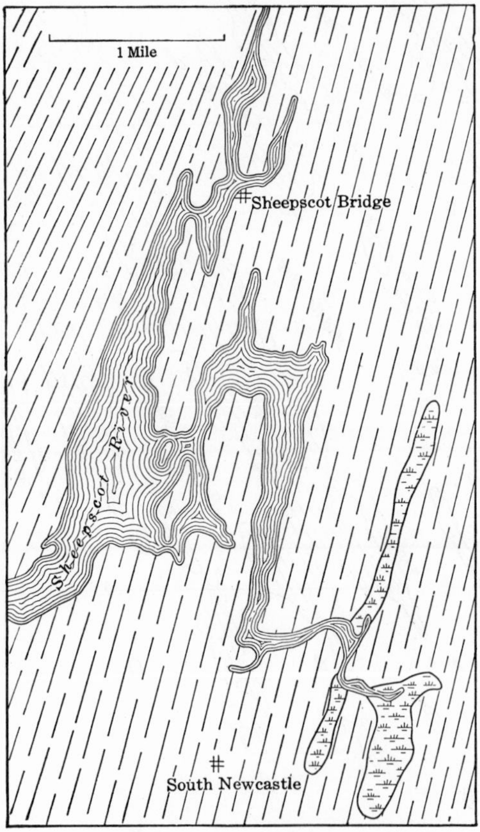

Fig. 6. Drowned valley of the Sheepscot River, east of Wiscasset, Maine, showing submergence of longitudinal (subsequent) valleys eroded on weaker rock belts.

In a preceding paragraph mention has been made of the fact that in Massachusetts the parallel rock belts, resulting from the

folding of the different formations, deviate from the usual southwest-northeast trend to curve more strongly eastward in the
vicinity of Cape Ann.   This is but one of a number of places

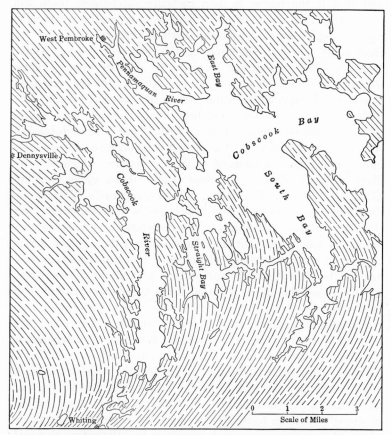

FIG. 7.   Young shoreline of submergence of the Cobscook Bay region near
Eastport, Maine, showing concentrically curving bays, peninsulas and
islands due to partial submergence of curving valleys and ridges developed by normal erosion on folded rocks of varying resistance.   (The
rocks are mainly shales, slates and sandstones with interbedded volcanics,
which strike northwest-southeast, gradually changing to south and
southwest, due largely to a broad anticlinal fold pitching toward the
northeast.   See U. S. G. S. Folio No. 192 for detailed geology.)

where one may observe such local deviations, quite normal to a
great series of rocks which have been subjected to mountain-
making processes involving crumpling, bending and warping.   It

is obvious that where a series of alternately resistant and less
resistant rock belts is very strongly curved, stream erosion will
produce a strongly curved parallel system of ridges and valleys;
and that if the region is then partially submerged, there will
result a curving series of concentric bays separated by parallel
curving peninsulas and islands. Such is the explanation of the
remarkably striking shoreline of the Eastport region, Maine
(Fig. 7). The dependence of shoreline pattern upon geologic
structure is clearly shown on the geologic map of the region by
Bastin and Breger, constituting part of the Eastport folio.[7]

**Résumé.** — In the foregoing brief analysis it has been shown
that the broader characteristics of the New England-Acadian
shoreline are a product of the partial submergence of a complex
mountainous mass of rocks of variable resistance, which were reduced to a peneplane at the close of one erosion cycle, then uplifted and maturely dissected in a subsequent cycle. The shoreline thus appears to be a true " shoreline of submergence." We
shall later see that it belongs in the sub-class of " ria shorelines."
Whatever modifications it may have suffered through the action
of waves or currents since submergence brought the sea surface
against the New England-Acadian land area at the present level,
it is clear that the salient features of the initial shoreline have not
been wholly destroyed, for the shoreline today still shows that
remarkable dependence upon geologic structure which is the most
striking characteristic of an initial shoreline of submergence
bordering a dissected mass of faulted and folded rocks. This is
especially noticeable where the sea borders the resistant uplands
and has occupied depressions eroded on its weaker belts; and we
have cited a sufficient number of instances of geological control
of shoreline pattern to make clear both the degree of dependence
of initial shore form upon rock structure, and the extent to which
this dependence is still clearly manifest in the shoreline that
particularly claims our attention.

BIBLIOGRAPHY

1. MEINHOLD, FELIX. "Die Küste der Mittleren Atlantischen Staaten
    Nordamerikas," 89 pp., Crimmitschau, 1904.
2. WEIDEMÜLLER, C. R. "Die Schwemmlandküsten der Vereinigten
    Staaten von Nordamerika," 58 pp., Leipzig, 1894.
3. DAVIS, W. M. "The Physical Geography of Southern New England."
    Nat. Geog. Mon., I, 269–304, 1895.

4. DALY, R. A. "The Physiography of Acadia." Bull. Mus. Comp. Zoölogy, XXXVIII, 73–104, 1901.
5. GOLDTHWAIT, J. W. "Physiography of Eastern Quebec and the Maritime Provinces." Twelfth Inter. Geol. Cong., Guidebook No. 1, Pt. I, 16–24, 1913.
6. GOLDTHWAIT, J. W. "The Physiography of Nova Scotia." Manuscript copy of a volume to be issued by the Geological Survey of Canada.
7. BASTIN, E. S., and WILLIAMS, H. S. "Eastport Folio." U. S. Geol. Surv., Folio 192, 1–15, 1914.

# CHAPTER II

## RECTILINEAR SHORELINES

**Advance Summary.** — Included among the segments of shoreline that together constitute the New England-Acadian shoreline of submergence are certain long, comparatively straight stretches of shore, relatively free from embayments, which contrast strongly with the more irregular, drowned-valley pattern characterizing the remainder of the sea margin in question. These rectilinear shorelines usually border upland areas of resistant rock, and both on the map and in the field they readily attract the attention of the student of landforms. It has often been assumed, both in this country and abroad, that rectilinear shorelines indicate the presence of earth fractures, along which it is sometimes further assumed that parts of the continental mass have foundered, thus permitting the sea to wash against those portions of the mass which did not participate in the subsidence. This idea, both in the more moderate and in the more extreme form, is so frequently encountered in the literature of shorelines that it deserves special attention here; particularly because the assumptions referred to, if invalid, necessarily involve fundamental misconceptions as to the origin and development of the shorelines affected. It is the purpose of the present chapter to enquire into the possible origins of rectilinear shorelines, and, so far as may seem feasible, to assign to earth fractures, including faults, their relative importance in producing shorelines of this type, especially in the New England-Acadian region. Inasmuch as certain rectilinear shorelines of the latter region have been specifically correlated with earth fractures, in a series of papers which constitute the most complete statement of the fracture theory of origin for rectilinear earth lineaments, it is only proper that our analysis of the problem should include a full consideration of the arguments set forth in those papers.

**Origin of Rectilinear Shorelines.** — Straight shorelines may be produced on a partially submerged coast in a variety of ways. Under wave attack irregularly projecting headlands may be cut back to a simple or relatively straight shoreline in the mature

18

stage of shoreline evolution. Manifestly this is not the case with the coast in question, for the New England-Acadian shoreline shows every evidence of being in a very youthful stage of development, having suffered but moderately from wave erosion. If a recently uplifted, undissected broad coastal plain, or a partially submerged peneplane of exceptionally smooth surface slopes down into the sea, the shoreline will be comparatively straight. But here again the explanation cannot apply to the New England-Acadian shore, for there is no broad coastal plain involved, and the seaward sloping peneplane is maturely dissected; and while the contact of this dissected peneplane with the sea may explain the generally rectilinear course of parts of the shoreline which in detail are very irregular, it cannot help us to understand the type of shoreline, straight even in detail, which we are here considering. Only when steeply tilted can a partially submerged dissected peneplane give a fairly simple shoreline; and the inclination of the New England-Acadian upland peneplane is nowhere steep.

Straight contacts between rock masses of different degrees of resistance to erosion will give straight shorelines, if, after normal erosion has reduced the weaker formation to a low level and left the more resistant as an upland terminating in a straight scarp at the plane of contact, submergence permits the sea to come to rest against the face of the scarp. As this is one of the most frequent causes of straight escarpments on all land areas, we must expect it to be a common cause of straight shorelines bordering lakes and seas. Several sub-classes of such shorelines might be imagined:

**Sedimentary Contact Shorelines.** — The simplest case is that in which, in a normal sedimentary succession, resistant layers are associated with non-resistant layers. If the series is tilted or folded, and erosion removes weaker beds and leaves resistant ones little affected, submergence of the area will give straight shorelines along the sedimentary contacts with the resistant formations (Fig. 8). The initial shore will be steeply or gently inclined, according as the sedimentary contact was steeply or gently tilted. Hyde[1] states that the straight northeast-southwest shorelines bordering both sides of Boularderie Island in the Bras d'Or Lakes region of Cape Breton Island (Fig. 9) are of this class, the island being the erosion remnant of a northeastward pitching syncline of resistant Carboniferous sandstones and Sub-carboniferous limestones underlain by gypsum. Many of the straight shorelines bordering narrow embayments resulting from submergence of valleys eroded on weak-rock belts, whether parallel to the coast as in the St. John region (Fig. 10), or more or less nearly at right angles to it as in Maine (Figs. 3 and 5), are likewise to be included in this class.

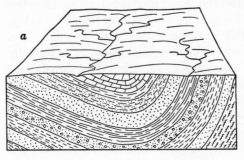

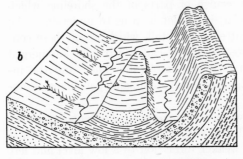

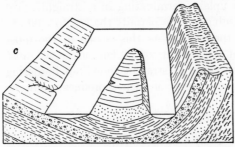

FIG. 8. Successive stages in the formation of sedimentary contact shorelines. (a) Folded or tilted beds of varying resistance (b) suffer differential erosion which leaves the resistant members in relief bordered by more or less pronounced rectilinear scarps along the contacts with the extensively eroded weaker beds; (c) partial submergence of these scarps gives sedimentary-contact shorelines.

*Northern Shoreline of Gaspé Peninsula.* — The northern shore of the Gaspé Peninsula (Fig. 11), forming a beautiful arc which in general parallels the arcuate trend of the sedimentary belts of the peninsula, may be of essentially similar origin. It is doubtful whether the "St. Lawrence fault" can be held directly responsible for the form of this shore. It seems more reasonable to suppose that the drowned valley of the St. Lawrence was eroded on a rock belt weaker than that part of the sedimentary series which remains to form most of the upland of the peninsula. One must not forget that the weaker formation may have been brought into contact with

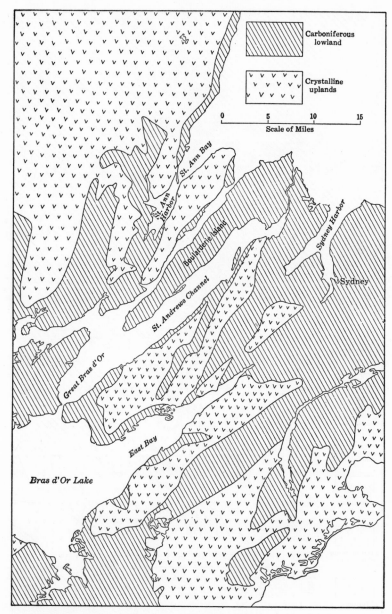

Fig. 9. Portion of the Bras d'Or Lake region, Cape Breton Island, showing partial submergence of a lowland eroded mainly on folded and faulted Carboniferous rocks (the limited areas of other Paleozoic rocks are not differentiated on map) between crystalline uplands. As in the Narragansett Bay region (Fig. 28), unsubmerged portions of eroded folds, some of which bring the underlying crystallines to the surface, give islands and peninsulas trending with the structure. (Geology generalized on basis of more detailed maps by Fletcher et al., Geological Survey of Canada.) (21)

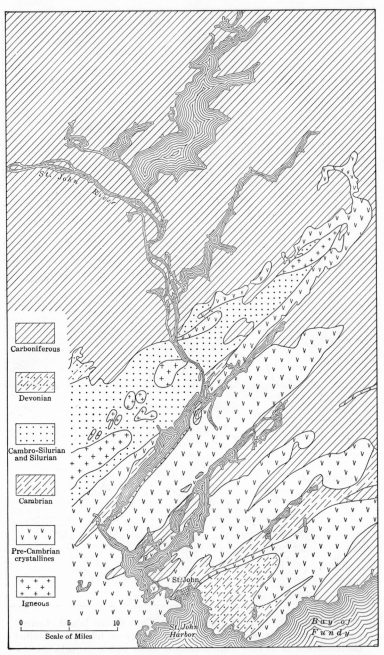

Carboniferous

Devonian

Cambro-Silurian
and Silurian

Cambrian

Pre-Cambrian
crystallines

Igneous

0    5    10
Scale of Miles

St. John River

St. John

St. John
Harbor

Bay of
Fundy

FIG. 10. Drowned valley shorelines of the lower St. John River, showing
parallel bays or lakes due to the submergence of rectilinear valleys eroded
on parallel belts of weak rock. (Geology modified after Ells and Broad.)

(22)

the resistant beds by extensive faulting for the existence of
which much evidence has been reported; but it is not necessary to invoke faulting to explain the broader shoreline relations actually observed.   In any case submergence of the lowland eroded on the weak rocks would cause the shoreline to
follow, in a general way, the contact line between weak and resistant formations, which in a normal sedimentary series would
be parallel to the structural belts of the region.   Absolute parallelism should not necessarily be expected, and the degree actually
exhibited seems sufficient to lend support to the interpretation
here tentatively suggested.   On the basis of this interpretation

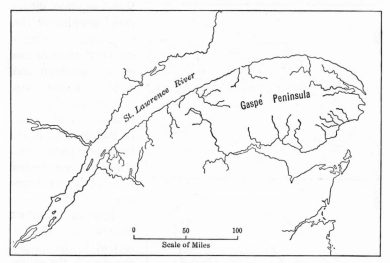

FIG. 11.  Gaspé Peninsula, showing arcuate northern shoreline, and more
irregular eastern and southeastern shorelines.

the eastern and southeastern shores of the peninsula, obliquely
truncating the rock structure, should show an alternation of
peninsulas and bays contrasting strongly with the smooth shoreline parallel to the structure; and this is precisely what we find
to be the case.   Indeed, the contrast is so obvious that students
of the region have sought to account for it; and certain among
them have invoked subsidence of the eastern and southern shores
in excess of that registered by the northern shore, apparently on
the basis of the assumption that pronounced subsidence must
give an irregular shoreline.[2]   But it would seem, from what has
been said above, that this assumption is not justified; and it is

clear that the regularly curved northern shoreline is itself a shoreline of submergence.

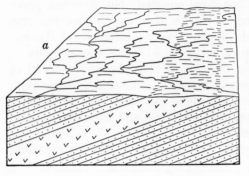

Nor does it appear
that a further depres-
sion of the northern
side of the Gaspé Pen-
insula would give any
bays comparable to
those indenting the
southern and eastern
coasts. It would seem,
therefore, that differ-
ential warping of the
peninsula, involving a
degree of submergence
on the southern and
eastern coasts not
experienced by the
northern coast, must
be indicated, if at all,
by other phenomena
than the contrasted
forms of the two shore-
lines.

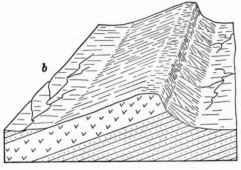

**Igneous Contact
Shorelines.** — Closely
related to the forego-
ing class is the shore-
line which is produced
by the partial sub-
mergence of the more
or less steep slope left
by removal of weak

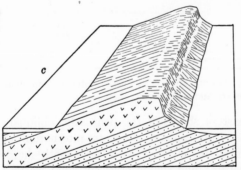

Fig. 12.   Successive stages in the formation of
igneous contact shorelines.   At the left the
shoreline borders directly the exposed contact
plane, while at the right the direction and character of the shoreline are indirectly controlled
by the contact.

beds from one side of
a straight igneous con-
tact (Fig. 12).   Inter-
bedded lava sheets,
either extrusive or in-
trusive, and dykes are

most apt to give rectilinear contacts.   Shorelines of this group may
result from the sea's coming to rest directly against the exposed

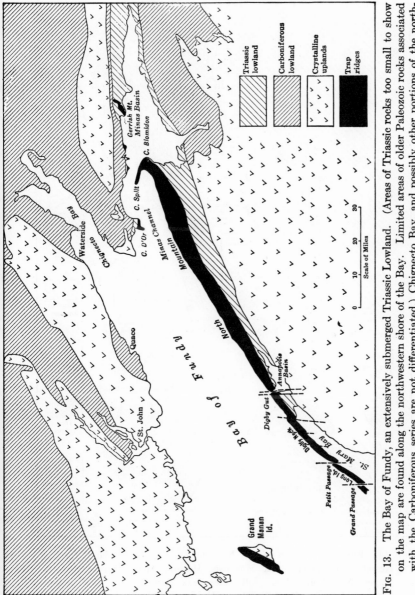

Fig. 13. The Bay of Fundy, an extensively submerged Triassic Lowland. (Areas of Triassic rocks too small to show on the map are found along the northwestern shore of the Bay. Limited areas of older Paleozoic rocks associated with the Carboniferous series are not differentiated.) Chignecto Bay, and possibly other portions of the northwestern side of the Bay of Fundy, represent, in part at least, submerged lowlands eroded on Carboniferous rocks. Broken lines show faults clearly indicated by the topography. (Geology generalized on basis of work by Geological Survey of Canada.)

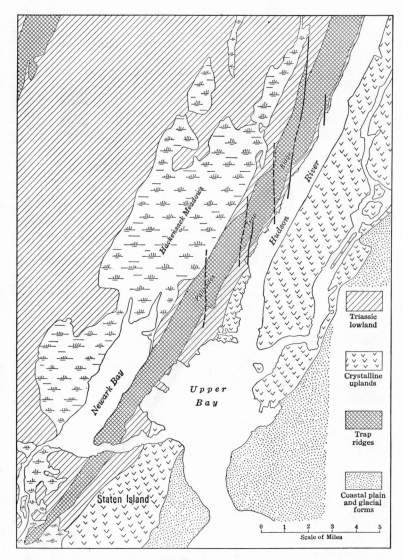

FIG. 14.  Embayed portion of the New Jersey Triassic Lowland, forming
Newark Bay, Hackensack Meadows, Hudson River, and part of the
Upper (New York) Bay.  Solid lines show known faults; broken lines
show additional faults suggested by the form of the trap ridge.  (Based
on maps of New York, New Jersey, and U. S. Geological Surveys.)

contact surface, as in the case of the long, straight southeast shore of the Bay of Fundy (Fig. 13) and the southeast shore of the Newark Bay-Hackensack Meadows embayment (Fig. 14), both of which shorelines border the gentle backslope of a trap ridge from which overlying weak sandstones have been removed by erosion, as described on later pages.   Or the shoreline may not actually touch the contact surface, yet have its course indirectly determined by it, as is the case with the straight northwestern shores of the Hudson River embayment (Fig. 14) and St. Mary Bay (Fig. 13).   Where dykes are intruded into more resistant material, their removal by erosion may form chasms, the straight sides of which give igneous contact shorelines if the chasms be submerged.   As a rule, however, these last are miniature features, often developed by wave erosion during the process of shoreline development, and are too small to deserve more than passing mention in the present connection.

**Resurrected Peneplane Shorelines.** — Where a series of sedimentary beds is deposited upon a peneplaned oldland of resistant rocks, and the buried peneplane is later tilted and resurrected by removal of the sedimentary covering, the sea coming to rest against the inclined resurrected peneplane as a result of submergence will give a shoreline which may be remarkably straight for long distances (Fig. 15).   As Davis[3] has named the topographic form resulting from the resurrection of a peneplane under the conditions shown in Fig. 15, *a, b, c,* a " morvan," we might call this special class of resurrected peneplane shorelines, " morvan shorelines," were it not for the fact that two intersecting peneplanes are necessary to produce the morvan, only one of which directly affects the form of the shoreline.   This one peneplane may be present without the other, as in Fig. 16, in which case there is no morvan, although the shoreline is similar in character and origin with that in Fig. 15.   Resurrected peneplane shorelines appear to be fairly common along the coast of Acadia.   Hyde[1] is of the opinion that many of the northeast-southwest shorelines of Cape Breton are essentially of this origin, although he believes that the old surface may have had considerable relief in places.   Where the shoreline is relatively straight the relief could not have been very rugged, since the partial submergence of a resurrected surface of mature aspect would give an irregular shoreline.   It may well be, however, that the peneplaned surface was warped along northeast-southwest axes before or during

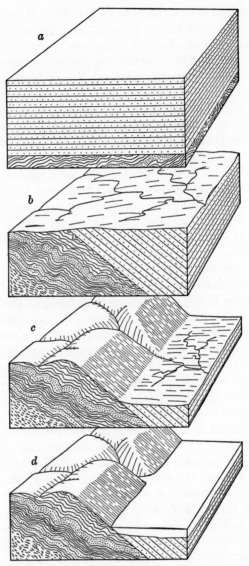

FIG. 15. Successive stages in the formation of a resurrected peneplane shoreline of the morvan type. (*a*) A peneplaned mass of resistant rocks is buried under later non-resistant beds, (*b*) the whole then tilted and peneplaned a second time, (*c*) and subsequently uplifted, permitting erosion to reduce the weak-rock area to a lowland, thereby exposing the older peneplane as a scarp bordering the resistant rock; (*d*) partial submergence of this produces a resurrected peneplane shoreline.

deposition of the Carboniferous beds, thus giving pronounced
unconformities and overlaps of Carboniferous beds upon the old
crystalline surface, without implying that the contact between
the two was necessarily irregular.   Hyde reports strong evidence
in favor of such unconformities and overlaps in Cape Breton[1] in
close association with the rectilinear resurrected peneplane shorelines, the linear extent of which he places at more than 200 miles.
He includes in his figure many miles of shore along which the water
does not come in direct contact with the older crystallines, being
separated from them by a narrow band of the Carboniferous weak
rocks not wholly removed by erosion, on the ground that the

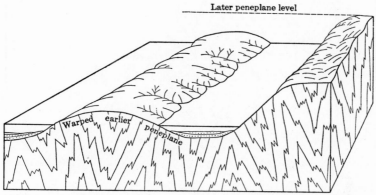

Fig. 16.   Resurrected peneplane shorelines.   At the right the shoreline
    borders a "morvan" where the resurrected earlier peneplane is inter-
    sected by one of later date; but the arched portion of the earlier pene-
    plane, bordered on either side by a resurrected peneplane shoreline, is
    below the level of, and unaffected by, the later peneplane.

contact of the weak rocks with the tilted peneplane surface is in
either case the important factor responsible for the rectilinear
shore.   Among the resurrected peneplane shorelines described by
Hyde are those bordering the southeast coast of the peninsula
of northern Cape Breton from White Point to St. Ann Harbor
(Fig. 17), the southeastern shore of St. Ann Bay and Harbor (Fig.
9), part of the northwest shore of Great Bras d'Or, parts of the
southeast shore of St. Andrews Channel, of both shores of East Bay,
and of the northwest and southeast shores of West Bay.   Where
the old peneplane surface was tilted up steeply, the removal of the
weak Carboniferous beds has left a steep, bold shore, as southward
from Smoky Cape, in which region is the great rectilinear scarp

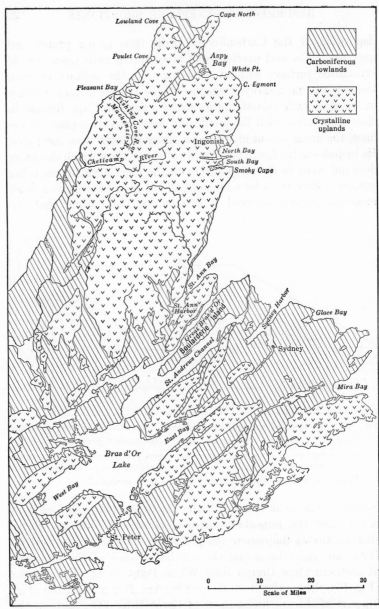

FIG. 17. Portion of Cape Breton Island, showing lowlands eroded on weak beds mainly of Carboniferous age and hence called "Carboniferous Lowlands" on the map (earlier Paleozoic beds occur, especially in the southeast); and uplands of resistant crystalline rocks, designated as "Crystalline Uplands." (Generalized from a more detailed geologic map prepared by the Geological Survey of Canada on the basis of work by Fletcher, Faribault, Bailey, and others.)  (30)

bounding the view as one looks westward from Point Aconi; where the tilting was of moderate amount, the crystalline upland slopes down gently into the sea, as around Neil Harbor[1] (Fig. 18). It is important that the observer should not mistake the steep slope of the first case for a fairly youthful wave-cut cliff, nor the second case for a late mature or old cliff of similar origin. Both slopes being resurrected peneplanes of ancient date, the angle of slope toward the sea depends entirely on the accidents of folding during orogenic movements long prior to the beginning of the present cycle.

FIG. 18.   Crystallines of Cape Breton Island, south of Neil Harbor, sloping gently downward to pass under the sea without being extensively cliffed by wave action. The surface is believed to be, not the so-called Cretaceous peneplane, but one of older date resurrected by removal of weak Carboniferous beds, and then partially submerged. Photo by J. E. Hyde, Geol. Surv. Canada.

While the shores of Cape Breton Island appear to be exceptionally rich in resurrected peneplane shorelines, because of the pronounced folding of the peneplaned crystalline mass and its sedimentary cover, good examples are not lacking in other parts of the New England-Acadian region. The southeastern shores of St. Mary Bay and of the Hudson River, where weak Triassic sandstones seem to have been removed from the tilted crystalline floor on which they were deposited, are long rectilinear shores apparently belonging to this type. It is possible, also, that limited sections of the shores of Narragansett Bay, where the Carboniferous beds have been nearly or quite stripped from the tilted crystalline floor on which they were laid down, should likewise be classed here.

**Fault Shorelines.** — Several important subclasses of rectilinear shorelines are controlled by faults. If a portion of the coast is dropped below sealevel by faulting, thereby admitting the sea against the fault plane, there will be produced a *fault shoreline*. This is a shoreline belonging to the major class of Neutral Shorelines[4] in which no pre-existing land surface is partially submerged, as in the class of Shorelines of Submergence;* and no seabottom plain emerges, as in the class of Shorelines of Emergence. True fault shorelines must be rare phenomena, and the majority of shorelines described as such prove on critical examination to belong to other types. So far as the writer is aware, no fault shoreline occurs in the New England-Acadian region; but Cotton[5] has described as fault shorelines certain rectilinear sea margins of New Zealand.

**Fault-scarp Shorelines.** — If faulting develops a true fault scarp on any land surface (Fig. 19, *b*), and depression of the land or elevation of the sealevel partially submerges this land surface in such manner as to bring the sealevel to rest against the scarp, there will result a *fault-scarp shoreline*. In this case the shoreline is not the direct result of faulting, as in the case of the true fault shoreline, but of a general change in the relative level of land and sea which brings the sealevel against a pre-existing topographic form (the fault scarp) which may have been produced by independent movements long before. The fault-scarp shoreline is a true Shoreline of Submergence, and must not be confused with the Neutral Shoreline (fault shoreline) which it resembles, but which has a very different history. As the New England-Acadian region does not appear to have been one of very active faulting on an extensive scale in recent geological times, true fault scarps are rare or of insignificant size, and, as should be expected under these conditions, fault-scarp shorelines are here practically unknown.

**Fault-line-scarp Shorelines.** — A far more common type of fault-control of rectilinear shores is that represented in Fig. 19, *e*. As shown by the successive diagrams of this figure, the shoreline in question is the result of a long and somewhat complicated geological history involving faulting to bring weak beds opposite some resistant formation, peneplanation of both to a common level, elevation to permit reduction of the weak-rock area to a lowland

---

* The downfaulted block is completely submerged, so has no shoreline; the surface of the stationary block is not reached by the sea, so no shoreline is developed against it; while the fault plane was not a land surface prior to the faulting which originated the shoreline.

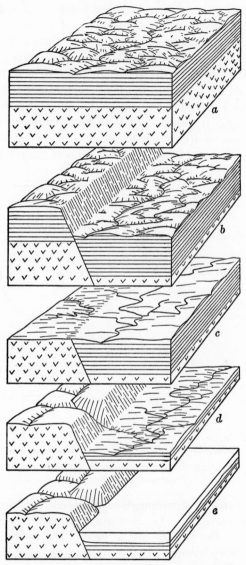

FIG. 19.  Successive stages in the formation of a fault-line-scarp shoreline.
(a) A mass of resistant rock overlain by weaker beds is (b) faulted, producing a true fault scarp which is, however, extinguished when (c) peneplanation reduces the whole region to a common level.  Later uplift
permits erosion (d) to remove the weaker beds from one side of the fault
line, producing a fault-line scarp, (e) partial submergence of which gives
a fault-line-scarp shoreline.

with resulting exposure of a fault-line scarp by this differential erosion, and finally, partial submergence of the resultant topographic form to bring the sealevel to rest against the fault-line scarp.   Thus is produced the *fault-line-scarp shoreline*.   It differs from the fault shoreline in that submergence and not recent faulting caused it; and from the fault-scarp shoreline in that the thing partially submerged was caused by differential erosion and not by faulting.   It differs from both fault shorelines and fault-scarp shorelines in frequency of occurrence, being much more common than either.   In form the differences are often obscure,

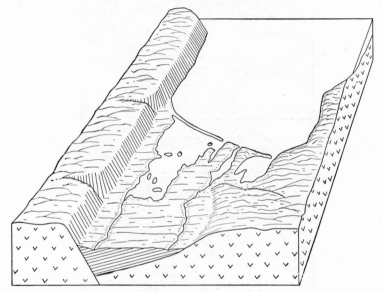

FIG. 20.   The Aspy embayment, showing fault-line-scarp shoreline
on northwest (left).

although features of discriminative value may be present, just as fault-line scarps may be distinguished from recent or older fault scarps on the surface of the land.   The resemblances are sufficiently close, however, easily to lead the observer astray; and many fault-line-scarp shorelines have been described as fault shorelines or fault-scarp shorelines, a quite erroneous physiographic history being thus assigned to the coasts in question.

*Aspy Bay Shoreline.* — In the Acadian region faulting not infrequently determined the contact between weak Carboniferous beds and resistant crystallines (*D*, Fig. 1), and the later reduction of the Carboniferous beds to a lowland usually left the crystalline upland bordered by a relatively straight fault-line scarp overlooking the lower land. Submergence of the lowland later permitted the sealevel to come to rest against the scarp, giving a relatively straight, bold shore. Such a fault-line-scarp shoreline is found in the northwestern wall of Aspy Bay (Figs. 20 and 29). Here the seaward margin of the crystalline upland is notably rectilinear, and precisely in line with the nearly straight northwestern border of the Carboniferous rocks of the Aspy lowland (Fig. 21), and with the prolongation of North Aspy River in a straight line several miles to the southwest of the Carboniferous area: an assemblage of features undoubtedly controlled by a prominent northeast-southwest fracture and displacement of the rocks. Partial submergence of the much reduced Carboniferous area here permitted the sea to flow against a fault-line scarp which was steep and forbidding; and the geological map of the region prepared by Hugh Fletcher for the Geological Survey of Canada some forty years ago, while indicating no fault, carries this legend along the straight shore in question: " Shore high and inaccessible except at the mouths of the brooks." Hyde[1] has observed the crushed zone along the great fault plane. The portion of the scarp still projecting above the sea rises to a height of more than a thousand feet, and provides one of the most magnificent examples of shoreline scenery along the Atlantic coast.

*Chedabucto Bay Shoreline.* — If the reader will glance at a map of Chedabucto Bay (Fig. 22), he will at once perceive a likeness in pattern to that of Aspy Bay. Again one side is remarkably rectilinear, the other far more irregular; and the two sides diverge as one passes seaward. At the very head of Chedabucto Bay there is a small patch of Carboniferous rocks in the vicinity of Guysborough Harbor. The whole suggests strongly that here we have to deal with another and greater infaulted and peneplaned block of weak Carboniferous strata, the subsequent erosion of which produced a lowland, later almost completely drowned to form Chedabucto Bay. The principal differences from the Aspy Bay case are the location of the fault on the south side of the basin, and the fact that either erosion of the Carboniferous beds was more complete or submergence was more extensive in the Chedabucto example.

Hyde early recognized the fault-line character of the south shore of Chedabucto Bay, as well as the submerged lowland character of the bay, basing his opinion on the truncation of later Paleozoics by the rectilinear contact with the gold series which continues far inland the strike of the southern shore, as shown on geological

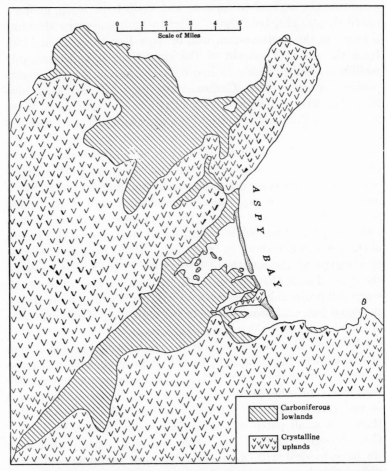

FIG. 21. Aspy Bay, formed by partial submergence of a small lowland eroded on Carboniferous rocks. The straight northwest wall of the lowland is apparently determined by a fault line, prolonged northeastward along the base of the straight and steep northwest wall of Aspy Bay, and southwestward (beyond the limit of the map) along the upper course of North Aspy River. (From geological map by Hugh Fletcher.)

maps; on the reported disturbed attitude of the beds near the contact; on the lowland topography continued west of the bay between the gold series on the south and the Cobequid intrusives

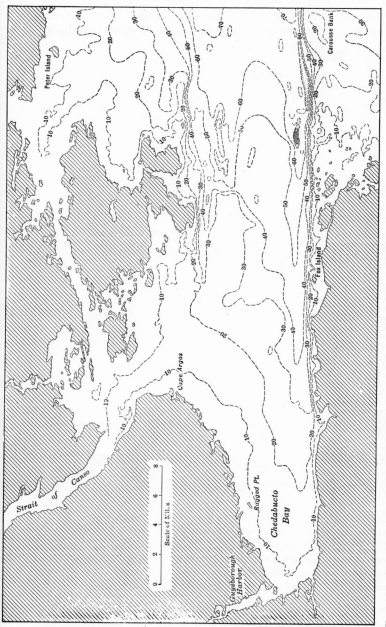

FIG. 22. Chedabucto Bay, showing rectilinear south shore and more irregular north shore. Compare with Aspy Bay (Fig. 21) and Miramichi Bay (Fig. 159). Note the submarine continuation of the rectilinear south shore eastward beyond Carousse Bank. The bay is believed to represent an eroded and partially submerged fault-block basin of weak rocks (Carboniferous ?).

on the north; and on the form of the submerged portion of the scarp as revealed by the hydrographic charts. That the bay is an eroded and submerged fault-block basin of the type believed

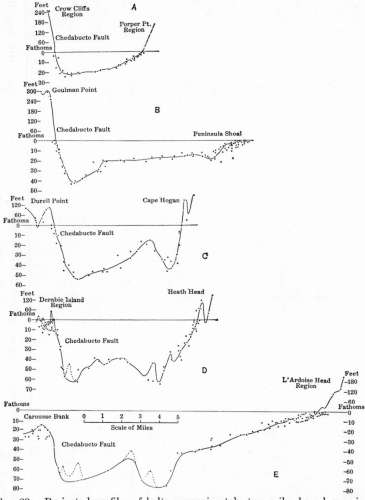

Fig. 23.   Projected profiles of belts approximately two miles broad, running from south to north across Chedabucto Bay, showing the partially submerged Chedabucto fault-line scarp. Vertical exaggeration approximately ×50.   Based on U. S. Hydrographic Chart No. 1236.

to occur at Aspy Bay, receives confirmation not only from the irregular pattern and divergent course of the northern shore, but also from the form of projected profiles across the basin from north to south (Fig. 23). These show a steeper southern and (in general) less precipitous northern wall for the depression, a feature apparent in the submarine contours far out in the Atlantic. Off Cape Canso, Carousse Bank drops down steeply on the north over what seems clearly to be the completely submerged seaward portion of the great fault-line scarp that farther west rises partially above sealevel to form the southern shore of the bay, and at the head of the bay wholly emerges from the water. We may conveniently designate the major fracture along which this scarp is located by calling it the "Chedabucto fault." The general relations are shown by Fig. 22, on which I have drawn submarine contours at 10-fathom intervals on the basis of soundings shown on the hydrographic chart of the bay. While these contours make no pretense to detailed accuracy, it is believed that they show with essential correctness the general form of the basin. It will be seen that the deepest soundings are at the base of the steep and remarkably straight scarp which, counting its westward extension along Salmon River, bounds the basin on the south for a distance of more than fifty miles. That the floor of this great eroded fault-block basin has a number of rocky ridges, as well as "deeps" probably representing partially obstructed valleys, is indicated by the soundings. The more gently sloping northern side of the basin is especially well shown in profile *E*.

*Other Fault-line-scarp Shorelines.* — According to Goldthwait[6] those portions of the straight western coast of northern Cape Breton Island (Fig. 17) between Lowland Cove and Poulet Cove, and between the mouths of the Mackenzie and Cheticamp Rivers, are probably fault-line-scarp shorelines. The straight shore south of South Bay, Ingonish, on Cape Breton Island, is tentatively placed in this class by the same authority, although it seems not improbable that it may prove to be a resurrected peneplane shoreline. The straight western side of the Cape George Peninsula (Fig. 31) in Antigonish County, Nova Scotia, from Malignant Cove northeastward, is doubtless a fault-line-scarp shoreline, as recognized by Goldthwait, Hyde, and Williams, the landward extension of the fault having been fully described by the last named writer.[7] To the same class possibly belongs part of the northwest shore of Great Bras d'Or, Cape Breton (Fig. 24), although farther south it appears to be continued as a resurrected peneplane shoreline. As will later be shown, there is good reason to believe that the straight, bold shore of New Brunswick, from

Quaco to Salisbury Bay, and its continuation on the Maine coast
from West Quoddy Head to Machias Bay, is a fault-line scarp
shoreline along which weak Triassic sandstones have been removed
from a fault contact with crystallines. Segments of the Massachusetts shore from near Lynn to Cape Ann, and from near
Quincy to Cohasset, while very irregular in detail, may have
their general courses determined by extensions of fault-line scarps,
if the interpretation of the Boston Basin as a depressed block of
weak Carboniferous rocks bounded on the north and south by
faults, be correct.

Fig. 24. Rectilinear northwest shore of Great Bras d'Or channel, viewed
from near Boularderie Centre, Cape Breton Island. Possibly a fault-
line-scarp shoreline. Photo by J. E. Hyde, Geol. Surv. Canada.

**Fault-line-valley Shorelines.** — Rectilinear shorelines indirectly
dependent upon faulting may result from the partial submergence
of a valley which has been eroded along the crushed zone of a
fault, or along a narrow strip of infaulted weak rock. Such
*fault-line-valley shorelines* are especially well developed in northeastern Nova Scotia (Fig. 25), where Indian Harbor, part of
Country Harbor, Isaac Harbor, and New Harbor Cove are partially drowned fault-line valleys. Farther southwest the upper
half of Sheet Harbor (Fig. 2) and Ship Harbor are of the same
origin, while to the northwest the drowned valley of Salmon
River, on the great Chedabucto fault, belongs in this class. One
might be tempted to assign a fault origin to all of the northwest-
southeast trending embayments and rivers; but an examination
of geological maps prepared by the Geological Survey of Canada

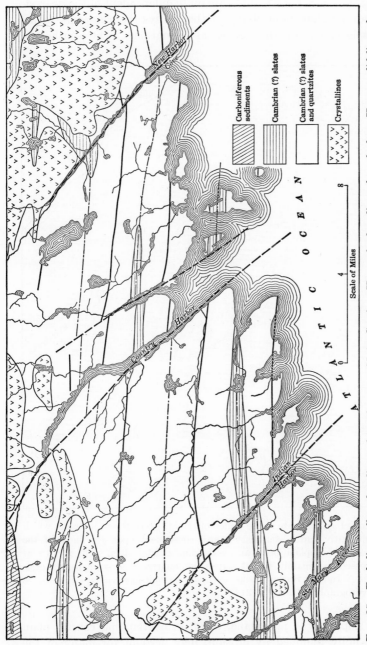

FIG. 25. Fault-line-valley shorelines of northeastern Nova Scotia. Heavy broken lines show faults. Heavy solid lines show anticlinal axes, light broken lines synclinal axes, and help to make clear the displacements due to faulting. Note northward offsetting of general position of shoreline at each fault, as well as drowned valley located along each displacement. Geology from map by Fletcher and Faribault, Geol. Surv. Canada.

shows that many known faults are quite independent of the nearest valleys, and that along many of the valleys there appears to be no displacement of the geological formations. The southeast-

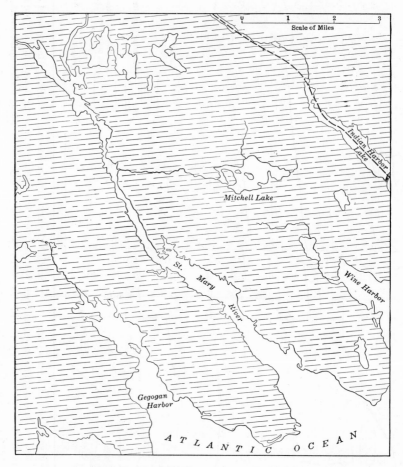

FIG. 25a.  Partially submerged valley of the St. Mary River, a stream which apparently had a southeast course consequent upon the slope of the Acadian peneplane or of an overlapping coastal plain. The rocks now exposed are mainly folded slates and quartzites striking nearly east-west. Indian Harbor Lake occupies a fault-line valley. See U. S. Hydrographic Chart No. 2127.

ward slope of the peneplane, or of an overlapping coastal plain now wholly removed by erosion, may account for many of the parallel northwest-southeast trending valleys (Fig. 25a). Where true fault-line-valley shorelines exist, they should not be confused with shorelines caused by the submergence of valleys or basins produced directly by recent faulting. It not infrequently happens that a fault-line valley is described as a fault valley, notwithstanding the fact that the former is an erosion feature and the latter a tectonic feature, and that the faulting in the first case is of far more ancient date. We may note in passing that lakes as well as bays may mark the fault-line valley (Fig. 119).

**Extension of the Fracture Theory of Earth Lineaments.** — The question naturally arises whether still larger elements of the New England-Acadian shoreline may not have been determined, directly or indirectly, by extended earth fractures. An affirmative answer is presented by Hobbs in his discussion of " Lineaments of the Atlantic Border Region."[8] According to this author the relatively straight southeastern shore of the Bay of Fundy and the north shore of Long Island Sound west of New Haven Harbor mark distant parts of a fracture line which elsewhere limits for a short distance part of the Triassic Lowland in southern Connecticut, follows a section of the " fall line " farther south, and corresponds more or less closely with parts of certain river courses and with the western border of the Piedmont Belt (Fig. 26). Another hypothetical fracture line is drawn along the northern shore of Long Island Sound eastward from New Haven Harbor and prolonged to coincide with the southern margin of the glacial outwash plain of Cape Cod, while a parallel line is supposed to follow the axis of the Sound and farther west to limit the New Jersey Triassic Lowland on the northwest. The north-south Hudson estuary is represented as the locus of one of many north-south fracture lines, four others of which follow the estuaries of the Thames River in Connecticut, of the Kennebec and Penobscot Rivers in Maine, and of the St. John River in New Brunswick. Finally, northwest-southeast fractures are drawn through the lower Connecticut River below Middleton, and along parts of the St. Croix River and Bay, the latter fracture following " the southwestern shore of Nova Scotia so as to terminate the trap walls, and at the same time the Newark basin of that province " and to indicate offsets in other geological formations of southwestern Nova Scotia. If Hobbs' interpretation be correct, it is evident that many elements of the New England-Acadian shoreline are determined by earth fractures. Furthermore, it is his

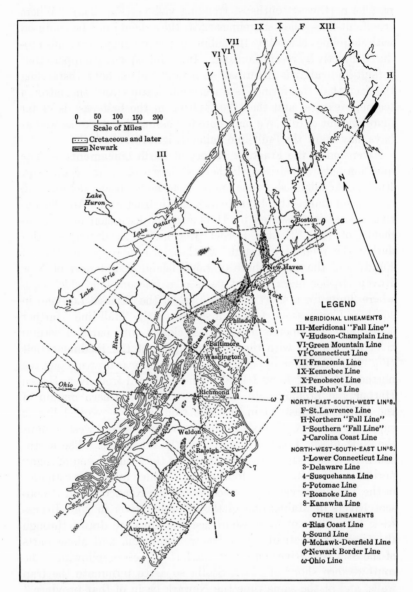

FIG. 26. Lineaments of the Atlantic border region according to Hobbs. (Bulletin of the Geological Society of America, XV, 1904.) More numerous lineaments, forming a more complex system, are shown on a later map by the same author ("Earthquakes," New York, 1907, p. 114).

opinion that other large sectors of the Atlantic shoreline have a similar origin.

Hobbs' work has demonstrated that it is possible to draw a series of straight lines for long distances across the map of the Atlantic border region which will coincide more or less closely with a variety of earth lineaments. He does not maintain that a single, clean-cut fault or fracture need be identifiable for great distances; nor does he claim absolute coincidence of fracture and lineament line, for he recognizes that the lineament may be a zone in nature[9] and includes as part of a given lineament topographic features which are some miles distant from the axial line drawn. Thus he says of his " Northern Fall Line " that " its course is along the remarkable series of sharp and straight arms of the Delaware River and the drowned Susquehanna and Potomac," although the portions of these rivers in question are located anywhere from 5 to 20 miles or more southeast of the line as shown on his map;[10] and other features 5 to 15 miles distant are correlated with other fracture lines. He also recognizes that a feature making a marked angle with a given lineament line may nevertheless be correlated with it, on the ground that " a line of dislocation is not straight, but made up of a number of straight elements composing a series of zigzags," as, for example, in the case of the lower St. John River, where the lineament is drawn as a nearly north-south line through the zigzag course of the stream which here for the most part follows pronounced northeast-southwest and northwest-southeast lines.

It is a legitimate line of argument to show that a network of straight lines may be so drawn on the map as to parallel more or less closely a large number of topographic features; to hold that the coincidences thus brought out cannot properly be explained as merely the result of chance; and to claim that in earth fracturing we find the most plausible explanation of the observed facts. How far this argument carries conviction will depend first on the number and perfection of the coincidences revealed; and second, on how fully the fracture theory is supported, and other explanations are excluded, in the development of the argument. While fully recognizing the suggestiveness of Hobbs' interpretation, I am unable to agree with his conclusions; and it is therefore pertinent to explain the grounds of this disagreement, particularly as related to the question of origin of certain New England-Acadian shorelines.

*The Rôle of Chance in the Extension of Earth Lineaments.* — It has already been shown that there are many rectilinear features of the earth's crust known to be produced by other causes than fracturing and faulting. These lines, extended indefinitely, must through mere chance here and there coincide more or less closely with other topographic lineaments, such as parts of river courses, crests of ridges, geological formation contacts, plateau or mountain scarps, and shorelines. This will give an appearance of order which is in part the result of design in selecting certain rectilinear features as starting points, and in part due to the impossibility of drawing any line for scores or hundreds of miles across country without its coinciding more or less closely with some of the many topographic or geologic features in its course. When the lineament is broadened to a zone, and features from 5 to 20 miles away are included; and when features making an angle with the lineament line are included as elements of a zigzag course for the lineament, the perfection of the coincidence suffers. It is true that some fracture zones may be broad, and that some fractures may follow a more or less zigzag course. But when one includes specific distant topographic features as parts of supposed lineaments on this ground, he inevitably weakens the force of his argument; for he thereby makes his " lineament " a zone so broad that in the course of hundreds of miles it could hardly escape including a certain number of more or less obvious topographic elements. Whether or not in any given case there is a significant coincidence in the alignment of these elements must remain a matter of individual opinion. On this point I can only say that after a careful study of Hobbs' lineaments in the New England-Acadian region I am unable to see in them any coincidences which are not explicable on the ground that if we select a rectilinear earth feature and prolong it for a great distance, the prolongation may happen to pass through or near other more or less linear earth features. Thus, while I recognize that strikingly rectilinear topographic features of considerable length are characteristic of parts of the region in question, and that some of them are the indirect result of faulting, it does not seem to me that the great extension of these features to form a network of intersecting lineaments, some of them many hundreds of miles in length, rests upon a sufficiently sound basis.

*Orientation, Parallelism, and Spacing of Lineaments.* — Nor am I convinced of the validity of the grounds on which Hobbs gives to his lineament lines the orientation, parallelism, and spacing shown on his map, and which he believes to be significant of their origin.   It seems to me that other lineaments could be added to his map on grounds as good as, or better than, those for lineaments already drawn (in some cases better because based on known fractures), the results of which additions would be to destroy the supposed orderliness of orientation, parallelism and spacing, and to emphasize the greater complexity which seems actually to be present in Nature.   This is a test of the fracture theory which the reader can readily apply for himself.   It has in a measure been applied by Hobbs, for in a later edition of his map, illustrating the discussion of lineaments in his book on " Earthquakes," he has added many new lineament lines to show a relation between such lines and earthquake epicenters.[11]   Comparison of the two maps shows that the simplicity and regularity of the original is seriously compromised in the later edition; for while the essentially parallel and somewhat regularly spaced lines of the former remain, the addition of new lineaments already partially obscures them.   Thus, of the southwest-northeast lineaments there are one or more having, as nearly as can be measured on so small a map, the following directions:  S 4 W, S 13 W, S 26 W, S 33 W, S 37 W, S 44 W, S 54 W, S 58 W, S 63 W, S 75 W, S 84 W, S 87 W, as well as others varying but one or two degrees from these.   Perhaps Hobbs would group some of these in the same system; but the important point is that there is not a ten-degree interval in the quadrant through which he does not draw one or more lineament lines.   One may perhaps consider that there are regularly spaced systems of fractures parallel to each of these directions; or that the multiplicity of directions represents variations from a few standard directions; but either alternative leaves a much weakened support for the theory so far as inherent evidence of system in orientation, parallelism, and regularity of spacing is concerned.   The weakness increases just in proportion as one adds other lineaments based on known or probable faults and extended in the manner employed by Hobbs; or based on straight river courses or other prominent rectilinear topographic features, and similarly extended.

*Nature of the Argument Relating to Specific Lineaments.* — If we restrict consideration to those undoubtedly significant rectilinear features of the New England-Acadian topography which apparently served as the groundwork of Hobbs' more extended lineament lines, the strength of the fracture theory as applied to them must rest upon the completeness with which the fracture origin of each such feature is demonstrated, or else upon the certainty with which other possible explanations are excluded. If I have correctly interpreted Hobbs' suggestive essay, he does not attempt to demonstrate by actual evidence the presence of a fracture along most of the lineaments described by him, although he does do so in certain cases, some of which are mentioned below; nor does he seem to consider the many alternative explanations which might reasonably be offered to account for rectilinear earth features, and indicate why they should be excluded. If I rightly understand his treatment of the problem, it consists in naming and classifying into groups the linear features which are in line with, or parallel to, each other; in showing that limited portions of the features thus classified are coincident with, or parallel to, fault or joint fractures; in citing other cases in which topographic form has been strongly influenced by faults or joints; in arguing that faults would show such a rough approximation to uniformity of spacing as is believed to occur in the spacing of the supposed lineaments; and in concluding, on the basis of this reasoning, in favor of a specifically indicated geometric network of earth fractures as a major element in determining the topography of the Atlantic border region. It should be noted, however, that each individual link in this chain of reasoning, up to the final conclusion, might be sound,* and yet the linking of them together as a chain of evidence be unsafe, and the conclusion to which one is thus led be wholly unsound. Not until the fracture origin of a proportion of the lineaments sufficiently great to imply such an explanation for all be demonstrated, or until reasons be shown why alternative explanations will not apply, can the interpretation of the lineaments as due to fractures be regarded as valid. Inasmuch as the problem is one of much importance in connection with the New England-Acadian coast, I give herewith somewhat fully the reasons for my inability to accept the fracture network theory as a sound basis for interpreting the rectilinear shorelines of this province.

*Alternative Interpretations of Supposed Fracture-Controlled Lineaments.* — The intersection of two planes is a straight line. The

---

* In the writer's opinion, however, both the contentions that faults should be more or less uniformly spaced and that the rectilinear features of the earth are thus spaced, are open to question.

intersection of a peneplane with the plane of sealevel may therefore give a shoreline nearly straight in its general pattern, wholly
unrelated to any system of fractures. Hence the comparatively
straight shoreline of southern New England (Fig. 43), where the
peneplane of that region slopes down beneath the waters of Long
Island Sound, does not in itself seem to offer any evidence in favor
of the fracture theory. The same holds true with regard to the seaward margin of a coastal plain, which must afford examples of relatively straight segments of shoreline, whether or not the region has
ever suffered from fracturing. Sloping peneplanes and coastal plains
will normally have parallel rivers flowing in more or less rectilinear courses down the slope to the sea, and hence at right angles
to shorelines which may be relatively straight. There is, therefore, no tectonic significance in the fact observed by Hobbs that
" series (of lineaments) directed nearly at right angles (to the
series paralleling the shore) are hardly less in evidence"; and his
statement that " Examination of the rivers of the Atlantic border
region . . . furnish(es) evidence that dislocations approximating to the northwest-southeast direction have controlled,"
seems open to question in view of the obvious possibility, and
even strong probability, that the slope of the land, rather than
dislocations of the earth's crust, exerted the control in question.
The general southeast course of the St. Croix River seems to
accord with the southeast slope of the Acadian peneplane, while
both it and the rectilinear southeast course of the lower Connecticut River may have been determined either by the southeast slope of the peneplane, or by the similar slope of an overlapping coastal plain from the surface of which the stream cut
down into the underlying crystallines, as has been suggested by
Davis for the case of the Connecticut.[12] The St. Croix " lineament " is supposed by Hobbs to be continued southeastward as
a line of dislocation which " terminate(s) the trap walls and at
the same time the Newark basin of that province (Nova Scotia)";
but Daly has shown that the trap ridge and crystalline upland
of Nova Scotia are warped down so as to disappear gradually
under the sea;[13] and, as will later be shown, there is evidence
that the Newark (Triassic) basin is not terminated in this region,
otherwise than by submergence beneath the sea.

In Canada the longest of the supposed lineaments is represented
as tangent to " the basalt bluffs forming the steep southeast
shore of the Bay of Fundy"; but the steep bluffs of North Moun-

tain are on the opposite side of this trap ridge from the line drawn by Hobbs, which follows the more gentle backslope of the ridge where the overlying weak Triassic sandstones were doubtless in contact with the trap sheet before erosion removed them. Even were it drawn tangent to the line of bluffs on the east, there would still be no evidence that it was here associated with faulting; for the west dipping trap sheet is bordered on this side also by west dipping weak Triassic beds (Fig. 13), erosion of which. must produce a rectilinear contact, and so give a rectilinear shoreline (Fig. 12), irrespective of whether or not there had been fracturing or faulting. The only known faults in the region cut obliquely across the ridge; and as Powers[14] has pointed out, " there is a lack of evidence of any major fault parallel to North Mountain." In other words, the linear element of the shore is here apparently due to a long, nearly straight contact between rock formations of varying resistance quite independent of faulting.

The estuaries of both the Kennebec and Penobscot Rivers conform in general direction with the trend of the geological structure in adjacent parts of southern Maine. The remarkable agreement between the trend of the rock belts and the trend of islands, peninsulas, and bays in the Casco Bay region (Fig. 5) near the mouth of the Kennebec, in the Cobscook Bay region near Eastport (Fig. 7), and in other parts of the Maine coast, is most reasonably explained on the ground that in these regions the alternation of linear elevations and depressions is largely dependent upon alternation of more resistant and less resistant rock belts; and it is equally reasonable to suppose that the drowned valleys of the Kennebec and Penobscot Rivers may similarly depend upon this type of rock structure, rather than upon earth fractures. As early as 1836 Edward Hitchcock apparently correctly interpreted the relation of the rectilinear features of the Maine coast to rock belts of varying resistance, although he exaggerated the amount of erosion accomplished by wave action, and underestimated the importance of normal stream erosion followed by submergence. " In sailing among the islands in Casco Bay, said to be as numerous as the days of the year, I was struck with the fact that their longitudinal direction is almost always from southwest and northeast; and the same thing is generally true of the numerous islands and capes along the coast, as far, at least, as the mouth of Penobscot River. The explanation of this fact depends in a measure, I am persuaded, upon the fact that the strata run in that direction. For the water gradually encroaches upon the softer portions of the strata, the harder ridges resisting its power much more successfully, and thus a succession of gulfs and capes is formed, running in the same direction as the strata. In a variety of ways these capes may be cut off, so as to become islands in the course of centuries."[15]   Ogilvie[16] has shown that in the Boothbay region (Fig. 3) the principal valleys are determined by the strike of bands of weak rock.   Long Island Sound (Fig. 43) has long been recognized as the drowned inner lowland of a coastal plain, the cuesta of which appears mantled over with glacial débris in Long Island, while the crystalline uplands of New England constitute the oldland; as such inner lowlands are the normal product of stream erosion upon a weak-rock belt, the existence of the somewhat rectilinear Sound affords no evidence of earth fracturing.   The influence of alternate belts of weak and resistant rock upon topography is beautifully shown in the lower course of the St. John River (Fig. 10) where successive parallel arms of the drowned valley are nicely adjusted to parallel strips of easily eroded material.   While one may not agree with all the details of process as described by him, it would seem that Ganong[17] interpreted the general physiographic history of this region with essential correctness when he wrote: " According to our theory, these valleys originated on a southeasterly sloping surface as it arose from the sea.   Had the underlying rocks been uniform in texture and hardness, those rivers would doubtless have kept those courses to the present day.   But the rocks were not of equal hardness, but on the contrary consisted of bands of harder and softer rocks running for the most part directly across the courses of these rivers.   In the process of erosion these softer bands were cut down rapidly, forming large right-angled branches to the older valleys.   Ultimately these branches were able to cut back into neighboring valleys and frequently to capture their head waters.   It is in this erosion by branches of the main valleys along the softer rocks crossing from valley to valley that we have the explanation of the changes which have altered the original arrangement to the conditions that we find at the present day, for all of the river courses of this system seem to lie either in the ancient northwest and southeast valleys across the rock bands, or in northeast and southwest valleys following the general direction of the softer rocks."

*The Case of the Lower Hudson.* — The drowned valley of the
lower Hudson, — straight, narrow and long, — constitutes, as we
shall see on a later page, one of the most picturesque and interesting elements of the New England-Acadian shoreline.   Here again
we find that Hobbs has drawn one of his earth fractures; and in
this case he presents specific arguments in support of his interpretation.   " In its southern section, near the City of New York,
the writer has shown that it represents a line of dislocation along
which the Newark formations of New Jersey are set down into
the crystalline rocks lying to the east of the Hudson."[18]   For
proofs the reader is referred to an earlier paper, where one reads:
" The writer has modified the sketch of the New York-New
Jersey area by adding a fault along the eastern margin of the
Palisades, because not only does the topographic break at the
border of the system seem to require such a fault, but parallel
faults observed by the writer during the past summer on New
York Island increases the probability of this structural break."[19]
Several years later Hobbs stated still more fully his reasons for
drawing a fault along the Hudson: " The origin of the North
River (Hudson River) channel is sufficiently accounted for, however, by its position along the contact of the Newark beds with
the crystallines.   That this border is a fault border seems to be
abundantly proven, not only by its markedly rectilinear extension,
by the great scarp of basalt, and by the inferior position of the
newer terrane as revealed by surface development, but especially
by the new borings along the line of the proposed tunnels of the
Pennsylvania Railroad Company."[20]
     In these several statements there are advanced six arguments
in support of the fault theory, as follows: (1) the rectilinear
extension of the border between the Triassic beds and the crystallines proves the contact is a fault; (2) the topographic break at
this border seems to require a fault; (3) the great scarp of basalt
proves faulting; (4) faults parallel to the Hudson trench are
known to occur on New York (Manhattan) Island; (5) the newer
terrane (Triassic) occupies an inferior position in respect to the
surrounding crystallines; and (6) borings for a tunnel under the
river prove that a fault must be present.   As pointed out in
earlier paragraphs, rectilinear contacts, both sedimentary and
igneous, which have no connection with faulting, are among the
commonest of geological phenomena, they being much more usual
than fault contacts.   It is not clear, therefore, how the " markedly

rectilinear extension " of the border of a formation can be regarded
as an indication of faulting.  A topographic break normally
occurs at all contacts, sedimentary or igneous as well as fault
contacts, where the rocks are of markedly unequal resistance and
erosion has had an opportunity to operate.  " The great scarp
of basalt " is a perfectly normal erosion feature, the inevitable
result of differential denudation operating upon a tilted trap sheet
enclosed above and below in weak sandstones and shales.  The
sharpness of the scarp is quite expectable in view of the steeply
inclined, well developed columnar structure, while its straightness
depends on the straight contact between the intrusive sheet of
resistant rock and the weak sandstones below (Figs. 12c and 33).
All the essential features of the Palisades scarp are many times
duplicated in nature, independently of faulting, and hence cannot
be regarded as proof of faulting in any given case.  That faults
parallel to the Hudson are found on Manhattan Island seems no
more a proof that the Hudson valley was determined by faulting,
than is the well-known occurrence of belts of weak rock on Manhattan Island and farther north, also parallel to the Hudson, a
proof that the Hudson valley was determined by normal stream
erosion along a belt of weak rock.  It is pertinent to note, however, that a belt of weak rock has actually been observed at
many points under the Hudson valley, both exposed along the
western margin of the river and reached by drilling beneath the
water; while no important fault has yet been observed there.
Newer terranes occupy an inferior position with respect to older
rocks whenever there is tilting, warping, or folding of the two
formations, as well as when there is faulting.  The same is true
when the newer beds are deposited in an estuary, a favorite theory
of origin for the very beds (the Triassic) which Hobbs is discussing.
It is not easy to see, therefore, how the inferior position of the
Triassic beds affords any evidence in support of the fault theory.
There remains, then, only the evidence of the borings along the
line of the Pennsylvania tunnels.  On this point Hobbs refers to
the description and figure of a section across the Hudson River
showing the geological structure as revealed by the borings.
Hobbs' drawing is here reproduced as the solid-line portion of
Fig. 27.  It shows on the west the westward-dipping weak Triassic sandstones and associated resistant traps; on the east the older
crystallines of Manhattan Island.  The débris partially filling the
Hudson depression completely covers the bedrock over a zone

nearly 3500 feet broad in the middle of the valley, effectually
concealing the nature of the contact. It is obvious from an
inspection of the figure, however, that this contact may be a
normal sedimentary contact, the Triassic sandstones having been
deposited upon the crystallines and the whole then tilted to the
west, as suggested by the dotted portion of the figure. In other
words, the results of the borings appear to give no indication of a
fault along the Hudson. On the contrary, the borings show con-
clusively the presence of a belt of weak sandstones under the
trap, the erosion of which would be sufficient to produce the
valley, whether or not there was any faulting. It is believed
that the Triassic series of this region was deposited directly upon
the crystallines, the whole then tilted to the west, and later

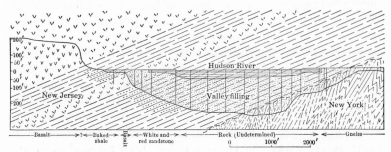

Fig. 27. Section across Hudson River on line of Pennsylvania tunnels.
Solid lines show section as given by Hobbs on basis of drawing furnished
by engineer in charge of borings. Broken lines have been added to show
that the facts as revealed by the borings may be normally interpreted
without assuming the existence of a fault under the river.

peneplaned, in such manner as to expose a belt of weak sandstones
between the trap and the crystallines, which belt was eroded,
following subsequent uplift of the land, to give the Hudson valley.
Even if a fault were to be discovered along the line of the Hudson
it would seem that its presence there must be purely incidental
to the major fact that the valley owes its origin to the easily
eroded belt of sandstone.

    *General Conclusions.* — That there are earth fractures, both
great and small, which have profoundly affected the topography
of the earth's surface, is not open to doubt; and I have already
shown that some of these are indirectly responsible for the form
of significant portions of the New England-Acadian shoreline.
That such fractures sometimes run in parallel series is equally

certain; and examples are found in the region now under consideration (Figs. 13 and 14). That the vast majority of fractures are so hidden or obscured that even where faulting along the fracture has occurred, direct stratigraphic evidence of the break is but rarely obtainable, is a commonplace of geological experience; and the value of physiographic evidence of fractures as an aid to their discovery cannot be too strongly emphasized. That fault fractures are vastly more numerous than many have suspected, seems to me unquestionable; and I believe many of them are discoverable by the aid of physiographic evidence, and by such evidence alone. That the physiographic evidence of faulting, properly interpreted, is as reliable as such stratigraphic evidence as is usually available, I am convinced. It should be clear from this that my inability to follow Hobbs in his interpretation of earth lineaments is not due to any hesitation to utilize topographic as well as other evidences of fracturing. Lest, therefore, the foregoing analysis of the lineament theory as applied to the Atlantic shoreline appear merely an academic discussion in which minor differences of detail are unduly emphasized, the following explicit statement seems desirable:

In so far as the idea of a systematic network of earth fractures, related to centers of seismicity, is put forward as an hypothesis which may account for various rectilinear features of the earth's surface, it seems to me of real value; for it not only emphasizes the probability that faults and other fractures are far more numerous than those we know, raises the important question of their possible great extension across country where concealed by surface débris, stresses the need of utilizing topographic as well as stratigraphic evidence of faulting, and focuses attention on interesting problems of tectonics and seismology; but it also directs the attention of the investigator to specific local field phenomena by suggesting the possibility of a fracture interpretation of them, and so promotes those tests of the hypothesis which, while either disproving it or raising it to the rank of a theory, will incidentally add greatly to the sum of geologic and geographic knowledge. But if the hypothesis is raised to the rank of a theory before adequate field tests are made, and on its basis vast numbers of specific earth features are definitely interpreted as the product of earth fractures, not only in the absence of supporting local evidence but even when local conditions clearly indicate some other origin as possible or even probable, then as a theory it would seem to me dangerous, both in principle and in practice. In principle it seems objectionable because of the undue weight of the personal equation necessarily involved, especially in the selection of many lineaments not pre-determined by long, rectilinear earth features, but based on widely separated shorter features connected by straight lines across broad stretches of country; because of the great weight and far-reaching importance of the superstructure, as compared with the very limited foundation of known geologic facts; and because most of the rectilinear earth features used as the basis of the lineaments are merely assumed to represent fracture lines, without critical enquiry as to whether they may not be the product of one of the many other causes of rectilinear earth forms. In practice the theory seems dangerous because of the inevitable tendency, once it is accepted and applied, to regard as proofs of fracture or faulting, and hence as confirmation of the theory, evidence which *permits* a given interpretation, but which has in reality no *determinative* value; and because the results derived from it in concrete cases do not seem satisfactory. Except for short stretches of shore in the vicinity of Boston Bay, and the northwest shore of the Bay of Fundy (not shown as a lineament on Hobbs' original map but added on the later edition), all of the rectilinear features of the coast on Hobbs' lineament map of the Atlantic border (Fig. 26) appear to be better interpreted as the normal product of the known physiographic history of the region, rather than as the product of extended fractures, of the existence of which there is no satisfactory evidence; although, as shown on earlier pages, there are other parts of the shoreline which may safely be regarded as fault-line-scarp or fault-line-valley shorelines.

**Résumé.** — In the present chapter we have considered the genesis of rectilinear shorelines and have found that shores presenting very similar topographic aspects may characterize coasts which have experienced very different geologic histories. From this it would appear that the tendency to regard rectilinear shorelines as indications of earth fractures, a tendency noted in certain quarters both in America and abroad, is not justified. It would seem, rather, that by far the greater number of rectilinear shorelines must be wholly unrelated to earth fractures; and that among the minority of shorelines which are directly or indirectly dependent upon fracturing, those resulting from the submergence of previously formed fault scarps, and differential erosion scarps developed in faulted rock masses, are much the more numerous. If our analysis of the problem be correct, shorelines due directly to fracturing, or true fault shorelines, should be among the rarest of physiographic phenomena. In respect to the New England-Acadian shoreline, it has been shown that the theory of a geometric network of parallel and more or less regularly spaced and definitely oriented systems of extended earth fractures does not seem to apply; and that almost all of the rectilinear shorelines of this province which on the basis of this theory have been correlated with such fractures, seem to find a normal and reasonable explanation, independently of fracturing, in the known physiographic history of the region.

## BIBLIOGRAPHY

1. HYDE, J. E. Personal communication, by permission of the Director of the Geological Survey of Canada.
2. COLEMAN, A. P. "Physiography and Glacial Geology of Gaspé Peninsula, Quebec." Geol. Surv. Can., Bull. 34, 6, 1922.
3. DAVIS, W. M. "Relation of Geography to Geology." Bull. Geol. Soc. Amer., XXIII, 117, 1912.
   DAVIS, W. M. "A Geographical Pilgrimage from Ireland to Italy." Assoc. Amer. Geog., Annals, II, 93, 1912.
4. JOHNSON, DOUGLAS. "Shore Processes and Shoreline Development," 189, 397, New York, 1917.
5. COTTON, C. A. "Fault Coasts in New Zealand." Geog. Review, I, 20–47, 1916.
6. GOLDTHWAIT, J. W. "The Physiography of Nova Scotia." Manuscript copy of a volume to be issued by the Geological Survey of Canada.
7. WILLIAMS, M. Y. "Arisaig-Antigonish District, Nova Scotia." Geol. Surv. Can., Mem. 60, 93–95 and maps, 1914.
8. HOBBS, W. H. "Lineaments of the Atlantic Border Region." Bull. Geol. Soc. Amer., XV, 483–506, 1904.
9. HOBBS, W. H. "Lineaments of the Atlantic Border Region." Bull. Geol. Soc. Amer., XV, 494, 1904.
10. HOBBS, W. H. "Lineaments of the Atlantic Border Region." Bull. Geol. Soc. Amer., XV, 491 and Plate 45, 1904.
11. HOBBS, W. H. "Earthquakes," 114, New York, 1907.
12. DAVIS, W. M. "The Triassic Formation of Connecticut." U. S. Geol. Surv., 18th Ann. Rept., Pt. II, 155, 165, 1898.
13. DALY, R. A. "The Physiography of Acadia." Bull. Mus. Comp. Zoölogy, XXXVIII, 88, 1901.
14. POWERS, SIDNEY. "The Acadian Triassic." Jour. Geol., XXIV, 258, 1916.
15. HITCHCOCK, EDWARD. "Sketch of the Geology of Portland and its Vicinity." Bost. Jour. Nat. Hist., I, 342, 1837.

16. OGILVIE, I. H.   "A Contribution to the Geology of Southern Maine."
    N. Y. Acad. Sci., Ann., XVII, 519–562, 1907.
17. GANONG, W. F.   "The Origin of the Fundian System of Rivers."   Nat.
    Hist. Soc. New Brunswick, Bull., V, No. XXII, 208, 1904.
18. HOBBS, W. H.   "Lineaments of the Atlantic Border Region."   Bull.
    Geol. Soc. Amer., XV, 489, 1904.
19. HOBBS, W. H.   "Former Extent of the Newark System."   Bull. Geol.
    Soc. Amer., XIII, 143, 1902.
20. HOBBS, W. H.   "Origin of the Channels Surrounding Manhattan Island,
    New York."   Bull. Geol. Soc. Amer., XVI, 180, 1905.

# CHAPTER III

## INITIAL SHORELINES BORDERING WEAK-ROCK LOWLANDS

**Advance Summary.** — Thus far we have dealt primarily with the crystalline uplands and their associated shorelines, and only incidentally with the lowland districts. We now turn our attention more specifically to the so-called Carboniferous and Triassic Lowlands, and in the present chapter will consider first the character of the initial shoreline in these areas. Similar lowlands which have experienced similar physiographic histories should possess shorelines showing analogous features, and our analysis will in part be directed to the elucidation of such analogies. Finally, the question of the supposed great antiquity of the depressions containing the weak rock masses will briefly be touched upon, although this is a question lying too far outside the scope of the present work to receive the fuller treatment its importance merits.

**The Partially Submerged Carboniferous Lowlands.** — The extensive areas underlain by comparatively non-resistant Carboniferous rocks and associated formations (especially Devonian and Permian) were reduced to lowland surfaces during the long period of erosion which followed the uplift of the peneplane now in part preserved on the crystalline uplands, and were maturely dissected in the new fluvial cycle initiated by a later subordinate uplift. These " Carboniferous Lowlands," as they have conveniently been called because of the supposed preponderance of Carboniferous sediments under their floors, constituted one of the chief elements of the subaërial topography prior to the initiation of the present shoreline cycle. One would expect that the subsequent partial submergence of the region would permit the sea to drown, or partially drown, the lowland areas (*B* and *D*, Fig. 1). Such is the origin of Narragansett Bay (Fig. 28), where the seaward portion of a lowland developed on Carboniferous rocks has been partially submerged. Erosion was not so complete and submergence not so extensive but that large areas remain above water to form islands trending nearly north-south with the

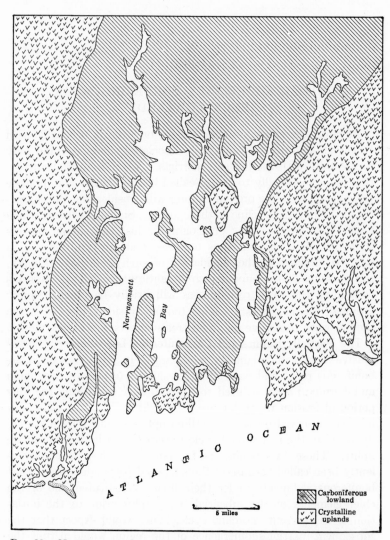

FIG. 28.   Narragansett Bay, a partially submerged lowland on Carboniferous
rocks between crystalline uplands.   Unsubmerged portions of the eroded
north-south folds give north-south islands and peninsulas.   (Geology
modified after Emerson.)   Compare with the Bras d'Or Lakes region,
Fig. 9.

folded structure. Boston Bay is of similar origin, the sea having partially submerged a lowland eroded on Carboniferous rocks between slightly higher crystalline uplands, where the rock belts deviate from their usual southwest-northeast course to curve strongly eastward. Here the harder portions of the Carboniferous series remaining above water are of more limited extent, projecting eastward from the mainland as relatively unimportant peninsulas or rising from the sea to form irregularly distributed small islands. Chaleur Bay, between New Brunswick and the Gaspé Peninsula, is bordered on either side by larger or smaller remnants of Carboniferous rocks, a relation which suggests that this bay also is chiefly the result of extensive submergence of a lowland eroded on Carboniferous formations. Indeed, the broad southern embayment of the Gulf of St. Lawrence, lying between the Gaspé Peninsula and Cape Breton Island, and including Northumberland Strait, appears to represent the drowned seaward portion of the great Carboniferous Lowland of New Brunswick and Nova Scotia. The shores of Cape Breton Island are indented with a number of small bays which have resulted from

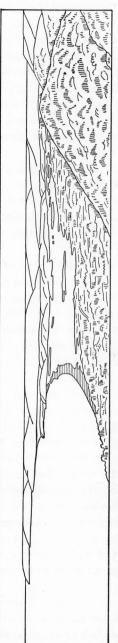

FIG. 29. The partially submerged Carboniferous Lowland of the Aspy Bay region, Cape Breton Island, looking southeast. The higher skyline indicates the remarkably level peneplane surface of the crystalline upland; in the right foreground one gets a glimpse of the steep fault-line scarp bounding the lowland on the northwest; the middle ground shows the lower dissected and partially submerged peneplane developed on the infaulted wedge of weak rock (Carboniferous). Drawn from photos by J. E. Hyde, Geol. Surv. Canada.

the partial submergence of small lowlands developed on Carboniferous beds folded into, or faulted into, the massive crystalline rocks
of that region. Aspy Bay (Fig. 29), North and South Ingonish
Bays, and St. Ann Bay are examples. The Bras d'Or Lakes region
(Fig. 9), with its parallel channels and peninsulas, may best be compared with Narragansett Bay, both regions representing incompletely submerged Carboniferous Lowlands in which the more resistant Carboniferous rocks and occasional patches of crystallines
project above the water as islands and peninsulas elongated in the
direction of the rock folds. In the Cape Breton case the rocks,
usually closely folded, occasionally are flat over fairly large areas,
in which case the river valleys, and hence the bays due to their
partial submergence, have the dendritic, branching pattern characteristic of valleys cut in horizontal rocks. According to Goldthwait[1] the branching pattern of Sydney Harbor is thus to be
explained.

The long southeast shore of Nova Scotia, while broken by
innumerable bays of moderate size, is in its general pattern made
up of two relatively straight segments which meet at a slight
angle some distance southwest of Halifax. Just at the intersection there occurs the great double re-entrant in the shore
formed by Mahone and St. Margaret Bays, the dimension of
which is manifestly out of harmony with the smaller embayments
common to this coast. The shores of both Mahone and St.
Margaret Bays are bordered in places by Carboniferous beds resting on the older crystalline series. Hyde[2] has directed my attention to the significance of this distribution of Carboniferous rocks,
and has suggested that these bays and others along this coast
might represent the pre-Carboniferous topography, exposed by
removal of the weaker beds and then partially submerged. One
may recognize the double embayment as an almost completely
submerged lowland developed on Carboniferous rocks, without
necessarily implying the existence of such a topographic feature in
pre-Carboniferous times. The smaller bays of the coast seem, for
the most part at least, to belong to a distinctly different order, and
may have had no relation to previous lowlands of Carboniferous
or earlier time.

Where areas of Carboniferous rocks bordering extensive crystalline masses are reduced to a low level but not wholly submerged,
we find a low shelf or bench along the coast terminated inland by
a more or less pronounced escarpment rising to the crystalline

upland (Fig. 30).   This is a characteristic element in the coastal
scenery of Cape Breton Island and of other parts of the New
England-Acadian region.   In northern Cape Breton the crystalline
upland (the so-called Cretaceous peneplane) stands 1000 to 1200
feet above sealevel, and on all sides its seaward border is frequently
fringed by narrow strips of Carboniferous lowland.   To one standing upon the upland and looking out over its nearly level surface
(Fig. 29), it presents a monotonous appearance, as different from

FIG. 30.   New Campbellton district, on the Great Bras d'Or channel, Cape
Breton Island.   In the foreground one sees a narrow strip of the Carboniferous Lowland bearing glacial débris and partially submerged at
the left; to the right a steep fault-line scarp rises to the crystalline
upland.   Photo by J. E. Hyde, Geol. Surv. Canada.

the popular conception of mountains as one can well imagine.
But when observed from the sea, the crystalline scarp back of
the lowland strip often rises to the upland level as a rugged and
precipitous slope of very impressive dimensions.[3]   Still more
imposing is the shoreline scenery when submergence has been so
complete that no Carboniferous Lowland shelf remains above
water, and the sea washes directly against the steep crystalline
slope, as in the case of the resurrected peneplane shorelines and
fault-line-scarp shorelines described on earlier pages.

*Southern Embayment of the Gulf of St. Lawrence.* — In the
Carboniferous Lowland which was submerged to form the southern
embayment of the Gulf of St. Lawrence, the beds over broad
areas were exceptionally little disturbed, and there was a central
area of moderately resistant red sandstones, somewhat younger
in geological age (Permian), the whole series lying nearly horizontally, but with a faint dip downward toward the north.

As so often happens in the case of such a structure, erosion fashioned these gently inclined beds into an asymmetrical upland or cuesta, the steeper side of which faced southward, while the gentle backslope descended almost imperceptibly toward the north. Although the northerly dip was thus sufficiently pronounced to determine the major topographic form of the region, the beds lay so nearly flat that streams cutting back into the upland from both the north and the south branched irregularly in all directions, giving the typical dendritic drainage pattern characteristic of horizontal formations, and cutting the upland into a maze of hills with gentle slopes which soon became cloaked with red soil. When submergence drowned the northern section of the lowland to make part of the Gulf of St. Lawrence, as well as a strip of the southern portion which became Northumberland Strait, the cuesta upland remained above water to form Prince Edward Island (Fig. 31). The crescentic form of the Prince Edward Island cuesta and of the drowned lowland of Northumberland Strait suggests that the rock layers, in addition to their slight northward dip, are bent into a shallow downfold or syncline, pitching northward. This would explain, at least in part, the concave form of the southern shore of the Gulf of St. Lawrence, the concave northern shore of Prince Edward Island, and its convex southern shore. In detail the shores of the island are deeply indented by branching bays of a markedly dendritic pattern wherever the sea drowned the dendritic valley systems. Cascumpeque Harbor (Fig. 162) and Malpeque (or Richmond) Bay are exceptionally beautiful examples. The shores of these bays are particularly picturesque, bordered as they are by low hills whose ruddy slopes bear evergreen forests, while shore cliffs and outlying sand reefs glow with a richer red against the blue background of the sea.

While it is true that the remarkable concentric arcs formed by the shores rimming the great southern embayment of the Gulf of St. Lawrence and the southern and northern shores of Prince Edward Island, indicate that the major pattern of the shoreline is determined by a very broad, northeast-pitching syncline, the student of shoreline physiography is impressed by a marked contrast in the pattern of the eastern and western shores of the embayment. The western or New Brunswick shore is less regular; and it would be still less so if spits and bars built by the waves were removed and headlands cut away by the waves were restored (Fig. 31); while the eastern, or Nova Scotia-Cape Breton

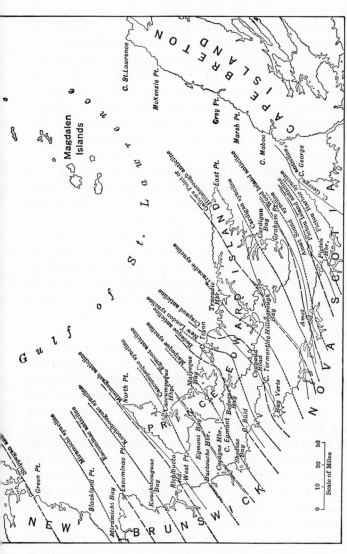

FIG. 31.  Southern embayment of the Gulf of St. Lawrence, showing general arcuate pattern of initial shorelines, apparently due to partial submergence of an eroded broad, shallow, northeast-pitching syncline.  Note initial contrast in detail between the irregular western and central shorelines, and the more simple eastern shoreline;  also relation of headlands and embayments to minor anticlines (broken lines) and synclines (dotted lines), the positions of which are here tentatively located on the basis of shore forms.  The locations of anticlinal axes as given by Ells on the basis of field studies of the poorly exposed structures, shown by solid lines.  Spits and bars have been eliminated, and eroded headlands partially restored to show approximate initial form of the shoreline.

shore is remarkably simple, and would be approximately the same if the effects of wave action were eliminated.  Since there is no difference in exposure to wave attack which could produce a mature shoreline on the east while that on the west remained youthful or submature, the student of shorelines is led to infer an initial difference in pattern due to a difference in geological structure.  The dendritic pattern of the irregularities of the western shore, duplicated in the shores of Prince Edward Island, are of themselves sufficient to suggest that the rocks forming the western and central portions of the basin are but slightly tilted; whereas the initially rectilinear shorelines southwest of Cape George, Nova Scotia, and along the west side of Cape Breton suggest that on this side of the basin the rocks have been steeply tilted or faulted.  The facts appear to support these deductions, for both in eastern New Brunswick and in Prince Edward Island the rocks are known to be more or less nearly horizontal over broad areas, although low anticlines and shallow synclines are reported by Dawson and Harrington,[4] Ells,[5] and others; whereas the rocks of northern Nova Scotia and Cape Breton show the folded structure, accompanied by faulting, typical of the Appalachian province. The importance of faulting in determining indirectly the rectilinear pattern of the shoreline bounding Cape George Peninsula and parts of Cape Breton Island on the west, has already been emphasized.

*Rôle of Shallow Folds in Determining Shore Form.* — Even in shoreline features of the second magnitude there is a suggestion of order which plausibly relates itself to rock structure.  Mention has been made of low anticlines and shallow synclines into which the Carboniferous and Permian beds of New Brunswick and Prince Edward Island have been warped.  The axes of these folds trend southwest-northeast, and the direction of pitch is, like that of the major synclinal basin, gently downward to the northeast.  It is obvious that where erosion has removed weak-rock belts to form lowlands which have later been partially submerged (and such submerged lowland belts are represented by Northumberland Strait and the embayment north of Prince Edward Island), the location of the shallow folds, where they pass obliquely across the lowlands, might be revealed in the pattern of the shorelines.  Thus synclines should, if the soft rocks in the core of the basins are more or less completely etched out, show embayments on northeast-facing shores, like those of New

Brunswick and northern Prince Edward Island; and conversely, (especially where a distinctly resistant member forms a cuesta between the lowlands), southwest-facing shores, like the southern side of Prince Edward Island, should show broad, blunt headlands, or round-pointed " canoe " ends.   Anticlines should show the reverse, — headlands on northeast-facing shores and embayments on southwest-facing shores.

Something clearly suggestive of such a pattern was evident in the initial shorelines of New Brunswick and Prince Edward Island (Fig. 31), and still persists in spite of the modifying influence of wave action.   The Miramichi embayment suggests the presence of a southwest-northeast trending wedge or trough, possibly bounded by a fault on the northwest, while the projecting headlands on either side suggest the presence of parallel anticlines, one of which extends northeast toward the Miscou-Shippegan headland, the other northeastward to form the Escuminac headland.   A Shippegan anticline and a Miramichi syncline have been reported to exist by Robb, whose manuscript notes on the stratigraphy and structure of this part of New Brunswick are quoted by Dawson.[6] South of the Escuminac headland comes the Kouchibouguac embayment suggestive of a syncline, and the Richibucto headland, through which passes the Miminegash anticline of Ells.[7]   Dawson and Harrington[8] draw the axis of this anticline farther southeast, making it pass through the Buctouche embayment; but the physiographic evidence is against this interpretation and in favor of that given by Ells; it even suggests that the axis may possibly be slightly northwest of the position assigned to it by the latter authority.   The Buctouche embayment should then represent a syncline, and across the Strait we find more or less concentric with it the pronounced headland of West Point on Prince Edward Island, with the typical " canoe end " form of a broad, shallow syncline, and definitely shown by Ells to be synclinal in structure. In line with its northeastward prolongation we should expect to find an embayment on the north coast of the island; and precisely at the expected point is one of the chief bays of this coast, the reentrant of Cascumpeque Harbor.   We may therefore call this fold the Cascumpeque syncline.   Cocagne Harbor, south of Buctouche on the New Brunswick shore, has a peculiar rectangular form, is bounded on the east in part by land 100 feet high, and has its main axis extended north-south, all of which suggest that it is an abnormal feature, due possibly to structural conditions, such as faulting, which have here influenced erosional processes more than have the shallow folds. Accepting this interpretation, and noting the position of the high Cocagne headland opposite to, and roughly concentric with, the Egmont embayment on the south coast of Prince Edward Island, the shore forms suggest another anticline on the axis Cocagne headland-Egmont Bay. Ells finds such a structure, and names it the " Egmont anticline." Its prolongation to the north shore of the island should correspond with a headland, and this it appears to do, as Ells represents it as passing through the central portion of the broad headland between Cascumpeque and Malpeque Bays.

Shediac Harbor shows a fairly rectilinear western side, in alignment with the east side of Cocagne Harbor and possibly related to it structurally; but the larger Shediac Bay is a great re-entrant in the coast roughly concentric with the even more striking Cape Egmont headland on the opposite side of the strait. The form on both shores is clearly suggestive of a syncline, and when we find that the prolongation of this axis passes, as should be expected, through a pronounced embayment on the north shore of the island our hypothesis is strengthened. We may call this the Malpeque syncline, from the embayment last mentioned, which is the second of the two major embayments of the north shore. Cape Bald headland is opposed to the Bedeque embayment, and while the opposition is not so clean-cut as in previous cases, it suggests the presence of an anticline the axis of which is deflected more to the east. Stratigraphic evidence seems to support the physiographic interpretation of the structure, for Ells[7] shows his Bedeque Bay anticline as passing through the localities mentioned, and prolonged to reach the north coast of the island at Cape Tryon headland.

Eastward the deflection of the folds, both as indicated by the form and position of headlands and bays, and as represented by Ells on his map of anticlines showing strike and dip of the beds, is more strongly to the east, and hence more obliquely across the strait of Northumberland. The physiographic indications of the folds also become less pronounced than farther west, and do not wholly agree with Ells' conclusions, as will be seen by referring to Fig. 31, where the locations of fold axes as suggested by shoreline form are given for comparison with the axes as reported by Ells. The chief discrepancies are found where Ells prolongs his Tryon anticline to reach the north coast of Prince Edward Island

in an embayment instead of at a headland as we should expect;
and where he prolongs his Gallows Point anticline to be embayed
east coast instead of along the upland to the main headland of
the north coast.   In respect to both of these localities Ells comments on the fact that the shores are low, exposures less frequent,
and the folds apparently flatter, — all conditions tending to make
the solution of structure by stratigraphic methods a particularly
trying matter.   Other workers in the New Brunswick and Prince
Edward Island region emphasize the great difficulty of locating
the folds by observing the strike and dip of beds, a difficulty
which any one who has seen the poor character of the exposures
along the shore, and the abundance of false bedding in the deposit, will fully appreciate.   While the distinction of different
stratigraphic horizons is possibly of greater value in working out
the structure, this also is frequently a matter of difficulty, and
doubt is often expressed as to the certainty of conclusions reached.
Under such circumstances it seems possible that the geologist
may derive much help in his structural studies from the forms of
the shoreline; but here also caution must be observed when the
shallowness of the folds and the lack of striking differences in
rock resistance may permit other factors in the development of
the shoreline to obscure the effects of structure.   The careful
worker will know how to profit by every line of evidence available,
giving each its proper weight, and checking one against the other
in his effort to discover the true relations.   In many cases he will
find the physiography of the shoreline helpfully suggestive;   in
some, of decisive value.

**The Partially Submerged Triassic Lowlands.** — Another important series of red sandstones makes up the great thickness of
easily eroded " Red Beds " of still more recent geological age
(Triassic) which unconformably overlie both the complexly folded
older crystallines and the less strongly folded Carboniferous
formations, and which usually occur in a gently tilted or warped
attitude occupying a limited number of broad basins in the earlier
rocks, produced by warping or faulting (3, Fig. 1).   We have
seen that erosion readily reduced broad areas of these weak rocks
to lowlands of faint relief.   These are the " Triassic Lowlands "
of Acadia, New England, and New Jersey, each of which is bordered
on either side by uplands of the more resistant crystalline rocks,
and each of which has rising from its nearly level floor prominent
ridges (" trap ridges ") formed by the protruding edges of uptilted layers of resistant volcanic rock.

Partial submergence of the Triassic Lowlands (*E*, Fig. 1) would give bays of varying dimensions, the size of the bay depending upon the size of the lowland, the perfection of its reduction to or near sealevel, and the extent of the vertical movement causing the submergence.   If the seaward portion of the lowland were narrow, and if its reduction to sealevel were incomplete, a slight

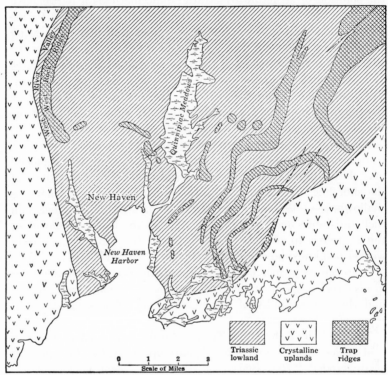

FIG. 32.   New Haven Harbor, formed by partial submergence of the narrow southern end of the New England Triassic Lowland.   Broken lines show faults (West Rock Ridge is traversed by seven or more northeast-southwest faults just north of border of map).   Geology modified after Davis, Gregory, Robinson, and Longwell.

submergence would produce a small bay only.   Such is the case of the Triassic Lowland of New England, the narrow southern end of which, imperfectly reduced (possibly because it was drained by streams that reached the sea by flowing across the resistant crystallines), gave as the result of slight submergence the small New Haven Harbor (Fig. 32).   The Triassic Lowland of New

Jersey is very broad, and in the region west of New York City appears to have been worn down to a very low level. Whether the relative change of sealevel causing submergence was greater here than at New Haven is not easily determined, but it is not necessary to assume a greater change in order to account for the much more extensive submergence of the New Jersey Lowland. Difference in the perfection of baselevelling is alone sufficient to explain the large drowned area represented by part of Upper New York Bay, Hudson River, Newark Bay, and the salt marshes of the Hackensack Meadows (Fig. 14). The influence of rock structure on shoreline form is unusually clear in this region, the parallel sides of the Hudson River and of the Newark Bay-Hackensack Meadows depression being determined by parallel ridges of older crystallines, intrusive igneous rock, and fairly resistant sandstone layers, following the normal northeast-southwest trend of the New England-Acadian structure.

A broad Triassic Lowland well worn down and deeply submerged would give a bay of very large dimensions ($E$, Fig. 1). Such is the Bay of Fundy (Fig. 13). The occurrence of Triassic beds on both sides of the basin, especially on the southeastern side where they may be observed dipping northwestward under the waters of the bay along its entire length, and analogy with the partially submerged Triassic Lowlands described above, justify the conclusion that much of the area is underlain by the weak Triassic formation. It is not practicable to state how far the extensive submergence of the Acadian Triassic Lowland is due to more perfect planation of the weak sandstone series and how far it depends upon a greater vertical change in relative sealevel than occurred in the southern New England and New Jersey regions; but there is reason to suspect a distinctly greater vertical change of sealevel, possibly including a further downwarping along the axis of the Bay.

**Analogous Shorelines of the Partially Submerged Triassic Lowlands.** — The closely analogous geological conditions in the three great Triassic areas discussed above is reflected not only in the formation of a bay in the submerged portion of each Triassic Lowland, but in the whole physiographic aspect of the three regions, even to certain striking details of shore form. The generalized section shown in Fig. 1 will help us to trace this analogy. In this figure $HI$ represents in Acadia the crystalline upland of Nova Scotia sloping southeastward under the waters of the open Atlantic; in the New Jersey section, the crystalline upland of Manhattan and adjacent areas sloping southeastward under East River and Long Island Sound; and in the southern New England region, the crystalline upland of eastern Connecticut sloping southeastward under the Sound. West of this upland one finds in each case the broad Triassic Lowland; and farther west another crystalline upland (*CC*, Fig. 1), the southeastern highlands of New Brunswick in Acadia, the highlands of northern New Jersey in the second case, and the highlands of western Connecticut in the third.

*Subdivision of the Lowlands by Trap Ridges.* — In the lowland itself the projecting edge of a prominent lava sheet, forming a trap ridge (*F*, Fig. 1), separates a broad section of the lowland (*E*) from a long but very narrow section (*G*). In the Acadian region it was the almost complete submergence of this broad section which formed the Bay of Fundy (Fig. 13); in New Jersey very moderate submergence transformed part of it into the Newark Bay-Hackensack Meadows embayment (Fig. 14). When we examine the New Haven region we must remember that in the Connecticut Valley Lowland the Triassic rocks dip in the opposite direction from those in the Acadian and New Jersey Lowlands, with the result that the order of topographic features within the lowland is reversed. Here the broad section of the lowland is *east* of the particular trap ridge in question (West Rock Ridge) and the portion of it drowned by the slight submergence forms part of New Haven Harbor and the Quinnipiac meadows (Fig. 32). The long, narrow section of lowland (*G*, Fig. 1), eroded on the strip of weak sandstones exposed between the lava sheet and the near-by crystallines, was extensively submerged in both the Acadian and New Jersey regions, to give a long, narrow and picturesque body of water. In the Acadian region this water body is interrupted by a low divide (Fig. 34) which rises above sealevel and separates it into two parts, St. Mary Bay in the south and the Annapolis Basin in the north. On the eastern edge of the New Jersey Lowland the narrow embayment is uninterrupted from Staten Island to the Highlands, forming the so-called Hudson River. It is interesting to note that whereas in the Acadian example it is the broad western lowland which is almost completely submerged while the narrow eastern strip is but partially drowned, in the New Jersey case it is the eastern strip which is continuously under water, while the broad western lowland is only partially submerged.   In the New Haven region, where the dip of the Triassic rocks is reversed and the narrow lowland is on the west, the submergence was not sufficient to turn the latter into a narrow arm of the sea.   The lower course of the West River, which drains the narrow belt in question, is drowned and occupied in part by salt marsh; but the waters of the sea do not invade the main West River Valley (Fig. 32) where the lava sheet of West Rock ridge on one hand and the crystalline upland on the other enclose between them a narrow lowland strip otherwise analogous to the drowned valleys of St. Mary Bay-Annapolis Basin and the Hudson River.

*Similarity of the Trap Ridges and Their Bordering Shorelines.* — The trap ridge which separates the broad from the narrow lowland is known in its different sections as North Mountain, Digby Neck, Long and Brier Islands in the Acadian example; as the Palisades ridge in the New Jersey case; and as West Rock ridge in the New Haven case.   In all three the form of the ridge is remarkably similar, and photographs of one might easily be mistaken as representing one of the others.   All three, where typically developed, show a precipitous cliff of columnar igneous rock as the upper part of the front face, with a steep but less precipitous slope below, the latter sometimes covered with a talus of débris from the upper cliff, sometimes exposing to view the underlying red sandstones.   Along the eastern base of the North Mountain ridge (North Mountain, Digby Neck, etc.) the foot of the steep slope is bathed by the waters of St. Mary Bay and Annapolis Basin.   At the eastern base of the Palisades it is the embayed Hudson River which washes the foot of the scarp (Fig. 33).   The rocky crags of the upper cliffs frowning down upon the narrow water body give in each case a bold and picturesque shoreline. If the sealevel were to rise another hundred feet or so in the New Haven region the same shoreline forms would again be duplicated there.

Southward the West Rock ridge trap sheet terminates on land, but the North Mountain and Palisades ridges decline gradually toward the southwest until they pass below sealevel.   This results in bringing the sea directly against the nearly vertical upper cliff with its striking columnar structure, and in the case of the southwestern extension of North Mountain gives a shoreline of imposing beauty where one may see " the Atlantic swell bursting in all its grandeur on these iron-bound shores."   Unfortunately in the

Palisades case a position sheltered from the waves of the open ocean, the water-front structures of a great port, an unsubmerged remnant of adjacent rocks, and an area of salt marsh, all combine to rob this part of the shoreline of an impressiveness which it would otherwise possess. A curious feature of the North Mountain trap sheet is its double character in the Digby Neck-Long Island-Brier Island section, where an upper and a lower hard portion are separated by an intermediate vesicular phase of the trap which is easily eroded to form a ravine along the summit of the ridge. The effect of this upon the shoreline is readily

FIG. 33.    Rectilinear shoreline of the Hudson River embayment at base
of Palisades, above New York City.

apparent at the ends of Brier Island and the southwest end of Long Island, where the sea invades the ravine to give a little bay flanked by capes representing the double crest of the ridge (Fig. 34).

In all three of the cases under consideration the top of the trap ridge is more nearly flat than it would otherwise be, due to the bevelling effect of the erosion which once planed all the rocks down to the level of the crystalline upland (Fig. 12); and in all three the backslope of the ridge, declining downward with the dip of the beds, is typically more gentle than the front face. It should be noted, however, that faulting (see below), steepening of the dip of the beds, and other factors may operate locally to make the backslope quite steep.

*Effects of Oblique Faulting.* — In all three cases the trap ridge is repeatedly cut across obliquely by transverse faults in some sections, and bent or warped in others; and in the North Mountain and Palisades examples, where submergence has brought the sea against the trap ridges, these geological structures have intimately affected the form of the shoreline. The oblique faults

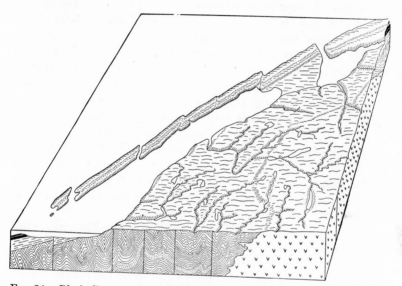

FIG. 34. Block diagram of the North Mountain-Digby Neck trap ridge and associated features, showing peneplaned crystalline upland of Nova Scotia, northwest-dipping Triassic series with double trap sheet, narrow embayed lowland of St. Mary Bay and Annapolis Basin, part of submerged broad lowland of Bay of Fundy, and north-south faults responsible for oblique offsetting of trap ridge. Based in part on an unpublished diagram by Goldthwait.

or breaks in the continuity of the trap ridge sometimes involve but little apparent displacement, and are evident mainly from a slight offset or jog in the face or backslope (or both) of the ridge. Such is the case with the Palisades ridge, and the slight offsets are repeatedly accompanied by slight but distinct offsets of the western shoreline of the Hudson River embayment (Fig. 14). It is easy to see that if streams had carved important valleys along the fault lines, the continuity of the trap ridge would be interrupted, and submergence might transform the ridge into a succession of islands, separated by broad or narrow straits depending on the width of the fault-line valleys, and offset more or less according to the amount of the displacement. Turn now to a map of the Bay of Fundy (Fig. 13), and note how significant is its eastern shoreline. The great trap ridge of North Mountain is repeatedly offset in a manner which is frequently more striking than in the Palisades case; and at some of the offsets the sea breaks through, with the result that the southwestern portion of the ridge is broken up into the peninsula of Digby Neck and two islands, Long and Brier. The lozenge-shaped form of the islands and of the Neck, the approximately parallel position of the straits of Digby Gut, Petit Passage and Grand Passage, and the systematic offsetting of the shore to the north as one passes southwestward, are precisely what should be expected if the trap sheet were cut by a series of north-south faults, the western block raised in each case, the whole then peneplaned, uplifted, dissected, and partially submerged (Fig. 34). At several places on Digby Neck the North Mountain trap ridge is offset by faulting where there are no straits, because there were no through-going valleys, or none deep enough to be submerged; but the shoreline offsets in sympathy with the fault structure, just as in the case of the Palisades ridge.*

*Effects of Warped Portions of the Trap Sheets.* — Near its northern end the Palisades trap sheet was warped into a shallow downfold or syncline, the axis of which pitches downward toward the west-southwest. As a result, when bevelled by the erosion which planed the region down to a nearly level surface ("Cretaceous" peneplane), the outcrop of the trap sheet curved strongly around to the north, northwest and west; and when uplift permitted further erosion to reduce the weak red sandstones on both sides to a new lowland level, this part of the trap sheet remained as a prominent ridge curving in the direction indicated. Had sub-

---

* Stratigraphic evidence of faulting is obscure or lacking at many of the offsets and transverse gaps; but the physiographic evidence of faulting is so clear that the position of the fault and the direction of displacement may be determined with much confidence, as has been recognized by Daly[9] and others. Bailey's suggestion[10] that the transverse valley and straits (the trend of which he correlates with the direction of glacial striæ in the region) may be partly or wholly due to the excavating action of glacial streams, would account for part of the phenomena only; and no evidence is presented which indicates that the ice or glacier-borne streams have greatly modified the forms produced by normal stream erosion upon a faulted trap sheet.

mergence of the New Jersey Lowland been more extensive, the northern end of the Palisades would now form a peculiar curving peninsula or island, tapering to a point somewhere southwest of Haverstraw (Fig. 35).

That the northern end of the North Mountain trap sheet is similarly warped into a shallow syncline, the axis of which pitches west or possibly slightly south of west, is clearly suggested by the shore form which outlines a peculiar peninsula curving north, northwest and west, to end in a point at Cape Split (Fig. 13). It is the blunt eastern arc of the curve, near the axis of the syncline where the face of the trap ridge looks eastward up the Basin of Minas, that is called Cape Blomidon. The Basin of Minas itself has a form and position which harmonize

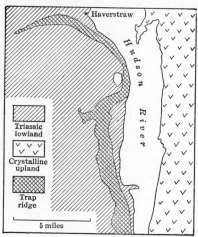

Fig. 35.   Curved northern end of Palisades trap ridge due to warping of Triassic formation (after New Jersey Geological Survey).   Compare with northern end of North Mountain trap ridge, Nova Scotia (Fig. 13).

with the interpretation that it is a drowned lowland excavated on weak Triassic sandstones of the Cape Blomidon syncline prolonged eastward, an interpretation early recognized and partly confirmed by the finding of Triassic sandstones on both sides of the Basin dipping toward its centre.   The other chief branch of the Fundy depression, known as Chignecto Bay, exhibits somewhat different relations, and seems to have resulted from the submergence of a lowland developed on Carboniferous and Permian beds.

*Three Parallel Trap Ridges.* — If the Triassic Lowland of Connecticut were to be more deeply submerged, the faulted and warped trap ridges of that region would give a remarkable series of islands separated by fault-line straits and sharply offset one from the other, and a number of beautifully curving peninsulas or islands.   But the best cases of curved forms would be found in connection with another series of trap ridges, not yet discussed, which lie some distance across the lowland, east of West Rock

(Fig. 32).   These ridges represent the exposed edges of three principal trap sheets found higher up in the sandstone series, above the
West Rock sheet.[11]   In the New Jersey Triassic Lowland we find
a similar series of additional ridges, likewise developed on three
trap sheets higher in the series than the Palisades sheet, but
lying west of the Palisades because of the westward dip of the
New Jersey Triassic.[12]   At first glance the analogy seems to fail
when we come to the Acadian area, where the three ridges formed
by higher trap sheets should, if present, appear to the west of
the North Mountain-Digby Neck ridge.   But note the words
of Perley[13] in his report on the fisheries of New Brunswick, which
have a peculiar significance for us in the present connection:
" From Black Rock (near the northeastern end of North Mountain ridge) down to Brier Island, along the whole south shore
(of the Bay of Fundy), there are three fishing banks or ledges,
lying parallel to the shore, outside each other;  their respective
distances from the coast have acquired for them the designations
of the three-mile ledge, — the five-mile ledge, — and the nine-
mile ledge.   Between these ledges there are sixty fathoms of
water, but on the crown of each ledge, thirty fathoms only. . . .
Each of these ledges is about a mile in width, the outer one something more."   We may have here, wholly submerged beneath the
waters of the Bay, the three trap ridges which are required to
complete the analogy between the trap ridge topography of the
Connecticut, New Jersey and Acadian Triassic Lowlands.   It is
possible, as Russell[14] has pointed out, that faulting might cause
the North Mountain-Digby Neck trap sheet to be repeated three
times to the westward;  but to account for three ridges paralleling
the coast for great distances by the fault hypothesis requires that
the faults should all be parallel strike faults with a fairly uniform
displacement throughout the distance in question.   It would
seem more reasonable to regard the ridges as independent features,
analogous to the series of three such ridges known to occur above
the lower trap sheet in the Connecticut and New Jersey cases.
It should be pointed out, however, that the coast charts fail to
indicate any such pronounced and continuous submarine ridges
as Perley describes.

   *Isolated Remnants of Trap Ridges.* — Inasmuch as the groups
of three trap ridges observed in the Connecticut and New Jersey
Lowlands are not reached by the sea at any point, while in the
Acadian Lowland the corresponding group, if it exists, is completely

covered by the sea, we have no present shore forms to study in connection with these series. There are, however, in the Acadian area, several disconnected remnants of trap ridges the precise relations of which are not clear, but which materially affect the form of the shoreline. An interesting series of these trap remnants is found scattered along the northern shores of the Basin of Minas and Minas Channel, where their extremely resistant character tends to make them stand forth from the mainland as salient peninsulas or capes, or to rise as islands some distance out from shore. Thus the trap ridge of Gerrish Mountain (Fig. 13), the easternmost of the series, not only projects southwestward from the main- land as a blunt cape, but is continued westward for four miles into the sea by a succession of trap ridge islands, believed by Powers[15] to be separated from each other by faults. " To a traveller who . . . toward the close of day ascends the steep side of Gerrish's Mountain, the view which greets him at the summit is of the most grand and striking character. The rocky chain of the Five Islands, and the pretty inlet and settlement on the shore within them, lie at his feet. In front are the waters of Minas Basin stretching far to the westward. On the one hand is the rugged and picturesque trappean shore extending (west- ward) toward Parrsboro, with the Cobequid Mountains ranged behind it. On the other, Blomidon and Cape Split tower in the distance. I may remark here, that for grandeur and beauty of coast scenery, this part of Minas Basin and the Minas Channel are not surpassed by any part of the eastern coast of North America."[16]

The " trappean shore extending toward Parrsboro " refers to the succession of islands and headlands projecting out to sea which constitute the most striking element in the coastal scenery for the next fifteen miles or more to the westward. Clarke Head, Par- tridge Island (a trap island now tied to the mainland by a wave- built beach or tombolo), and Cape Sharp are the most prominent of these trap projections, the latter two being particularly noted for the bold cliffs on their seaward faces. But most impressive of all is the great trap mass of Cape d'Or, much farther west and standing far out into the Minas Channel. The prominence of Cape d'Or as a shore feature is accentuated by the fact that just back of it the mainland consists of the weak Triassic sandstones worn down to a very low level, a condition which we recognize as the normal, expectable thing; and which indeed is likewise partly responsible for the bold appearance of Partridge Island and Cape Sharp.[17]

A dozen miles to the westward of Cape d'Or the little Isle Haut rises alone from the broad expanse of the Bay of Fundy, bravely opposing its precipitous trap walls to the angry waves attacking it from all points of the compass; while far away to the southwest, the large island of Grand Manan[18] shows the last of the trap remnants of this region in the wild and picturesque crags which rim its northern and western sides for a distance of many miles. The western side " presents a bold front of overhanging cliffs and lofty mural precipices of majestic grandeur and beauty. . . . Deep caverns are worn out of the solid base of the lofty wall, which tumbles headlong into the sea beneath. . . . The northern side of the island will average from three to four hundred feet in height. Its lofty mural cliffs stand like rude imitations of masonry, and rival in grandeur those of the celebrated Cape Blomidon in Nova Scotia. The rock at many places is perfectly basaltic, and appears like large pieces of squared timber placed upright side by side, with a perfection and beauty equal to the basaltic columns of Staffa. These are met by enormous blocks of rhomboidal and amorphous trap, which from their architectural arrangement appear to have been laid by the skill and ingenuity of man. At Northern Head . . . the precipice will average two hundred and forty feet in height, and stands majestically fronting the sea."[19] Powers[20] states that the straight western side of Grand Manan is a fault-line scarp, but as he fails to give the evidence upon which his conclusion is based, one is left in doubt whether he regards the rectilinear form of the shore as sufficient indication of faulting, or whether he found other proof.

*Fault-Line Scarps Bordering the Lowlands.* — When the Triassic beds of the Connecticut Valley and New Jersey regions are followed down the dip, they appear to be cut off by major faults where they come in contact with the crystallines. Partial removal of the weak Triassic sandstones and shales has thus exposed to view a fault-line cliff on the eastern side of the Connecticut Valley Lowland, and on the western side of the New Jersey Lowland. The remarkable analogy between the three great Triassic basins which we have discussed would at least suggest that the Triassic beds of the Acadian region might likewise be cut off down the dip, or on the northwest, to give a fault contact with the crystallines of New Brunswick. While there are but few areas of Triassic preserved on the northwest side of the Bay of Fundy which might show the nature of this contact, those few appear to support the theory of an important fault or fault zone bordering the New Brunswick coast, along which line of fracture Triassic beds to the southeast were dropped (relatively) downward, and the crystallines to the northwest were raised.[21]    There is other evidence that the New Brunswick shoreline, which maintains a fairly straight northeast-southwest course for many miles, represents a fault-line scarp, now much worn by erosion, against which the sea came to rest as a result of the extensive submergence of the Acadian Triassic Lowland.   Much of this shore is characterized by rocky cliffs from 50 to 200 feet high, while the straightest part of the shore, between small Triassic exposures at Quaco and Waterside, is a nearly continuous line of cliffs rising 400 feet above the sea.[22]   This rectilinear line of cliffs appears to be part of a dissected fault-line scarp which continues far to the southwest under the sea off the coast of Maine, marking what I have called the "Fundian Fault," described at some length in a later chapter.

**Supposed Antiquity of the Carboniferous and Triassic Basins.** — In closing our consideration of the initial shore features produced by the partial submergence of the Carboniferous and Triassic Lowlands of the New England-Acadian region, it is desirable to refer briefly to the great antiquity assigned to the basins containing those rocks by many of the geologists who have dealt with them. It seems to be generally accepted that the great Bay of Fundy depression, for example, is much older than the post-Triassic down-warping or down-faulting which gave the beds of that region their present attitude, — very much older, even, than the Triassic period during which those beds were deposited.   Dana[23] assumed an "Acadian Channel," including the site of the present Bay of Fundy, as having been formed between Archæan ranges in northwestern New Brunswick and in Nova Scotia as early as the end of Archæan time.   Bailey[24] has discussed "The Bay of Fundy Trough in American Geological History," at some length, showing that Dana's ideas require much revision, but himself concluding that the northwestern border of the Bay of Fundy trough was outlined, approximately in its present position, at the opening of the Cambrian era; and that this trough was a subsiding geosyncline from Precambrian times through the Triassic.   The position of the southwest border of the trough is considered doubtful until late Devonian or Carboniferous time, when it

was fixed not far from where we now find it. Daly[25] accepts
Bailey's conclusion that the Bay of Fundy trough was delimited
on the northwest by the beginning of Cambrian time and on the
southeast during the late Devonian; and says "the estuary was
filled with Lower Carboniferous sediments" which were first
folded and then partially eroded, after which the estuary witnessed the deposition of Triassic beds upon the remnants of the
Carboniferous. Powers[26] seems to favor the interpretation of the
Bay of Fundy region as a slowly subsiding geosyncline, in Triassic
time at least. These are but random examples of a conception
which constantly recurs, in one form or another, throughout the
literature describing the geological history of Acadia, — the conception that the Bay of Fundy is an ancient trough which has
persisted more or less successfully throughout vast geological ages,
repeatedly serving as a local basin or estuary in which successive
geological formations were deposited, contorted, and partially removed by erosion. The same interpretation is frequently applied
in greater or less degree to the Carboniferous basins, including
very small basins like that of the Aspy district (Fig. 21), the
margins of these lowlands being interpreted as shorelines of an
embayment in the Carboniferous sea. Even parts of the present
river valleys are in some cases assumed to have been in existence
in Carboniferous, Devonian, or more remote geological eras, as in
the case of St. John River, to sections of which Bailey,[27] Matthew,[28]
and others assign such ancient dates. Clarke[29] describes the
basins of Gaspé Bay and Mal Bay as representing two of the
"very few places in this world where the ancient topography of a
country which it acquired in the very making has been unaltered
with time and is still retained in the present configuration."
But elsewhere he recognizes that the present outlines of these
basins are probably "of comparatively recent date" and due in
part to relatively recent submergence.[30] That the Connecticut
Valley Lowland was an estuary like the Bay of Fundy in Triassic
times, is a favorite theory with a number of the geologists who have
concerned themselves with the origin of the New England Triassic,
and the same theory has been applied to the New Jersey Triassic.

It seems doubtful whether local basins of moderate size, much
less very small basins and sections of narrow river valleys, can
survive a long geological history known to have involved several
periods of profound disturbance of the beds, separated by periods
of peneplanation and renewed deposition. The discussions in

which an ancient date of origin is attributed to present topographic forms rarely take sufficient account of the fact that these forms may perhaps be explained as the product of erosion upon infaulted or infolded belts of weak rock which reached their present position at some date later than that in which the beds concerned were deposited. In some of the cases, at least, there is clear evidence that the margins of the basins are not old shorelines or valley sides of ancient date, but fault lines of much more recent origin, or sedimentary contacts more recently tilted to a steep angle during a period of active disturbance of the strata. Russell[31] has advanced arguments in support of the contentions that the Triassic deposits originally formed a broad terrane extending far beyond the present limits of the formation, and that these present limits have been in large part, if not wholly, determined by faulting and erosion. In support of these conclusions Hobbs[32] and Grabau[33] have added some further considerations. The evidence presented in support of an ancient date for the basins and valleys in question does not seem wholly convincing, even when we give full weight to that furnished by marine faunas, and to the physical evidence of conglomerates adjacent to the supposed ancient shorelines or basin margins. Faunal evidence seldom is sufficiently determinative to permit the drawing of land outlines with precision and confidence, as the constantly changing interpretations of paleogeography sufficiently attest; while Davis[34] and Russell[35] have argued that the conglomeratic phases of the Triassic cannot safely be interpreted as indicating the former margins of the deposit. The presence of Triassic, Carboniferous, and older deposits on both sides of a basin, whether dipping toward the centre of the basin or not, affords no proof that there was a similar basin in existence when those beds were deposited; for later warping, folding, or faulting may at one and the same time have given to the beds their present attitude and have brought them in considerable part so low that still later peneplanation left them as an unremoved belt of weak rocks. Subsequent erosion in a new cycle following uplift would, by removing the weak rocks in whole or in part, give to the basin its first existence as a topographic feature.

In view of the greatly increased knowledge of conditions of sedimentation, principles of paleogeography, and physiographic processes which modern students possess as compared with the earlier workers in this region, it would seem advisable critically to re-examine the question of origin of each of the basins and valleys supposed to date from very ancient geological times. While there is nothing inherently improbable in the conception that so large a basin as that of the Bay of Fundy might repeatedly be an area of subsidence in the course of geological history, the possibility of an alternative interpretation should be held clearly in view until evidence of compelling value shall demonstrate the correctness of the theory of ancient origin and long persistence. It seems not improbable that when the problem is critically re-examined, it may be found that most of the smaller basins and valleys, and possibly some of the larger ones as well, will date no farther back than the erosion period following uplift of the so-called Cretaceous peneplane. Nor should it seem surprising if the ultimate conclusion was to the effect that few if any of the larger basins had outlines closely resembling those of the present at any earlier date than the Tertiary, although Barrell,[36] Longwell,[37] Foye,[38] and W. L. Russell[39] have presented evidence which seems to indicate that during part at least of Triassic time one border of the Connecticut Triassic basin, the eastern, was already determined by the fault which now marks the eastern wall of the lowland. To pursue this problem further here, would carry us too far afield from our study of present day shorelines.

Résumé. — In the preceding paragraphs we have considered the origin of some of the most important embayments of the New England-Acadian shoreline, and have briefly noted the initial characters of those segments of shoreline bordering the embayed lowlands. Our study has revealed the existence of analogies of shoreline pattern and shore form which might escape the notice of the casual observer. Thus the resemblances between the Narragansett Bay, Boston Bay, and Bras d'Or Lakes shorelines are found to be much closer than might at first appear. The close analogy between Aspy Bay and Chedabucto Bay was revealed in the preceding chapter; but it still remained to point out the most remarkable analogy of all, — that existing between the shorelines of the partially submerged Triassic Lowlands of the Bay of Fundy, the Connecticut Valley, and the Newark Bay-Hudson River region. The effects of folded, faulted, and horizontal structures upon details of shoreline pattern in the lowlands have been noted, and on a larger scale the arcuate shorelines of the Northumberland Strait embayment and Prince Edward Island have been explained as the normal consequence of partial submergence of a curved cuesta and lowland eroded on a broad and shallow pitching syncline. The great antiquity sometimes assigned to the basins containing the Carboniferous and Triassic sediments has tentatively been questioned, especially in the case of the smaller basins and restricted portions of river valleys; but no attempt has been made to solve this one of the many problems presented by the lowland areas.

## BIBLIOGRAPHY

1. GOLDTHWAIT, J. W. "The Physiography of Nova Scotia." Manuscript copy of a volume to be issued by the Geological Survey of Canada.
2. HYDE, J. E. Personal communication, by permission of the Director of the Geological Survey of Canada.
3. WRIGHT, W. J. "Geology of Clyburn Valley, Cape Breton." Geol. Surv. Can., Summ. Rept. for 1913, 271, 1914.
4. DAWSON, J. W., and HARRINGTON, B. J. "Report on the Geological Structure and Mineral Resources of Prince Edward Island," 51 pp., Montreal, 1871.
5. ELLS, R. W. "Report on the Geology of Prince Edward Island with Reference to Proposed Borings for Coal." Geol. Surv. Can., Summ. Rept. for 1902, 367–377, 1903.
6. DAWSON, J. W. "Acadian Geology," 2nd Ed., 228, London, 1868.
7. ELLS, R. W. "Report on the Geology of Prince Edward Island with Reference to Proposed Borings for Coal." Geol. Surv. Can., Summ. Rept. for 1902, 367–377, 1903. See map.
8. DAWSON, J. W., and HARRINGTON, B. J. "Report on the Geological Structure and Mineral Resources of Prince Edward Island." 51 pp., Montreal, 1871. See map.
9. DALY, R. A. "The Physiography of Acadia." Bull. Mus. Comp. Zoölogy, XXXVIII, 92, 1901.
10. BAILEY, L. W. "Preliminary Report on Geological Investigations in Southwestern Nova Scotia." Geol. Surv. Can., Ann. Rept. for 1892–93, VI, Rept. Q, 16, 1895.
    BAILEY, L. W. "Notes on the Geology and Botany of Digby Neck." Nova Scotian Inst. Sci., Proc. and Trans., 2nd Ser., II, 74, 1898.
11. DAVIS, W. M. "The Triassic Formation of Connecticut." U. S. Geol. Surv., 18th Ann. Rept., Pt. II, 9–192, 1898.
12. DARTON, N. H. "The Relations of the Traps of the Newark System in the New Jersey Region." U. S. Geol. Surv., Bull. 67, 84 pp., 1890.
13. PERLEY, M. H. "Reports on the Sea and River Fisheries of New Brunswick," 2nd Ed., 159, Fredericton, 1852.
14. RUSSELL, I. C. "The Newark System." U. S. Geol. Surv., Bull. 85, 80, 1892.
15. POWERS, SIDNEY. "The Acadian Triassic." Jour. Geol., XXIV, 25, 26, 257, 1916.
16. DAWSON, J. W. "Acadian Geology," 2nd Ed., 101, London, 1868.
17. DAWSON, J. W. "Acadian Geology," 2nd Ed., 105–107, London, 1868.

18. BAILEY, L. W. "On the Physiography and Geology of the Island of Grand Manan." Can. Nat., N. Ser., VI, 43–54, 1872.

19. GESNER, ABRAHAM. "First Report on the Geological Survey of the Province of New Brunswick," 33–36, St. John, 1839.

20. POWERS, SIDNEY. "The Acadian Triassic." Jour. Geol., XXIV, 10, 1916.

21. POWERS, SIDNEY. "The Acadian Triassic." Jour. Geol., XXIV, 1–26, 105–122, 254–268, 1916.

22. POWERS, SIDNEY. "The Acadian Triassic." Jour. Geol., XXIV, 3, 1916.

23. DANA, J. D. "Manual of Geology," 4th Ed., 461, New York, etc., 1895.

24. BAILEY, L. W. "The Bay of Fundy Trough in American Geological History." Roy. Soc. Can., Proc. and Trans., 2nd Ser., III, Sec. IV, 107–116, 1897.

25. DALY, R. A. "The Physiography of Acadia." Bull. Mus. Comp. Zoölogy, XXXVIII, 85, 1901.

26. POWERS, SIDNEY. "The Acadian Triassic." Jour. Geol., XXIV, 255, 1916.

27. BAILEY, L. W. "On the Physical and Geological History of the St. John River, New Brunswick." Roy. Soc. Can., Proc. and Trans., I, Sec. IV, 281–284, 1882.

28. MATTHEW, G. F. "The Outlets of the St. John River." Nat. Hist. Soc. New Brunswick, Bull., III, No. 12, 43–62, 1894.

29. CLARKE, JOHN M. "L'Île Percée," 108, 159, New Haven, 1923.

30. CLARKE, JOHN M. "Early Devonic History of New York and Eastern North America." N. Y. State Mus., Mem. 9, Pt. 1, 17, 1908.

31. RUSSELL, I. C. "The Newark System." U. S. Geol. Surv., Bull. 85, 101–107, 1892.

32. HOBBS, W. H. "Former Extent of the Newark System." Bull. Geol. Soc. Amer., XIII, 139–148, 1902.

33. GRABAU, A. W. "Text Book of Geology," II, 613, 1921.

34. DAVIS, W. M. "The Structure of the Triassic Formation of the Connecticut Valley." U. S. Geol. Surv., 7th Ann. Rept., 461, 1888.

35. RUSSELL, I. C. "The Newark System." U. S. Geol. Surv., Bull. 85, 105, 1892.

36. BARRELL, JOSEPH. "Central Connecticut in the Geologic Past." Conn. Geol. and Nat. Hist. Surv., Bull. No. 23, 44 pp., 1915.

37. LONGWELL, C. R. "Notes on the Structure of the Triassic Rocks in Southern Connecticut." Amer. Jour. Sci., 5th Ser., IV, 223–236, 1922.

38. FOYE, W. G. "Origin of the Triassic Trough of Connecticut." Jour. Geol., XXX, 690–699, 1922.

39. RUSSELL, W. L. "The Structural and Stratigraphic Relations of the Great Triassic Fault of Southern Connecticut." Amer. Jour. Sci., 5th Ser., IV, 483–497, 1922.

# CHAPTER IV

## INITIAL SHORELINES DETERMINED BY GLACIAL FORMS

**Advance Summary.** — Thus far we have dealt with the broader features of the New England-Acadian shoreline as determined by submergence of what we might term the " bedrock topography " of the province. We have still to consider the rôle of an unconsolidated formation which in a variety of forms has materially affected the detailed character of parts of the shore. This is the *glacial drift* which during the glacial period was spread as a discontinuous sheet of variable thickness and composition over both New England and Acadia, and which necessarily determined in some degree the initial form of the shoreline wherever the sea came to rest against portions of the coast mantled over with glacial deposits. In a later chapter we shall see that the sequential forms of the shoreline are of particular interest where carved in glacial deposits, for the reason that shoreline development proceeds much more rapidly in non-resistant than in resistant materials. Here we are primarily concerned with the initial shoreline. Consideration is first given to the possible effects of glacial erosion upon the initial shore forms, particularly in the case of the so-called " fjord coasts " of Maine and Nova Scotia. The characteristic features of moraine shorelines, outwash plain shorelines, drumlin shorelines, delta plain shorelines, kame and esker shorelines, and ground moraine shorelines are then described, and attempts made to reconstruct the initial forms of some of these shorelines where the present form is the result of extended wave erosion.

**Initial Shoreline as Affected by Glacial Erosion.** — Before considering the initial shore features due to glacial deposition, it is pertinent to enquire whether glacial erosion materially affected the New England-Acadian shoreline. It is a well-known fact that nearly all, if not all, of the New England-Acadian province was overrun by ice moving outward from a main centre of accumulation east of Hudson Bay, and possibly also from a local centre in the highlands of northern New Brunswick and the Gaspé

Peninsula. Goldthwait[1] has presented evidence which seems to disprove the theory of J. H. Wilson[2] that a great centre of accumulation in Newfoundland was the source of the ice which passed over Cape Breton Island and Nova Scotia. The direction of ice advance was eastward, southeastward and southward over most of Acadia and New England, or in general more or less nearly at right angles to the trend of much of the shoreline. Thus the ice would not only have the usual opportunity to remove the deep residual soil formed in pre-glacial times, and to smooth the deeper fresh rock into the grooved and polished roche moutonnée forms which are so familiar a feature of the rocky coasts of this region; but one must consider the possibility that where it moved along the valleys of seaward-flowing streams, it might erode them more effectively than if it were moving at right angles to them, and might even send long glacier tongues down such valleys to the shore and beyond. Under these conditions the maximum differential effects of ice erosion upon the land might be expected, and hence the greatest modifying effects of ice upon the shoreline which resulted from partial submergence of the land.

There can be no doubt that the ice sheet has determined certain minor characteristics of the New England-Acadian shoreline. The " bold and rocky shores " which figure so prominently in descriptions of this coast often owe their barren surfaces and minor details of form largely to ice erosion. Even where the waves have stripped away glacial deposits and left the bedrock bare, as is the case with some of the outer islands and other exposed portions of the coast, it was the ice sheet which changed a deeply soil-covered upland to a smoothly scoured ledge of undecayed rock, and then mantled it over with a coat of loose débris. As a rule these glaciated ledges have not been greatly altered by post-glacial wave erosion, and the modelling of the icy finger can readily be traced in many shore details.

When we approach the question of possible major effects of the ice sheet upon shore forms, the problem is not so simple. If glacial erosion operated uniformly over the whole surface, planing all parts down in equal measure, it is obvious that we would have today shore forms identical with those of pre-glacial times, but shifted inland little or much according as the amount of land surface evenly removed was small or great. In these circumstances, however, there would be no measure of glacial modification, and one would perforce remain in doubt as to whether the ice had merely removed the soil cover, or had cut far into the unaltered rock.   In other words, the shore would not be different in kind as a result of glaciation, and doubt must exist as to whether it was even appreciably different in position.

Very different is the case where restricted portions or currents of the ice sheet cut more deeply than adjacent portions, whether because these currents occupied pre-glacial valleys and were therefore of greater thickness, or because belts of weak rock were more deeply excavated when the erosive force applied to them was the same as that exerted on adjacent hard-rock areas, even when the two rock types originally had the same surface level.   The last supposition is more theoretical than practical, for it assumes that pre-glacial weathering and erosion had failed to reduce the weak-rock belts to a lower level than that of the resistant formations, an assumption of doubtful validity except in special rare instances.   The usual condition will be that in which the ice sheet finds an uneven land surface much dissected by valleys developed along weak-rock belts and elsewhere.   There can be no doubt that this was the situation in the New England-Acadian region when the glaciers advanced over it.

Where the ice moved transversely across the valleys of such a region it would seem that the conditions favoring glacial erosion must be at a minimum in the valleys, where stagnant or slowly moving ice would work with little efficiency, while the hill tops might be extensively planed down.   The net result of glaciation in this case would be to reduce the relief of the land by an amount equal to the total amount of glacial erosion on the upland, and thus to leave the topography more subdued than it was in pre-glacial times.   On the other hand, if the ice flowed as thick glacial streams along the valleys, and on the intervening uplands it was thin, or stagnant, or wholly wanting, the valleys would suffer deepening while the uplands remained unmodified; and the net result would be an increase of the topographic relief, equal to the total amount of glacial erosion in the valleys.   If the ice moved parallel with the valley system, both on the upland and in the valleys, the greater thickness in the valleys might not cause markedly greater erosion there, especially if the ice over both upland and valleys was very thick.   In this case both the net change in the relief and the total amount of erosion would remain a matter of doubt.   It is obvious that regions of high relief, in which lofty uplands alternate with deeply trenched valleys, would be more apt to witness intense and long-continued glaciation in the valleys with little or no ice action on the uplands, than would regions of faint relief where shallow valleys and low divides must be buried under an almost equal thickness of ice for an equal period of time.

*Supposed Fjord Coasts of New England and Acadia.* — It has sometimes been assumed that in the region under discussion the surface of the land was profoundly modified by the continental ice sheet, and that the general character of the shore is the result of glacial action. Of the deeply indented coast of southwestern Nova Scotia Bailey writes: " The indentations referred to are veritable fjords, and even were there no other evidence than that of position, form, and depth, they would at once be recognized as marking a former period of excessive glaciation."[3] Of the Yarmouth section of this coast, where " the shore is wonderfully broken and ragged, presenting a continuous succession of bays and inlets," he says: " No more remarkable illustration of the effects of glacial action in modifying ocean contours could well be found."[4] In an account of the coast of Maine and adjacent areas Shaler[5] wrote: " The outline of this coast . . . is believed to be mainly the product of the peculiar form of erosion brought about by one or more glacial periods;" and he cited the Maine embayments as especially good examples of ice-carved fjords. The " fjords of Cape Ann," Massachusetts, he attributes to a combination of stream and ice erosion.[6] In a curious article entitled " Untersuchungen der Fjorde an der Küste von Maine," Otto Remmers[7] devotes a great deal of space to proving mathematically the degree of parallelism of the Maine embayments and islands; then argues that water cannot produce such parallel forms because it is too easily displaced, whereas the more rigid ice is capable of this type of erosion; and finally concludes that the Maine embayments are ice carved, the direction of the embayments and islands showing that the ice spread out radially from the centre of glaciation, with the axes of movement departing only slightly from parallelism. Other writers cite the sea border of Nova Scotia, Maine, and other sections of the shore as " typical fjord coasts," and though not all of them make clear what they mean by the term " fjord," some of them at least consider profound modification of the coast by glacial erosion to be a necessary element.

*Significance of the Term " Fjord."* — The loose and variable ways in which the term " fjord " is applied to portions of the

New England, Acadian, and other shorelines often make it difficult to know just what is a given author's conception of the origin
of these shores.  Differences of opinion as to the origin of the
type fjord coast of Norway is in a measure responsible for the
confusion which persists in the use of this important term.  The
theory that waves and tides have cut these deep re-entrants into
the rocky land has not lacked its supporters, and is considered
worthy of mention as a possible contributing cause of fjord formation in the modern revision of Le Conte's textbook of geology.[8]
Dana,[9] Upham,[10] Fairchild,[11] and others have been impressed with
the element of valley submergence on the Norwegian and similar
fjord coasts, and have invoked subsidence of the land as the
essential cause of fjord topography; whereas Shaler[12] and Gilbert[13]
have shown that fjords may be produced without any change in
the relative level of land and sea.  Still others have noted particularly the evidences of glaciation of the Norwegian coast, and
have seen in glacial erosion the sole and sufficient cause of fjords,
ignoring the rôle of pre-glacial stream action in determining the
depressions which ice later transformed into the forms we see today.  For J. W. Gregory[14] and some earlier writers the rectangular pattern of certain Norwegian fjords dwarfed every other
consideration, and these authors have defended the theory that
faulting is the fundamental cause of fjords.  To some of those
who hold the theory which in the light of modern physiographic
science seems most reasonable, — that fjords are partially submerged glacial troughs formed by the erosive action of ice occupying pre-existing river valleys, — the overdeepening action of the
ice is especially emphasized, and the presence of deeper water in
the body of the embayment than exists near its opening into the
ocean, is adopted by them as the distinguishing feature of fjords.
This seems to attach undue weight to a single element of fjord
topography, and, it may be pointed out, to an element which
might be lacking in a true fjord, and present in a submerged valley
obviously unrelated in origin to typical fjords.

    The history of the fjord problem I have elsewhere outlined at
greater length.[15]  Suffice it to say here that if the Norwegian
fjord be taken as the type of the landform to which the term
" fjord " shall be applied, as seems the most reasonable course
to pursue, then we must define a fjord as " *a partially submerged
glacial trough*."  While glacial troughs, submerged and unsubmerged, exhibit much variety in details of form, the assemblage

of features characteristic of them is pretty clearly understood. High and steep rocky side walls from which projecting, interlocking spurs have been cut away, and on the face of which lateral troughs or valleys open with markedly discordant junctions (hanging valleys); a cross-profile the bottom of which approximates more or less closely a catenary curve, according to whether the trough is mature or young (U-shaped valley); a longitudinal profile characterized by reversed slopes which give rock-basin lakes if above sealevel, or, if submerged, greater depths in the body of the embayment than near its mouth: these compose the assemblage of features normally found in glacial troughs. And while it is possible that one of these elements might be lacking in a particular trough, it is scarcely conceivable that all of them could be lacking from any valley so much overdeepened by ice as to entitle it to be called a glacial trough; nor that any one of these elements could be wanting in a whole series of such troughs. Physiographers are pretty well agreed that profound modification of pre-existing river valleys by ice erosion is the only cause adequate to explain the significant features of glacial troughs, submerged or unsubmerged. Fjords are, therefore, an indication of profound modification of a shoreline by ice erosion.

*The Coast of Maine.* — When we turn to the so-called fjord coast of Maine, and apply the criterion: *a fjord is a partially submerged glacial trough,* grave doubts immediately arise as to the appropriateness of using the term " fjord " in connection with this part of the New England-Acadian shoreline. It is to be noted, in the first place, that the low relief of this coast, which resulted from the dissection of a low erosion plane lifted but slightly above sealevel, practically precluded the possibility of glacial trough formation, since it offered no opportunity for large and therefore powerful ice-streams to concentrate their activities in the valleys to the exclusion of the uplands. This matter of the relation of pre-glacial topography to glacial trough and fjord development, one of prime importance, is too often neglected by those who assume the glacial origin of embayed shores in glaciated areas. In the present case due consideration of this element of the problem leads one to doubt, on *a priori* grounds, the possibility of finding true fjords on most of the Maine coast.

An examination of the topography of the coast confirms the doubt. With the possible exception of the Mount Desert region, to which special attention will be given, the walls of the Maine embayments are neither so steep nor so high as is usual in glacial troughs.   Where the walls are free from projections, their comparative straightness seems to be related to rock structure, rather than to be the result of removal by ice erosion of interlocking spurs encountered by the glacier.   Hanging valleys are conspicuous by their rarity, one might almost say, by their absence; for while the lower courses of certain streams are somewhat oversteepened (due, in part at least, to a cause unconnected with glacial erosion, as will later appear), true hanging valleys of the type so commonly associated with glacial troughs appear to be unknown on the Maine coast.   The catenary curve is certainly simulated locally, but so far from its being in any sense the normal, or even a frequent cross-profile for valleys of this coast, the usual form is rather that of normal river valleys.   Shaler's statement[5] that the valleys of this coast usually have a U-shaped cross-section is apparently the result of generalization from the exceptional case of Mount Desert Island, to which he gave special study. Soundings reveal the existence of local depressions in some of the embayments which are 20, 40, or even more feet deeper than other parts of the embayment floor near the open sea; but since tidal scour of soft bottom deposits, unequal distribution of sediments by marine currents, unequal deposition of glacial débris by the ice sheet, and possibly other causes, are competent to explain most of these moderately overdeep areas, one must hesitate to accept them as proof of extensive glacial erosion in the absence of definite proof that they are true rock basins.   In any case, it is clear that long and deep rock basins of the type associated with glacial trough topography are practically unknown on the Maine coast.

Local studies further confirm the opinion that the continental ice sheet did not greatly alter the character of the pre-glacial valleys.   In many places where the embayments are typically developed, the direction of ice advance appears to have been across the trend of the ridges and valleys, the direction affording a minimum of opportunity for ice erosion in the valleys.   In the Casco Bay region (Fig. 5), for example, where the ridges and valleys trend northeast-southwest, the direction of the glacial striæ as reported by Katz[16] is S to S 25 E.   Striæ may be expected to indicate only the later movements of the ice, but there is little probability that here the major direction of ice advance was at any time southwestward.   Smith[17] is of the opinion that

in the Kennebec River basin (adjacent on the east, and perhaps
more favorably situated for glacial erosion of the valleys than the
Casco Bay region) " before the first invasion of the ice the hills
and mountains of this basin rose more abruptly above the valleys,"
and that " the first effect of the occupation of the basin by the ice
sheet from the north was the planing away of the decomposed
rock and the smoothing down of the outlines of the hills and
mountains." We have already seen that it is to be expected
that ice moving transverse to the valleys and ridges, as was the
case in the Casco Bay region even more than in the Kennebec
basin, should erode the ridges and decrease the topographic
relief, precisely the reverse of what happens under the conditions
in which fjords are usually produced. Bastin,[18] in a brief statement on the geology of the Penobscot River basin, says that
" the ice mass also in many places lowered and reshaped the land
surfaces, *particularly the hills* " (the italics are mine); and the
Penobscot Bay folio, by Smith, Bastin, and Brown[19] limits glacial
action to reducing the irregularities and more jagged prominences
of the hills and " filling some of the depressions." In an account
of the Fox Islands in Penobscot Bay Smith[20] writes: " During
the ice invasion of Glacial time, some modification of the older
topography may have resulted. It is to be noted, however, that
the characteristic features of Mount Desert, interpreted by Pro-
fessors Shaler and Davis as due to glacial erosion, are not represented on these islands." Of the Eastport region Bastin says:
" The larger topographic features are closely related to the structure of the bedrock, and the fact that these features had relatively
slight influence on the direction of ice movement indicates that,
far from being accentuated, they were probably somewhat subdued by the glaciation;"[21] and he evidently holds the same opinion
as to the effects of glaciation in the Rockland area.[22] When we
consider that in southern Maine the direction of ice advance was
in general at a marked angle to the principal valley systems, that
the pre-glacial topography was as a rule of low relief, and that the
region was probably not at a very great distance from the thinning
southern edge of the ice sheet much of the time when it was covered by ice, we cannot be surprised that detailed geological studies
along the coast confirm the view that the valleys of this coast did
not suffer profoundly from the glacial occupation. The drowning
of the valleys would therefore seem to be an evidence of a sinking
of the land or of a rise of the sealevel, and not of glacial erosion.

The origin of the deeply embayed coast of Maine has been considered at such length because of the widespread misconception as to its supposed fjord character, and because this same misconception persists in respect to other similar coasts. To continue to cite the Maine embayments as examples of fjords, as is done in certain of our textbooks, is to mislead the student as to the critical distinctions between fjords (partially submerged glacial troughs) and rias (partially submerged normal valleys). The former require profound glacial erosion, but not a relative change of sealevel, although such a change may take place in the history of a fjord; the latter require a relative change of sealevel, but no glacial erosion, although limited glacial modification is not excluded from the history of a ria. The Maine coast consists of a complexly folded mountain mass which has been peneplaned, slightly uplifted, maturely dissected by normal stream erosion, then *modified to a very limited extent* by continental glaciation, and partially submerged. It would seem, therefore, that the term " fjord coast " cannot appropriately be applied to the coast of Maine. It is an excellent example of a *ria coast*, whether one uses that term in the restricted sense first proposed by von Richthofen, or in the broader sense advocated by the present writer in his classification of shorelines.[23]

*Mount Desert Island.* — There is one limited area on the Maine coast which may be said to exhibit a minor, local example of fjord shoreline. On Mount Desert Island (Fig. 36), a high east-west trending ridge of resistant granite, which stands as a monadnock above the New England peneplane, here sloping southeastward into the sea, is cut across by a series of north-south notches trenched deeply into the mass. These notches have high and steep walls; cross-profiles the lower parts of which in several cases at least approximate a catenary curve, thus giving so-called U-shaped valleys; and longitudinal profiles, the median portions of which show pronounced overdeepening. The glacial form of the notches is clearly apparent, whether viewed from Baker Island (Fig. 37) or some other point to the south, or examined more closely (Fig. 38). On account of the limited upland area, there was little opportunity for the development of streams which might have hanging valleys; but several obliquely transverse depressions which may be remnants of an older drainage system, and some short streams enter the notches with distinctly discordant junctions. One seems justified in saying that the high

Fig. 36.   Portion of Mount Desert Island, Maine, showing east-west ridge of resistant rock cut transversely by glacial troughs which are partially drowned by trough lakes or by the sea.

granite range of Mount Desert is trenched by parallel glacial troughs trending nearly north-south, parallel to the direction of ice advance in this region, and containing rock-basins which in

FIG. 37.   Mount Desert Range viewed from Baker Island, showing glacial notches.   *Courtesy* Lafayette National Park.

FIG. 38.   Glacial notch near north end of Jordan Pond, Mount Desert Island, showing typical trough profile.   *Courtesy* Lafayette National Park.

most cases are occupied by typical trough lakes, but in one, Somes Sound (Fig. 39), by an arm of the sea.   And while one would certainly hesitate to cite Somes Sound as a typical example of fjord topography, it may not be amiss to include it in the

generic class of fjords.  Its eastern wall at one place rises over
one thousand feet above the bottom of the trough, which in its
central portion is a little over 125 feet deeper than where it begins
to open out to the sea on the south.  It is true Shaler states that
all of the overdeepened troughs are real rock basins and are not
walled in by mounds of glacial débris, " with the possible exception of Somes Sound;"[24] but even if some glacial or other
deposits help to make shallower the " Narrows " at the mouth
of the Sound, which is by no means certain, it seems not improbable that much, if not most, of the overdeep central part of
the Sound has the same origin as the undoubted rock basins on
either side associated with it.  All of them are explained by

Fig. 39.    Somes Sound, Mount Desert Island, as seen from the
south.    *Courtesy* Lafayette National Park.

Shaler,[25] apparently with good reason, as the product of excavation
by glacial erosion;  and Davis[26] recognized in the form of the
notches an evidence of ice scouring far more vigorous than was
usual on the Maine coast.  It is admitted, however, that the original valley cross-profile of Somes Sound has clearly been less modified by the ice than have the profiles of the other notches.

The conditions for glacial trough formation were locally exceptionally good.  When the advancing ice sheet reached this
part of the coast, its progress was obstructed by the highest rock
barrier on the entire Atlantic shoreline of the United States.
Whereas the coast of Maine as a whole averages but a hundred
feet or so above sealevel, in the Mount Desert range the ice en-

countered an obstacle eleven miles long (Fig. 36) rising well over one thousand feet high in many places, and to a maximum height of 1532 feet. Cutting across this range are a series of dykes which have courses between N 20 W and N, and which according to Shaler decay more readily than dykes trending in other directions. " The presence of these dykes seems in certain cases to soften the granitic rock, possibly through a process of kaolinization of the feldspar it contains. Furthermore, these dyke injections appear to increase the jointing of the country rock on either side of the injection, and so, by these several actions, the granitic rock in the neighborhood of the dykes has its resistance to the several kinds of decay diminished."[25]   Bascom[27] notes that the north-south system of joints is more strongly developed than the other principal system, running east and west. The present writer would add the suggestion that faults, striking slightly west of north, may also have been responsible for zones of weakness in this direction, the weakness being due either to crushed zones along the displacements, or to the infaulting of weak rocks overlying the granite, long since removed by erosion. The suggestion is based on the fact that the topography of certain of the peaks (e.g., the double-crested Beech Mountain) is that which should be produced by faults striking in the direction indicated, with downthrows on the east. As the occurrence of dykes in fault fissures is a common geological phenomenon, it seems possible that the north-south dykes (one of which passes through the notch on Beech Mountain) and the increased jointing (crushed zones?) on either side of the dykes, both phenomena noted by Shaler, may be incidental to faults which had a major rôle in creating the weak zones in question.

The pre-glacial erosion which reduced the lands north and south of the Mount Desert range to the low level of the peneplane, leaving the resistant granitic mass standing up in bold relief as a monadnock ridge, must inevitably have discovered the weak zones trending nearly north-south across the range, and have worn them down somewhat to produce transverse notches in the ridge crest, some of them shallow perhaps, others possibly of considerable depth. It seems to the writer very unlikely that during recent geological time the land ever sloped continuously southward from the northern side of the island, or that a series of north-south parallel streams ever flowed from a high northern side of the island southward to the sea, the whole headwater area of these streams being later removed by glacial erosion, as Bascom's earlier interpretation of the drainage history required.[28]  Neither does it seem probable that in post-glacial time the south-flowing streams could have pushed their headwaters northward to any appreciable extent, to effect the river captures described by that author. The shortness of post-glacial time and the inappreciable changes effected by post-glacial erosion on stream divides, even when these are located in weak material, as well as the expectable behavior of streams believed to occupy old, beheaded valleys, are strongly against such an interpretation.  When the ice advanced to Mount Desert Island it must have found the broader topographic relations similar to those we see today, — an east-west ridge of resistant granite flanked on either side by lower land, having its crest notched more or less deeply by transverse depressions eroded on weak belts trending slightly west of north; but the notches were not nearly so deep as today, and streams heading in or near them doubtless flowed away from the ridge in opposite directions, northward on the northern side of the island, southward on the southern side.

As the ice of the advancing glacier banked up against the northern side of the Mount Desert mass, it must have been deflected to the east and west around the ends of the barrier.  Observed directions of glacial striæ are in accord with this view. But as the ice rose higher and higher upon the northern flank of the range, it would reach the level first of one notch, then of another, and pour southward through the depressions, until six or eight principal ice tongues were, like local alpine glaciers, grinding their way through the narrow passes and eroding with marked rapidity the weak zones which weathering and normal stream erosion, working far more slowly, had incompletely reduced in pre-glacial time.  The grinding action continued until the trough form typical of ice-stream erosion was fairly well developed, before the melting of the ice put an end to the process.  Drowning of the bottoms of the troughs, by lake waters or by the sea, gave trough lakes or fjords as the case might be.  When the submergence was more extensive than now, as was the case for some time after the retreat of the ice, there were more fjords, and therefore fewer trough lakes, than today.  At the present time Somes Sound is perhaps the only embayment which deserves to be placed in the fjord class.

If the above interpretation be correct, the Mount Desert

region alone affords a possible exception to the statement that the term fjord cannot properly be applied to the coast of Maine; and this exception is due to an unusual combination of geological and topographical conditions which exist only on this part of the coast.   Elsewhere the embayments are normal drowned valleys, too little modified by ice action to transform them into fjords. It is most appropriate that the remarkable scenic features of Mount Desert should form the basis of the only National Park on the Atlantic Coast, the Lafayette National Park.

*Gorge of the Hudson through the Highlands.* — Southward from Maine the conditions were as a rule even more unfavorable for glacial overdeepening of coastal valleys, and nothing resembling a fjord is to be found on this part of the outer coast.   But fifty miles up the Hudson embayment local conditions afforded opportunity for another exceptional case.   The southward moving ice found its progress obstructed by the great crystalline barrier of the Highlands north of Peekskill, rising 1100 to 1200 feet above sealevel with peaks 1400 to 1600 feet high, through which the Hudson River had cut a narrow gorge in pre-glacial time.   Before the ice overtopped the barrier in its advance, and after it had retired behind it during its retreat, — possibly also during the time that the barrier was completely buried, — a tongue of ice must long have flowed through the river gorge. The present form of the gorge suggests some modification by ice erosion (Fig. 40).   Kemp[29] and Berkey and Rice[30] are convinced that glacial overdeepening and widening have both occurred, and report the presence of small hanging valleys, some of which have the form characteristically produced by glacial erosion. At the Storm King crossing of the Hudson, where the Catskill aqueduct passes under the river, borings demonstrated that the bottom of the bedrock channel lies between 765 and 950 feet below sealevel.   As the bedrock channel opposite New York City is only about 300 feet deep so far as known (a small gap of 1100 feet still unexplored exists in the series of borings into bedrock), it seems probable that the former stream channel was deepened several hundred feet by glacial scour.   The hypothesis, entertained by Fuller[31] and others, that a narrow inner gorge is entrenched in the bottom of the Hudson valley opposite New York is open to more serious objections than any these writers have opposed to the theory of glacial overdeepening at the Storm King crossing.   Since the greatest unexplored belt opposite New York

FIG. 40.   Gorge of the Hudson River through the Highlands of New York.   The lower lands represent the dissected and partially submerged Tertiary peneplane.   Photo by New York Board of Water Supply.

is only 1100 feet broad, if we assume the depth to bedrock at Storm King as but 800 feet, the gradient of the stream as only 1 foot per mile, the brink of the inner gorge to be barely within the bedrock encountered 300 feet below sealevel at the two borings 1100 feet apart, and the stream to be narrow and to have no valley floor, — all conditions the most favorable to the inner gorge theory, — then the walls of the gorge will have a slope of 45°. Now a stream so youthful as to have walls of such steepness normally has a gradient many times steeper than 1 foot per mile, — twenty, thirty, or more feet per mile would seem more appropriate. But calculations based on these figures greatly deepen the hypothetical gorge, and so greatly steepen its walls as to make it a rather unusual type of erosion phenomenon. To invoke an unusual type of gorge, located within the narrow limits of a specific unexplored zone under specialized conditions, rather than to credit a restricted ice stream with several hundred feet of erosion at the Storm King crossing, is to create a large difficulty in order to escape a lesser. Warping might account for the observed difference of level in the bedrock channel, but there is general agreement that the evidence is against warping. Glacial erosion alone offers at once a complete and satisfactory explanation for all of the observed facts. There is thus some ground for calling that portion of the embayed shoreline of the Hudson situated in the Highlands, a fjord shoreline (Fig. 40). That it is not a typical fjord shoreline is obvious, for the amount of glacial modification of the Hudson gorge is very moderate.

Nowhere else south and west of Maine does the New England shore afford an example of a drowned valley which could properly be called a fjord. Shaler[32] speaks of the Thames estuary, Connecticut, as having been " enlarged and deepened and widened by the action of the ice and probably sunk below its ancient level"; but the form of this valley affords no evidence that the amount of glacial modification was sufficient to alter materially its preglacial form. It has every appearance of being a normal drowned river valley. Boston Bay, which Shaler[33] ascribed to ice erosion without presenting evidence in support of his conclusion, seems best interpreted as a partially submerged normal erosion lowland.

*The Coast of Acadia.* — What has been said on earlier pages concerning the almost complete absence of fjords from the coast of Maine and other parts of New England, applies with equal

force to the coast of Acadia. The embayed southwestern and
long southeastern coasts of Nova Scotia in particular have been
referred to by some geologists and geographers as fjord coasts,
and in some cases cited as remarkable examples of profound
glacial erosion. But these coasts are low and of slight relief, a
condition generally unfavorable to the excavation of glacial
troughs. The topography of the embayments is distinctly that
of normal river valleys, little modified by ice action, submerged
by a relative change in sealevel, and bears little resemblance to
fjord topography when critically examined. Goldthwait[34] specifically points out the lack of opportunity for concentration of ice
flow on the low relief of much of the Nova Scotian coast, and
states that the deepest and steepest-sided estuaries like Country

FIG. 41. South Bay near Ingonish, Cape Breton Island, looking toward
its head. Photo by Goldthwait, Geol. Surv. Canada.

Harbor, and even canyon-like valleys such as South Bay at
Ingonish (Fig. 41) and Mabou Harbor, show no overdeepening by
ice. While admitting that " the continental glacier gave finish-
ing touches to the outlines of the shore," he states: " The idea
that the ice sheet carved out the valleys which indent the southern
coast is a mistaken one. These valleys are plainly the work of
rain and rivers, during the period preceding the ice age, drowned
and subsequently altered in detail only, by the activity of the ice
sheet. They are not true glacial fjords like the famous fjords of
Norway and Alaska." Even in Cape Breton Island, where the
strong relief of parts of the dissected crystalline plateau near the
coast offered the best opportunity along the Acadian shore for
vigorous erosion by local ice tongues, Goldthwait notes the

absence of glacial troughs; and while at one time he was inclined
to the theory of marked glacial overdeepening in the Bras d'Or
Lakes region,[35] he later rejected the glacial origin of the local
deeps in these lakes, because " all other signs point to weak
glaciation."[34]  Hyde[36] thinks that these deeps may in part at
least be the result of submarine solution of the gypsum and limestone series of the Carboniferous formation known to be present
under the lake waters.  In New Brunswick and Prince Edward
Island the conditions were even less favorable for glacial overdeepening of coastal valleys, and we find no embayments which
can properly be called fjords.  Everywhere, except on Mount
Desert and in the Hudson Highlands, the topography is that of
normal river valleys, little affected by glaciation, which have
been drowned by a depression of the land or a rise of sealevel.
Occasionally the valleys thus submerged have a youthfulness
which suggests a late glacial or post-glacial origin, as for example
the long, narrow, rock-walled channel of Little Bras d'Or, connecting St. Andrews Channel with the ocean, through which the
tides rush violently in and out of the Bras d'Or Lakes,[36] and the
origin of which has been discussed by Goldthwait.[34]

**Initial Shoreline as Affected by Glacial Deposits.** — While the
continental ice sheet affected the New England-Acadian shoreline
only in a minor degree by its erosive action, it materially affected
it through glacial and fluvio-glacial deposition.  Terminal moraines and their associated outwash plains, as well as groups of
drumlins, gave to extensive sections of the initial shoreline of submergence a very special character.  To a lesser degree eskers,
kames and glacial delta plains determined the outline of smaller
segments of the shore.

*Moraine Shorelines.* — The edge of the ice sheet lay close to
the southern border of the New England upland for a relatively
long period, and it is there alone that we find extensive terminal
moraines and outwash plains.  As shown by Fig. 42, two principal positions were maintained by the ice front for periods sufficiently prolonged to permit in each case the irregular deposition
directly from the melting edge of the ice of a long hummocky
ridge or terminal moraine, while the streams born of the melting
glacier spread in front of each moraine a southward sloping
alluvial deposit known as an outwash plain.  When submergence
brought the sea to rest against the moraines and outwash plains
at the present level, the resulting initial shoreline of submergence

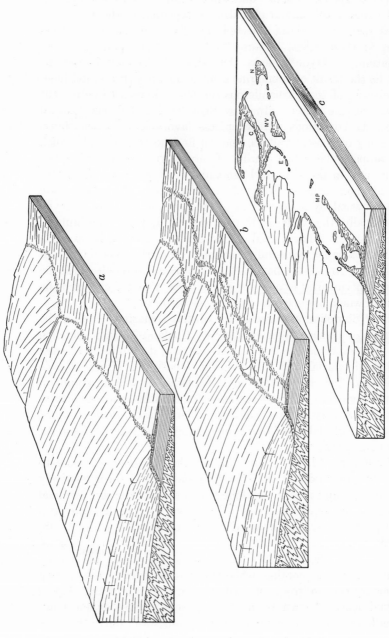

FIG. 42. The continental ice sheet apparently made two halts in this region, the earlier being the farther south (a), the later farther north (b). Two belts of terminal moraines resulted (c), the Ronkonkoma moraine represented in Montauk Point (MP), Marthas Vineyard (MV) and Nantucket (N); and the Harbor Hill moraine represented in Orient Point (O), the Elizabeth Islands (E) and Cape Cod (C).

was extremely irregular where it bordered the moraines, but of more simple pattern where it lay against the outwash plains, although the drowning of some valleys cut in these plains produced irregularities in places. Long stretches of both moraines, with adjoining portions of their associated outwash plains, were completely submerged. That part of the earlier or southern moraine (known to geological students of Long Island as the Ronkonkoma moraine) which remains above sealevel forms the southern or Montauk fluke of the fish tail of eastern Long Island, and appears again on Block Island, Marthas Vineyard and Nantucket. Bits of the outwash plain remaining above the sea make the nearly flat southern parts of the two islands last mentioned. In Nantucket the principal deposition may have been just back of the ice margin, giving a kame-moraine rather than a typical terminal moraine; but the difference in the character of the initial shoreline would be negligible. Both moraines rest in places upon irregularly pushed and disturbed older deposits, sometimes unconsolidated sands and clays of the coastal plain, sometimes earlier glacial deposits. But here again the resulting shoreline topography is much like that where the sea borders pure moraine; and for our purposes it will be sufficiently accurate to denominate the resulting shorelines as moraine shorelines.

The later or northern moraine (Harbor Hill moraine) forms the northern fluke of the fish tail of eastern Long Island, and is recognizable again on Fishers Island, as the moraine on the extreme southern margin of the New England mainland just west of Narragansett Bay, in the long string of Elizabeth Islands, and as the ridge making the " upper arm " of Cape Cod from which it disappears seaward at the elbow or bend of the arm. The ice front appears to have been lobate in both of the principal positions described. Marthas Vineyard, lying in the angle between the two lobes when the ice occupied the more southerly position, acquired the marked angle of its northern coast, which with the shoreline of the outwash plain on the south gives to the island its triangular form. The lobate pattern is again reflected in the angle between the northeastward curving outline of the Elizabeth Islands and the east-west course of the " upper arm " of Cape Cod. Thus both the pattern of the landforms bordering New England on the south, and the character of their shores were profoundly affected by the double stand of the ice sheet in this region.

Toward the west on Long Island the margin of the ice appears to have rested upon the gentle southward slope of a cuesta (left side of Fig. 43), the steeper northern scarp of which faced the inner lowland that became Long Island Sound when submerged. This cuesta had been much modified by still earlier ice advances, particularly by the deposition of thick deposits of outwash gravels from certain of the earlier ice sheets. If all of the glacial deposits were removed, there would still remain a cuesta to form Long Island, and an inner lowland submerged to form Long Island Sound; hence the broader features were not essentially changed by glacial deposition. But the size of Long Island would be much diminished if the glacial deposits were taken away, and the detailed form of the shore would notably be changed.

On Marthas Vineyard, Block Island, the Elizabeth Islands, and possibly on Nantucket, Cretaceous or Tertiary beds, or both, are present beneath the glacial drift, suggesting that these may be parts of the eastward prolongation of the main cuesta of Long Island, or possibly a subordinate cuesta sufficiently high in the east to rise above sealevel in places. The disturbed nature of the Cretaceous and Tertiary deposits has been interpreted to mean that the continental glacier in its advance wrinkled these beds and pushed them up into ridges, some of which ridges may thus first have acquired their observed elevation above sealevel. The northeastward continuation of the cuesta of the drowned coastal plain, as will later be pointed out, appears to be represented by the famous "banks" lying off the New England-Acadian coast. In all of the cases where the cuesta remnants rise above sealevel, the terminal moraine and outwash plain appear to have effectually mantled over the older form, and to have determined the detailed character of the initial shoreline.

What this character was initially, may be inferred with some confidence from an examination of those parts of the shoreline bordering terminal moraine or outwash plain which have been least affected by post-glacial wave erosion. On the line of the southern or Ronkonkoma moraine the irregular inner shoreline on the northern side of the Montauk Point peninsula of Long Island, and the similar shoreline in the Nashaquitsa region of southwestern Marthas Vineyard, give a fair idea of the original character of the terminal moraine shoreline. In both places, however, the sea has cut away outlying islands and projecting points of the shore and built sand bars across some of the embay-

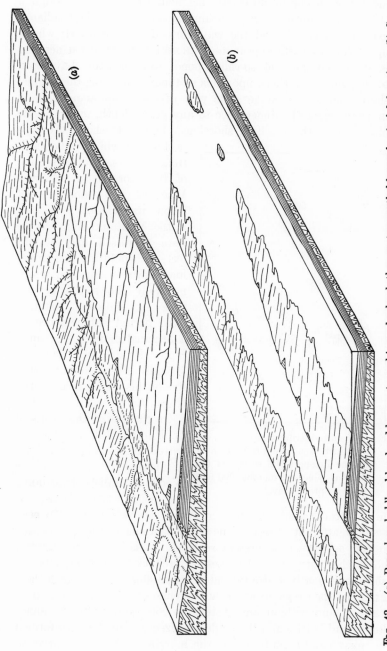

FIG. 43.  (a) Peneplaned oldland bordered by cuesta and inner lowland, the cuesta mantled by early glacial deposits.   (b) Same partially submerged.   Long Island and Long Island Sound present the relations shown in the second diagram.

ments; so, if one would correct his mental picture of the original shoreline, he must imagine certain islands restored, the headlands extended seaward, and the wave-formed bars removed; whereupon the shore will appear much more irregular than it actually is at present, and the so-called ponds will constitute bays open to the sea.   As a check upon this method of restoring the original shore, one may imagine some part of the terminal moraine to undergo renewed submergence to any given depth, and note the character of the resulting shoreline.   Figure 44 shows the type

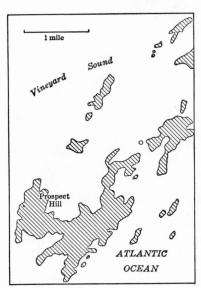

of shoreline which would result from depression of a section of the moraine on Marthas Vineyard two hundred feet below its present level.   Or if the Montauk Point region were depressed only twenty feet, we would get the shoreline shown in Fig. 45, which not only shows the general type of shoreline resulting from partial submergence of a terminal moraine, but must represent fairly well the major features of the actual shoreline of this region in its initial stage.

Fig. 44.  Initial terminal-moraine shoreline which would result from depressing the Prospect Hill section of the Marthas Vineyard moraine 200 feet below its present level.

On the line of the northern or Harbor Hill moraine the extremely irregular shorelines of Fishers Island, and of the Woods Hole district including the neighboring islands, exhibit features similar to those mentioned above.   Figure 47 represents an attempt to restore the initial shoreline of the Woods Hole region as] formed at present sealevel.   It is based on map and coast chart studies, and makes no pretense to accuracy; but it shows sufficiently well a typical morainal shoreline.   In all of these examples the irregularities of the shoreline are of small and medium pattern, and without any system, to correspond with the minor knobs and kettles and the moderate-sized morainal masses formed in unsystematic confusion at the margin of the ice.   Curves of larger and somewhat more regular pattern may occasionally mark sections of the shoreline which border ice-contact slopes at the northern side of the moraine where the ice front was more or less scalloped; and it is possible that part of the southern, marshy shore of the Barnstable Harbor embayment on Cape Cod should

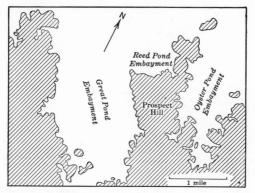

Fig. 45.   Initial terminal-moraine shoreline which would result from a depression of the Montauk Point region 20 feet below its present level. The actual initial shoreline in this region must have been very similar. Compare with present shoreline, Fig. 46.

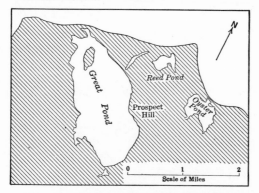

Fig. 46.   Present shoreline of part of Montauk Point moraine.

be so interpreted.   Where the summit portions only of a very irregular moraine remained above sealevel, they formed groups of small morainal islands.   The Cuttyhunk Island section of the Harbor Hill moraine was of this type (Fig. 49).   Some of the former islands have since been completely washed away, and the

FIG. 47.  Restoration of the initial terminal-moraine shoreline in the Woods Hole region, Massachusetts, showing extreme irregularity at this stage. Compare with Fig. 48.

FIG. 48.  Present shoreline of moraine in Woods Hole region.

remainder reduced in size and tied together by wave-built bars or tombolos.

There is little doubt that the terminal moraine ridges described above continue eastward under the sea, beyond their last appearance on Nantucket Island and Cape Cod.   A variety of crystalline rock fragments brought to the surface by fishermen, and the very irregular bottom indicated by soundings on parts of the submarine " banks," are probably best explained as marginal deposits of the continental ice sheet.   But the idea, apparently entertained by Shaler[37] and others, that the great ridges of these banks are in considerable part terminal moraines, probably exaggerates the volume and importance of the morainal deposits.   Here presumably, as certainly on the land farther west, the moraines are

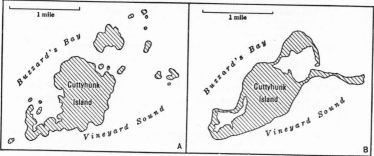

Fig. 49.   (A) Restoration of the initial terminal-moraine shoreline in the Cuttyhunk Island region, showing irregular character of initial shoreline of this type.   (B) Present outline of Cuttyhunk Island.

of but slight thickness, and owe their elevation above adjacent areas in large part to the fact that they rest upon topographic eminences of very different origin, particularly the cuesta of a drowned coastal plain.

*Outwash Plain Shorelines.* — The outwash plain of a continental ice sheet is not normally a perfectly smooth, sloping surface, but usually consists of a series of coalescing alluvial fans, each of which rises toward the moraine, and some of which at least head in distinct notches cut through the moraine by glacier-born streams.   Toward their distal portions the fans unite to form a single plain, but even here the identity of many of the fans is still recognizable, the plain being in reality composed of segments of a number of extremely low, flat cones some of which are arched enough to give a faintly scalloped pattern to a contour map of the slope. It is obvious that if the sea came to rest against such a plain, the initial shoreline would be scalloped. Parts of the outwash plain shorelines which have been preserved from wave attack because of outlying bars show this scalloped pattern quite distinctly. Enough of the southern shore of Marthas Vineyard has been preserved to enable us to restore its initial pattern (Fig. 50),

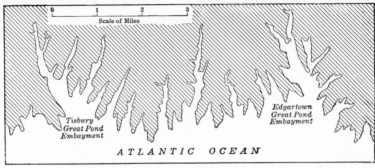

Fig. 50. Outwash plain shoreline (initial stage), south side of Marthas Vineyard, restored to show major lobate form due to coalescing alluvial fans of plain, and minor embayments due to partial submergence of valleys carved by glacier-born distributary streams. Compare with Fig. 51.

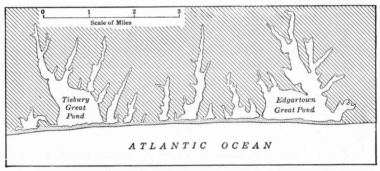

Fig. 51. Present shoreline bordering outwash plain, south side of Marthas Vineyard.

and to note that it exhibited one good scallop in the centre with parts of others, poorly formed, on either side. The scallops themselves are fringed by small embayments, because the glacier-born streams, supplemented perhaps in some measure by post-glacial streams in certain cases, cut shallow valleys on the fans, and these valleys were partially drowned by the later submergence.

The inner shore of the south side of Long Island, back of the offshore bar, shows with great distinctness both the major scallops of the coalesced fans and the minor embayments fringing their margins.  The south shore of Nantucket has obviously been too greatly modified by wave erosion to show the scallop pattern distinctly, even if it were well developed originally.  Along the northern outwash plain, associated with the Harbor Hill moraine, scalloped shorelines are shown, though obscurely, in the Peconic

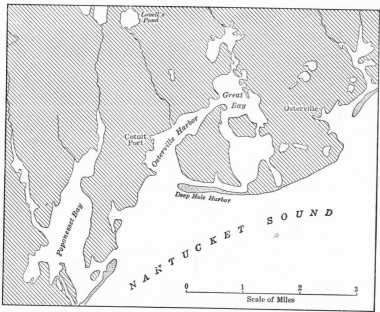

FIG. 52.  Kettle-hole shorelines of partially submerged pitted outwash plain, "upper arm" of Cape Cod.  The short, broad, rounded embayments east and north of Great Bay, southwest of Poponesset Bay, as well as parts of the bays themselves, appear to be partially submerged kettle holes.  The ponds occupy other kettle holes not reached by the sea.

Bay region, Long Island, and on the south shore of the upper arm of Cape Cod, especially toward the western part of this shore. Here, as elsewhere, the minor embayments of the small valleys are superposed upon the broader feature of the scallops, like the ornamental fringe which adorns the margin of a scalloped curtain. In addition to the valley embayments of fairly regular forms, there are along parts of the outwash plain shoreline shorter, generally

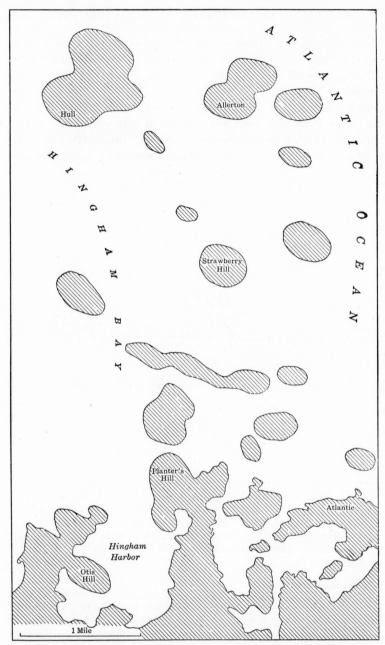

Fig. 53. Restoration of initial drumlin shoreline of the Nantasket region, Boston Harbor, showing drumlin curves on part of mainland, and drumlin islands. The irregular sectors of the shoreline are partly on rock shores and partly on irregular deposits of glacial drift. For successive stages of development to present shoreline, see Figs. 230–235. (116)

more irregular, sometimes rounded embayments, resulting from
the partial submergence of ice-block kettle holes in the plain.
Examples of these may be seen along the south shore of the
upper arm of Cape Cod (Fig. 52).

*Drumlin Shorelines.* — Where the ground moraine of the continental ice sheet was molded into drumlins, and these smooth,

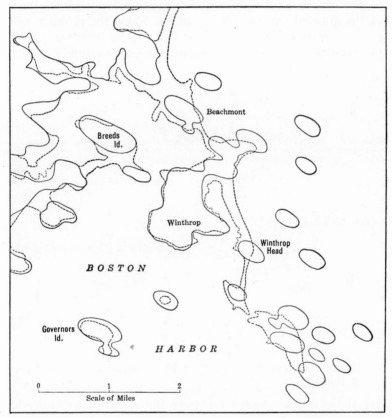

FIG. 54.   Restoration of initial drumlin shoreline of the Winthrop region,
Boston Harbor.   Broken lines show present form of shoreline.   In
centre of map is a glacial delta plain on which the village of Winthrop
is located.

oval hills were partially submerged by the sea, the initial shoreline possessed a very peculiar and picturesque character.   Drumlins are apt to occur in groups, with the result that while many
miles of shoreline show no trace of them, locally the aspect of
the shore changes completely, and both projecting headlands and

numerous off-lying islands show the graceful, symmetrically arched forms of these " whalebacks " as they are sometimes called, all with their long axes parallel to each other and to the direction of ice movement when they were formed.   Their oval outlines give a large proportion of graceful curves in the initial shoreline, and where several drumlins are in contact these curves may combine to give several small scale scallops convex toward the sea.   When to the graceful curves of these hills is added the pleasing color contrast of dark green forest cover and blue surrounding sea, the picture formed by the drumlin shoreline is one of exquisite beauty.

Fig. 55.  Hog Island drumlin, surrounded by salt marsh, near Ipswich, Massachusetts.  In the foreground are the sand dunes of Castle Neck Beach, a continuation of the Plum Island offshore bar.  Photo by G. K. Gilbert.

Like the terminal moraine deposits, the unconsolidated material of the drumlins has yielded readily under the attack of the waves, causing rapid and extensive alterations of exposed parts of the original shoreline; but the general character of the initial drumlin shoreline may be determined with some approximation to accuracy by restoring the drumlins and parts of drumlins removed by wave erosion.   As will later appear, the form and position of old seacliffs, beaches, bars, and shoals sometimes enable us to make such restorations with great confidence, as in the Nantasket and Winthrop sections of Boston Bay (Figs. 53 and 54).   Even here one cannot always be sure of the former size of drumlins now nearly or wholly destroyed, and in certain cases doubt must persist as to whether all lost drumlins have been restored, or as to the validity of some of the restorations attempted.   There can be little doubt, however, as to the substantial accuracy of the *type* of initial shoreline represented in the restorations.   Drumlin shorelines of similar type were less strikingly developed in the Ipswich and Scituate regions of the Massachusetts coast (Fig. 55).   In the Mahone Bay region of Nova Scotia drumlins were even more numerous than on any part of the New England coast,[34] and the initial shoreline, like that of the present, must have been largely dominated by drumlin outlines (Fig. 56).   The oval hills (Fig. 57) of dark-green forest or light-green fields bathed by the blue waters from Chester to Lunenburg, seen under the clear light of a summer day, make a picture the sheer beauty of which will live long in the observer's memory.   Goldthwait's work on Nova Scotia drumlins shows that other excellent examples of drumlin shorelines are to be found in the Yarmouth Harbor-Chebogue Harbor-Tusket Islands region at the southwestern end of Nova Scotia; in Halifax Harbor and east of its entrance where are the Cow Bay drumlins described by McIntosh;[38] at Three Fathom Harbor a short distance farther east, where drumlins block the entrance to the drowned valley of Porter Lake; along the shores of Chedabucto Bay at the northeastern extremity of Nova Scotia, Cape Argos and Glasgow Head on opposite sides of the entrance to the bay being formed by half-consumed drumlins; and in the St. Peters region of southeastern Cape Breton Island, where Cape Rond and Brickery Head are among the drumlin headlands.   As at Boston, so at Halifax, the forts defending the Harbor are based on drumlin islands, and in both Boston and Mahone Bays two drumlin islands tied together by a wave-built beach have given rise to the obviously appropriate designation of " Spectacle Island."

*Delta Plain Shorelines.* — The influence of fluvio-glacial delta plains upon the initial shoreline of submergence was in general less striking, but there is one portion of the New England coast where plains which apparently belong to this class controlled the form of the initial shoreline.   The " forearm " of Cape Cod, from the elbow northward to the wrist, is composed of stratified clays, sands, and gravels which are generally interpreted as delta deposits built into some water body by streams from the melting

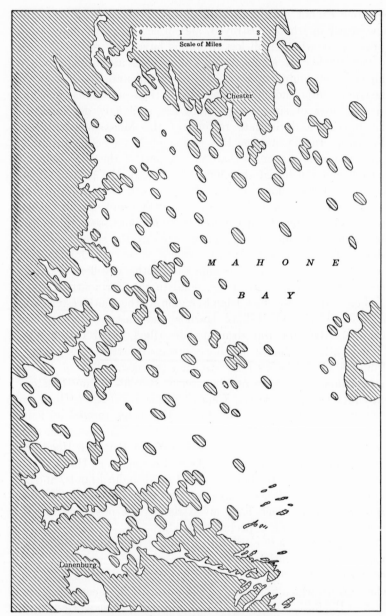

Fɪɢ. 56. Remarkable drumlin shoreline of the Mahone Bay region, Nova Scotia, restored to show initial character of shoreline. Restoration (approximate) based in part on manuscript map of drumlins by J. W. Goldthwait, and in part on submarine contours of hydrographic charts.

Fig. 57.    Drumlin shoreline near Chester, Nova Scotia.    Photo by J. W. Goldthwait, Geol. Surv. Canada.

ice. Whether that water body was a lake held in between ice-lobes of such peculiar arrangement as was supposed by J. H. Wilson[2] or was of some other type, and what was the nature and position of the ice margin when the deposits were made, is not clear. Hence it is not possible to determine the location or the form of the initial shoreline on the ice-contact side of these plains with any degree of correctness. The ice contact appears to have been on the east, and if this be true more doubt must

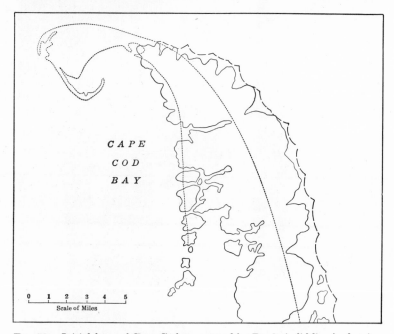

FIG. 58.    Initial form of Cape Cod as restored by Davis (solid lines), showing irregular glacial delta plain shorelines. Broken lines show suggested alternative restoration of eastern shoreline. Dotted lines show present outline, which especially on the east indicates a remarkably simple, mature shoreline.

attach to Davis's suggested reconstruction of the initial shoreline on this side of the cape than attaches to the same operation on the western side. It is not clear, for example, that the restored eastern shoreline should be " indented toward the various troughs and valleys that break the general surface of the mainland."[39] In pattern that shoreline may have been a succession of shallow concave embayments corresponding to the scalloped

margin of the ice, with projecting headlands between the concavities, where there used to be re-entrants in the ice border, the
stream channels on the delta plain occupying no special position
with respect to these features, and their higher, eastern portions
not necessarily being drowned by the partial submergence of the
plains. The restoration of the western shoreline presents less
difficulty, and in its initial stage this shoreline must have cor-
responded in general character to the form as reconstructed by
Davis (Fig. 58).

When delta plains are well formed there is a distinct contrast
between the ice-contact slope, where the sand and gravel banked
up against the frequently more or less minutely lobate front
of the glacier, and the frontal slope, where distributaries of the
glacier-born stream built
forward into the water
body a corresponding ser-
ies of lobes of the grow-
ing delta plain. With the
disappearance of the ice
and the water body, the
delta plain will remain as
a sandy table land, often
of somewhat irregular
outline, but with its steep
ice-contact slope marked
by concave scallops and
its more gently inclined
frontal slope by convex
scallops representing the
frontal lobes. Delta plain
shorelines may therefore

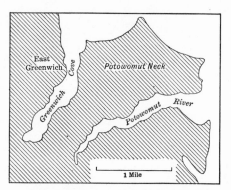

FIG. 59.   Scalloped glacial delta plain shorelines of part of Narragansett Bay region,
partially restored to show approximate
initial form.   Concave scallops represent
ice-contact-slope shorelines; convex scallops, frontal-lobe shorelines.

be characterized by concave or convex scallops, according to
which part of the plain the sea rests against as a result of partial submergence.

Woodworth[40] has described a series of glacial delta plains in
the Narragansett Bay region, some of which are sufficiently well-
formed to give the shore contrasts just described. Thus the
south shore of the Potowomut drowned valley (Fig. 59) shows
the shallow concave embayment of a typical ice-contact slope of
one delta plain, while the north shore was originally scalloped by
the southward-projecting frontal lobes of another similar plain

deposited farther north.   The ice-contact slope of this latter plain
determined the southeastern shoreline of Greenwich Cove.   Other
neighboring coves show shorelines of the same type, all of them
more or less modified by post-glacial wave erosion.   The shores
of Boston Harbor furnish several examples of delta plain shorelines, among which the North Weymouth and Quincy Neck shores
of Weymouth Fore River and the south shore of Town River
Bay (Fig. 60) are among the best, while the Winthrop example
(Fig. 54) is less typical in its development.

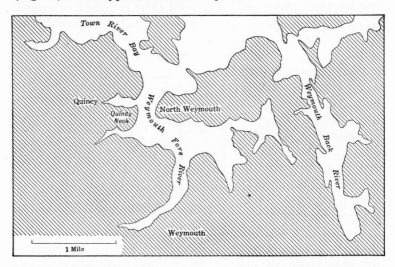

Fig. 60.   Glacial delta plain and esker shorelines of the Weymouth region,
Boston Harbor, partially restored to show approximate initial form.
The concave scallops on south side of Town River Bay, and north side
of Quincy Neck and North Weymouth, are ice-contact-slope shorelines;
convex scallops on south side of Quincy Neck and North Weymouth are
frontal-lobe shorelines; the narrow points projecting into Weymouth
Back River are due to eskers, as is also the point extending northwest
from the North Weymouth plain.

*Kame and Esker Shorelines.* — Kames and eskers determined
the initial form of limited sections of the New England-Acadian
shoreline.   Irregular masses of kames give a shoreline which
closely resembles that bordering partially submerged moraines.
The northeast side of Country Harbor (Fig. 25) owes the detailed irregularities of its shoreline to the partial submergence of
kames.[34]   The elongated ridge of a typical esker is more peculiar,
and no doubt esker shorelines constituted a recognizable element

in the initial stage of shoreline development in this province; but as waves very quickly destroy narrow ridges of unconsolidated sand and gravel, only those eskers in protected situations have survived to the present. Traces of esker shorelines may be recognized at occasional points along the New England coast, as for example on the shores of Weymouth Back River and the northern shore of North Weymouth (Fig. 60), where they formed narrow projecting points in the initial shoreline; but nowhere do they now constitute an important element of the shoreline topography. In Cape Breton part of the South Arm of Sydney Harbor has its shoreline characterized by long, narrow projecting points which according to Goldthwait[34] in part at least represent eskers. Other examples are known, both in Acadia and New England; but these minor features of the shoreline deserve no more than passing notice.

*Ground Moraine Shorelines.* — Where irregular masses of glacial drift mantled the rocks of the mainland at the level reached by the sea as a result of submergence, the resulting shoreline was irregular, and without definite system. If the deposit was thin, or of limited lateral extent, the form of the shore differed but little from what it would have been had the bedrock topography free from its glacial covering been submerged to the same extent. Thus we find that in an island fringe like that of the Casco Bay region (Fig. 5), where the exposed outer islands have had their glacial drift covering largely stripped off by the waves while the more protected inner islands still retain parts of such a covering,[41] no striking contrast in the two groups of islands is noticeable on the map.

Occasionally the drift became responsible for peculiar features of the shore. Some lakes (e.g., Porter Lake east of Halifax) would be bays of the ocean were they not separated from the sea by masses of glacial deposits. The remarkable reversible falls at the mouth of the St. John River, where the sea through a narrow rocky gateway flows into the inner harbor at one stage of the tide, while the harbor pours back into the sea at other times, is believed to be the result of glacial débris damming the former course of the river, forcing it to find a new and narrow outlet across a rocky barrier.[42] So narrow is the new channel that the tidal waters cannot pour through it fast enough to raise the water level in the drowned valley harbor as fast as it rises in the open ocean; hence a rush of water from the ocean into the harbor.

Later, as the tide in the ocean falls, the harbor water cannot escape seaward through the channel rapidly enough to lower the water level inside as quickly as it is lowered outside by the falling of the tide; and so in a short time there is a swirling torrent passing from the inner harbor into the ocean.

**Résumé.** — The considerations set forth in the preceding paragraphs have led us to conclude that the New England-Acadian shoreline was but little affected by glacial erosion, although profoundly affected by glacial deposition. True fjord coasts are practically non-existent in the province under investigation, the possible significant exceptions being found in the Mount Desert Island embayments of Maine and the drowned gorge of the Hudson in the Highlands of New York. On the other hand the terminal moraines, outwash plains and drumlins of the Pleistocene ice sheet are bordered by shorelines which in their initial stage were highly characteristic, and strikingly different one from the other. In less degree fluvio-glacial delta plains, kames and eskers impressed their stamp upon the initial shoreline, while both directly and indirectly the ground moraine deposits are responsible for minor peculiarities of the sea border zone, such as the " reversible falls " at St. John, New Brunswick.

## BIBLIOGRAPHY

1. GOLDTHWAIT, J. W. "Physiography and Surficial Geology of Nova Scotia." Geol. Surv. Can., Summ. Rept. for 1913, 244–250, 1914.
   GOLDTHWAIT, J. W. "The Physiography of Nova Scotia." Manuscript copy of a volume to be issued by the Geological Survey of Canada.
2. WILSON, J. H. "The Glacial History of Nantucket and Cape Cod, with an Argument for a Fourth Center of Glacial Dispersion in North America," 90 pp., New York, 1906.
3. BAILEY, L. W. "Notes on the Surface Geology of Southwestern Nova Scotia." Nova Scotian Inst. Sci., Proc. and Trans., VIII, 3, 1891.
4. BAILEY, L. W. "Report on the Geology of Southwest Nova Scotia." Geol. Surv. Can., Ann. Rept. (1896), N. Ser., IX, Report M, 15, 1898.
5. SHALER, N. S. "Remarks on the Geology of the Coast of Maine, New Hampshire, and that part of Massachusetts north of Boston." U. S. Coast Surv., Coast Pilot for the Atlantic Sea-Board: Gulf of Maine and its Coast from Eastport to Boston (1874), 883, 1875.
6. SHALER, N. S. "The Geology of Cape Ann, Massachusetts." U. S. Geol. Surv., 9th Ann. Rept., 562, 1889.
7. REMMERS, OTTO. "Untersuchungen der Fjorde an der Küste von Maine," 63 pp., Leipzig, 1891.
8. LE CONTE, JOSEPH. "Elements of Geology," 5th Ed., 39, 597, New York, 1910.

9. DANA, J. D. "Manual of Geology," 4th Ed., 948, New York, etc., 1895.
   DANA J. D. "Geology," U. S. Exploring Expedition during the Years 1838 to 1842 under the Command of Charles Wilkes, X, 675, Philadelphia, 1849.

10. UPHAM, WARREN. "Fjords and Hanging Valleys." Amer. Geol., XXXV, 312–315, 1905.
    UPHAM, WARREN. "The Fiords and Great Lake Basins of North America considered as Evidence of Pre-glacial Continental Elevation and of Depression during the Glacial Period." Bull. Geol. Soc. Amer., I, 563–567, 1890.

11. FAIRCHILD, H. L. "Ice Erosion Theory a Fallacy." Bull. Geol. Soc. Amer., XVI, 13–74, 1905.

12. SHALER, N. S. "Evidences as to Changes of Sealevel." Bull. Geol. Soc. Amer., VI, 141–166, 1895.

13. GILBERT, G. K. "Glaciers and Glaciation." Harriman Alaska Expedition, III, 1–231, 1904.

14. GREGORY, J. W. "The Nature and Origin of Fjords." 542 pp., London, 1913.

15. JOHNSON, DOUGLAS. "Shore Processes and Shoreline Development." 176–186, New York, 1917.

16. KATZ, F. J. "Preliminary Report on the Geology of the Portland and Casco Bay Quadrangles." Maine State Water Storage Commission, 3rd Ann. Rept. (1912), 179, 1913.

17. SMITH, G. O. "Geology (of the Kennebec River Basin)." U. S. Geol. Surv., Water Sup. Paper, No. 198, 6, 1907.

18. BASTIN, E. S. "Geology (of the Penobscot River Basin)." U. S. Geol. Surv., Water Sup. Paper No. 279, 12, 1912.

19. SMITH, G. O., BASTIN, E. S., and BROWN, C. W. "Penobscot Bay Folio." U. S. Geol. Surv., Folio 149, 1, 1907.

20. SMITH, G. O. "A Geological Study of the Fox Islands, Maine." Colby College Bulletin, I, Sup., 9, 1901.

21. BASTIN, E. S., and WILLIAMS, H. S. "Eastport Folio." U. S. Geol. Surv., Folio 192, 14, 1914.

22. BASTIN, E. S. "Rockland Folio." U. S. Geol. Surv., Folio 158, 1, 1908.

23. JOHNSON, DOUGLAS. "Shore Processes and Shoreline Development," 173, New York, 1917.

24. SHALER, N. S. "The Geology of the Island of Mount Desert, Maine." U. S. Geol. Surv., 8th Ann. Rept., Pt. II, 1006, 1889.

25. SHALER, N. S. "The Geology of the Island of Mount Desert, Maine." U. S. Geol. Surv., 8th Ann. Rept., Pt. II, 1007, 1889.

26. DAVIS, W. M. "An Outline of the Geology of Mount Desert." Flora of Mount Desert Island (by E. L. Rand and J. H. Redfield), 67, 1894.

27. BASCOM, F. "The Physiography of Mount Desert." Bull. Geog. Soc Phil., XVII, 122, 1919.

28. BASCOM, F. "The Physiography of Mount Desert." Bull. Geog. Soc. Phil., XVII, 117–130, 1919. See also "Second Reprint" published in pamphlet form in 1923, with revised account of drainage history.

29. KEMP, J. F. "Buried Channels Beneath the Hudson and its Tributaries." Amer. Jour. Sci., 4th Ser., XXVI, 301–323, 1908.
    KEMP, J. F. "The Storm King Crossing of the Hudson River, by the New Catskill Aqueduct of New York City." Amer. Jour. Sci., 4th Ser., XXXIV, 1–11, 1912.
30. BERKEY, C. P., and RICE, M.  "Geology of the West Point Quadrangle." N. Y. State Mus. Bull. 225–226, 12, 145, 1921.
31. FULLER, M. L. "The Geology of Long Island, New York." U. S. Geol. Surv., Prof. Paper No. 82, 62 et seq., 1914.
32. SHALER, N. S. "The Geological History of Harbors." U. S. Geol. Surv., 13th Ann. Rept., Pt. 2, 169, 1893.
33. SHALER, N. S. "Remarks on the Geology of the Coast of Maine, New Hampshire, and that part of Massachusetts north of Boston." U. S. Coast Surv., Coast Pilot for the Atlantic Sea-Board: Gulf of Maine and its Coast from Eastport to Boston (1874), 884, 885, 1875.
34. GOLDTHWAIT, J. W. "The Physiography of Nova Scotia." Manuscript copy of a volume to be issued by the Geological Survey of Canada.
35. GOLDTHWAIT, J. W. "Physiography (of Eastern Quebec and the Maritime Provinces)." Twelfth Inter. Geol. Cong., Guidebook No. 1, Pt. I, 24, 1913.
36. HYDE, J. E. Personal communication, by permission of the Director of the Geological Survey of Canada.
37. SHALER, N. S. "Remarks on the Geology of the Coast of Maine, New Hampshire and that part of Massachusetts north of Boston." U. S. Coast Surv., Coast Pilot for the Atlantic Sea-Board: Gulf of Maine and its Coast from Eastport to Boston (1874), 885, 1875.
    SHALER, N. S. "The Geological History of Harbors." U. S. Geol. Surv., 13th Ann. Rept., Pt. 2, 163, 1893.
    SHALER, N. S. "Report on the Geology of Martha's Vineyard." U. S. Geol. Surv., 7th Ann. Rept., 304, 1888.
    RUSSELL, I. C. "North America." 8, New York, 1904.
38. McINTOSH, D. S. "A Study of the Cow Bay Beaches." Nova Scotian Inst. Sci., Proc. and Trans., XIV, Pt. 2, 109–119, 1916.
39. DAVIS, W. M. "The Outline of Cape Cod." Amer. Acad. Arts and Sci., Proc., XXXI, 310, 1896.
40. WOODWORTH, J. B. "The Retreat of the Ice Sheet in the Narragansett Bay Region." Amer. Geol., XVIII, 150–168, 1896.
41. LORD, E. C. E. "On the Dikes in the Vicinity of Portland, Maine." Amer. Geol., XXII, 337, 1898.
42. MATTHEW, G. F. "The Outlets of the St. John River." Nat. Hist. Soc. New Brunswick, Bull., III, No. 12, 43–62, 1894.

# CHAPTER V

## INITIAL SHORELINE AS MODIFIED BY MINOR CHANGES OF LEVEL

**Advance Summary.** — We have seen that the initial shoreline of the New England-Acadian region was determined primarily by partial submergence of a mountainous oldland of complexly folded and faulted rocks upon which several cycles of erosion had developed a variety of clearly defined topographic forms, and secondarily by the fact that this same submergence in places brought the sea to rest against unconsolidated glacial and fluvio-glacial deposits having very different but equally characteristic topographic expressions. It is pertinent now to enquire whether this submergence, admittedly the major factor in determining the class (Shorelines of Submergence) to which the New England-Acadian shoreline belongs, is the only change of level which has materially affected the form of this shoreline. In the present chapter we shall first answer the question whether the change of level which determines the primary characteristics of a shoreline is necessarily the only change, or the latest change, which affects it. The causes of changes of level to which the New England-Acadian shoreline may have been subject will then briefly be reviewed, and the literature descriptive of changes of level in this region summarized. The complexity and difficulty of the whole problem of changes of level will be emphasized and illustrated, and suggestions will be offered as to the conditions requisite to the definitive solution of the problem. Finally, the observed effects of subordinate changes of level on the character of the New England-Acadian shoreline of submergence, including the influence upon shore form of the rate at which such changes take place, will receive attention.

**Relation of Changes of Level to Classes of Shorelines.** — It should clearly be understood that the change of level of land or sea which causes a shoreline of submergence or a shoreline of emergence is not necessarily the only change of level, nor even the latest change of level, which has affected the region. The fact that the shoreline of Maine is classed as a *Shoreline of Submergence* does not imply that the Maine coast may not have witnessed various oscillations of level, involving repeated emergences; nor is it inconsistent with the contention that the latest movement along this coast was one of emergence.   The genetic class to which any shoreline belongs is determined by the movement which is primarily responsible for its major features.   If those features, as in the case of the Maine shoreline, are obviously the result of partial submergence of a former land area, we have a shoreline of submergence, regardless of the number or recency of oscillations of level which may have affected the coast.   And if the last movement on this coast should prove to be one of emergence, it would merely mean that the emergence was so limited in amount and occurred so soon after the major submergence in point of time, that it is still the partially submerged and substantially unaltered land topography which controls the form of the shoreline, and that no typical seabottom plain has yet been formed and emerged to give a different type of coast.   In other words, the emergence in effect merely decreased the total amount of submergence, without altering the essential fact that the shoreline resulted from the sea's resting against a partially submerged land area.

Had the emergence been greater in amount, bringing up the old seabottom plain of marine deposits farther out; or had it been of the same amount but occurred later, after the submerged land topography had been buried by new offshore deposits to form a normal submarine plain, then the emergence of typical seabottom would have controlled the form of the shoreline, giving a *Shoreline of Emergence* of wholly different type.   A minor submergence, especially if it followed so soon after emergence that the emerged coastal plain was little affected by the ordinary processes of erosion operative upon the land, might produce no great change in the shoreline.   Such shallow valleys as had been formed would give slight embayments, but the simple shoreline characteristic of an upraised seabottom, perhaps with the offshore bar and lagoon which develop early in the youth of such a shoreline, would still remain the dominant feature of the shore.   Thus it is that the shoreline of southern New Jersey is properly classed as a shoreline of emergence, although a later slight submergence caused partial drowning of the valleys back of the offshore bar and lagoon.

If neither submergence of a former land surface, nor emergence

of a former subaqueous surface causes the shoreline, it belongs
in the class of *Neutral Shorelines*. Deltas built forward into a
stationary water body, island volcanoes building their cones outward by continued addition of erupted materials, and fault cliffs
newly formed and exposed to the sea by subsidence of the down-
dropped block completely below sealevel, are examples of neutral
shorelines; for in none of these cases does the shoreline border a
partially submerged former land area or a partially emerged
former seabottom; and the shorelines have special features quite
unlike those characteristic of either shorelines of submergence
or shorelines of emergence. On the other hand, if both submergence and emergence have determined major features of the
shoreline, we have a *Compound Shoreline*. Such is the shoreline
of North Carolina, which combines large and extensively branching drowned valleys due to submergence of a dissected coastal
plain, with a beautiful cordon of offshore bars due to emergence
of a comparatively smooth seabottom. Other types of compound
shorelines are known, but need not concern us here.*

The New England-Acadian shoreline is, as we have seen,
clearly a shoreline of submergence. If it has been affected by
emergence, the results are so small as not materially to have
modified the salient characters produced by submergence. Obviously they were not sufficiently important to throw the shoreline
into the compound class. At best they are but minor features
superimposed upon the major forms due to extensive encroachment of the sea over the margins of a dissected landmass. Yet
no description of a shoreline can be complete which ignores minor
forms produced by a relative change of level opposite to that
which is primarily responsible for the character of the shore.
Hence we turn aside for the moment to enquire what changes of
level have in recent geological time affected the New England-
Acadian coast, and whether these have left their imprint upon
the form of the present shoreline.

**Possible Causes of Changes of Level.** — That the New England-
Acadian coast has witnessed repeated oscillations of level in glacial
and post-glacial times is indicated both by theoretical considerations and by the evidence which various students of the problem
have collected and analyzed. The abstraction of vast quantities
of water from the ocean to form the great ice sheets of the glacial

* For a full discussion of the genetic classification of shorelines, see the
author's "Shore Processes and Shoreline Development," pp. 171–192.

period must have lowered the sealevel, possibly as much as a few hundred feet; and the return of this water to the ocean consequent upon the melting of the ice must similarly have raised sealevel. The weight of the ice may have depressed the earth's crust beneath it, while beyond the ice margin the crust may have been bulged upward in a low, broad arch due to the transfer in depth of material pressed out from beneath that part of the earth's crust which yielded under its burden of ice. When the ice melted the depressed area would rise again; but, as Barrell has shown, the rising central area might carry the marginal bulges upward with it, causing a further rise of areas already appreciably elevated. Later these marginal areas might be expected to subside. The mass of the ice, by the attractive force which it exerted upon the waters of adjacent parts of the ocean, must materially have raised the sealevel along coasts near to the ice margin; and with the disappearance of the ice sheet the waters must have fallen. During these changes in the relative level of land and sea, there may have been others quite unrelated to glaciation, such as broad continental and suboceanic movements involving isostatic readjustment of large sections of the earth's crust, more limited compressive movements associated with earth shrinkage and often tending to destroy rather than to establish isostatic equilibrium, the rise of sealevel due to partial filling of the ocean basins by sediments washed in from the lands, and possibly a further slow rise due to secular gain in the volume of the ocean water.[1]

**Evidences of Changes of Level.** — It is obvious that some of these various changes of level may have, and indeed certain of them must have, operated simultaneously, tending either to accentuate or to neutralize each other. Others operated at different times. One can hardly escape the conclusion that the net result must have been a series of oscillations of level, of submergences and emergences, of extreme complexity. The results thus far secured by students of this problem seem to establish both the fact of oscillations of level and their complex nature. Barrell's[2] work on the Pleistocene and older terraces cut in the hard rocks of the New England upland, supplemented by that of Hatch;[3] the studies of De Geer,[4] Chalmers,[5] Daly,[6] Goldthwait,[7] Fairchild,[8] Johnston[9] and many others on the elevated beaches, seacliffs, deltas, and wave-washed surfaces observed on or near the coasts of New England and eastern Canada; the descriptions of post-glacial marine clays bordering parts of these same shores, published by Logan,[10] Stone,[11] Davis,[12] Chalmers,[13] Upham,[14] Keele,[15] and others; and the accounts of submarine valleys given by Dana,[16] Lindenkohl,[17] Spencer[18] and Poole,[19] to name but a few of those who have considered such phenomena, and to say nothing for the present concerning more voluminous evidence of post-glacial subsidence: these are some of the investigations which together have demonstrated that in geologically recent times the margin of the continent in the New England-Acadian region has experienced repeated submergence and emergence.

**Unsatisfactory Nature of Part of the Evidence.** — It is true that both the evidence and the arguments presented by the several investigators named, and by a large number of other observers who have contributed toward the elucidation of various aspects of the problem, are of very unequal value. Submarine canyons have been contoured to enormous depths on the basis of evidence which appears to be inadequate. Critical students are not convinced that the argument for submergence based on well established cases of submarine trenches is valid, and Davis[20] has remarked, in a recent commentary on the subject, that the whole problem of submarine trenches " is evidently open rather than closed," and that it may be found advisable " to explain them all as of submarine origin, without the aid of changes of level." Former marine submergence of large areas of Long Island and southern New England has been postulated on lines of reasoning some of which appear to the writer to be unsound. The lack of agreement among students of the problem in respect to the number, nature, and dates of oscillations of level is an indication not only of the complexity of the problem, but also of its difficulty. The distinction between marine and freshwater elevated shorelines is often extremely delicate, a serious matter in a region which has suffered extensively from obstructed drainage in the glacial period, as well as from streams marginal to the ice at various elevations; and we find the same phenomena cited by some investigators as proof of the former existence of a temporary lake or stream, and by others as proof of former marine submergence of the area. Analysis of the problem is further complicated when one investigator endeavors to utilize the observations of another, due to the fact that such observations are of unequal value; and it is often difficult, if not impossible, on the basis of the written text alone, to discriminate those observations which are reliable from those which are of doubtful value or wholly

FIG. 61. Chimney Rock, Mount Desert Island, sometimes interpreted as a marine stack marking an elevated shoreline. *Courtesy* Lafayette National Park.

unreliable.   Thus Fairchild's[22] isobase of 500 feet for the St. Johns area, Newfoundland, based on figures suggested by Daly after brief observation of a region where conditions are highly specialized, becomes of doubtful significance with the latter's revision of his figures following more detailed studies;[21] and indeed Fairchild's whole series of isobases for Newfoundland, drawn to harmonize with Daly's earlier figures for various points on the coast, are incompatible with the latter's revised observations, Daly's zero isobase, or line of no uplift, passing squarely through the center of Fairchild's area of maximum uplift as indicated by his 600-

Fig. 62.   Rifting of granite along joint planes, on summit of Champlain Mountain (1050 feet), Mount Desert Island, Maine.   In the distance the New England peneplane is seen sloping down to the sea.   *Courtesy* Lafayette National Park.

foot isobase.   Goldthwait[23] has recently reviewed the problem of changes of level as related to the Nova Scotian area, and has commented on the important questions there awaiting answers.

**Supposed Elevated Shorelines of Maine.** — As a concrete example of the difficulties attendant upon the determination and correlation of higher marine levels, we may instance the unsatisfactory character of the evidence upon which some of the famous elevated shorelines of Mount Desert Island are postulated.[24]   The " Chimney Rock " (Fig. 61), often interpreted as a marine stack in front of an ancient seacliff, appears to be more reasonably explained as a joint block rifted from the main granitic mass and creeping slowly down a sloping bed-joint surface under the influence of frost action and gravity. No indication of marine action is observable at the base of either supposed seacliff or supposed stack, whereas the control of rifting along joints in the granite is strikingly obvious (Figs. 62 and 63), not only here but at levels far above that generally admitted as the upper marine limit for the most extensive post-glacial submergence. The theory that the top joint-block of the " stack " was twisted out of its normal position by wave action or some other natural force, loses much weight in view of the reported fact that recently this block was tilted off its pedestal and precipitated to the ground below by some mischievous youths, and later replaced by their more sober minded elders. The broken corners of the block as well as the scars on the face of the " stack " are suggestive reminders of the fact that hands which could hurl down and lift up again this interesting object, could easily have twisted it upon its base. Post-glacial submergence may have brought the sea to the level of the Chimney Rock for a relatively brief period, but if so the fact must be demonstrated by other evidence, and cannot be substantiated by the occurrence of forms thoroughly typical of subaërial agencies.

The Cadillac Cliffs (Fig. 64), a far more imposing scarp commonly attributed to marine erosion at higher levels than the present, show on a grand scale the normal results of rifting along vertical joint planes when prominent bed-joints inclined downhill permit the rifted blocks to migrate down the slope. Every gradation may be found from blocks moved but an inch or two from the parent mass, through great masses separated by chasms one foot or several feet wide, to other masses tumbled forward and shattered on the gentle granite slope in front. Nowhere does the scarp show the characteristic features of a wave-cut cliff. There are layers of the almost horizontally jointed mass which are weathered into the rounded forms so characteristic of granite, while other layers are weathered out to form horizontal clefts or chasms; but this is true of the whole face of the cliff, at the top as well as at the bottom. On the other hand there is no pronounced or even moderately continuous notch at the cliff base; and the base instead of being approximately horizontal, varies extensively and abruptly in elevation. So far as its physiographic aspect is concerned one

FIG. 63. Rifting of granite along joint plane, with down-hill movement of
detached block, steep eastern slope of Flying Squadron Mountain,
Mount Desert Island. *Courtesy* Lafayette National Park. (137)

FIG. 64. The Cadillac Cliffs, Mount Desert Island, interpreted by some as ancient marine cliffs bordering an elevated shoreline. The cave shown in Fig. 65 is at the base of the cliffs. Note the vertical joint plane separating the stack-like mass from rest of cliff at right. *Courtesy* Lafayette National Park.

would scarcely hesitate to ascribe the shattered scarp to weathering of the jointed walls of an oversteepened glaciated valley, unmodified by marine action.

There is, however, a local detail which may, not without reason, cause one to invoke the aid of the sea at the base of the Cadillac Cliffs. At one point a cave extends back under the mass some distance, and in the rear of this cave large rounded boulders are visible (Fig. 65). Bascom,[25] following Shaler, considered both cliffs and cave to be of marine origin; but she recognized the rounded boulders as normal decomposition products of disintegrating granite. In company with Mr. William Campbell of the Lafayette National Park I examined the recesses of this cave back of the boulders visible from the entrance, and found a large quantity of water - rounded cobbles and larger boulders representing a variety of rocks foreign to the locality. The roof of the cave showed distinct exfoliation phenomena, and curving plates of the granite were dislodged without difficulty. Similar evidence of exfoliation was observed on the rounded granite boulders, some of which still retained slight portions of one

or more joint faces.   Thus one might explain both the cave and the
rounded granite boulders as normal weathering phenomena.   But
this explanation cannot be invoked for the mass of water-worn erratic material of varying composition.   That this material represents beach gravel and cobbles driven back into the head of a sea
cave under the impact of wave action is perhaps the most obvious
explanation which occurs to one.   But against this interpretation
there must be urged the absence of any clear indication of wave
erosion at the cave or elsewhere, the variable elevation of the cliff
base, and the fact that the steep descent in front of the cave makes
it doubtful whether the waves, after working on a steep granite

Fig. 65.   Cave at base of Cadillac Cliffs, Mount Desert Island, showing
    rounded boulder of weathered granite.   The hat gives a scale for com-
    parison of dimensions.   Farther back in the cave, out of sight, are
    water-worn boulders representing several types of rocks.   *Courtesy*
    Lafayette National Park.

slope long enough to carve a cave, could find and bring to the
mouth of the cave erratic material without losing it in deep water
beyond the reach of effective wave movement.   A more likely
source is perhaps to be found in waters from the melting ice,
swirling past and into the cave and leaving part of their load at
its inner end.
    Another possibility should not be overlooked: the cave is in
the base of a great block of the granite rifted from the main
mass along a master joint (Fig. 64) which passes not far back of
the inner end of the cave.   The rift shows as an open chasm into

which, in case it existed at the end of the glacial period, glacial waters may have poured, together with their load of gravel and cobbles.  Any connection of moderate size with the nearby rear end of the cave would adequately account for the presence of the erratics where found.  If such connection existed, movement of the granite mass in the rear or deposition of débris in the chasm, or both, must effectually have sealed it, for no gleam of light penetrates the cave from above, although I observed in the rear of the roof inconclusive evidence of a zone of crushed rock.  One should also consider the possibility that temporary marine submergence of a cave produced by weathering might wash into it glacial erratics from the adjacent slope.  The finding of an Indian arrow-head in the débris by Mr. Campbell emphasizes the question as to whether the water-rounded erratics may not also have been introduced into the cave by human agency.  But because of the difficulty of reaching the rear of the cave (which is a mere slit between nearly horizontal joints in the granite), the quantity and size of the débris in question, and its appearance when found, it seems difficult to doubt the natural origin of the deposit.  At the same time I regard the supposed marine origin of cliff, cave, and deposit as in the highest degree doubtful.

**Difficulties of the Problem.** — I have selected the foregoing supposed indications of elevated beaches for emphasis in order to make clear the unsatisfactory character of the evidence upon which former marine levels are often postulated.  Many supposed former shorelines, on Mount Desert and elsewhere, rest on evidence far less convincing than that described above.  On the other hand I have seen on the lower slopes of this interesting island, and in other parts of New England, what appeared to be valid evidence of elevated strands, and other more equivocal indications of earlier sealevels.  Such observations, incomplete and fragmentary as they are, convince one of the desirability of reviewing the whole problem of elevated shorelines along the Atlantic Coast in the light of a critical examination and analysis, in the field, of all the available evidence.  That the higher stand of the sea was very temporary and the changes of level comparatively rapid, would seem to be suggested by the extent to which glacially striated bare rock slopes, both steep and gentle, are preserved below the known marine limits.

Enough has been said to indicate some of the difficulties which confront those studying past oscillations of level along the New

England-Acadian coast, and to make clear the present unsatisfactory status of the question.   It is not my intention to attempt any solution of this complex problem.   Even if it did not lie without the scope of this work (which is confined to a study of the present shoreline and the light which it throws upon the question of subsidence in recent times), I have not made the critical studies which would give me competence for the task.   My observations of phenomena attributed to former higher water levels on the coasts of the United States, Great Britain, Sweden, and elsewhere have been sufficient to convince me that while there is obvious valid evidence of emergence on the coasts named, a considerable portion of the phenomena attributed to marine action at higher levels had no such origin.   But I have been unable to prosecute the detailed investigations necessary to separate valid from fictitious indications of emergence, and thus to make a constructive contribution toward the solution of the problem.   It may not be impertinent, however, for one who frankly admits his own incompetence to discuss the subject, but who has seen something of the difficulties of the problem in several fields, and who has encountered somewhat similar difficulties in a critical investigation of the supposed evidences of modern coastal subsidence, to suggest the procedure which seems most likely to solve definitively the complex problem of recent oscillations of level, particularly those involving coastal emergence.

**Conditions Requisite to the Solution of the Problem.** — The delicate nature of the evidence requires that a single investigator, or two or more investigators so closely associated in all phases of the work that they see absolutely " eye to eye " in observing the field evidence, shall so far as possible cover the whole territory under discussion.   This is made necessary by the fact, already referred to, that it is difficult if not impossible to employ the results of a variety of investigators with confidence, when critical discrimination of the field evidence at each point is absolutely essential to the proper establishment of the fundamental data of the investigation.   A considerable proportion of the errors involved in previous work on the subject is chargeable to the acceptance of conclusions of other observers, when personal examination in the field would have led to the modification or rejection of those conclusions.   It is also essential that the investigator or investigators should be well trained in physiography, and possess a special acquaintance with shore phenomena.   One may be pardoned for stressing the seemingly obvious point that those thoroughly familiar with shore processes and forms will best be qualified to attempt the difficult discrimination of obscure shore features inland.  And since the arguments upon which marine submergence is postulated necessarily involve the interpretation of broad areas which must have been seabottom according to one theory and land surface according to another, one with physiographic training should be most competent to deal with these vitally important aspects of the problem.  Justification for this requirement is found in the fallacious arguments not infrequently advanced in support of submergence or emergence by excellent investigators insufficiently familiar with physiographic principles. The problem is for the most part essentially physiographic in nature, and the best abilities of the trained physiographer will be fully taxed by its more difficult phases.  For the proper discrimination of marine and non-marine water levels, the investigator needs a broad and thorough personal familiarity with the field relations and appearance of erosional and depositional forms of various types produced by streams marginal to the ice and in other positions, by wave action on temporary lakes, and by marine action under different exposures and on different types of shores.  In making discriminations in the field, it is most necessary that the investigator should first relentlessly exclude from his list of marine levels not only all dubious cases of shore phenomena, but likewise all undoubted shore forms which admit of a non-marine interpretation, all phenomena which merely " fall in with " levels indicated by other data, and all evidence which for any reason is only of permissive, not of probative value.  There will remain a residue of valid evidence of recent changes of level which in volume will be meagre as compared with the large mass of evidence and argument thus far printed on the subject, but which will have a definite, known value.  Critical analysis of it, unhampered by the mass of doubtful, erroneous, and misleading observations which now complicate the problem, may be sufficient to establish the number, nature and dates of the oscillations in question.  In any case, it can hardly fail to clarify the problem, and to establish clearly the lines on which a solution must be found, if at all, through the discovery of additional evidence having critical value.  To bring so much order out of the confusion of present conflicting theories is a task well worthy the ambition of any student.  The excellent results already secured by a few competent investigators on certain sections of the coast, point the way toward the final solution of the problem for the entire New England-Acadian province along the lines indicated above.

**Effects of Emergence and Submergence upon the New England-Acadian Shoreline.** — Despite the present unsatisfactory state of the problem of oscillation of levels along the New England-Acadian shoreline, there is no room to doubt the reality of both post-glacial emergence and submergence. Whatever the number and extent of these oscillations, they now concern us only in so far as they have left their impress upon the present shoreline. The reader who would follow the problem into other fields will find abundant literature on the subject, much of which is opened to him through the works cited at the close of this chapter. Of particular service will be the bibliography of works dealing with post-glacial continental uplift prepared by Fairchild,[26] and that relating to submarine valleys prepared by Spencer.[27]

Submergence additional to that which produced the characteristic features of the New England-Acadian shoreline of submergence already described in earlier pages, would operate chiefly to confirm or intensify those features. It might carry below sea-level marine cliffs and other features produced by waves and currents along the shoreline of submergence during a somewhat higher relative stand of the land. But it does not appear that any striking peculiarities of the shore would result from further submergence of an already partially submerged coast of the New England-Acadian type still in a youthful stage of development, although certain details of more than usual interest must claim our attention whenever we attempt to discriminate between evidences of geologically recent (post-glacial) subsidence, and proofs of subsidence within the modern or historical period.

Emergence, on the other hand, would add elements of a new and distinct order. It is true that the elevated cliffs, benches, and sea-beaches would appear simply as minor details on hillsides or valley walls, unless a still-stand of the land sufficiently long for the sea to cut deeply into the coast preceded each emergence. This apparently was not the case, for according to the preponderant weight of evidence the elevated shorelines are as a rule so faintly developed as to require much care for their proper interpretation. There are, it is true, a few reported cases of prominent coastal terraces at high levels, but these may be open to interpretation as of non-marine origin, as will later be explained; and

Goldthwait,[28] Daly,[29] Stone,[11] and other students of elevated shorelines about the Gulf of St. Lawrence, along the Labrador coast, on the coast of Maine and other parts of northeastern North America, repeatedly emphasize the prevailing absence of elevated strands possessing " enough individuality of character, enough strength of expression, or enough continuity to indicate a long stand of the sea at any level," and cite indications that the sea " has stood at or near its present position many times as long as at any higher level." These conditions are in general characteristic of the whole New England-Acadian coast, although Daly[30] has suggested that a temporary upward bulging of the Banks enclosing the Gulf of Maine may have prevented the waves of the open ocean from breaking on the New England coast for a part of post-glacial time, thus accounting for an apparent unusual weakness of the elevated strands of that region.* But even in Labrador, where he believes no such protection occurred, he finds " no sure evidence of pronounced halts in the uplift " of the land. The Micmac Terrace (Figs. 115 and 116), described by Goldthwait[28] as bordering the shores of the Gulf of St. Lawrence for a distance of more than two hundred miles in the form of a pronounced cliff or scarp with its base about twenty feet above sealevel, fronted by a bench or flat of variable width, may owe its striking form to slight modification of subaërial terraces partially drowned when the sea entered the terraced valley of the St. Lawrence River, as will more fully appear on a later page.

*The Terraces of Anticosti Island.* — Among descriptions of higher terraces of great breadth attributed to marine erosion by those who have investigated them, one of the most recent and best relates to the terraces of Anticosti Island by Twenhofel and Conine.[32] These authors describe in some detail a series of benches found at twenty-two different levels, but imperfectly correlated because of the difficult nature of the country. The highest attains an elevation of more than 400 feet above sealevel, and several of the broadest measure 1.5 miles, 2 miles, and in one case several miles across from front to rear. A structural origin

---

* More vigorous shore erosion due to intense frost action in more northern latitudes as described by Nansen,[31] exposure to northeast storms, less protection by offshore islets and reefs, and other favorable factors may account for the apparent great vigor of wave attack on the Labrador coast, independently of a hypothetical bulging of the Banks region to afford protection to the New England coast.

for these benches is excluded on the ground that they truncate the rock formations. As favoring a marine origin it is pointed out that gravel occurs on most of them; some of the scarps, especially the lower ones, are cliffs " such as could have been developed only by the waves"; shell bored rocks have been found in one region up to at least 85 feet above sealevel; and on the Mingan Islands to the north " flowerpot " rocks, believed to be stacks carved by waves, are found at or below the 50-foot level, while a stack-like structure is also found more than 400 feet above sealevel on the top of a cliff at another locality. The gravel is said to be " beach gravel," but the evidence on which this conclusion is based is not made clear, except that it resembles the gravel along the present coast, and is more or less weathered on the higher and older beaches. " Boulder beaches or lines " were not discovered. The evidence on which the terrace scarps are considered as necessarily due to wave action is not stated; but elsewhere overhanging cliffs fronted by talus are said to occur at the back of the lowest terrace, only 5 or 6 feet above sealevel. The features of the " flower-pot " rocks which caused them to be regarded as marine stacks are not described. One must not forget that, in the field, evidence is often more complete and more conclusive than would appear from a condensed statement on the printed page; but when it is remembered that in the absence of beach forms the discrimination of beach gravels from other gravels is not an easy matter; that in the region in question the known physiographic history afforded on the one hand ample opportunity for the distributing over the terraces of freshwater gravels, and on the other hand equal opportunity for the deposition of marine gravels upon any terraces of non-marine origin which were involved in the post-glacial submergence; that overhanging cliffs quite similar to marine forms are sometimes produced by normal weathering in crystalline rocks, and much more frequently in horizontal or gently inclined sedimentary rocks like those of Anticosti; that some of the forms closely resembling marine stacks (Figs. 61 and 86) are perhaps better to be interpreted as products of subaërial weathering agencies; that the post-glacial submergence of Anticosti, even if unaccompanied by long stands of the sealevel at any particular horizons, would afford sufficient opportunity for the making of shell borings and for the sharpening of pre-existing cliffs and the notching of their bases where conditions were favorable; and that evidences of such long-continued wave cutting as would be required to produce terraces from one to several miles broad in solid rock above present sealevel are generally lacking on neighboring coasts; it seems permissible to suspend final judgment as to the extent of wave action on the Anticosti terraces until they have been further examined in the light of the considerations here set forth, and those developed at greater length in connection with the supposed wave-cut submarine shelves bordering the mainland shores of the St. Lawrence embayment, to be discussed in a later chapter of this volume. It must not be forgotten, however, that both in character of rock and in exposure to wave attack Anticosti Island is better situated to record marine erosion than are some of the other coasts cited above.

*The Post-Glacial Marine Coastal Plain.* — In its effect upon the present shoreline the emergence of submarine deposits to form a coastal plain was more important than the lifting above sealevel of ancient strand lines. Such emergence of seabottom deposits occurred along the coasts of Maine and New Brunswick, of Chaleur Bay, in the Annapolis Valley of Nova Scotia, in the valley of the St. Lawrence, and to a limited extent on other parts of the New England-Acadian coast. The floor of the Annapolis Valley is in large part formed of marine clays and sands of limited thickness mantling over the subdued topography of the valley floor. How far the shoreline here owes its character to submergence of the valley floor, and how far to the emergence of the marine deposits, has not been determined. In the valley of the lower St. Lawrence an uplifted plain of marine sands and clays is from eight or ten miles up to twenty or thirty miles broad on the northern side of the estuary, where it rises from an elevation of 15 or 20 feet close to the water, to an altitude of 400 or 500 feet at the base of the Laurentide hills.[13] The initial shoreline formed against this plain has been cut back some distance wherever exposed to the waves of the embayment, and the rocks beneath often exposed. As the principal development of this plain is on the northern side of the St. Lawrence estuary, and thus outside the territory here under discussion, it need not further concern us.

The coastal plain of glacial and early post-glacial marine clays and sands bordering the irregular coast of Maine and New Brunswick is of more than ordinary interest. Following the major submergence which determined the chief characteristics of this indented coast, there accumulated on the rugged seabottom pro-

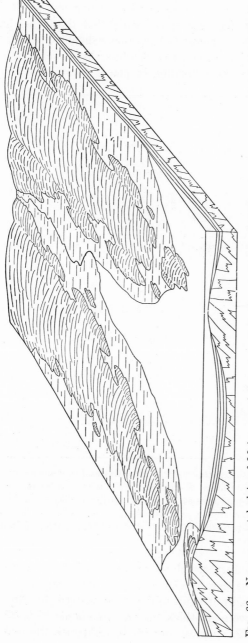

FIG. 66.  Narrow coastal plain of Maine, consisting of partially emerged post-glacial marine clay and sand incompletely filling the drowned valleys of an embayed mountainous coast.  The initial shoreline here represented bordering this fringing coastal plain was much more simple than the former unmodified shoreline of submergence bordering the rock hills.

duced by the drowning of a dissected land area, a thickness of clays and sands which was only sufficient partially to fill the submerged hollows and valleys, and which left the higher hills projecting through the deposit to form rocky shoals or islands.   With subsequent partial emergence, which brought above water a coastal plain fringe (Fig. 66) extending in places twenty-five miles, fifty

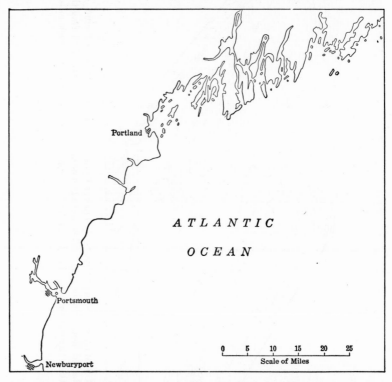

FIG. 67.   Contrasted portions of the New England shoreline of submergence. The section southwest of Portland is far more regular than that to the northeast, in part because it is more nearly parallel to the strike of the rock structure, and in part because it has been simplified by limited emergence of post-glacial marine clays to form a narrow, fringing coastal plain.

miles, or even further inland along principal embayments, the shoreline at the new level presented certain novel features.   It was still markedly irregular in general pattern, for the clay and sand deposits were not thick enough (commonly 15 to 35 feet, but in places 50, 75, or even more[33]) to obliterate the embayments caused by submergence; and the emergence was not extensive enough (between 200 and 300 feet vertical change[34]) to carry the new shoreline seaward beyond them.   On the other hand, many of the minor branch embayments of the rocky coast were not represented in the new shoreline bordering the uplifted marine clays. Thus southwest of Portland, Maine, the sea came to rest against a nearly flat plain five to ten miles in breadth, through which as a rule only small and isolated hills of hard rock projected, and the shoreline was so markedly simplified as a result of emergence that the effects are recognizable in the present form of this shore (Fig. 67).   Since elsewhere the new shoreline still bordered rocky islands or peninsulas, either portions of the dissected peneplaned oldland or monadnocks rising above the peneplane,[35] it is evident that in its initial stage it must have been curiously composite in character.   Just as the coastal plain of Maine has been described by Davis[12] as the type example of a narrow coastal plain of thin deposits fringing an extremely irregular oldland, so we may take the associated shoreline as the type of a shoreline of submergence moderately simplified in its initial stage by limited emergence.   That much of this moderate simplicity may be lost in later stages of the shoreline's development will be shown in following pages, where we shall find that the shoreline of Maine is in places much more irregular in detail than it was immediately following the limited emergence here under consideration.   We shall also see that subsequent minor submergence apparently has caused the drowning of the lower courses of certain valleys cut in the coastal plain.

**Effects of the Rate of Emergence and Submergence.** — There remains to be considered, in connection with the initial shoreline, the effects of the *rate* of emergence and submergence upon the character of the initial shore forms.   Thus far we have discussed the initial shoreline as though it were the result of a submergence which brought the sea to rest against the dissected landmass more or less suddenly; and in the same way we have described the modifying effects of limited emergence as though no appreciable time were consumed in this change of level.   A moment's thought, however, will remind us that with a given amount of submergence or emergence, the results at the moment the change is arrested will be profoundly different according to whether the change took place very rapidly or very slowly.   If the change be rapid, the waves will have time to do very little work during the progress of the movement, and when the movement terminates the new shoreline will rest against a dissected landmass or an uplifted seabottom which is as yet practically unaffected by wave action. But when the change of level takes place slowly, the waves may cut the shoreline back into the land faster than the movement of submergence would transfer it backward; or a slowly emerging seabottom might be profoundly altered by wave erosion or deposition, or by both, before it rose out of the water. In either case the shoreline formed at the instant the movement ceased would be a shoreline already advanced some distance in its evolutionary history. It would never have had a truly initial stage at that level.

To take a concrete example: The moraine shoreline which is represented in Fig. 44 as the initial form which would result from a depression of part of the Marthas Vineyard moraine 200 feet below its present level, would have that form only if the submergence took place rapidly. If the change of level were gradual, permitting extensive wave erosion and deposition, by the time the water reached the level in question projecting headlands would be cut back, embayments possibly blocked by bars, and some of the islands might be entirely swept away. In other words, the shoreline would appear materially different from Fig. 44; and although it would be the shoreline as first established at that level, it would not be " initial " in any proper sense of that term. Similarly, the initial drumlin shorelines shown in Figs. 53, 54, and 56, assume a relatively rapid submergence; for it is obvious that if the change were slow some of the drumlins must have been partly cut away, others perhaps wholly so, by the time the actual level of land and sea was established.

There is abundant evidence that the rate of the principal submergence which gave to the New England-Acadian shoreline its major features, was relatively rapid. Even today the waves have not succeeded in cutting back rocky headlands to any great extent, and the shoreline is throughout most of its length in very early youth. Where unusually weak rocks occur, the results of wave attack are, as we shall see, much more pronounced; and moraines, drumlins, and other unconsolidated glacial deposits have suffered severely, wherever well exposed to open water. But much of what has been accomplished certainly occurred after the present level of land and sea was established, for there is strong physiographic evidence indicating that for several thousand years at least there has been no appreciable change in that level. We are probably not far wrong, therefore, in depicting the initial stage of the shoreline of submergence as the shoreline formed at or near the present level following a comparatively rapid encroachment of the sea upon the land. If an element of error is involved for those shorelines bordering unconsolidated glacial deposits, it probably is not of great magnitude; and in any case we have presumably correctly pictured the type of the initial shore, even if the initial form was developed earlier at a somewhat lower level. As regards the modifications due to limited emergence, the evidence is clear that while the emerging plain of post-glacial marine clays was sufficiently acted upon by waves and currents to have shore forms developed on it at various levels, the movement was so rapid that nowhere was the plain greatly altered by marine agencies. Hence the description of the initial shoreline of submergence as modified by limited emergence, given on preceding pages, may be considered as reasonably accurate.

**Résumé.** — We have found that the major change of level which determines the primary character of a given shoreline need not be the only change, nor even the last change affecting the region in question. In the New England-Acadian area various causes of changes of level apparently have operated, and there is evidence that the oscillations of the shoreline have been many and complex. The problem thus presented to the students of changes of level is a difficult one, and has not yet received a satisfactory solution. It appears, however, that the initial form of the New England-Acadian shoreline of submergence has not been profoundly modified by minor oscillations of level. Moderate emergence has adorned the land margin with some elevated strands, although many of the supposed elevated shorelines are of doubtful validity; and a narrow coastal plain of glacial and post-glacial date has been raised above the water along certain parts of the coast. Minor submergence has added slightly to the embayment of the coast, and has drowned the lower reaches of some of the valleys cut in the narrow coastal plain. But none of the forms resulting from these subordinate changes of level are of major importance, for the essential character of the shoreline remained unchanged by these movements. It appears, further, that the rates of the changes of level, whether of the principal submergence which determined the primary character of the shoreline or of the subordinate oscillations, were not such as to require us to make special allowance for possible modifying effects upon the initial shore forms.

## BIBLIOGRAPHY

1. BARRELL, JOSEPH. "Factors in the Movements of the Strand Line and their Results in the Pleistocene and Post-Pleistocene." Amer. Jour. Sci., 4th Ser., XL, 21, 22, 1915.

2. BARRELL, JOSEPH. "The Piedmont Terraces of the Northern Appalachians." Amer. Jour. Sci., 4th Ser., XLIX, 227–258, 327–362, 407–428, 1920.

3. HATCH, LAURA. "Marine Terraces in Southeastern Connecticut." Amer. Jour. Sci., 4th Ser., XLIV, 319–330, 1917.

4. DEGEER, GERARD. "On Pleistocene Changes of Level in Eastern North America." Bost. Soc. Nat. Hist., Proc., XXV, 454–477, 1892.

5. CHALMERS, ROBERT. Numerous articles and reports, appearing principally in publications of the Geological Survey of Canada, the Transactions of the Royal Society of Canada, the American Geologist, and the American Journal of Science, during the period 1882–1905.

6. DALY, R. A. "The Geology of the Northeast Coast of Labrador." Bull. Mus. Comp. Zoölogy, XXXVIII (Geol. Ser. V), 205–270, 1902.
   DALY, R. A. "A Recent Worldwide Sinking of Ocean-Level." Geol. Mag., LVII, 246–261, 1920.
   DALY, R. A. "Oscillations of Level in the Belts Peripheral to the Pleistocene Ice-Caps." Bull. Geol. Soc. Amer., XXXI, 303–318, 1920.
   DALY, R. A. "Post-Glacial Warping of Newfoundland and Nova Scotia." Amer. Jour. Sci., 5th Ser., I, 381–391, 1921.

7. GOLDTHWAIT, J. W. "The Twenty-foot Terrace and Sea-cliff of the Lower St. Lawrence." Amer. Jour. Sci., 4th Ser., XXXII, 291–317, 1911.
   GOLDTHWAIT, J. W. "The Physiography of Nova Scotia." Manuscript copy of a volume to be issued by the Geological Survey of Canada.
   GOLDTHWAIT, J. W. Numerous articles in the publications of the Geological Survey of Canada for the period 1911–1915, and in Guidebooks Nos. 1 and 3 of the Twelfth International Geological Congress, 1913.

8. FAIRCHILD, H. L. "Pleistocene Marine Submergence of the Connecticut and Hudson Valleys." Bull. Geol. Soc. Amer., XXV, 219–242, 1914.
   FAIRCHILD, H. L. "Pleistocene Uplift of New York and Adjacent Territory." Bull. Geol. Soc. Amer., XXVII, 235–262, 1916.
   FAIRCHILD, H. L. "Post-glacial Marine Submergence of Long Island." Bull. Geol. Soc. Amer., XXVIII, 279–308, 1917.
   FAIRCHILD, H. L. "Post-glacial Uplift of Northeastern America." Bull. Geol. Soc. Amer., XXIX, 187–234, 1918.

9. JOHNSTON, W. A. "Late Pleistocene Oscillations of Sea-Level in the Ottawa Valley." Geol. Surv. Can., Mus. Bull. No. 24, 14 pp., 1916.

10. LOGAN, W. E. "Geology of Canada," 915–926, Montreal, 1863.

11. STONE, G. H. "The Glacial Gravels of Maine and their Associated Deposits." U. S. Geol. Surv., Mon. XXXIV, 54–58, 1899.

12. DAVIS, W. M. "Un Exemple de Plaine Côtière: la Plaine du Maine." Annales de Géographie, VIII, 1–5, 1899.

   DAVIS, W. M. "Die Erklärende Beschreibung der Landformen," 532–539, Leipzig and Berlin, 1912.

13. CHALMERS, ROBERT. "Notes on the Pleistocene Marine Shorelines and Landslips of the North Side of the St. Lawrence Valley." Geol. Surv. Can., Ann. Rept., N. Ser., XI, for 1898, 63J–70J, 1901.

14. UPHAM, WARREN. "Late Glacial or Champlain Subsidence and Re-elevation of the St. Lawrence River Basin." Amer. Jour. Sci., 3rd Ser., XLIX, 17–18, 1895.

15. KEELE, J. "Preliminary Report on the Clay and Shale Deposits of the Province of Quebec." Geol. Surv. Can., Mem. 64, 42–106, 1915.

16. DANA, J. D. "Manual of Geology," 1st ed., 441, Philadelphia, 1863.

   DANA, J. D. "Manual of Geology," 4th Ed., 18, 745, 949, New York, etc., 1895.

   DANA, J. D. "Long Island Sound in the Quaternary Era, with Observations on the Submarine Hudson River Channel." Amer. Jour. Sci., 3rd Ser., XL, 425–437, 1890.

17. LINDENKOHL, A. "Geology of the Seabottom in the Approaches to New York Bay." Amer. Jour. Sci., 3rd Ser., XXIX, 475–480, 1885.

   LINDENKOHL, A. "Notes on the Submarine Channel of the Hudson River, and Other Evidences of Post-Glacial Subsidence of the Middle Atlantic Coast Region." Amer. Jour. Sci., 3rd Ser., XLI, 489–499, 1891.

18. SPENCER, J. W. "High Continental Elevation Preceding the Pleistocene Period." Bull. Geol. Soc. Amer., I, 65–70, 1889.

   SPENCER, J. W. "Submarine Valleys off the American Coast and in the North Atlantic." Bull. Geol. Soc. Amer., XIV, 207–226, 1903.

   SPENCER, J. W. "The Submarine Great Canyon of the Hudson River." Amer. Geol., XXXIV, 292–293, 1904.

   SPENCER, J. W. "The Submarine Great Canyon of the Hudson River." Amer. Jour. Sci., 4th Ser., XIX, 1–15, 1905. Geog. Jour. (London), XXV, 180–190, 1905.

19. POOLE, H. S. "A Submerged Tributary to the Great Pre-glacial River of the Gulf of St. Lawrence." Roy. Soc. Can., Proc. and Trans., 2nd Ser., IX, Sec. IV, 143–147, 1903.

20. DAVIS, W. M. "The Abyss of Cap-Breton, Bay of Biscay, and a New Explanation of the Origin of Submarine Trenches." Geog. Review, XII, 501, 1922.

21. DALY, R. A. "The Geology of the Northeast Coast of Labrador." Bull. Mus. Comp. Zoölogy, XXXVIII, (Geol. Ser. V), 257, 1902.

   DALY, R. A. "Post-glacial Warping of Newfoundland and Nova Scotia." Amer. Jour. Sci., 5th Ser., I, 382, 1921.

22. FAIRCHILD, H. L. "Post-glacial Uplift of Northeastern America." Bull. Geol. Soc. Amer., XXIX, 202, 204, 1918.

23. GOLDTHWAIT, J. W. "The Physiography of Nova Scotia." Manuscript copy of a volume to be issued by the Geological Survey of Canada.

24. SHALER, N. S.  "The Geology of the Island of Mount Desert, Maine."
U. S. Geol. Surv., 8th Ann. Rept., Pt. II, 987–1061, 1889.
BASCOM, F.  "The Physiography of Mount Desert."  Bull. Geog. Soc.
Phil., XVII, 117–130, 1919.
25. BASCOM, F.  "The Physiography of Mount Desert."  Bull. Geog. Soc.
Phil., XVII, 117–130, 1919.
26. FAIRCHILD, H. L.  "Post-glacial Uplift of Northeastern America."  Bull.
Geol. Soc. Amer., XXIX, 229–234, 1918.
27. SPENCER, J. W.  "Bibliography of Submarine Valleys off North America."
Amer. Jour. Sci., 4th Ser., XIX, 341–344, 1905.
28. GOLDTHWAIT, J. W.  "The Twenty-foot Terrace and Sea-cliff of the
Lower St. Lawrence."  Amer. Jour. Sci., 4th Ser., XXXII, 291–317,
1911.
29. DALY, R. A.  "A Recent Worldwide Sinking of Ocean-level."  Geol.
Mag., LVII, 246–261, 1920.
30. DALY, R. A.  "Oscillations of Level in the Belts Peripheral to the Pleistocene Ice-Caps."  Bull. Geol. Soc. Amer., XXXI, 303–318, 1920.
31. NANSEN, FRIDTJOF.  "The Strandflat and Isostasy," 28, Christiania, 1922.
32. TWENHOFEL, W. H., and CONINE, W. H.  "The Post-glacial Terraces of
Anticosti Island."  Amer. Jour. Sci., 5th Ser., I, 268–278, 1921.
33. BASTIN, E. S.  "Rockland Folio."  U. S. Geol. Surv., Folio 158, 1–15,
1908.
KATZ, F. J.  "Preliminary Report on the Geology of the Portland and
Casco Bay Quadrangles."  Maine State Water Storage Commission,
3rd Ann. Rept. (1912), 170–184, 1913.
DAVIS, W. M.  "Die Erklärende Beschreibung der Landformen," 532,
Leipzig and Berlin, 1912.
34. STONE, G. H.  "The Glacial Gravels of Maine and their Associated De-
posits."  U. S. Geol. Surv., Mon. XXXIV, 54–58, 1899.
BASTIN, E. S.  "Rockland Folio."  U. S. Geol. Surv., Folio 158, 1–15,
1908.
KATZ, F. J.  "Preliminary Report on the Geology of the Portland and
Casco Bay Quadrangles."  Maine State Water Storage Commission,
3rd Ann. Rept. (1912), 170–184, 1913.
DAVIS, W. M.  "Die Erklärende Beschreibung der Landformen," 533,
Leipzig and Berlin, 1912.
35. DAVIS, W. M.  "Un Exemple de Plaine Côtière: la Plaine du Maine."
Annales de Géographie, VIII, 1–5, 1899.

# PART II

## SEQUENTIAL FORMS OF THE NEW ENGLAND-ACADIAN SHORELINE

# CHAPTER VI

## EROSIONAL FORMS BORDERING THE
## RESISTANT UPLANDS

**Advance Summary.** — Thus far our attention has been focused on the genesis of the New England-Acadian shoreline, and on the initial forms which characterized this shoreline as a consequence of the genesis described. Only incidentally have we noted certain transformations of the margin of the lands resulting from wave attack. It now becomes our duty to enquire more specifically into those transformations, and to note just how far wave attack has altered the nature of the shore. After a summary statement of the factors affecting shoreline evolution, we shall consider the progress thus far accomplished in such evolution along the margins of the hard-rock uplands, as revealed by a study of maps and charts, and by the field investigations of various observers. We shall soon discover a marked discrepancy in the estimates of marine erosion made by different students of the question, and as this is a matter of prime importance in the interpretation of many shore forms, it will become our duty to analyze the problem with some care in order to determine the cause of the discrepancy, and which conclusions most strongly commend themselves to our reason. In this connection a certain number of peculiar shore features bordering the New England-Acadian coast will be described, and the question of their origin will be considered at some length.

**Shoreline Evolution.** — The principles of shoreline development have been set forth at some length in the author's volume on "Shore Processes and Shoreline Development," and need not be repeated here. It is sufficient to note that the progressive passage of a shoreline through a systematic and orderly series of changes under the influence of wave action, is as well established a fact as is the systematic evolution of a landscape under the influence of stream action. The observer who from some lofty promontory surveys a broad sweep of interlocking bays and hills where rugged lands come down to meet the sea, finds in wave-cut cliff, sandy

157

beach, and shingle bar abundant proof that he beholds an ever-changing scene. The shoreline stretching in intricate pattern on either hand is not the same shoreline as yesterday, nor the one which will border the lands tomorrow. The eye of the imagination, schooled in the principles of shoreline development, enables our observer to see not merely the fact of change, but better still the order of its progress. He can penetrate the past, and know with some confidence what were the shore forms of yesterday, before the waves had cut the cliffs, or built the bars and beaches. He can pierce the future, and tell with equal confidence what forms will mark the shore in epochs yet to come, if land and sea maintain a constant level. All this because the shoreline of today is in some certain *stage* of its development, preceding which it must have passed in orderly sequence through other stages to attain its present form; and succeeding which still later stages must run their systematic course. Thus in the most complicated pattern of the coastal margin may one trace successive phases of shoreline evolution, and so find in apparent chaos, order and the majestic beauty of natural law.

It is obvious that the evolution of a shoreline must proceed more rapidly where the sea encounters a landmass composed of weak rocks, and more slowly where the rocks are resistant. It is likewise true that against low-lying lands shoreline evolution is more rapid than against high lands, for the simple reason that waves have vastly more material to remove when the land is high. Since under the influence of fluvial denudation weak rocks are apt to be worn down to lowlands, while resistant rocks still stand up as highlands, the partial submergence of a much eroded landmass of complex structure will usually give some shorelines bordering land which is both weak and low, others bordering land which is both resistant and high. The contrasted rates of development in such diverse areas should be doubly striking. This, of course, assuming equal exposure to the marine forces; for if a shoreline bordering a lowland of weak rock is for any reason protected from vigorous wave attack, it may develop more slowly than the shoreline bordering an exposed coast of resistant highlands.

In earlier chapters we have seen that partial submergence of the New England-Acadian shoreline brought the sea to rest against resistant crystalline uplands along some parts of the coast, against lowlands of weak Carboniferous or Triassic rocks elsewhere, and against very weak, unconsolidated clays or glacial drift in still other places. We are accordingly prepared to find that the shorelines bordering the resistant uplands are in a decidedly more youthful stage of development than those bordering the weak-rock lowlands, wherever there is adequate exposure to the sea; and that the lowland shorelines are more youthful than those developed against unconsolidated clays or glacial drift under similar conditions. Let us now examine these several shoreline types, to ascertain the developmental stage of each, beginning with the

## Shoreline Bordering Resistant Uplands

**Youthfulness of Shoreline as Indicated by Maps and Charts.** — A very brief inspection of large scale maps of those parts of the New England-Acadian coast where the sea rests against crystalline or other resistant rocks is sufficient to show that there the shoreline is in an extremely youthful stage of development. The intricate pattern of the coasts of Maine and southeastern Nova Scotia are such as should characterize the initial stage of a shoreline of submergence trending across the geological structure in the one case (Figs. 3 and 5) and parallel with the structure in the other (Figs. 2 and 4); and the maps alone are quite sufficient to show that in these cases shoreline development has progressed but very little beyond the initial stage. The Connecticut shoreline is less intricate, due in part to the fact that here the sea came to rest against a peneplaned upland of resistant rocks and low relief which was not deeply dissected, and which therefore was not subject to deep embayment. The possibility that the peneplane involved in this case is not the same as that sloping down beneath the sea along the coasts of Maine and southeastern Nova Scotia, but an older and more steeply sloping peneplane passing southward under the coastal plain deposits of Long Island, and to the north intersecting the present upland surface at a low angle, may also help to account for the simpler character of the Connecticut shoreline; for of two planes equally dissected, the more steeply inclined will give the less intricate shore pattern. Where glacial deposits border the Connecticut shore, the simplicity is due to a more advanced stage of shoreline development, as will be made evident in a later section; but the rocky upland descends into the sea without showing any evidence of extensive modification by wave action. Only when observing the relatively straight, steep coasts of resistant rocks bordering parts of the Bay of Fundy, northeastern Nova Scotia including Cape Breton Island, and the Gaspé Peninsula, could one entertain for a moment the illusion that the sea had cut back an originally irregular shoreline to a simple line of wave-cut cliffs; and in all these cases the illusion would quickly be dispelled by finding that the geological structure and the physiographic history of the regions concerned had given them rectilinear shorelines in the initial stage, as already set forth in Chapter II.   Nowhere in New England or Acadia is there any evidence that an initially irregular shoreline bordering uplands

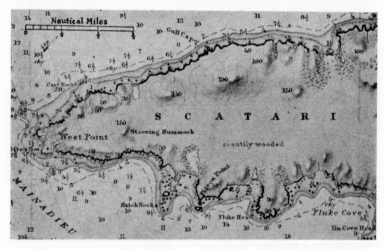

Fig. 68.  Portion of Scatari Island, Cape Breton, showing low cliffs and crenulate shoreline indicative of limited wave erosion of resistant rocks at present sealevel.  Young shoreline of submergence.  From U. S. Hydrographic Chart No. 1097.

of resistant rock has been transformed into a simple shoreline (submature or mature stage) by the action of the sea.   Everywhere the evidence points to a very youthful stage of development for these shorelines.

*Comparison of Cliff Height and Height of Hillslopes.* — The small amount of wave cutting on hard-rock coasts is shown on the Hydrographic and Coast Survey charts, and on the topographic maps, not only by the irregularity of the shoreline, but also by the fact that the wave-cut cliffs are of moderate height in comparison with the height of the hillslopes which they truncate.   The Hydrographic charts in particular are apt to be deceptive as regards their representation of cliffs, scarps 100 feet or more in altitude often appearing no higher than others which are relatively insignificant; but the fact that the cliffs are cut back but a moderate distance into hillslopes of much greater elevation is often made sufficiently clear. Thus the charts of Scatari Island (Fig. 68) off the Cape Breton Coast, of the Cape St. Mary region (Fig. 69) on the Nova Scotia coast, and of L'Etang Harbor (Fig. 70) on the New Brunswick coast, are typical of many others which show that the seacliffs are normally minor scarps cut but a short distance into much higher hillslopes of the partially submerged landmass. Similarly, both charts and topographic maps of the New England coast show that cliffs cut back far enough in the resistant rocks to have altitudes comparable with those of the higher hills or upland summits, are conspicuously rare. The charts of Scatari and the Cape St. Mary region also show what appears to be the "crenulate shoreline" typical of a very youthful shoreline of submergence when cut in hard rock exhibiting inequalities of resistance due to variable composition, jointing, or other causes.

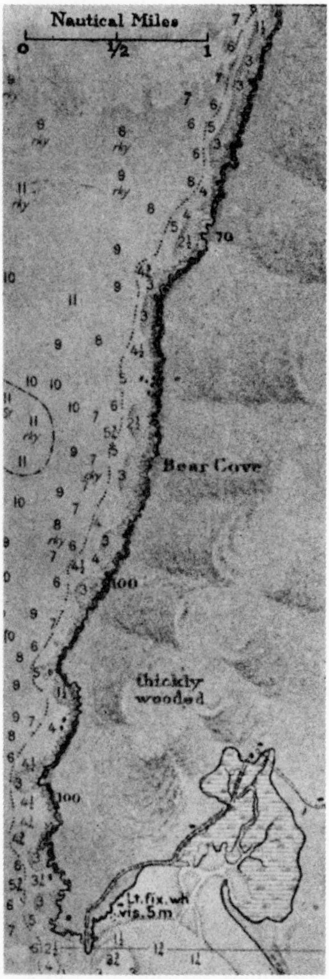

**Youthfulness of Shoreline as Observed in the Field.** — The relatively small amount of erosion

FIG. 69. Crenulate shoreline north of Cape St. Mary, Nova Scotia, with cliffs of moderate height cut in lower part of steeply sloping upland of resistant rocks, indicative of limited wave action at present sealevel. From U. S. Hydrographic Chart No. 2134.

of resistant rocks accomplished by marine forces at the present sealevel, as indicated by maps and charts of the New England-

Acadian coast, is strikingly evident to the field observer. Exception made of bold coasts the steepness of which is obviously the result of other than marine agencies (e.g. fault-line-scarp shorelines, resurrected peneplane shorelines, etc.), the crystalline upland usually descends into the sea unmarked by prominent cliffs (Fig. 71). That this should be the case along the Connecticut shore might be explained as the result of protection from the open sea afforded by Long Island; but no such explanation can be invoked in the case of the Massachusetts and other coasts where such protection is lacking. An observer

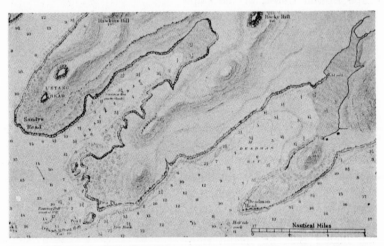

Fig. 70. Portion of the New Brunswick coast near L'Etang Harbor, showing low cliffs at base of higher hillslopes, characteristic of an early stage in the development of a young shoreline of submergence. From U. S. Hydrographic Chart No. 1054.

stationed on one of the islands in Boston Harbor and looking southward to the higher land south of the Boston Basin, has a distinct impression of a gently undulating plateau-like upland declining gradually toward the east until it passes under the sea with scarcely a break in its surface slope. Or let him stand on one of the monadnocks of the Mount Desert region rising above the New England peneplane (Figs. 62, 72 and 84) near where it passes beneath the Gulf of Maine. From such vantage point the impression of a gently undulating land surface sloping downward under the water unbroken by any significant marine cliffing is most vivid; and the validity of the impression can amply be confirmed by numerous views from nearer sealevel (Figs. 71 and 76) showing in profile the gradual descent of the peneplane to the water, instead of its termination seaward in such a lofty and more or less continuous scarp as should exist had the waves cut deeply into the land.

On the southeastern shores of Nova Scotia the story is the same. Here monadnocks are few in number and low in altitude, and the perfection of the peneplane developed on the crystallines is very impressive. But still more impressive is the manner in which this gently tilted surface slopes seaward into the ocean

FIG. 71. Young shoreline of submergence near Gloucester, Massachusetts, showing typical rocky coast without imposing cliffs where the upland peneplane passes into the sea.

with scarcely a trace of marine abrasion where it touches the water. One who looks eastward across the Halifax embayment from the vicinity of the fort north of Herring Cove; or westward from Ketch Head to where Morris Point and the outlying Sambro Islands and shoals reach far out to sea; or westward across Liverpool Bay to the peninsula ending in Western Head; or from the seaward end of Lockeport Island eastward toward Black Point; or westward toward the Western Head of that locality (Fig. 73); or indeed east or west from almost any exposed point along this rocky coast, will secure excellent views of a remarkably fine peneplane sloping very gently into the sea unbroken by any important

FIG. 72. New England peneplane, surmounted by the Blue Hill monadnock, sloping southward to pass under the sea, embayments of which are visible in the distance. Looking northwest from Acadia Mountain, Maine. *Courtesy* Lafayette National Park.

marginal cliff.  That the observer is not the victim of an optical illusion may be demonstrated by a visit to the extremities of the rocky headlands, where he will see the glaciated ledges pass under water with only the very faintest indications of marine abrasion.  (Figs. 74, 75, 77 and 78.)  The apparent exceptions do not seem numerous along this part of the coast, and where best observed, in the Chebucto Head-Ketch Head region west of the entrance to the Halifax embayment, the higher cliffs are, as in similar cases from the Maine coast discussed more fully on another page, related to steep, glaciated slopes which are quite independent of the present marine cycle, and which were already in existence when the sea assumed its present level.

Fig. 73.  Upland peneplane of Nova Scotia sloping southeastward under the sea without showing appreciable cliffing by waves.  Looking westward from Lockeport Island toward Western Head.

**Conclusions of Other Observers.** — Many observers have been impressed with the slight evidence of marine abrasion of the resistant rock shores.  Of the coast north of the Boston Basin in the region of Cape Ann, Shaler[1] writes: " Considering the shore as a whole, not more than a tenth of its line exhibits marine benching of a distinct character.  On by far the greater portion of the line the original glacial form remains."  This notable absence of effective marine erosion Shaler attributes in part to the brevity of the time in which the sea has operated at its present level, and in part to the fact that rapid erosion depends upon a combination of favorable physical conditions rarely found along this coast.  The following description of the shores of the Fox Islands, in the mouth of Penobscot Bay, given by Willis,[2] will apply to

FIG. 74.  Seaward extremity of Western Head, Nova Scotia, showing absence of appreciable cliffing by wave action where the Nova Scotian peneplane passes into the sea.

FIG. 75.  Seaward extremity of Lockeport (or Lockes) Island, Nova Scotia, showing gradual disappearance of upland peneplane under the sea.  The alternate bands of resistant and less resistant rock were eroded into parallel minor ridges and valleys, the partial submergence of which produced parallel lines of narrow peninsulas and islands separated by bays, the whole being at right angles to the general direction of the shore in this region, which shows no important seacliffs.

much of the Maine coast: " The present shores are of very youthful aspect, deeply sinuous in water line, and not conspicuously remodeled by wave action either through the development of seacliffs or the construction of spits. . . . Neither waves nor streams appear to have accomplished much in the post-glacial interval." On the exposed eastern coast of northern Cape Breton Island, near Neil Harbor (Fig. 18), Hyde[3] finds that the resurrected pre-Carboniferous peneplane developed on granite, slopes gently eastward into the sea with " practically no cliffs." Such testi-

Fig. 76.   South shore of Baker Island, Maine coast, showing beach of giant granite blocks.   Although the waves of the Atlantic have the power to rift these huge blocks from the parent mass and hurl them in a confused heap upon the shore, this portion of the upland surface slopes into the sea without appreciable evidence of marine cliffing.   Glacial striæ can in places be traced almost to the water's edge.   The well-developed joint planes sloping toward the sea are here especially unfavorable to rapid marine erosion.

mony might be extended indefinitely.   My own field studies have convinced me of the small rôle played by the waves in developing the present shoreline bordering the crystalline uplands.   While wave-cut cliffs are found in many places, it is more characteristic for the upland to descend into the sea as a gently inclined, irregular surface of barren rock, such as may be seen at Gloucester, Massachusetts (Fig. 71), on Baker Island, Maine (Fig. 76), near Lockeport, Nova Scotia (Fig. 74), and at countless other points along our northeastern coast; or as a sloping surface of rock, itself uncliffed, projecting from beneath a mantle of glacial débris

FIG. 77.  Nova Scotian coast near Chebucto Head, showing rounded glaciated surface of crystalline upland slightly notched at base by marine erosion at present sealevel.  On more exposed parts of the coast outside this slight embayment, the rocks are bare to greater heights, but the amount of wave work is scarcely more impressive.  Compare Fig. 97.

which is cut back by the waves to give a distinct scarp. Where the slopes are steeper, they usually represent normal hillsides formed by stream erosion on the land prior to its partial submergence, or glacially steepened slopes but moderately affected by marine action (Fig. 77). Where the rock ledges were grooved and striated by the overriding glacier, the glaciated surfaces may remain but little modified by the waves (Fig. 78), a fact not always to be explained on the ground that such surfaces were until recently heavily covered with glacial débris competent to protect them from wave attack.[1]

Fig. 78.   Glacially grooved and striated surface near seaward end of Lockeport Island, descending uncliffed under the waters of a bay fairly open to the sea.

**Testimony in Favor of More Extensive Marine Erosion.** — It is true that some authorities credit marine erosion with a far greater amount of work than is admitted above. As an example of the most extreme view we may cite the explanation of the irregular shores of New England, Nova Scotia, and other shorelines of submergence as the product of differential wave erosion, assisted by the tides. The theory that waves can cut far into the land along belts of weak rock, leaving peninsulas of resistant rock projecting far out to sea, is not only opposed to fundamental principles of shoreline physiography,[4] but as applied to the cases mentioned, it ignores the obvious physiographic history of these coasts. One would suppose that the theory had long since become obsolete, but in a recent revision of one of our older text-books of geology one reads: " The form of the whole New England coast is largely determined by this cause. The softer parts are worn away into harbors by the waves and scoured out by the tides, while the harder parts reach out like rocky arms far into the sea." The irregular shores of Lake Superior are in this same text attributed to differential wave erosion alone.[5]  Bailey[6] appears to invoke this same explanation for the irregular shores of New Brunswick. In all these cases the facts observed are doubt-less correctly reported; but they seem more reasonably to be explained as the result of partial submergence of a landmass on which normal stream erosion had developed valleys separated by hard-rock ridges. Edward Hitchcock[7] at a much earlier date thought wave erosion might be responsible for the embayment of Boston Harbor, or even for most of Massachusetts Bay. A corresponding exaggeration of the constructive work of waves is found in his apparent implication that all of Cape Cod is a beach formation.

Other observers, while assuming no such wholesale marine erosion as that implied in the citations of the preceding para-graph, admit a very considerable amount of wave work at certain localities.. According to Ogilvie[8] " seacliffs are notable features of the present erosion cycle " in the Boothbay region, Maine. Shaler[9] states that on the Maine coast " at one point we may find that the sea has carved its way back, so that a majestic precipice 100 feet high faces the ocean, while a few hundred feet away the waves beat against rocks which still bear the glacial scratches." The Otter Cliffs (Fig. 79) on Mount Desert have been figured by Shaler,[10] Bascom,[11] and others as striking examples of marine erosion at the present sea margin; and Davis,[12] writing of marine erosion about these shores, says that " a rocky bench is formed a little below water level, surmounted by such vertical faces as Great Head and Otter Cliffs." An interesting example of the divergence in the views of those who recognize at most only moderate marine erosion, is found in the writings of other observers of the Maine coast who have compared the amount of wave cut-ting at present sealevel with that accomplished in late glacial time when the sea stood higher than now. Willis[13] found in a rock bench at Ames Knob evidence that " the sea stood long " at the higher level, and added that he did not know of " any bench of similar width cut in equally hard rocks on this coast in post-

FIG. 79. Otter Cliffs, Mount Desert, Maine. Marine cliff of exceptional prominence bordering the seaward margin of the New England upland. Weathering of the crystalline rock along vertical joint planes has greatly facilitated the work of the waves. *Courtesy* Lafayette National Park.

glacial time." On the contrary Davis[14] believed that " the depression of the land about the close of the glacial period cannot have been maintained long at any one level, for nowhere on the slopes of the island (Mount Desert) are there shorelines of as great distinctness as those which mark the present margin of the sea"; and Stone[15] writes: " When we compare the ragged and uneven cliff of erosion at the present beach with the still moutonnéed ledges at higher levels, it becomes evident that the sea has stood at or near its present position many times as long as at any higher level." The high cliffs bordering Grand Manan Island are in part developed in rock which, although of Triassic age, is of a resistant igneous type; so it may be pertinent to mention here that these cliffs have been cited as remarkable illustrations of marine erosion.[6]

*The Gaspé Region.* — Without doubt the best descriptions implying extensive wave action at the present level are to be found in Clarke's charming accounts of the country about Percé, at the eastern extremity of the Gaspé peninsula.  Both along the mainland and about outlying islands are some of the most picturesque and imposing seacliffs to be found anywhere on the Atlantic Coast of North America; picturesque because " clothed in tints of red and yellow, . . . and veined with streaks of white, the colors of the cliffs change with every passing cloud"; and imposing because in places they rise sheer for hundreds of feet above the water. *Le Rocher Percé*, or Pierced Rock (commonly called Percé Rock), is the most remarkable of the scenic features of this coast (Fig. 80).  It is a long, narrow island, connected with the mainland by a slender bar at low tide, bounded by vertical cliffs from 150 to nearly 300 feet high, and pierced by a lofty archway through which boats may pass.  At its seaward end is an isolated stack or chimney, formed when the roof of another arch fell more than half a century ago.  There are records which indicate that other arches were earlier in existence, and the disappearance of that part of the rock in which these were located, coupled with the form of the rock, suggests very extensive wave erosion on this part of the coast.  Clarke writes: " All other presentments of the gnawing power of the ocean which the writer has studied on American shores, in northern Scotland at Scrabster and Caithness, in Hoy and the other islands of the Orkneys, are surpassed in magnitude and effect by this leviathan rock."[16]  " Exposed to the full potency of the sea, few places display with more com-

FIG. 80. Percé Rock, Gaspé. The marine arch which pierces the rock transversely and gives to it its name, is near the farther end. Limestone beds, tilted to a vertical position, favored the development of imposing marine cliffs.

pelling effect than this broken and deeply gnawed coast, the tremendous destructive power of the ocean."[17]  " At Percé it has cut away Bonaventure Island from along the flanks of Mt.

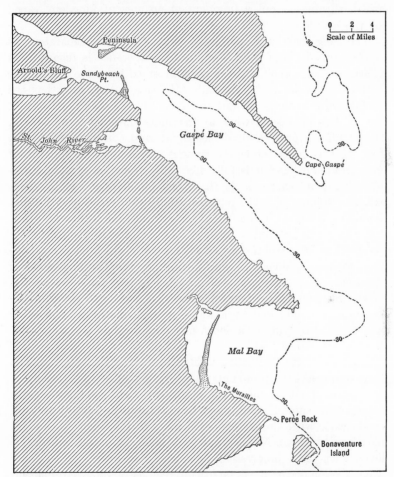

F<small>IG</small>. 81.   Eastern end of the Gaspé peninsula.   The unnamed headland, between Percé Rock and Cape Gaspé, is Point Saint Peter.   Note the bars at the head of Mal Bay and the mouth of the St. John River embayment, and the cuspate bars and spit in upper part of Gaspé Bay.

Ste. Anne and the shores of the South Bay, by a channel three miles wide, from which remnants of the old rock still project above the water; it has cut away the Pierced Rock from the Headlands of Mt. Joli and Cape Canon, with which it once formed a now lost mountain; it has eaten away another and greater mountain above the North Beach, leaving to the present only the ragged Murailles, which formed its southern flanks."[18]  "The Percé which survives is but a fragment of an ancient kingdom, raped by the sea."[19]

The long, narrow Cape Gaspé (Fig. 81) which separates the outer part of Gaspé Bay from the St. Lawrence is regarded by Clarke as but a remnant of high land saved from the destructive action of the waves.[20]  He calls attention to the fact that the 30-fathom contour is far out to sea on the exposed northeastern side of this peninsula, while at the shore the land terminates in sheer cliffs several hundred feet high; and continues: " At the foot of this inaccessible escarpment the seabottom falls away very gradually, and it is fully five miles from the present coastline before it reaches a depth of one hundred and eighty feet. All this volume of rock, represented by the width of five miles bounding the coast and a height far greater than a thousand feet, has the ocean gnawed away from Cape Gaspé in comparatively recent time."[21]  Still more vast is the work which Clarke attributes to waves along the north shore of the Gaspé peninsula: " sea erosion, however, has been so efficient that the lower reaches of the St. Lawrence River which washes the north shore of the peninsula are bounded by a wave-cut rock platform in places 8 miles in width, lying at a depth of not more than 300 feet below the present water level."[22]

**Analysis of the Conflicting Evidence.** — How shall we reconcile these evidences of profound wave erosion at certain localities, with little or no marine action elsewhere?  Differences in degree of exposure cannot be invoked in explanation, since these contrasts exist with similar exposure both to the open sea and to northeast storms.  Neither can we assume favorable changes of level, such as a progressive subsidence, at those places where wave erosion seems most rapid; for regions of rapid erosion and regions of little or no erosion are often situated but a few hundred yards apart, under similar conditions of exposure; and in a later companion volume to the present work evidence will be adduced in favor of a long-continued stability of the coast including those parts where wave attack appears to be most vigorous.

*Effect of Variations in Initial Shore Profile.* — A partial explanation is undoubtedly to be found in the variable nature of the initial shore profile.  Where the sea came to rest against a nearly vertical rock wall, formed by subaërial agencies before the partial submergence of the land, oscillatory waves would be reflected back without doing much damage, provided the water were deep.[23] Waves impinging on a gently sloping surface of smooth rock will sweep up that surface without marked erosive power. Where the waves are unarmed with rock débris, whether because of great depth of water near shore or for other reasons, the erosive work accomplished will be less than where the waves find an abundance of cutting tools with which to work. A moderate slope of the upland into the sea, with moderate water depth and a sufficiency of

Fig. 82. South coast of Iron Bound Island, Frenchmans Bay, showing how vertical joint planes favor the formation of vertical wave-cut cliffs. At left a chasm eroded on weak zone. *Courtesy* Lafayette National Park.

rock débris close in shore, will facilitate rapid marine erosion. But while these differences in physical conditions may explain the contrast between little or no erosion at some points and distinct evidence of marine cliffing at others, they will not explain the major contrasts which we have considered in preceding paragraphs.

*Effect of Rock Structure.* — A factor of very real importance is the structure of the rock on the shore subjected to wave attack. Of two granitic masses, one little broken by joints may remain scarcely affected by the waves, while the other, divided into small blocks by intersecting joint systems, is having a prominent seacliff cut into it.  In this work of cliff making, however, weathering along the joint planes, including loosening of the blocks by frost action, may accomplish a far greater proportion of the total than wave cutting.  If prominent joint planes dip gently toward the sea, no significant cliff may be developed (Fig. 76).  Joint planes dipping from the sea, into the land, favor the formation of a ragged cliff.  Vertical joints tend to give vertical cliffs (Figs. 79 and 82).  The great importance of joint structure in relation to wave work has been emphasized by Shaler in his reports on Cape Ann[24] and Mount Desert,[10] and by Bascom, who supplements Shaler's observations on Mount Desert with additional details.[11]

Fig. 83.  Margin of Carboniferous Lowland near Briton Cove, Cape Breton Island, showing details of shore form where beds dip steeply toward sea.  In middle distance the shoreline for a long distance coincides with a single bedding plane.  In foreground is a series of well-formed beach cusps.  Photo by J. E. Hyde, Geol. Surv. Canada.

Bedding planes, like joints, play their rôle in retarding or accelerating wave attack.  If they dip gently toward the sea, the waves operate at a disadvantage, being deflected up the slope and finding little opportunity for undermining.  Where the dip is away from the sea, the on-coming wave is directed toward the base of the slope, and undermining is favored.  Vertical or steeply inclined beds trending at right angles to the coast permit the waves to etch out the weak layers first, following which the resistant members more readily break down.  Vertical beds paralleling the shore give the most imposing cliffs, since the removal of weak formations back to a resistant stratum may leave the latter as a vertical wall of extremely forbidding aspect, even where the amount of marine erosion has not been excessive.    Horizontal beds favor effective undermining and rapid cliff retreat if the beds at or near sealevel are non-resistant; but not otherwise.    The precise form of the shore and the details of shoreline scenery may vary greatly with the attitude of the beds, as will be obvious from an inspection of some illustrations of the several types of shore (Figs. 75, 80, 83, 83a and 152).

Fig. 83a.    Sutherland Island    near    Sheet Harbor, Nova Scotia, showing effect of rock structure    on    detail of shoreline pattern. The rocks belong to the    quartzite and slate    gold - bearing series of Nova Scotia, and here form part of an east-west fold.

There can be no doubt that in rock struc- ture is to be found a partial explanation of some of the cliffs cited by different observers as proof of extensive marine erosion.    The important rôle which joints must have played in the formation of Otter Cliffs (Fig. 79) and similar scarps described by Shaler, Bascom, and others is sufficiently obvious from an examination of the descriptions and figures of the scarps; but if a wave-cut rock bench is present just below water level at the base of Otter Cliffs and Great Head, it must be very nar- row; for on the Coast Survey chart (No. 306) the 3-fathom line runs close to the cliff base, and depths of 13, $15\frac{1}{2}$, and 17 fath- oms of water are shown a short distance out.    If the cliffs on Grand Manan Island referred to as remarkable illustrations of erosion by the sea,[6] are the imposing cliffs of columnar trap which descend abruptly into the sea, then in the vertical columnar jointing of the trap we find a partial reason for their yielding to the attack of the elements.    Percé Rock (Fig. 80) is composed of limestone, the beds nearly vertical, with their flat sides parallel to Percé Bay on the south and Mal Bay on the north; a com- bination of physical conditions eminently suited to the develop- ment of vertical walls bordering the sea with a minimum expendi- ture of energy by the waves.    Furthermore, Clarke tells us that " Percé Rock is evidently bounded on its long sides by faults,"[25] and these displacements, whether marked by movements recent enough to have affected the present topography, or of ancient date but marked by zones of weakness, or of such nature as to have brought weaker formations next to the limestone on either side, may have had more to do with the character of the vertical cliffs than has wave erosion. Some of the other cliffs so graphically described by Clarke show structural conditions similar to those at Percé Rock.

*Fictitious Indications of Marine Erosion due to Partial Submergence of Subaërial Forms.* — We have yet to consider, however, the most important factor in reconciling appearances of extensive marine erosion at certain points, with little or no erosion elsewhere. Much of the argument in favor of profound wave erosion is based on two assumptions: first, that a high cliff bordering the sea implies that the waves have cut far into the land; and second, that a broad, sloping submarine platform offshore implies the removal of a corresponding breadth of land by wave action. That neither assumption is necessarily correct can readily be demonstrated by imagining the sea to rise, without appreciable marine erosion, until certain of the features of the present land surface, certainly of non-marine origin, become partially submerged. The southward moving ice sheet, by long-continued plucking of joint blocks from the southern or lee slopes of obstructions, and by oversteepening the walls of the valleys through which ice passed between such obstacles, left countless prominent rocky hills with bold cliffs or scarps at their southern ends or along their sides. Should the sea rise to the foot of such a scarp, it would have the appearance of a true seacliff; and after the waves had operated on it for a short time, it might be difficult for the most careful observer to decide whether he had to deal with a non-marine form modified by the waves during a short period of marine action, or with a seacliff cut deeply into the land by long-continued wave erosion. The submarine contours, if determined, might aid him toward a correct interpretation; but even this assistance would fail him in case the former topography of non-marine origin included a bench or sloping plane in front of the cliff, or if waves and currents had deposited sufficient débris offshore to build a submarine terrace, or if the submarine rock contours were otherwise obscured, as by a covering of clay deposits like that laid down along the Maine coast in glacial and early post-glacial time.

*Scarps of the Mount Desert Region.* — Mount Desert Island is characterized by an abundance of rocky scarps (Fig. 84) similar in aspect to the Otter Cliffs and others found along the present

Fig. 84. Steep southern face of Acadia Mountain, Maine. Dissected peneplane partially submerged in distance. Were the scarp in foreground
reached by the sea, it would appear as a seacliff of impressive magnitude,
suggesting extensive wave erosion. *Courtesy* Lafayette National Park.

(181)

shore, but occurring at all elevations above sealevel (see Charts
306 and 307, U.S.C. and G.S.).   Some of these have been interpreted as possible seacliffs formed during a higher stand of the sea;
but many others are not open to this interpretation because of
their position.   Yet if the sea were to rise, and waves were to
operate for a brief period at the foot of some of these scarps, they
would give an impression of long-continued wave erosion, far
stronger than that gained at any point along the present shore.

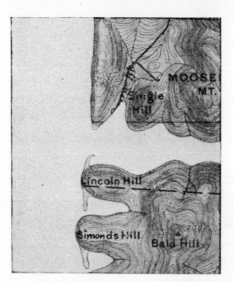

This is especially true because the contours of the
hills are such as to sug-
gest that large fractions
of their original bulk have
been eaten away.

If it be objected that
the scarps on Mount Des-
ert are open to suspicion
because of their proximity
to the sea and because of
the theory that the sea has
at least carved some cliffs
above its present level,
then one may imagine the
sea to rise until some of the
countless similar scarps in
the mountains of northern
New England or in the
higher Adirondacks would
assume the aspect of sea-
cliffs cut in bold promontories or outlying islands.
A certain Vermont scarp,
less elevated but unques-

FIG. 85.   Illusory appearance of a formerly
irregular shoreline of submergence cut
back to a simple line by extensive wave
erosion.   A scarp of subaërial origin near
Pawlet, Vermont, as it would appear if
the sea were to rise 800 feet above its
present position and permit a small
amount of wave work at the new level.

tionably of subaërial origin, would even give the appearance
of marine erosion so vast as to have cut away half of a prominent mountain and changed an initially irregular shore to one
relatively straight (Fig. 85).   In this case the effect would be
heightened because a very moderate amount of erosion of low
hilltops and filling of intervening depressions, such as might
be expected after the sea had remained for a time at its new
level, would give a submarine bench or terrace in front of the

scarp, easily mistaken as the product of the supposed extensive marine abrasion which cut away a former westward extension of the mountains.    Submergence of a flat-floored valley in Virginia would not only give a good " cliff and bench," but the detail of marine stacks or chimneys would be so closely simulated, especially after a little notching at the bases of the columns, as to mislead a very careful observer (Fig. 86).    The student who will conscientiously apply this method of comparing non-marine and marine forms, making due allowance for the changes in detail of

Fig. 86.   Limestone columns left by solution along joint planes, near Mt. Solon, Virginia.  Submergence of the flat valley floor, followed by slight notching of the bases of the columns by wave erosion, would give a fictitious appearance of a marine cliff with stacks or chimneys, fronted by a submarine bench.   Photo by F. J. Wright.

cliff and submarine contours readily effected by a very moderate amount of marine erosion and deposition, will become convinced that many of the scarps supposed to indicate extensive marine erosion at present sealevel, are equally well to be explained as slightly modified scarps of non-marine origin against which the sea came to rest when it rose to its present level.    I know of no prominent scarp on the coast of New England or Acadia supposed to indicate extensive marine erosion of resistant rocks, which may not more reasonably be thus explained.

*Scarps in Columnar Lava.* — If one be tempted to see in the frowning basaltic cliffs of Grand Manan or of Brier Island a proof of extensive wave action, let him remember that the subaërially formed cliffs of the Palisades along the Hudson River (Fig. 33), likewise developed on a columnar trap sheet, would give precisely the same appearance were the sea to rise until it rested against the nearly vertical upper portion of the escarpment. It should further be remembered that the cliffs on Grand Manan may be in part the result of faulting, or of erosion removing weak beds from one side of a fault line to produce a fault-line scarp.[26] The imposing cliffs against which the waves now break with a mighty display

Fig. 87.  Obsidian Cliff, Yellowstone National Park, as it would appear if the sea were to rise to its base, and waves cut a slight notch there.

of force, presumably exhibited the same general appearance as they do today, and occupied nearly the same position, when the sea first came to rest against them.   The amount of modification necessary to change such subaërial scarps into apparently typical seacliffs with features peculiar to marine erosion is very slight indeed.   If the sea were to rest against the base of the Obsidian Cliff in Yellowstone National Park (Fig. 87) and do no more than cut a notch at its base, few would hesitate to accept it as a marine cliff cut back into the land far enough to give a scarp of considerable height, were it not for the fact that here the surrounding topography would show the difficulties of such an interpretation.

**Analysis of Shore Cliffs of the Mount Desert Region.** — In the Mount Desert region of the Maine coast Otter Cliffs (Fig. 79) and the cliffs at Great Head (Fig. 88) are famous for their stern aspect, and have, as already noted, been cited as impressive examples of wave erosion.   The rugged cliffs of the southern coast of Iron Bound Island (Fig. 89), within the entrance to Frenchmans Bay, are popularly grouped with the preceding as the product of extensive marine abrasion of the coast, while the steep

FIG. 88. Shore cliff at Great Head, Mount Desert Island. Above the vertical cliff one sees a little of the older, rounded surface rising toward the summit of the hill. *Courtesy* Lafayette National Park.

FIG. 89.  Bold southern coast of Iron Bound Island, Maine, showing here and there traces of a very narrow wave-cut bench.  Apparently the waves have cut but a short distance into an already steeply sloping side of the island.  *Courtesy* Lafayette National Park.

FIG. 90.  Round Porcupine Island, near Bar Harbor, Maine, showing gentle northern and steep southern slopes antedating the present marine cycle. The waves have cut but a short distance into the glaciated mass, but the resulting cliffs are imposing where the slope was already steep. *Courtesy* Lafayette National Park.

southern slopes of the Porcupine Islands (Figs. 90, 91 and 93) are similarly deemed proofs that the sea has cut deeply into the land.   No one who picks his way over the ragged rocks at the base of these naked scarps, or from their crests looks down upon the surges thundering against their massive ramparts, can fail to be impressed with their imposing beauty.   But he who would justly evaluate their significance as a record of wave erosion must seek another point of view.   Let him take his stand upon a neighboring projection of the shore, or from a boat some distance out

Fig. 91.   In the distance, Sheep Porcupine Island showing gentle northern and steep southern slopes.   In the foreground, southern end of Burnt Porcupine Island, showing detail of weathering and wave work in crystallines.

study the profiles of these cliffs in their relation to the more ancient contours which streams and glacier gave to the hills and valleys of the resistant landmass.   Then will he discover that the Otter Cliffs represent but an insignificant notch cut in the base of a much higher hill (Fig. 92); that the cliffs at Great Head and Iron Bound, and those which rim the Porcupines (Fig. 93), are all minor elements which modify but slightly the form headlands and islands possessed when the glaciers first melted from the land and the sea first came to rest at the present level.   As the observer pushes his studies further he will be convinced that the frequent

occurrence of higher and bolder cliffs on the south than on the
north of the islands (as in the Porcupine Islands) is not a simple
record of difference in exposure to wave attack, for he will note
that at all levels the glaciers left many of the hills with steeper
southern (Fig. 84) and more gentle northern slopes.   Whether something in the structure of the mass permitted weathering and stream
erosion to develop such contrasted contours in pre-glacial times,
or whether glacial plucking on the lee sides of the much-jointed
rocky hills is alone responsible, one need not now inquire.   It is
sufficient for him to realize the obvious fact that the pre-marine
contours were often surprisingly steep on the south, and that
under these conditions a very slight incision by the waves must

FIG. 92.  Southeast coast of Mount Desert Island, showing in left center
distance Otter Cliffs as mere notch cut in base of steep slope of high hill.
*Courtesy* Lafayette National Park.

produce a cliff far higher than would a much more extensive
advance of the waves into areas of more gentle slope.   Thus in
the Mount Desert region the cliffs at the southern ends of the
Porcupines (Figs. 90 and 93), on the southwest side of Bear Island,
near Hunters Beach Head, and many others which might be
named, are high because the pre-marine contours, as shown
by the portion of them still preserved, were here exceptionally
steep.   Glacially rounded, grooved and striated surfaces far down
the steep slopes, sometimes to the very crest of the wave-cut
scarp, prove that a steep rocky slope existed prior to and wholly
independent of the advent of marine agencies.   Projection of the
steep pre-marine slopes to sealevel shows that the waves had to

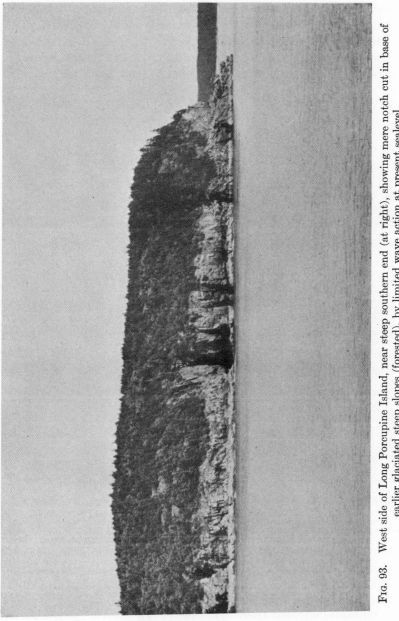

FIG. 93.   West side of Long Porcupine Island, near steep southern end (at right), showing mere notch cut in base of earlier glaciated steep slopes (forested), by limited wave action at present sealevel.

remove but a narrow wedge of rock to produce the cliffs as we see them today.   Marine benches in front of the cliffs are usually but a few feet, or at most a few hundred feet, wide; and are most often not clearly recognizable in the field or on profiles; and of the few which attract attention some at least are apparently slightly modified subaërial surfaces which seem to show traces of glacia-

Fig. 94.   The Thunder Hole, a chasm excavated by wave action along a jointed and crushed zone in the crystallines of Mount Desert Island. *Courtesy* Lafayette National Park.

tion.   Numerous stacks, chasms (Fig. 94), caves and arches prove that the cliffs rising from the water's edge are truly wave-cut; but other evidence as clearly demonstrates the very limited amount of such cutting.

Where ice streams passed down pre-glacial valleys, the bordering hillsides were often greatly oversteepened by glacial erosion.

Thus the east and west flanks of many hills, at all elevations from the highest to the lowest, exhibit steep slopes. Such of these steep slopes as are reached by the sea give comparatively high cliffs when but slightly cut by the waves. Otter Cliffs (Fig. 95) and the cliffs at Great Head (Fig. 88) and Schooner Head apparently belong to this class. Where the pre-marine slopes were gentle, the cliffs are low and inconspicuous, and the insignificant amount of erosion accomplished by the sea is clearly evident. This is true even when the exposure is to the open waves of the sea, as on the exposed southern side of the Schoodic peninsula and the south side of Baker Island (Fig. 76). In the latter case the power of the waves is sufficiently attested by the size of

Fig. 95.   Otter Cliffs, on one side of a partially drowned valley.
*Courtesy* Lafayette National Park.

the granite blocks torn from place and hurled up the slope; yet the shore is not perceptibly cliffed, partly because the gentle seaward inclination of the most important joint planes combines with the similar slope of the surface to make effective wave attack unusually difficult. But even where the jointing is favorable to rapid erosion and to the development of vertical cliffs, low shores, which should record the greatest encroachment of the sea, show that such encroachment has been slight. Everywhere one is impressed with the fact that the waves have barely begun their work, and have at best cut nothing more than an insignificant notch in the margin of the land, while in many exposed places one can follow beautifully glaciated ledges, marked by striæ and chatter-marks, practically to the water's edge.

When a region of normal hills and valleys is submerged and the sea first invades the valleys and comes to rest against the hill-slopes, there are no marine cliffs. Soon low cliffs will be produced wherever marine erosion is active; and as the waves cut farther and farther into islands and headlands the marine cliffs will progressively increase in height. So long as the extent of marine abrasion is not great, the marine cliffs will as a rule be cliffs of constantly increasing height (Fig. 96, *a*, *b*, *c*). But after the sea has cut deeply into the land, the shoreline will in many places have been pushed beyond the hill summits to the backslopes, and thus many of the marine cliffs will have become cliffs of progressively diminishing height (Fig. 96, *d*, *e*). The rocky shores of Maine, like those of the rest of the New England and Acadian hard-rock shores, are bordered, where cliffed at all, by marine cliffs which are for the most part cliffs of increasing

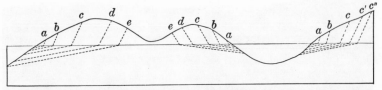

Fig. 96. Development of cliffs of increasing altitude (*a*, *b*, *c*), followed by cliffs of both increasing (*c'*, *c''*) and diminishing (*d*, *e*) altitude, with progressive wave erosion.

height (Figs. 88, 89, 90, 93 and 95), a fact which effectively confirms the impression that the waves have barely begun their work upon these coasts.

On the picturesque coast of Maine one should marvel, not at the occasional high cliffs which give a fictitious indication of profound marine abrasion, but at the clear evidence of the record as a whole that the sea rose against these shores only a few moments ago as the geologist counts time, and that thus far the waves have merely brushed the soil from the glaciated ledges, or at most have barely etched a fringe of ragged cliffs, usually low and inconspicuous, about the margins of the lands. Sea caves and chasms (Figs. 82 and 94), eroded where dykes or crushed zones produce lines of weakness readily attacked by the waves, are proper objects of interest and wonder; but more wonderful than these is the topographic contrast between glaciated upland slope and the marine etching at its very base which tells the story of a geologically recent drowning of the whole northeastern coast of North America.

**Analysis of Shore Cliffs of the Nova Scotian Coast.** — On the Nova Scotian coast, as has already been noted, the scarcity of good marine cliffs is even more impressive. There are places where the crystallines slope steeply into the sea, as for example southwest of Halifax where near the mouth of Halifax Harbor the granite shows fairly abrupt contours, with minor chasms and caves (Fig. 77). But in these cases it is obvious that glacial plucking on the lee sides of hills, steepening of valley walls by stream action, by glacial erosion or by some other non-marine agency, is mainly responsible for the abrupt topography; and as in the Maine examples cited above, the presence of glaciated surfaces well down these slopes, sometimes traceable practically to the water's edge, is sufficient proof that the steep slopes were in existence before the sea assumed its present level. From Chebucto Head westward the coast is bold, and several headlands in a fairly straight line present steep faces to the sea (Figs. 77 and 97). But the supermarine contours show that here we have an ancient scarp, possibly determined by faulting or more likely by erosion of weaker material from the seaward side of a fault or other contact; and the occasional presence of glacial grooves well down the face of the scarp proves that it was already fully developed before submergence brought the sea to rest against it at the beginning of the present shoreline cycle. Where the peneplane descended evenly to the sea (Fig. 73), unbroken by any such ancient scarp, the failure of the sea appreciably to modify the land brought within its reach by the submergence, is even more clearly evident. Thus the peneplane in the vicinity of Lockeport and Western Head, developed on highly tilted bedded sandstones striking at right angles to the coast, and later dissected to give minor ridges and swales, can be followed under the sea without a trace of anything worthy to be called a marine cliff (Figs. 74 and 75). Ridge after ridge stretches seaward to disappear gradually, sometimes reappearing in the form of linear islands or reefs beyond, sometimes failing again to rise out of the water; but never terminating abruptly in a bold seacliff. Only on the sides of these ridges, where exposure is less pronounced or where protection in closed bays may be quite perfect, but where pre-glacial erosion and glaciation carved steep slopes before the beginning of the present marine cycle, do we find significant scarps. And here the presence

Fig. 97. Exposed seaward end of Ketch Head, Nova Scotia, showing steep descent of crystalline upland into sea, but without evidence of important wave action. Glacially rounded and grooved surfaces well down the slope indicate that the form of the scarp has remained little changed since the glacial period.

of glaciated surfaces close to sealevel (Fig. 78) usually makes clear the fact that the waves have had very little to do with fashioning the surfaces which a casual observer might regard as the product of marine abrasion. Here, as on the New England coast, the student of shore forms is profoundly impressed with the wholly insignificant extent to which marine abrasion has affected the hard-rock coasts. Wave attack, aided by the frost and other weathering agencies working to advantage on the jointed rock masses, have begun the task of shattering the glaciated ledges and in favorable places have advanced a few feet into the land to give a marine cliff, high where the pre-marine slope was steep, low where that slope was gentle; but everywhere the marine cycle is obviously in the earliest days of its infancy.

**Analysis of Shore Cliffs of the Percé Region.** — Percé Rock is the remnant of a ridge formed of limestone tilted up on edge to a nearly vertical position, and attacked on both sides by the waves. That the adjacent rock on either side, whether there as a result of normal position in a sedimentary series or brought into contact with the limestone by the parallel faults mentioned by Clarke, was of inferior resistance, is indicated by a comparison of the geology of the region as deciphered by Clarke* with the pre-submergence subaërial topography as suggested by the present contours of the land. The Gaspé peninsula as a whole represents the seaward projection of a belt of folded Paleozoic rocks of variable resistance which was peneplaned, uplifted, and maturely dissected to give parallel, often steep-sided ridges of the more resistant layers, separated by parallel valleys or lowlands eroded on weaker beds. When the eastern portion of this belt, warped down lower than the rest, was invaded by the sea, the waters set far back into the valleys and lowlands to give such embayments as Mal Bay and Gaspé Bay (Fig. 81), while unsubmerged parts of the ridges projected seaward to form peninsulas like those of Percé, Saint Peter, and Cape Gaspé. From Percé south-

---

* Every student of the Gaspé region must acknowledge a special indebtedness to Dr. John M. Clarke for his studies of Gaspesian geology, based on 25 years' intimate acquaintance with its problems and forming the basis of many handsomely illustrated reports. If, on the basis of a study of these reports and a brief visit to the points here described, I have ventured to suggest a different interpretation for one of the most recent events in the long history deciphered by Clarke, let the reader not forget that such difference of interpretation is itself in no small measure based on the solid foundation of structural geology laid by that authority.

ward the Appalachian structure is more or less concealed, and the physiographic history accordingly modified, by a great thickness of nearly horizontal red sandstones and conglomerates which Clarke believes once filled some, at least, of the embayments in the older Paleozoics.  We are now concerned, however, only with exposed areas of true Appalachian structure, where as a result of submergence the sea came to flank ridges of tilted resistant rock.  It is true that these ridges oppose to the waves a less serious obstacle than the much harder crystallines; but they belong in the class of rocks which remain to form uplands rather than with those which weather away to produce lowlands, and the effects of wave action upon them may most conveniently be

FIG. 98.  The Murailles, a seacliff of diminishing altitude cut chiefly in the side of a ridge of upturned limestone forming the northern edge of the Percé peninsula.  The little bayhead beach is known as North Beach.

treated here if we keep in mind the fact that the areas composed of them should record a somewhat greater advance of the sea than do the crystalline areas.

It is obvious that where a gentle dip of the beds or the weathering of surface slopes to low gradients resulted in a gently sloping ridge side, the waves must cut far into the land before a high cliff will be produced.  Such seems to be the case along the southern sides of the Saint Peter and Cape Gaspé peninsulas, where rocks dipping southward with moderate inclination were observed during a brief reconnaissance of the region, and where the cliffs are as yet comparatively low (due partly, however, to difference of exposure).  On the other hand, where steep dips or scarp slopes gave a precipitous inclination to the subaërial ridge flank, a limited incision of the waves must give marine cliffs of great height. The high cliffs bordering Percé Rock (Fig. 80) and the Murailles (Fig. 98) on the north side of the Percé peninsula are cut in the flanks of a steep-sided ridge of vertical or nearly vertical limestone; those of even greater height along the north flank of the Cape Gaspé ridge are cut in the scarp slope eroded on the upturned edges of the southward dipping limestones of the Cape.

*Cliffs of Increasing and Diminishing Altitude.* — Even with these facts of structure and topography in mind, it is difficult for the visitor to Percé to rid himself of the impression of enormous wave erosion on these coasts. We have already noted that where waves have cut but a short distance into an irregular landmass, the seaward ends of the hills alone are usually cliffed (Fig. 96), and that the cliffs must therefore increase in height with continued wave erosion until the highest part of the hill is attained. From that point onward continued erosion must be accompanied by a decrease of cliff height, as the backslope of the hill is consumed. From this fact, first clearly stated by Davis, we may deduce certain important generalizations for testing the extent of wave erosion on a coast:

I.   A maturely dissected landmass bordered by marine cliffs which are wholly or mainly cliffs of increasing altitude, has suffered comparatively little wave erosion.

II.   A coast on which cliffs of diminishing altitude are abundant has suffered appreciable marine erosion unless the hills bordering the coast (a) are prevailingly of small size, or (b) had forms presenting short, steep sides toward the initial shoreline.

III.   An approximate minimum measure of shore retreat may be secured by taking the average distance from seaward base to backslope of uneroded, comparable, neighboring hills.

IV.   Cliffs of diminishing altitude are not common along infantile shorelines, but may be abundantly developed along young, mature, or old shorelines.

At Percé the shoreline is young, but cliffs of diminishing altitude are the rule rather than the exception (Figs. 98, 100 and 101). Indeed, it is very doubtful if elsewhere on the Atlantic coast one can see so perfect an illustration of precisely that type of detailed shore topography which should characterize a land margin along which the waves have cut far back into the hills. The graceful curve of grassy slopes and the majestic grandeur of sheer precipices present a contrast eloquent of the two great forces of Nature which have shaped them; and no one who falls in love with the beauty of Percé would subtract one word from the effective descriptions which Clarke has given us of one of the most picturesque spots adorning any shore.

*Physiography of the Percé Region.* — To escape the spell of Percé's cliffs, and prosaically enquire whether these scarps of diminishing height prove considerable coastal erosion, or represent one of the two exceptions noted under II above, let the observer first visit the head of Mal Bay and see what type of subaërial topography is there descending under the sea. Enroute he will note that the country is one of steep cliffs and barren precipices, even far above the reach of the waves; and that a further rise of sealevel would transform many a scarp of subaërial origin into an apparent seacliff, were the ocean waters to bathe its base. Passing over the shoulder of Mount Ste. Anne (Percé Mt.) he will have a magnificent view to the northwest, with the level skyline of the summit peneplane in the distance; and nearer, below him, a broad lowland sloping gradually eastward to pass under the sea. This is the Mal Bay lowland, and he cannot fail to note that on the south it is bordered by a somewhat irregular ridge, of only moderate magnitude but often sharp crested, which eastward forms the northern side of the Percé peninsula, and westward continues until lost to view among the hills. Descending to the lowland he observes that on the south the ridge is separated from the main mass of the Percé peninsula by a depression which is neither deep nor continuous, but which is pronounced enough to serve as a passageway for a country road. The northern side of the ridge can well be seen from some point on the great cobblestone ridge which forms the bayhead bar near the inner end of Mal Bay. From such a vantage point it is clear that the north side of the ridge is even steeper than the south, not only eastward where above the wave-cut cliffs the earlier subaërial slopes in places still remain with their forest cover, but also westward (Fig. 99) beyond the reach of the sea, where the details of form of ridge face and lowland floor leave little doubt of their subaërial origin. The observer can now satisfy himself that although different formations are exposed in the cliffed northern face of the ridge, the ridge itself is more or less continuous eastward to Percé, and that the Murailles scarp is cut in its steep northern face.

FIG. 99.   Unsubmerged lowland west of Mal Bay (see Fig. 81), showing east-west ridge which bounds lowland on south and farther east forms northern edge (Murailles ridge) of Percé peninsula.

With the general relations of valley, ridge and lowland, so characteristic of folded Appalachian topography, clearly in mind, let the observer ascend to some high point farther east, whence, looking backward along the picturesque crest of the Murailles (Fig. 100), he can better reconstruct the topography of the past, and more accurately estimate the amount of marine erosion necessary to produce the stupendous scarps towering high above the breakers. On the right the multi-colored wall, — red, buff, grey, maroon, white, — presents to the north its inaccessible face, absolutely vertical in places. Toward the south grassy slopes (Fig.

Fig. 100.  Ridge of the Murailles, looking westward, showing vertical sea-cliffs on north and original steep slope of ridge on south.

101), broken here and there by patches of woodland, descend to the ravine that rapidly widens to a small lowland, over which is scattered in happy disorder the little village of Percé. Such is the Murailles ridge, dividing the broad, weak-rock lowland on the north, now drowned to form Mal Bay, from the less perfect and far less extensive lowland on the south, partially drowned to form Percé Bay and partially occupied by the village. The brook which drains the ravine and part of the small lowland apparently did not escape toward the southeast, but cut obliquely across the ridge toward the east. Through this gateway, possibly broadened by the ice sheet, the sea reaches southward a short distance over the lowland floor to give the pretty embayment at North Beach (Fig. 98).

As the observer studies the contours of the remarkable Murailles

FIG. 101.  In center of view, the village of Percé, North Beach, and partly submerged lowland forming Percé Bay.  To the right, the Murailles ridge cliffed on north by waves, and on south sufficiently steep for rapid washing to expose bare soil as white band (to left of wooded area on nearest part of ridge).  In foreground, wave-cut bench on vertical limestones.  To left, vertical beds of limestone forming northern face of Mt. Joli headland.

ridge he is impressed with the fact that its grassy southern slope, at first seemingly gentle in comparison with the precipitous bare wall facing north, is itself in reality very steep.  Here and there are broad patches of bare earth where the soil washes so badly that grass cannot take root; and occasionally the signs of incipient landslips meet the eye (Fig. 101).  From the bed of the ravine or the floor of the lowland to the crest of the Murailles one ascends to a considerable altitude in a comparatively short horizontal distance.  If the sea had spread far and wide from the southern base of this ridge, and if the narrower lowland and ravine had been on the north, it is clear that a relatively short horizontal advance of the waves would give south-facing cliffs of the same altitude as those which now face north.  If, therefore, the Murailles ridge

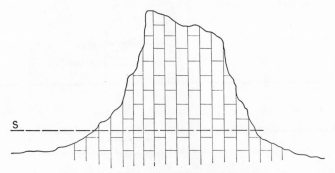

Fig. 102.    Theoretical cross-section of Percé Rock before submergence permitted the sea to cliff its base.

had in times past a northern slope as steep as its present southern slope (and we have seen that there is some evidence that it was even steeper), neither the great height of the cliffs we see today, nor the fact that they are cliffs of diminishing altitude, necessarily implies any great incision of the sea into the land.  They come under the exception recognized in IIb above; and the fact that cliffs of diminishing altitude find an exceptional development on the Gaspé peninsula is due to the fact that here, and here alone on the Atlantic coast, does the so-called Newer Appalachian belt of strongly contrasted ridges and valleys reach the sea.

*Percé Rock.* — Percé Rock (Fig. 80), in line with the southeastward projection of the Murailles, and composed of vertical beds of the same resistant limestone found in part of the Murailles scarp, doubtless marks the former eastward continuation of the

Fig. 103.   The "Stonewall," a hogback of nearly vertical strata (Dakota sandstone) west of Trinidad, Colorado.   A subaërial erosion form which, if submerged and slightly modified at the base by wave action, would give the appearance of cliffs due to extensive marine erosion, the submerged adjacent lowland or valley flats resembling in form a wave-cut bench.   Photo by N. H. Darton.

resistant Murailles ridge. Topographically it differs from the Murailles in the fact that the sea has here had access to the southern side of the ridge as well as the northern, due to the more complete submergence of the eastern part of the southern or Percé lowland. It is a double-faced " Murailles ridge." Just what was its form when first submerged no one can say. Like certain other vertical beds of resistant rock, the limestones of Percé may here have presented, in part at least, vertical faces of bare rock as a result of normal subaërial denudation. If we suppose that prior to sub-mergence Percé Rock was a ridge of the form shown in Fig. 102, bounded on either side by low land eroded on weaker beds, it will be evident that when the sea rose to the position indicated by the line SL, comparatively little wave work would be necessary to transform the ridge into the vertical-walled rock we see today. If the sea were to rise to the base of the subaërially formed ridge of " The Stonewall," Colorado (Fig. 103), no great amount of wave work would be required to change it into a rock which would have all the appearance of a small residual of a once far greater mass, reduced by wave erosion to insignificant proportions. The Percé Rock ridge was of greater thickness than the Stonewall, and its broader upland was fashioned into graded, grassy slopes; the flanking weaker beds may have risen higher on its steep walls, or may even have merged into the sloping upland surface; but even so, the amount of marine erosion necessary to remove the flanking beds and give the present form, is quite inconsiderable; and, as already noted, the little wave work required was enormously facilitated, and a resultant form of imposing abruptness was as-sured, by the nearly vertical bedding of the limestone.

The assumption that the striking form of Percé Rock was the product of extensive wave work would force one to choose be-tween these two alternatives: either the waves worked for a very long period of time at or near the present level, or they worked for a shorter period with exceptional vigor and rapidity. The first is negatived by the abundant evidence along most of the New England-Acadian coast indicating a very short period of marine erosion at the present level. The second receives no support from Clarke's study of the Percé region, for he tells us: " The wastage of Percé Rock under the impact of the waves is very slight. Freez-ing and thawing are more efficient agents, but during the past ten years not enough has fallen from all these causes combined to alter the outline of the cliff in any perceptible degree, and the line of the prow has not materially changed in 150 years."[27] The destruction of the thin seaward end of the rock, where were formerly the additional arches referred to in an earlier paragraph, necessarily caused more rapid changes in its appearance, as is fully recognized by Clarke;[28] but there is no reliable evidence of any such rapid marine erosion in this region as we shall find taking place under more favorable conditions in weaker materials.

*Partial Submergence of Subaërial Forms, followed by Moderate Marine Erosion.* — From the dilemma in which we are placed by the conclusion that in this locality wave erosion has been neither exceptionally rapid nor long-continued, we find a reasonable issue by recognizing that much of the work which we are at first tempted to attribute to marine agencies was accomplished by subaërial denudation prior to the submergence of the region. Thus we

FIG. 104. Bonaventure Island (see Fig. 81) showing cliffed northern end, and gentle western and southern slopes descending under the sea without indication of extensive cliffing.

seek the cause of the separation of Bonaventure Island from the mainland not in extensive wave erosion, but in the submergence which permitted the sea to flood a low sag or depression earlier etched out by weathering and stream action between the two, — a history which accounts for most of the islands of this submerged coast, and which seems indicated by the form of Bonaventure Island itself (Fig. 104). A narrow ravine, possibly developed along the fault which Clarke places between Percé Rock and the adjoining headland of Mont Joli (Fig. 101), may have separated these two before the waves, attacking the line of weakness from both sides of the ridge under exceptionally favorable conditions, still further widened the gap between them and carved the marine bench on which the shallow connecting bar of gravel, previously mentioned, appears to rest. Mont Joli headland, and Cape Canon just south are imperfectly developed parts of the lowland, formed of moderately resistant beds of more ancient date, and cut into by the waves to give cliffs of diminishing height. That the cutting required was not extensive is shown by the fact that just south of Cape Canon the lowland passes under the water unbroken by any appreciable cliff. The gradual eastward descent of the lowland beneath sealevel in this region, and the westward descent of the gentle backslope of Bonaventure Island (Fig. 104) with only moderate cliffing where it reaches the sea, are what should be expected if submergence drowned much of the Percé lowland to give Percé Bay in times geologically recent. The more imposing cliffs on the outer sides of this island may well be subaërial scarps, such as characterize the same geological formation high above the reach of the waves on the adjoining mainland, moderately trimmed by the sea in the short period since submergence brought Bonaventure hill within the reach of marine agencies. Similarly, the other major changes attributed to wave action at this remarkably interesting and picturesque locality appear to find a reasonable explanation in the partial submergence of an irregular land surface formed by subaërial agencies, followed by sufficient marine erosion to produce typical marine forms along the coast.

**Analysis of Submarine Shelf and Shore Cliffs of Cape Gaspé.** — The broad, shallow submarine shelf which fronts the precipitous northern side of Cape Gaspé, deserves our special attention; for nowhere else on the coast are cliffs so high (nearly 700 feet) associated with so broad a bench (approximately 5 miles), to give what appears to be a most imposing record of marine abrasion. From high points on the Percé peninsula one may see, looking northward across Point Saint Peter peninsula, a sharp-crested, moderately serrate ridge stretching along the northern horizon. It is another typical Appalachian ridge, and as he looks the observer realizes that it must be the one which reaches far out into the ocean to form Cape Gaspé. With the analysis of the topography of Percé fresh in mind, he cannot but speculate as to what lies beyond that barrier. If the submarine shelf shown on the chart be the stump of an old mountain mass planed off by the sea to a breadth of five miles, marine cliffs should rim the whole shore of the embayment, and there should be no close relation between the remaining land topography and the newly carved platform offshore. But if the law of Appalachian relief holds good, and the submarine shelf is merely the seaward end of a flat lowland drowned by the same submergence that embayed the rest of the Atlantic coast, then north of the barrier one should find the unsubmerged remnant of the lowland sloping gently downward toward the southeast to pass under the sea without appreciable cliffing; and the great cliffs bordering the north flank of the Cape, since they are on this interpretation largely subaërial forms, should extend inland as a steep wall bordering the lowland on the southwest.

With these criteria of two possible interpretations in mind the eager observer pushes northward along the shore, crosses the picturesque waters of Gaspé Bay with the southern side of the ridge now in full view, and hastens to the crest for a look into the

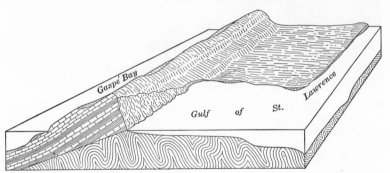

Fig. 105.  Monoclinal ridge of Cape Gaspé and the lowland to the north, partially submerged to form the cape and its bordering submarine shelf. Compare with Fig. 81.  Moderate wave incision into the steep scarp slope thus exposed to the sea produces imposing cliffs.  Geology after Clarke.

land which promises a solution for his problem.  Then instantly, as he tops the great southwest-dipping limestone ridge (Fig. 105), there bursts upon his vision a scene as beautiful as it is significant. From his feet the bare cliffs eroded on the uptilted edges of the limestone fall away sheer to where the waves are gnawing at their bases hundreds of feet below.  Off to the left he notes that the cliffs extend inland beyond the reach of the sea, and that from their base a flat lowland stretches northward (Fig. 106), a portion of which forms what Clarke[29] has aptly termed the "broad, flat triangle of Cape Rosier."  Southeastward this lowland declines gently under the sea, and the green of the fields gives place to the blue of the sea without any conspicuous scarp to divide them. Only here and there, as at Cape Rosier itself, minor elevations on the lowland floor terminate at the shore in cliffs of any size. Prominent cliffs such as should record a deep incision of the waves into the land are here absent from the lowland shores, while those features characteristic of a partially and, geologically speaking,

FIG. 106.  Cape Gaspé ridge in foreground.  In the distance the lowland north of the ridge slopes under the sea, unmarked by extensive marine cliffing.  View looking northwest.  Compare with Fig. 105.

FIG. 107.  Imposing cliffs due to limited marine etching of steep northern slope of Cape Gaspé ridge.  View looking east.  Compare left foreground of Fig. 105.

recently submerged Appalachian ridge and valley are strikingly apparent.  Where submergence brought the sea to rest against the scarp-like slope of the ridge bounding the lowland on the south, the imposing cliffs are found (Fig. 107); and here only because the form of the ridge, as subaërially developed, left little for the waves to do before imposing cliffs resulted. It is difficult to escape the conviction that the submerged lowland platform north of the Cape Gaspé ridge, like the lowland drowned to form Mal Bay north of the Murailles ridge, is of subaërial origin. They differ only in that the northern equivalent of Point Saint Peter ridge disappears in the vicinity of Cape Rosier, leaving the northern lowland open to the subaërially terraced and drowned valley of the St. Lawrence.

*Submarine Form of the Cape Gaspé Shelf.* — A more detailed examination of the Cape Gaspé submerged platform seems to offer some confirmation of its subaërial origin. Its surface is somewhat irregular, as is shown by the profiles in Fig. 108, *A, B, C.* At two points the 30-fathom contour makes marked re-entrants, one of which divides into two branches, thus giving a distinct suggestion of the presence of submerged valleys cut back into the bench (Fig. 81). The easternmost of these depressions heads close in against the edge of Cape Gaspé, and is there 10 fathoms or more deeper than adjacent portions of the platform. Thus, while the charts of this region are admittedly too inaccurate to permit one to draw definite conclusions as to submarine con-tours, there seems to be nothing in the form of the platform, as indicated by charts and profiles, incompatible with the interpreta-tion that it is a former land surface developed by subaërial agen-cies and later submerged. The irregularity of the surface and the presence of what appear to be submerged valleys favor this inter-pretation. Had waves cut four or five miles into the land, plan-ing off the mountain ridges to make a wave-cut bench, depressions extending back into the landmass for two miles or more must long ago have been filled with the products of so vast an erosion. The profiles drawn transversely across the platform (Fig. 109, *A, B, C*) are similar to those frequently found in regions of subaërial origin; indeed it is not difficult to find subaërial profiles (Fig. 109, *D-I*) which, if submerged, would give a stronger impression of a marine cliff and bench than do those of the Cape Gaspé region.

If the Gaspé platform is in large part a rock surface, some of the profiles in Fig. 109 are incomparable for the reason that they are developed on alluvium or glacial débris; but some are developed largely on bedrock, or with but an insignificant veneer of alluvium over bedrock, while the stripping off of the alluvium of others by wave action would reveal a similar bedrock profile. In other

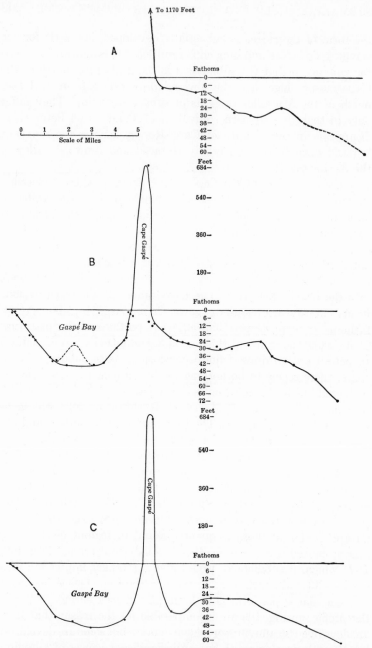

FIG. 108. Profiles across Cape Gaspé peninsula showing character of submerged platform and drowned valley of Gaspé Bay. Vertical exaggeration × 50. Based on British Admiralty Chart No. 1163.

A. Linear profile east across platform from Hill 1170 at base of peninsula.
B. Projected profile of a belt one mile broad from southwest to northeast across central portion of peninsula (Cape Bon Ami).
C. Linear profile from southwest to northeast across outer end of
peninsula. (210)

words, there are abundantly developed on land areas, by means of subaërial agencies, surfaces which if submerged and subjected to a moderate amount of marine erosion, would resemble the ideal wave-cut bench more closely than does the Cape Gaspé platform. While this in itself does not exclude the possibility of a wave-cut origin for the platform in question, it shows the difficulty of discriminating subaërial from marine forms; and taken in connection with the apparent presence of submerged valleys in the Cape Gaspé platform, strengthens the probability of its subaërial origin. It will be noted that no such broad platform is developed off the exposed shore of Bonaventure Island, where the 30-fathom contour is close to the island instead of five miles out, and the contours descend rapidly into deeper water. In the character of the sedimentary rocks found in the two areas we seem to find no adequate explanation for so great a difference of submarine form; and similarly the absence of any great amount of wave erosion along other parts of the shoreline bordering the uplands makes it seem more probable that the broad platform at Cape Gaspé is, like the broad valley bottoms and other submerged features of this coast, a subaërial form but moderately altered by wave action.

**Analysis of the Submerged Shelves of the St. Lawrence Embayment.** — The greatest breadth of the Cape Gaspé platform is approximately 5 miles from the shore to the 30-fathom line. Northwestward the platform rapidly narrows and soon disappears, profiles at various points along the north side of the Gaspé Peninsula, prepared by D. A. Nichols in connection with a graduate course at Columbia University and by H. G. Bray, Research Assistant in Physiography at the same institution, showing a fairly uniform steep slope into deep water (Fig. 110). It must be said, however, that for parts of this coast we have only small scale charts, on which the soundings do not show the bottom with sufficient detail for one to be sure that a very narrow shelf may not have escaped detection. The profiles of Figs. 110 and 111 are based on a chart of this type, and while they are open to the objection stated, there is no reason to doubt that they are correct in representing no broad shelf off the northern Gaspé shore, for numerous profiles from Cape Magdalen westward to Cape Balance, based on modern detailed charts, fully confirm the evidence of the older and poorer charts in this respect. Farther around to the southwest, in the narrower upper part of the St.

(*Continued on page 216*)

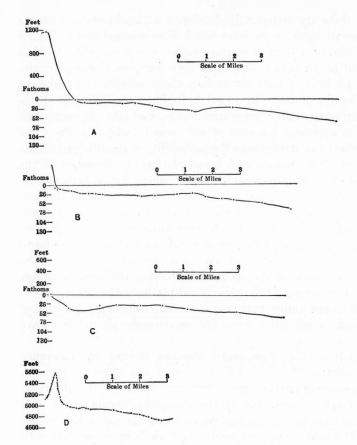

FIG. 109.  Profiles across the submerged shelf off Cape Gaspé (A, B, C) compared with subaërial profiles, showing closer approach of some of latter (D, E, H, I) to the ideal marine profile of equilibrium, and the small amount of wave work (cutting and filling) necessary to transform others (F, G) into marine profiles.  Vertical exaggeration × 10.  Profiles A, B and C are from Fig. 108, reduced to same vertical exaggeration as profiles D–I for direct comparison.

A. Linear profile from Hill 1170, Cape Gaspé, eastward.  Based on British Admiralty Chart No. 1163.

B. Projected profile of belt 1 mile wide from Cape Bon Ami northeastward.  Based on British Admiralty Chart No. 1163.

C. Linear profile from near outer end of Cape Gaspé northeastward. Based on British Admiralty Chart No. 1163.

D. Linear profile from hill west of Animas Valley, eastward.  Based on U. S. Topographic Quadrangle, Animas Peak, N. M.

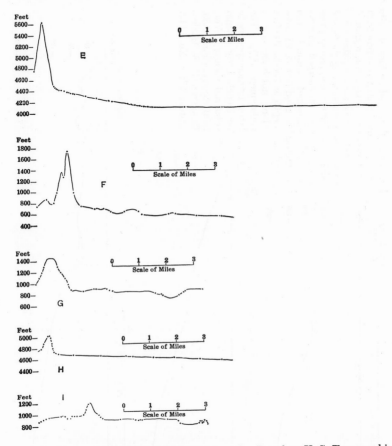

E.  Linear profile from Hill 5635 eastward.   Based on U. S. Topographic
    Quadrangle, Columbus, Ariz.

F.  Linear profile from Mt. Weisner northward.   Based on U. S. Topo-
    graphic Quadrangle, Fort Payne, Ala.

G.  Linear profile from near Devils Lake southward.   Based on U. S.
    Topographic Quadrangle, Baraboo, Wisc.

H.  Linear profile from near Hilo Peak northeastward.   Based on U. S.
    Topographic Quadrangle, Antelope Wells, N. M.

I.  Linear profile eastward across Coon Bluff.   Based on U. S. Topo-
    graphic Quadrangle, The Dells, Wisc.

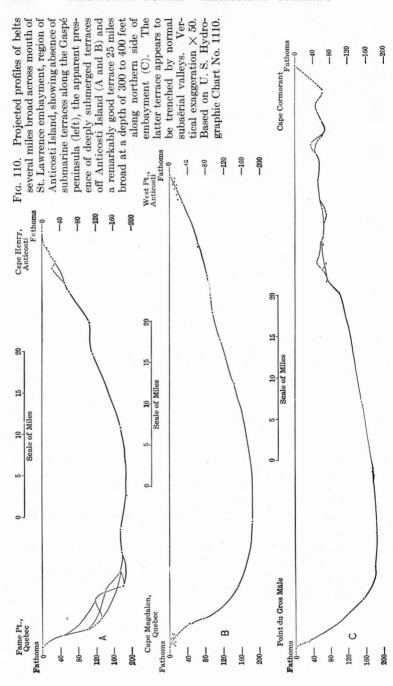

FIG. 110. Projected profiles of belts several miles broad across mouth of St. Lawrence embayment, region of Anticosti Island, showing absence of submarine terraces along the Gaspé peninsula (left), the apparent presence of deeply submerged terraces off Anticosti Island (A and B) and a remarkably good terrace 25 miles broad at a depth of 300 to 400 feet along northern side of embayment (C). The latter terrace appears to be trenched by normal subaërial valleys. Vertical exaggeration × 50. Based on U. S. Hydrographic Chart No. 1110.

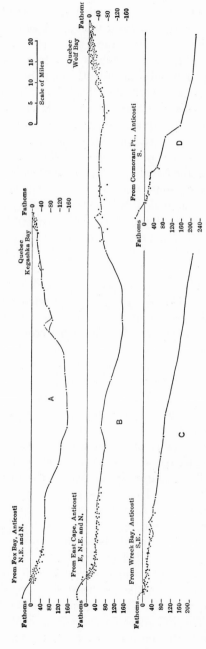

Fig. 111. Projected profiles of belts from 3 to 15 miles broad from the eastern end of Anticosti Island northeast, east, southeast, and south, showing terraces of drowned St. Lawrence valley. Note apparent absence of good terrace in profile C, where one or more might be found in deeper water if more soundings were available. Vertical exaggeration × 50. Based on U. S. Hydrographic Chart No. 1108.

Lawrence embayment southwest of Cape Chat (or Chatte), a shallow submerged shelf appears near Cape Balance, and broadens rapidly as one passes up the drowned valley.  A similar feature is found in places on the north side of the river, as is shown in some of the profiles of Fig. 112.  These shelves vary from less than a mile to as much as 7 or 8 miles in breadth, and their markedly even surfaces usually slope toward the axis of the embayment.

*Distribution of the Submerged Shelves.* — Certain characteristics of the shelves bordering the upper part of the St. Lawrence embayment deserve emphasis in the present connection.  As shown on the detailed charts issued by the Canadian Naval Service, the broad, shallow shelves are largely limited to the narrower upper part of the embayment, southwest of the sudden constriction which takes place in the region of Point-des-Monts and Cape Chat, being wonderfully developed along the shores bordering the more restricted waters as one passes up the river toward Quebec (Fig. 112), but only locally developed or wholly lacking about most of the broader expanse of the Gulf toward the northeast (Figs. 110 and 111.  The deeply submerged terraces are here not in question).  This is the opposite of what one would expect in the case of a wave-cut rock bench, which should be broadest where greater expanses of open deep water favor more vigorous marine erosion.  As already stated, large scale charts for the latter areas are not yet available; but the excellent charts for the Point-des-Monts and Cape Chat regions seem to show a gradual disappearance of the shelves as one passes eastward, while even on the old and decidedly inaccurate charts of the eastern waters shelves comparable with those in the upper part of the embayment would clearly be recognizable if they existed.

Within the more restricted waters of the upper embayment, for all of which excellent charts are available, the distribution of the shallow submarine shelves seems significant.  They are developed mainly along the southeast shore, appearing less frequently and usually with but limited breadth on the northwest shore (Fig. 112).  The northwest shore is for most of the distance much higher and bolder than the southeast, and plunges more steeply down into deep water; and it is noticeable, also, that where the shelves on the southeast shore begin to disappear eastward from the Cape Chat region, the coast becomes higher and bolder.  The difference in submarine contours does not seem attributable to differences in exposure to storm waves.

(Continued on page 220)

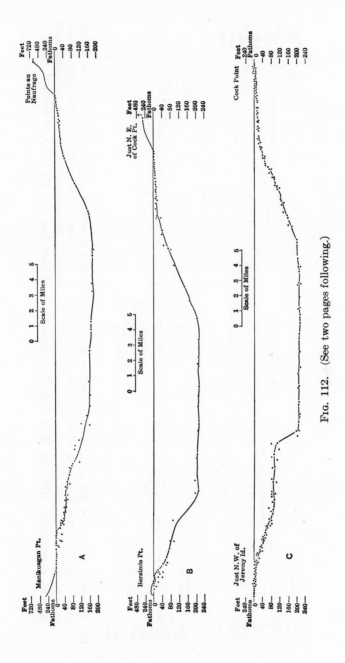

Fig. 112.  (See two pages following.)

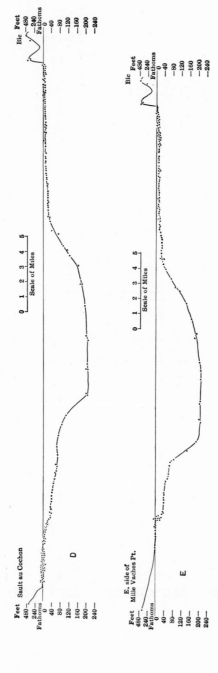

Fig. 112 continued (see pp. 217 and 219). Projected profiles (except I, which is a linear profile) of belts from one to four miles broad across the St. Lawrence embayment, drawn at intervals ascending the drowned valley from near Matane to Port Joli below Quebec, showing shallow shelves and deeply submerged terraces of subaërial origin. Vertical exaggeration approximately ×10. Based on Canadian Naval Service Charts Nos. 215, 210, 204, 201 and 207.

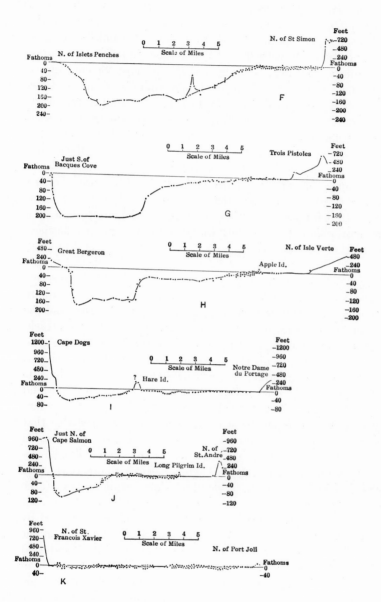

Fig. 112 continued (see pp. 217 and 218).

Both shores are partially open to attack from waves developed by storm winds blowing from the quadrant north to east; and the net differences in exposure to other storm winds would seem to be small in comparison with the great difference in submarine forms. Furthermore, the shore best exposed to the most violent storms, the northern side of the Gaspé peninsula from Cape Chat to Cape Magdalen and eastward, lacks the broad shelf found farther west. One might be tempted to explain the general absence of a shelf along the northwest shore on the theory that where, along the initial shoreline, the waves broke against a steep rock wall descending abruptly into deep water they could accomplish little erosion, both because they would be reflected back,[23] and because all débris would be in such deep water that the waves could not arm themselves with it for the most effective attack on the land; while on a more gently sloping shore they would work with great efficiency. But whether the contrast of no rock shelf on parts of the steep shore, with a shelf from 5 to 8 miles broad in places on the sloping shore, can adequately be accounted for on this basis seems open to doubt.   Neither does it seem possible to find an adequate explanation in the difference in height of the two coasts, and the consequent difference in rate of cliff recession under wave attack. There is a difference in the bedrock formations on the two sides of the embayment, the northwest shore bordering resistant crystallines (Precambrian), the southeast less resistant sediments of later date (Paleozoic).   But while the St. Lawrence Lowland presumably owes its existence to more ready removal of sedimentary beds by subaërial agencies, it does not seem probable that the contrast in resistance to wave attack is sufficiently pronounced to account for the remarkable contrast in the extent of shelf development on the two shores.   There are, furthermore, fairly wide shelves along parts of the crystalline shore, while parts of the shore bordering the sedimentaries show no shelf, or one of but narrow width.   It is noticeable that the low shores bordered by broad submarine shelves frequently show scarps labelled on the charts " clay cliffs," " sand cliffs," or " earth cliffs," and that surfaces of " swampy grass land," " flat cultivated land," or " grassy undulating land rising gradually to back ridges," are indicated here and there.   Evidently the low shores are in considerable part composed of unconsolidated materials overlying the bedrock formations discussed above, a fact readily verified on the ground.   Hence in some measure the real contrast is one between these unconsolidated deposits and the hard rock of the bolder and steeper shores, and this fact may explain certain details of form later to be considered; but it cannot account for the existence of the terraces, which are observed in the field to be cut in bedrock.

*Breadth of the Shelves.* — The breadth of the shallow shelves, where they are present, is extremely variable.   There is apparently some tendency for them to be widest opposite shallow embayments in the shore, while off exposed points they may be narrow or wholly wanting.   This does not favor the wave-cut theory of their origin, since waves should cut the broader benches off exposed points.   The maximum breadth, if we neglect minor channels cut in the shelf and occasional island ridges rising above it, is near the head of the embayment, not far below Quebec (Fig. 112, *K*), where on the basis of the wave-erosion theory the water body, before the cutting of the shelf, must have been so extremely narrow that the generation of waves competent to do the work would seem quite impossible.   Little help is secured by imagining this shelf to have been cut by waves formed on several narrow strips of water, as the volume of supposed wave cutting still remains enormous in comparison with the feeble waves capable of being developed in such narrow channels.   A few miles below Quebec the narrow channel between Orleans Island and the north shore is bordered on both sides by shelves, partly submerged and partly exposed, but believed to represent a single topographic feature, and seemingly identical with the broader shelves farther down the embayment.   Here the wave-cut theory of origin for the shelves would call for the development of benches having a total breadth much greater than that of the original water body.

Where islands rise from the waters of the upper part of the St. Lawrence embayment, it is sometimes observed that the shelf is very broad on that side of the island toward the narrower and shallower channel, but of limited breadth or absent from the side bordering the deeper and broader water body (Canadian Naval Service Chart Nos. 201, 204).   Furthermore, the shelf may be perfectly developed and continuous back of a long, narrow rock island bordering the mainland shore, but poorly developed on the opposite, exposed side of the island.   It is difficult to believe that waves could cut the land away to leave the island, or that they could form a broad bench by widening a pre-existing channel be-

tween island and mainland, and yet accomplish little or nothing
on much more exposed shores nearby.

*Deposits on the Shelves.* — The surfaces of the submarine shelves
are almost everywhere composed of sand or mud.  Away from the
main shores, islands, and occasional shoals, the charts seldom show
the symbol (*r*) for rock.  The charts thus give little support to
the hypothesis that the shelves are wave-cut rock benches; for
while it is theoretically conceivable that a rock bench might be
completely covered with a veneer of sand and coarser débris, or
with fine sand and mud in case there had been a complete change
in local conditions since the cutting took place, it does not seem
probable that a rock bench cut at the present level or a level
slightly lower, would have the rock surface so greatly obscured
by fine débris subject to easy removal.

It is worthy of note that as one follows the easternmost of the
shallow submerged shelves, on the south side of the St. Lawrence,
northeastward toward its extinction in the vicinity of Matane or
Cape Chat, the charts show that the deposit on the shelf changes
from mostly mud at the southwest, to mostly sand at the northeast.  This suggests the possibility that more vigorous wave action
here has removed the muds and left sands, or even prevented the
deposition of the muds in the first place.  It is in general true that
the proportion of mud decreases, and of sand increases, as one
follows the submerged shelves from the narrow head of the embayment near Quebec northeastward toward its broadly open
mouth.  Another significant fact is the presence of an unusually
strong current constantly flowing from west to east just off the
shore of the peninsula from the vicinity of Cape Chat eastward,
with velocities up to $3\frac{1}{2}$ knots per hour (Canadian Naval Service
Chart No. 213).  When one remembers that a current of 1 knot
per hour will move sand and fine gravel, while a current of $3\frac{1}{2}$
knots can even move angular stones an inch and a half in diameter,[30] the possible importance of the currents off the Gaspé coast
in preventing the formation of a submarine terrace of deposition,
or in removing such a terrace composed of fine débris, is obvious.
On the other hand, the charts occasionally show, in more sheltered
localities, current velocities as high as 3 knots over the surface of
the shelf, although in such places the current direction is usually
more variable.  These and other elements of the problem will all
have to be taken into account by the student who solves the
physiographic history of the St. Lawrence embayment.

*Down-valley Inclination of the Shelves.* — Some of the shelves show a pronounced down-valley inclination when followed along the shore, in addition to the usual slope from the shore outward toward the axis of the embayment. A beautiful case is shown on the Canadian Naval Service Chart No. 204, where a shelf which rises approximately 6 feet above mean low water in the vicinity of Green Island, declines gradually toward the northeast until in the vicinity of Bic Island it is 9 fathoms below the same datum plane (Fig. 113). This down-valley slope of 2 feet per mile (60 feet of descent in about 30 miles) suggests a river-cut terrace. Immediately to the southwest is a similar shelf, likewise sloping down-valley, but more irregular in form. One might, perhaps, assume that these shelves were wave-cut, and later warped into their present down-valley position, as well as broken into separate segments. Although the increasing depth of the shelves corresponds in some measure with a broadening of the embayment, one cannot attribute increasing depth to a greater exposure to wave attack, since the slope increases equally in exposed situations and under the lee of such protecting masses as Bic and Hare Islands and the reefs associated with the latter.

Goldthwait[31] locates two pro-

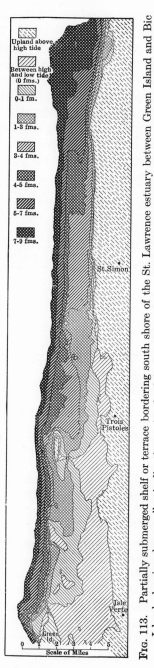

FIG. 113. Partially submerged shelf or terrace bordering south shore of the St. Lawrence estuary between Green Island and Bic Island, showing down-valley inclination. At the left (southwest) the shelf rises above low water level, but descends 2 feet per mile toward the right (northeast) until it is 54 feet below that level. Based on Canadian Naval Service Chart No. 204.

files (Fig. 114) of his "Micmac Terrace" on parts of the submerged shelf between Green Island and Bic Island, but does not mention the markedly inclined character of the shelf.  The results of this inclination are beautifully seen from some vantage point on the crest of the Micmac cliff at Isle Verte. Looking southwest up the valley (Fig. 115) one observes the sharply defined cliff with the broad, flat platform in front of it, covered with fenced fields obviously above the normal reach of the sea.  Turning toward the northeast, and following with the eye the course of the platform, one sees it slope gradually down into the sea, salt marsh and mud flats encroaching farther

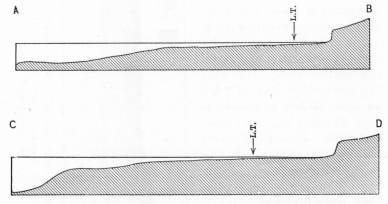

FIG. 114.  The Micmac terrace at Trois Pistoles and near Isle Verte on the Gulf of St. Lawrence (after Goldthwait).  Note that terrace is lower and low tide mark (L.T.) is closer to scarp at Trois Pistoles (AB, down-valley) than at Isle Verte (CD, up-valley).

and farther across its surface, ever pushing the zone of fenced fields back to a constantly narrowing remnant of the platform, until a few miles downstream the waves are almost within reach of the cliff base, and in favorable localities beyond seem actually to attain it.  In driving from Isle Verte to Trois Pistoles one may observe the descent of this platform to good advantage; and it is detectable in Goldthwait's profiles (Fig. 114).  If Goldthwait is correct in his conclusion that the Micmac shoreline maintains a remarkably uniform height of about 20 feet above sealevel, it would seem that the submarine shelf and the Micmac shoreline are independent features, the latter being etched by the waves obliquely across the inclined shelves, after the shelves had been formed, —

FIG. 115.   The Micmac Terrace at Isle Verte, looking up-valley.   To the right, fields cover the surface of the terrace platform, which declines down-valley soon to pass below sealevel.   In centre, the Micmac cliff.   To the left, the even surface of the next higher terrace.

possibly by non-marine agencies. If this interpretation be correct, Goldthwait's profiles involve two topographic forms which are so closely merged as to be almost indistinguishable as observed in the field. They are more easily separable through the interpretation of maps and charts, which permit a comparison of critical relations over broad areas.

**Origin of the Micmac Terrace.** — In this connection it should be pointed out that there seem to be as many difficulties in the way of accepting Goldthwait's theory that the waves cut a broad bench, much of it at least in rock,[32] twenty feet above the present sealevel, as we have found opposed to the theory of extensive wave erosion at the present level. The greater weight of evidence seems to indicate that even on exposed coasts no great amount of wave erosion is recorded at any of the higher levels where the sea is known to have stood in post-glacial time; nor do the submarine contours off such coasts indicate extensive wave cutting at any lower levels during the same period. Near the present level cutting on exposed coasts of unconsolidated materials has been extensive, in weak rock fairly pronounced, and in resistant rock almost negligible. Nowhere do we find any record of the excessive erosion of exposed rocky shores which should have taken place during the time waves in the more sheltered St. Lawrence are supposed to have cut benches a number of miles broad, much of the distance in fairly resistant rock. It would seem that the question of origin of the " Micmac terrace " might further be examined with a view to determining whether all the phenomena as observed in the field may not be accounted for on the assumption that the sea came to rest against terraces of non-marine origin bordering the St. Lawrence valley, cutting pronounced benches and cliffs in glacial débris, clay and sand deposits, and similar unconsolidated materials; but in bedrock merely sharpening hillslopes into marine cliffs, or cutting narrow benches which merge with non-marine terrace levels to give a fictitious appearance of extensive marine erosion. Certain passages in Goldthwait's excellent description of the Micmac shoreline suggest the possibility of such an interpretation; for while he speaks in some places of the waves cutting " far back into the fissile slate," and of " a wide expanse of mud-flats, through which appear here and there the truncated edges of upturned shale and sandstone layers, — as pretty an illustration of marine planation . . . as one could wish," elsewhere he records the weakness of wave attack, as near

St. Simon, at which point we are told "a long range of rocky ridges . . . forms a coast where instead of mature sea-cliffs the waves seem to have been able only to build pocket beaches among the ledges at the inner edge of the shelf," and at MacNiders, where the cliff is undeveloped, and only "ledges and obscure beaches occur at the twenty-foot mark."

*Higher and Lower Terraces Bordering the St. Lawrence.* — If there were only a single "Micmac terrace" to be considered in this region the difficulties encountered by the marine theory of origin would be sufficiently great. They become greater when one observes that we have here to deal with a remarkable series of terraces, some higher and some lower, which give to the sides of the St. Lawrence valley its most striking characteristics. The higher terraces may be studied in the field, where they are sometimes seen to attain breadths of several miles, and to bear a close resemblance to typical parts of the Micmac (Fig. 115). Lower members of the series are submerged and must be investigated through the media of charts and profiles. These show excellent terraces at different depths, one of which attains a breadth of at least 25 miles (Figs. 110 and 112). It does not seem possible to suppose that waves on the comparatively restricted waters of the St. Lawrence cut broad benches, not merely at a single level, but at many different levels, while the ocean waves left but slight traces of their presence on coasts far more exposed.

*Form of the Higher Terraces.* — The form of the St. Lawrence terraces suggests a subaërial rather than a marine origin. While some of them have remarkably smooth surfaces sloping gently toward the axis of the valley, others show significant departures from this type. Thus the surface may be characterized by low parallel ridges, such as are so commonly found on valley floors throughout the Appalachian belt. Sometimes one of these ridges rises high on the seaward margin of the terrace, in such manner as seemingly to exclude the possibility of effective wave action behind it. Cases of this kind are found on the third principal terrace (counting the "Micmac" near sealevel as the first) in the vicinity of Rivière du Loup, and on eastward toward Isle Verte. The long, narrow, rocky islands in the St. Lawrence are similar ridges on a lower terrace partially submerged; and profile *I* in Fig. 112, shows the relations which would exist near Rivière du Loup if the sea rose high enough to submerge slightly the third terrace and the base of its marginal ridge. In places the whole back portion of a terrace is lower than its seaward side, independently of the residual ridges. The traveller from Rivière du Loup to Isle Verte, traversing the surface of a beautiful terrace from one to three miles broad, notes that off to his right the landward portion of the terrace seems relatively low for a long distance, a fact more easily explained if the terrace be of stream origin than if we consider it the product of wave erosion. The terraces are variable in number, a single scarp repeatedly splitting up into two or more subordinate scarps, in a manner more common to stream terraces than to wave-cut benches. Thus near Rivière du Loup the scarp of the fourth terrace becomes double in places; at Isle Verte the second terrace is subdivided and the road follows near the crest of the upper scarp; near Trois Pistoles conditions are similar, while at the river of the same name is a whole succession of minor rock-defended terraces, undoubtedly carved by that stream. Although the major terraces frequently show rock in their scarps and on their platforms, and sometimes are clearly cut in rock, the minor ones and possibly some of the others may consist largely or wholly of unconsolidated débris. Where such nonresistant material is associated with outlying rock ledges, a " meander scarp " pattern sometimes characterizes the terrace front. Such forms were seen in both the Micmac and higher terraces; but while they seemed to me most probably the result of stream action, I could not be sure that wave erosion might not simulate the " meander scarp " pattern under the field conditions actually observed. The breadth of the terraces did not seem in any way related to varying exposures to wave action.

*Form of the Submerged Terraces.* — The submerged terraces revealed by the profiles (Figs. 110 and 112) are not symmetrically disposed on the two sides of the embayment, are not systematically related in different profiles on the same side, and are not to be correlated with different exposures to wave action. In some cases the terrace platform appears to be dissected by normal stream valleys (Fig. 110, *C*, and Fig. 112, *H, I, J*). The broad shelf shown in Fig. 110, *C*, has a very irregular surface and attempts to contour it on the basis of the inadequate soundings available, show the existence of pronounced ridges separated by partially filled valleys, with an occasional deeper trench cut far back into the mass, — the whole being most suggestive of a submerged and partially modified subaërial surface.

*Origin of the St. Lawrence Terraces.* — There seems to be no reason to doubt that both the benches exposed above present sealevel, and those drowned beneath the waters of the St. Lawrence, constitute a single series of terraces adorning the sloping walls of the great valley.   In the midst of this series we find one or another of the platforms near present sealevel, sometimes slightly above, sometimes slightly below the water surface.   It is very unlikely that the one or more examples now nearly or quite within reach of the waves should have a different origin from those above and below.   We have seen that as a whole the series seems to present the characteristics of subaërial terraces rather than those of wave-cut benches.   As for the examples now slightly submerged and therefore most apt to be credited to wave action: their apparent restriction to the narrower part of the embayment;  the fact that they are extremely broad in places where wave action is comparatively weak, and nearly if not wholly lacking where wave action is many times more vigorous;  their tendency, even where present, to be frequently wider in shallow embayments and narrower opposite exposed points along the shores, instead of wider off exposed points where waves act most effectively;  the prevalence of mud and sand on the surfaces of the best developed shelves and the almost complete absence of indications of rock in these same areas, especially when considered in connection with the known occurrence of a coastal plain of clay and sand covering a large section of the unsubmerged portion of the St. Lawrence lowland, with slopes toward the axis of the depression similar to those of the shelves in question;  the fact that the shelves where best developed show a marked inclination down-valley, whereas the latest known prominent wave-cut feature (the Micmac shoreline) is reported to be parallel to the present sealevel surface;  all of these considerations seem to me to argue strongly against the theory that the shallow submarine shelves of the upper St. Lawrence embayment are rock benches cut by waves at or near the present sealevel.

While the definitive solution of the problem of the St. Lawrence terraces requires a far more detailed investigation than I could give to a matter which manifestly lies beyond the scope of the present study, it seems to me probable that the observed facts will find their most reasonable explanation on the theory that a broad, terraced valley or lowland carved by the St. Lawrence River and somewhat modified by ice action, was deeply sub-

merged to give an embayment more extensive than the present
Gulf; that into this embayment streams from the land and perhaps also from the melting ice brought sands and silts, which
waves and currents distributed over the terraced submarine floor,
partially obscuring former stream valleys and cloaking the terraces with a mantle of marine sands and clays wherever the slopes
of the original lowland were gentle, but descending to the deeps
before coming to rest where the valley walls were high and steep;
that later partial emergence offered opportunity for limited wave
action during stages in the rise of the land from the water; that
ultimately the shoreline bordered the upraised terraced plain of sand
and clay where the slopes were gentle, the new water plane being
traced obliquely across the slightly inclined terraces so as to rest
against a scarp in one place, on a platform surface in another; but
that bold rocky shores existed where the slopes were steep and bare
and the deposits of sand and clay lay too deep to be raised to
the surface; that continued wave erosion more or less modified
the sand and clay shores, sharpening those terrace scarps against
which the new sealevel rested, while affecting but little the shores
of hard rock; and that minor oscillations of level, the presence of
glacial drift, rock ridges rising through both glacial and marine
deposits, and other factors added variety and complexity to the
resulting shore forms.  It may be that some such succession of
events will at the same time best account for the submerged
benches off the eastern end of Anticosti Island (Fig. 111), which are
continued above sealevel in the interesting terraces well described
by Twenhofel and Conine.[33]  For us, however, the important
point is this: There seems to be no valid evidence that the slightly
submerged shelves bordering the St. Lawrence embayment are
rock benches cut by wave action in post-glacial time, and hence
it does not appear that these shelves form any exception to the
rule that wave work at the present level has very slightly affected
hard-rock shores, especially in protected localities.

**Absence of Boulder Pavement in Front of Micmac Terrace.** —
There is some evidence that even in the matter of trimming back
the terrace scarps intersected by present sealevel or by a sealevel
possibly 20 feet higher in comparatively recent time, the waves
have accomplished but little.  Where seen by me east of Quebec
near Ste. Anne de Beaupré (Fig. 116), at Rivière du Loup, and
from Isle Verte to Trois Pistoles, the Micmac scarp certainly has
all the sharpness and freshness described by Goldthwait as charac-

teristic of this supposed wave-cut cliff.   In these localities, and I
believe generally, the scarp is cut largely in sand and clay, although bedrock not infrequently shows in its face, as for example
a few miles northeast of Isle Verte where slates and other fairly
resistant formations are exposed from the base of the scarp well
up toward its crest.   A typical section for this region, however,
shows blue and brown clays overlain by yellow sand and gravel.
At least one zone of the clay carries many large boulders, and
where a ravine trenches the scarp a great accumulation of these
big stones is usually concentrated in its bottom.   This suggests
that the cutting back of the deposit by waves should have left a

Fig. 116.   The Micmac cliff and bench near Ste. Anne de Beaupré,
east of Quebec.

prominent boulder pavement in front of the marine cliff, such as
we find in front of similar cliffs in drumlins, moraines, and other
bouldery deposits elsewhere along the coast.   Indeed, we should
expect a more impressive exhibition of the boulder pavement in
front of the Micmac scarp, for there the waves were far weaker,
due to the more protected situation and to the necessity of traversing a broad, shallow platform before reaching the cliff base; and
while they could perhaps readily dispose of the clay and sand,
they could hardly have dealt so effectively with large boulders.
But one of the impressive elements of the Micmac scarp is the
absence of a boulder pavement at its base.   There are, it is true,
large boulders scattered here and there over the broad platform,

which Goldthwait[34] and others have doubtless correctly attributed to ice-rafting; but no such concentration of boulders as
one should expect in front of a retreating scarp in bouldery débris
was found at the localities examined.  Near the cliff base one
might perhaps assume that the clay and sand washed down from
the scarp had buried an accumulation of boulders; but this would
not account for the relative scarcity of boulders farther out.  Apparently we must appeal to removal by ice of a boulder pavement
formerly present, or assume a very limited retreat for the Micmac
scarp under wave attack.

**Position of Base of Micmac Terrace.** — That in certain places
the apparent base of the Micmac scarp owes part of its elevation
above sealevel to the accumulation of débris washed down from
the scarp face and discharged from ravines heading a short distance back in the terrace above, would seem clear from the form
of scarp and platform where typically developed between Isle
Verte and Trois Pistoles.  The scarp often exhibits bare expanses
of clay from which every rain washes some of the finer material,
and evidence of slumping is occasionally seen.  Ravines are
numerous, and from each a small fan of débris issues from the
face of the cliff.  Near the cliff base the platform slopes more
steeply, and where it rises highest shows the form of inconspicuous
coalescing fans.  The crest of this alluvial slope, where it meets
the steeper scarp slope, seemed higher where the platform in front
was broad, and lower where the sea was close to the cliff; but
this was not verified by actual measurement.  It is obvious that
if the sea came to rest against the face of a terrace scarp cut in
loose débris, and the rate of removal of débris by weak wave
action was exceeded by the rate of supply from the scarp, the
alluvial slope might gradually rise higher on the scarp face, giving
the appearance of an elevated shoreline where no change of level
had occurred.  Where the original contact of terrace scarp and
fronting platform was slightly above sealevel, or reached only by
exceptional storm waves, the growth of the alluvial slope would
similarly give a fictitious appearance of substantial elevation.

Inasmuch as conditions in the St. Lawrence Valley appear to be
peculiarly favorable to the development of such fictitious indications of geologically recent slight emergence, and Goldthwait
failed to find the Micmac shoreline beyond the limits of this embayment, and also noted the absence of evidence of wave action
at the 20-foot level at a number of places within the embayment,

further studies of the Micmac cliff might perhaps consider (1) whether it actually represents a single terrace scarp, or different terrace scarps intersecting sealevel at different places; and (2) to what extent, if any, the elevation of the present base of the scarp above sealevel may be due to alluvial aggradation rather than to a change in the relative level of land and sea. I have not seen enough of the Micmac shoreline to judge whether or not alluviation is generally an important element in determining the elevation of the scarp base. The extension of a bedrock platform to the base of the scarp would exclude the possibility of error due to alluviation, although it would not demonstrate the marine origin of the scarp. Whether such a platform occurs at the cliff base some 20 feet above present sealevel is not clear from Goldthwait's account, as the rock platform areas specifically described by him all appear to be lower and farther out in the river. Daly[35] has tentatively correlated the Micmac terrace with other shorelines in various parts of the world apparently elevated from 5 or 10 to as much as 30 feet or more above present sealevel; and while some of these are developed in sand, clay, and glacial till, and therefore are open, in part at least, to the suspicion that an unknown fraction of their apparent elevation may be due to the causes we have been considering; and a few seem to be based on beach altitudes and thus are even more dubious measures of uplift, since waves at the present level may build bars and beaches with crests more than 30 feet above the sea; still others appear to be true wave-cut rock benches which are now obviously above the level at which they were formed.

**Résumé.** — If the arguments set forth in the present chapter are sound, not only do the maps and charts of the New England-Acadian coast clearly indicate that the shoreline bordering this coast is in an extremely youthful stage of development, but the field evidence establishes the fact that the sea surface came to rest against the lands at the present level a very short time ago. It is true, as we have seen, that some observers credit to marine agencies an amount of erosive work which would seem to require a long time for its accomplishment; but the discrepancy is largely accounted for when we take into consideration the effects upon the rate of marine erosion produced by variations in the initial shore profile and in rock structure and resistance, and more especially when we recognize that partial submergence of sub-aërial forms frequently produces a fictitious appearance of extended wave cutting. Thus the rocky cliffs bordering parts of the Maine and Nova Scotian coasts, the picturesque crags towering high above the waves in the Percé region, and the still loftier scarp along the northeastern side of Cape Gaspé, as well as the broad, submerged platforms off the latter cape and along the shores of the St. Lawrence embayment, all seemingly attributable to extended erosion of the lands by the sea, are found to be reasonably interpreted as the result of limited modification by marine agencies of forms earlier produced above sealevel by subaërial forces, and only recently brought within reach of the waves.

## BIBLIOGRAPHY

1. SHALER, N. S.  "The Geology of Cape Ann, Massachusetts." U. S. Geol. Surv., 9th Ann. Rept., 561, 1889.
2. WILLIS, BAILEY.  "Ames Knob, North Haven, Maine." Bull. Geol. Soc. Amer., XIV, 202, 1903.
3. HYDE, J. E.  Personal communication, by permission of the Director of the Geological Survey of Canada.
4. JOHNSON, DOUGLAS.  "Shore Processes and Shoreline Development," 74–76, 176, New York, 1917.
5. LE CONTE, JOSEPH.  "Elements of Geology," 5th Ed., 36–37, New York, 1910.
6. BAILEY, L. W.  "The Geological Factors in the Present Configuration of New Brunswick." Roy. Soc. Can., Proc. and Trans., 3rd Ser., III, Sec. IV, 60, 1910.
7. HITCHCOCK, EDWARD.  "On Certain Causes of Geological Change Now in Operation in Massachusetts." Bost. Jour. Nat. Hist., I, 75, 78, 1837.
8. OGILVIE, I. H.  "A Contribution to the Geology of Southern Maine." N. Y. Acad. Sci., Ann., XVII, 525, 1907.
9. SHALER, N. S.  "The Geology of the Island of Mount Desert, Maine." U. S. Geol. Surv., 8th Ann. Rept., Pt. II, 1011, 1889.
10. SHALER, N. S.  "The Geology of the Island of Mount Desert, Maine." U. S. Geol. Surv., 8th Ann. Rept., Pt. II, 987–1061, 1889.
11. BASCOM, F.  "The Physiography of Mount Desert." Bull. Geog. Soc. Phil., XVII, 117–130, 1919. Reprinted as pamphlet in revised form in 1923.
12. DAVIS, W. M.  "An Outline of the Geology of Mount Desert." Flora of Mount Desert Island (by E. L. Rand and J. H. Redfield), 70, 1894.
13. WILLIS, BAILEY.  "Ames Knob, North Haven, Maine." Bull. Geol. Soc. Amer., XIV, 204, 1903.
14. DAVIS, W. M.  "An Outline of the Geology of Mount Desert." Flora of Mount Desert Island (by E. L. Rand and J. H. Redfield), 69, 1894.
15. STONE, G. H.  "The Glacial Gravels of Maine and their Associated Deposits." U. S. Geol. Surv., Mon. XXXIV, 44, 1899.

16. CLARKE, JOHN M. "Percé: a Brief Sketch of its Geology." N. Y. State Mus. Bull. 80, 135, 1905.

17. CLARKE, JOHN M. "Early Devonic History of New York and Eastern North America." N. Y. State Mus., Mem. 9, Pt. 1, 47, 1908.

18. CLARKE, JOHN M. "The Heart of Gaspé," 5, New York, 1913.

19. CLARKE, JOHN M. "L'Île Percée," 178, New Haven, 1923.

20. CLARKE, JOHN M. "Early Devonic History of New York and Eastern North America." N. Y. State Mus., Mem. 9, Pt. 1, 22, 1908.

CLARKE, JOHN M. "L'Île Percée," 175, New Haven, 1923.

21. CLARKE, JOHN M. "The Heart of Gaspé," 6, see also p. 47, New York, 1913.

22. CLARKE, JOHN M. "Dalhousie and the Gaspé Peninsula." Twelfth Inter. Geol. Cong., Guide Book No. 1, Pt. I, 87, 1913.

23. JOHNSON, DOUGLAS. "Shore Processes and Shoreline Development," 57, New York, 1917.

24. SHALER, N. S. "The Geology of Cape Ann, Massachusetts." U. S. Geol. Surv., 9th Ann. Rept., 529–611, 1889.

25. CLARKE, JOHN M. "Dalhousie and the Gaspé Peninsula." Twelfth Inter. Geol. Cong., Guide Book No. 1, Pt. I, 102, 1913.

26. POWERS, SIDNEY. "The Acadian Triassic." Jour. Geol., XXIV, 10, 1916.

27. CLARKE, JOHN M. "Dalhousie and the Gaspé Peninsula." Twelfth Inter. Geol. Cong., Guide Book No. 1, Pt. I, 96, 1913.

28. CLARKE, JOHN M. "Early Devonic History of New York and Eastern North America." N. Y. State Mus., Mem. 9, Pt. 1, 53, 1908.

29. CLARKE, JOHN M. "Early Devonic History of New York and Eastern North America." N. Y. State Mus., Mem. 9, Pt. 1, 23, 1908.

30. HARRIS, R. A. "Manual of Tides, Part V." U. S. Coast Surv. Rept. for 1907, Appendix No. 6, 423, 1907.

31. GOLDTHWAIT, J. W. "The Twenty-foot Terrace and Sea-cliff of the Lower St. Lawrence." Amer. Jour. Sci., 4th Ser., XXXII, 291–317, 1911.

32. GOLDTHWAIT, J. W. "The Twenty-foot Terrace and Sea-cliff of the Lower St. Lawrence." Amer. Jour. Sci., 4th Ser., XXXII, 301, 303, 1911.

33. TWENHOFEL, W. H., and CONINE, W. H. "The Post-glacial Terraces of Anticosti Island." Amer. Jour. Sci., 5th Ser., I, 268–278, 1921.

34. GOLDTHWAIT, J. W. "The Twenty-foot Terrace and Sea-cliff of the Lower St. Lawrence." Amer. Jour. Sci., 4th Ser., XXXII, 300, 303, 1911.

35. DALY, R. A. "A Recent Worldwide Sinking of Ocean-level." Geol. Mag., LVII, 246–261, 1920.

DALY, R. A. "A General Sinking of Sealevel in Recent Time." Proc. Nat. Acad. Sci., VI, 246–250, 1920.

# CHAPTER VII

## WAVE-BUILT FORMS BORDERING THE RESISTANT UPLANDS

**Advance Summary.** — From the study of forms produced by wave erosion we turn naturally to a consideration of the very different forms resulting from the constructive action of the waves. In this chapter it will be our task to secure some idea of the variety of wave-built forms bordering the resistant upland shores, and to discover what conclusions of general interest may be derived from a knowledge of the character and quantity of these forms.

**General Considerations.** — A coast which has suffered but slight wave erosion at the present level should have but a moderate development of beaches, bars, forelands, and similar forms built by wave action. In general such features are not particularly prominent along those parts of the New England-Acadian shore bordered by resistant rocks of the crystalline upland. There are, it is true, many examples of practically every variety of these shore forms, but as a rule they are not conspicuous for their size and do not constitute as important an element of the shoreline physiography as is the case along shores of less resistant character. Even those which do occur are probably composed in large part of material derived from the glacial débris which covered much of the rocky surface when the sea came to rest against it, or from the erosion of neighboring areas of weak Carboniferous or Triassic strata. The volume of the beaches is materially augmented by the addition of pebbles and boulders rafted in from deep water offshore by seaweeds, in a manner which has briefly been described and illustrated elsewhere.[1] Shaler is of the opinion that "many of the pebbly beaches in New England are entirely supplied by the action of seaweeds,"[2] and considers the process a very important one along the rocky shores of Cape Ann.[3] These offshore pebbles and boulders may have been in part derived from submerged glacial deposits, and in part from material earlier eroded from the rocky upland.

A few examples of typical wave-built shore forms, composed of shore débris which presumably in most cases is derived only in part, and often only in very minor part, from wave erosion of the resistant rocks of the upland, will serve to illustrate the wonderful variety of interesting minor features which is normally characteristic of a young shoreline of submergence.[4]

**Bayhead Beaches.** — Of the several types of beaches formed directly against the upland (headland beaches, bayhead beaches, and bayside beaches*), the bayhead beaches, or pocket beaches, are most abundantly developed along the New England-Acadian coast. The innumerable small re-entrants or coves formed by partial submergence of small tributary valleys, ravines, or mere hollows in the land surface, have served to collect and hold the sand, gravel, and boulders driven into them by the waves. Where the embayment is not too deep in proportion to its breadth, the material is driven to its head to form a bayhead beach (Fig. 98). So abundant is this common type of beach that it requires no special comment, save where unusual features are developed. Clarke[5] describes Boom Beach, Isle-au-Haut, Maine, as a small example in which the reduction of rock fragments to symmetrical forms by vigorous wave action on a sloping rock floor bounded on either side by rock cliffs, has produced a tremendous accumulation of rounded boulders, many of which weigh 100 pounds or more. A bayhead beach near Manchester, Massachusetts, known as Singing Beach, has attracted attention because of the acoustic properties of its sand, which gives forth a musical sound when walked upon, agitated in a bag, or otherwise subjected to friction. This is a phenomenon reported from other localities on the New England coast and elsewhere, and has been studied by Bolton and Julien,[6] especially at the Manchester locality. A very small pocket beach of pebbles and sand near Kittery Point, Maine, attracted attention throughout the country in the autumn of 1905, because on two occasions it suddenly became covered with flames which played over the surface for the greater part of an hour. This " blazing beach " is well described by Penhallow,[7] who explains the phenomenon as due to the spontaneous ignition of gases generated by decaying vegetable and animal matter beneath the beach deposit.

* A discussion of the origin and development of the various types of beaches, bars, forelands, etc., will be found in the author's volume on "Shore Processes and Shoreline Development."

**Bayhead Bars.** — Good examples of bayhead bars are found at the head of Clam Bay, Nova Scotia, where one that might also pass as a tombolo because the eastern shore of the bay with which it connects is formed by an island, is labelled on the geologic map of Nova Scotia " beautiful sand beach " (Fig. 117). Farther to the southwest is the series of bayhead bars described by Fari-bault[8] in these words: " One of the remarkable features of the coast is the great number of beautiful white crescent-shaped sand beaches fringing the heads of coves and bays facing the broad Atlantic. The largest sand beaches are those of White Point, Summerville, Southwest Port Mouton, Little Joli Bay, Cadden Bay, and Sandy Cove. They generally consist of sand bars

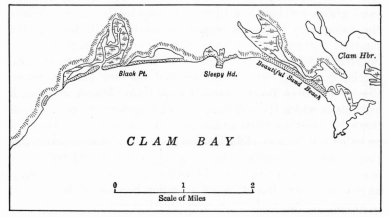

FIG. 117.   Bayhead bars at head of Clam Bay, Nova Scotia.

enclosing salt water ponds and marshes, and on some of these the action of the wind has developed prominent sand dunes, those of Port Mouton being especially remarkable for their altitude and their glistening whiteness." Bailey[9] has briefly described the dunes of Port Mouton, and the traveller along the coast of Nova Scotia finds that even on the smaller bars and beaches of minor re-entrants the dunes are an interesting and picturesque element of the shoreline scenery. Similar bayhead bars are to be found at many points along other sections of the Acadian shore, and bordering the coast of New England. Crescent Beach (Fig. 118) near the head of Seal Cove south of Portland, and the beach at the head of Howards Bay near Machias (U. S. Coast Survey Chart No. 303), are very pretty examples from the coast of Maine.

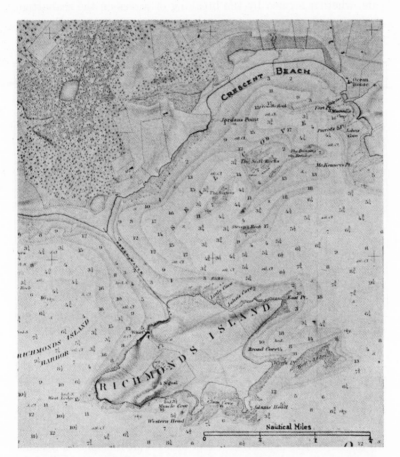

Fig. 118. Crescent Beach south of Portland, Maine, is a bayhead bar, back of which are a pond and marshes. Richmond Island is in process of being tied to the mainland by a submarine bar (uncompleted tombolo) upon which a breakwater has been constructed. From U. S. C. & G. S. Chart No. 327.

**Midbay Bars and Baymouth Bars.** — The breaking of waves on the floor of a bay to form a bar near its middle section rather than near its head, is less common; but examples of midbay bars are occasionally found, as witness the beautiful example in Indian

Harbor, Nova Scotia (Fig. 119).   Sandy Beach in Newport Cove, Mt. Desert Island, a favorite picnic ground for visitors to Lafayette National Park, may also be placed in this class.   Baymouth bars, whether formed by the breaking of waves on the seabottom at the mouth of the bay, or by longshore currents (usually wave currents) extending a spit or spits across the mouth of the bay

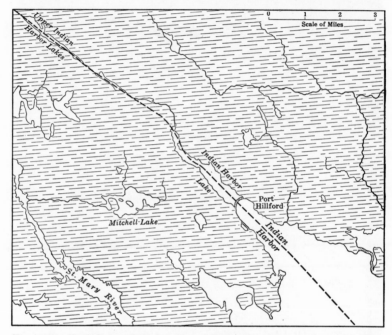

Fig. 119.   Fault-line-valley shoreline of Indian Harbor, northeastern Nova Scotia.   The rocks are mainly folded slates and quartzites striking nearly east-west.   Heavy broken line shows fault.   Note that lakes, as well as an arm of the sea, occupy the rectilinear valley eroded along this fault line.   Indian Harbor is divided at Port Hillford by a beautiful example of a midbay bar, which has transformed the upper half of the harbor into a freshwater lake.

until it is nearly or quite closed by a bar, are not numerous; but examples are found in the gravel bar at the mouth of St. John River on the south side of Gaspé Bay (Fig. 81); in the bar of red sand and fine gravel at the mouth of Grand Pabos River some thirty-five miles to the southwest, utilized by the railway as a means of crossing the bay; in the bar closing the mouth of Lang Pond, Nova Scotia (Fig. 137); and at Saint Esprit and adjacent

lakes or bays on the southern coast of Cape Breton; while a series
of small forms belonging in this class occur on the shores of Goose
and Harbor Islands (Fig. 120), near the mouth of Country Harbor,
Nova Scotia.  In some of the cases cited above the bar has been
explained as the result of the impact of heavy river discharge
against marine waters, a favorite theory often invoked, but
against which there lie serious objections, as I have elsewhere
pointed out.[10]  The embayed lower portion of Poquonock River

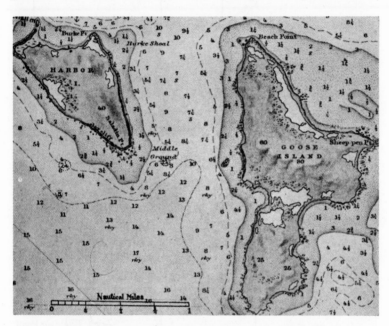

Fig. 120.  Small baymouth bars closing bays in the margins of two islands
near the mouth of Country Harbor, Nova Scotia.  The small island
south of Goose Island is united to the latter by a double tombolo.  Burke
Point at the northeast corner of Harbor Island is a good cuspate bar.
From U. S. Hydrographic Chart No. 1116.

near New London Harbor, Connecticut, is nearly closed by Bushy
Point Beach which is both a baymouth bar and a tombolo, since
near the western side of the bay it is attached to an island.  The
very limited development of baymouth bars along the hard-rock
shores of the New England-Acadian upland is a good index of the
extreme youth of this portion of the shoreline.  Those cited are
doubtless in part the result of wave action on weaker rocks as-

sociated with the upland series, or on glacial débris overlying both.

**Cuspate Bars and Forelands.** — Cuspate bars are somewhat more numerous, as they form quickly in the very earliest stages

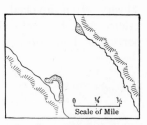

FIG. 121.   Green Point, N. S.   A cuspate bar, with small cuspate foreland opposite.

FIG. 122.   Cape Mocodome, N. S. A cuspate bar.

of shoreline development. Burke Point on Harbor Island (Fig. 120), Green Point in Country Harbor (Fig. 121), Cape Moco-

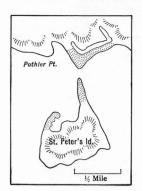

FIG. 123.   Cuspate bar on south shore of Cape Breton.   Two spits on island which may unite as looped bar, and connect with mainland cusp to form tombolo.

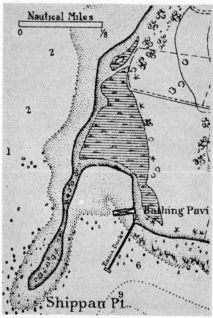

FIG. 124.   Cuspate bar near mouth of Stamford Harbor, Connecticut, extended in form of a spit.   From U. S. C. & G. S. Chart No. 269.

dome (Fig. 122) near mouth of same harbor, and the northern point of Tangier Island (U. S. Hydrographic Chart No. 1135) are good examples from the Nova Scotian coast; but while they are found on the rocky margin of the crystalline upland, the materials composing them were probably derived largely from glacial till and other unconsolidated deposits occurring nearby. Opposite St. Peters Island on the south coast of Cape Breton Island there is a cuspate bar (Fig. 123) which appears to represent the early stage of a tombolo that will ultimately tie the island to the mainland. The rocks here are believed to be Devonian metamorphics, but their relative weakness is such that this region may perhaps better be classed topographically with the Carboniferous Lowlands. The shores of Gaspé Harbor, bordered by typical high upland but associated with weak rocks and glacial deposits in their development, show what appear to be three cuspate bars (Fig. 81): on the north side the Peninsula, the western side of which is not wholly closed; on the south side a small closed bar west of Arnold's Bluff (not shown on the map); and the similar bar farther east from the apex of which the Sandy Beach spit projects a mile into the bay. A somewhat similar cuspate bar with apex extended in the form of a spit, although it may have originated as a tombolo, is found near Shippan Point (Fig. 124) at the mouth of Stamford Harbor, Connecticut. At-

tached to one of the northern members of the Blackstone Rocks off the Connecticut coast is a very pretty cuspate bar (Fig. 125) the two sides of which may be considered a double tombolo. Figure 126 shows a small but very perfect cuspate bar at the west end of Sutton Island, Maine. Small cuspate bars, and the forms built outward from the shore with little if any central lagoon or marsh, known as cuspate forelands, are not uncom-

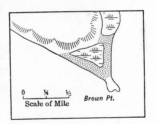

FIG. 125. Cuspate bar or double tombolo attached to one of the Blackstone Rocks, Connecticut.

mon. Morse Point and Popham Beach (Fig. 127) near the mouth of the Kennebec River, appear to be cuspate forelands determined by the presence of off-lying islands, with which they may in time be connected by tombolos, the beginnings of which are already developing in the form of submarine bars.

**Spits.** — More numerous than either baymouth bars or cuspate bars are the spits which may represent but an early stage in the development of such bars; or may connect islands with the

FIG. 126.  Rice Point, a small cuspate bar at the western end of Sutton Island, Maine, showing central lagoon which is flooded at high tide. *Courtesy* Lafayette National Park.

FIG. 127.  Popham Beach and Morse Point are cuspate forelands near mouth of Kennebec River, Maine.  Note submarine bars (beginnings of tombolos) extending from forelands to outlying islands.  From U. S. C. & G. S. Chart No. 314.

mainland or with other islands, thus becoming tombolos; or may continue to have an independent existence as embankments terminating with their free ends in open water. The spits forming Sandy Beach Point (Fig. 81) and Shippan Point (Fig.

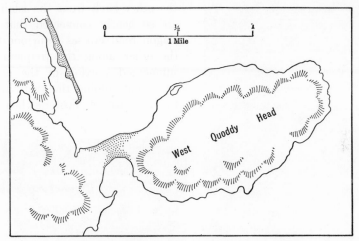

Fig. 128.   West Quoddy Head, Maine, united to mainland by a short tombolo.   From the northwest a compound recurved spit is growing southward parallel to the coast.

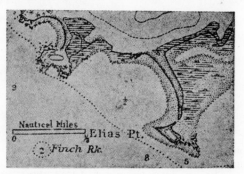

Fig. 129.   Elias Point region, Connecticut.   Spit representing incomplete tombolo at right.   Completed tombolo at left.   From U. S. C. & G. S. Chart No. 269.

124) have already been mentioned. South of Lubec, Maine, there is a narrow compound recurved spit growing southward along the coast toward West Quoddy Head (Fig. 128). Among the many spits forming between mainland and neighboring islands, possibly as first stages in the making of tombolos, attention

may be called to the spit built out from the Connecticut shore
nearly to the island at Elias Point (Fig. 129); to the Sears Island
case (Fig. 130) on the coast of Maine, where two spits, one building out from the mainland and
the other back from the island,
are so nearly connected that a
wagon road crosses from one to
the other along the frequently
submerged portion of the embankment joining the two; and
to the case of Foster's Island

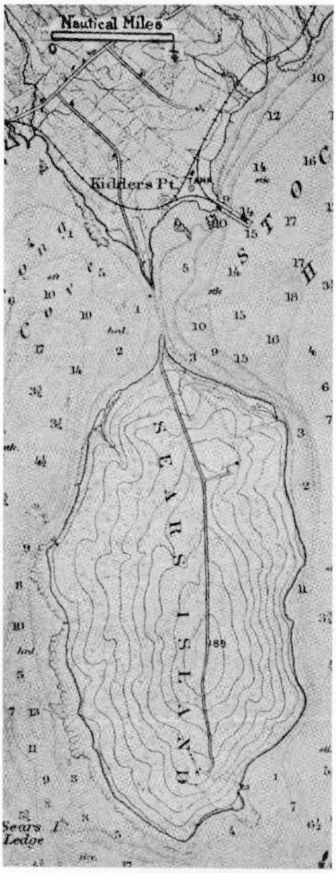

FIG. 130. Spits and submarine bar
representing incomplete tombolo
between Sears Island and Kid-
ders Point, Maine. Note wagon
road crossing on crest of bar below high tide level. From U. S.
C. & G. S. Chart No. 311.

FIG. 131. Starboard Island Bar, an
incomplete tombolo. North of Foster's Island there appears to be a
small spit, interrupted at one point,
extending landward over the rocky
ledges. From U. S. C. & G. S. Chart
No. 303.

(Fig. 131), where what appears to be a slender spit trailing back
from the island over a rocky bottom is breached at one point.

**Tombolos.** — Of tombolos there are numerous examples of
various types in different stages of formation. Reference has

already been made to examples of spits which appear to represent
early stages in island tying (Figs. 129 and 130). Starboard
Island Bar (Fig. 131) in Machias Harbor, Maine, marks a still
earlier stage, before the bar which is to tie the island to the
mainland has been built up to the surface, as do the similar
bars back of Richmonds Island near Seal Cove (Fig. 118), Great
Gott's Island (U. S. Coast Survey Chart No. 308) in Blue Hill Bay,
and Minister Island in Passamaquoddy Bay (U. S. Coast Survey
Chart No. 300), all three likewise on the Maine coast. In the
latter case a double tombolo may result, as two bars appear to be
forming beneath the water's surface. A bar is developing between

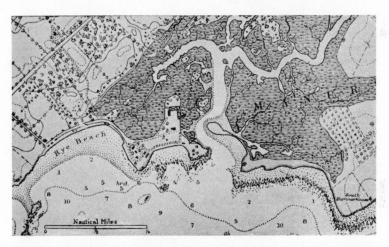

Fig. 132. Rye Beach, a bayhead beach extended as a tombolo to connect
a former island with the mainland of New York. From U. S. C. & G.
S. Chart No. 270.

Fox Island (Fig. 22) and the south shore of Chedabucto Bay
which seems to be a close parallel to the Starboard Island Bar
on the Maine coast. An irregular serpentine bar is forming
behind Gray Island, Nova Scotia (U. S. Hydrographic Chart No.
2132), to connect it with the mainland to the west. Crescent
Beach (poorly shown on U. S. Hydrographic Chart No. 2132),
tying Lockeport Island to the Nova Scotian mainland, is a beautiful cobblestone and gravel bar with a sandy beach along its seaward face and sand dunes on its crest, which would be classed as
a bayhead bar but for the fact that the head of the small embayment opens inward to Lockeport harbor. Among the numerous

completed tombolos one may cite Head Beach (U. S. Coast Survey Chart No. 315) tying a former island in Casco Bay to Cape Small, and the smaller bar nearby uniting the former Small Point island to the mainland; what appears be a short bar connecting West Quoddy Head (Fig. 128) with the mainland south of Lubec, Maine; and Rye Beach (Fig. 132) tying a former

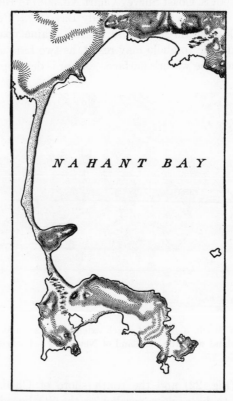

FIG. 133.  Tombolos uniting former island of Big Nahant with smaller island to the north, and latter with mainland of Massachusetts.

island to the New York coast.  Particularly fine examples are the slender beaches tying Nahant (Fig. 133) and Marblehead Neck (Fig. 134) to the rocky coast of Massachusetts.  The Marblehead and Nahant tombolos have frequently been cut through by the sea; and according to Sears[11] Graves Island was, more than half a century ago, connected with the mainland at Manchester by a similar tombolo, which has now been completely

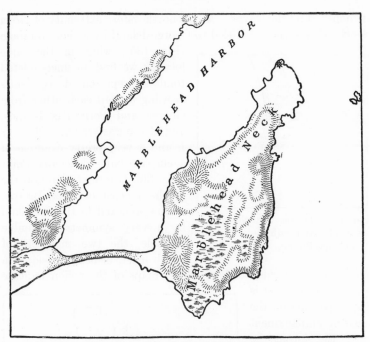

FIG. 134. Tombolo uniting former island of Marblehead to the
Massachusetts mainland.

FIG. 135. Islands off northeastern extremity of Nova Scotia. A short
tombolo unites Grassy Island to George Island, while between Petit
Pas and George Island an incomplete tombolo is represented by two
spits and their extensions toward each other as submarine bars. At
the western end of Grassy Island is a cuspate bar. From U. S. Hydrographic Chart No. 1074.

demolished by the waves.    At the northeastern extremity of Nova
Scotia, Grassy Island is tied to George Island by a short tombolo

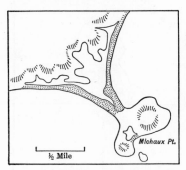

(Fig. 135), while in the same
locality we find an uncompleted
tombolo represented by spits
growing toward each other from
George and Petit Pas Islands,
and at the western end of Grassy
Island a very pretty example of
a cuspate bar.    Michaux Point
(Fig. 136), a former island off the
southern coast of Cape Breton,
is now annexed to the mainland

FIG. 136.    Double tombolo uniting
small island with southern coast
of Cape Breton.

by a very symmetrical double
tombolo, the two members of
which meet, or nearly meet, in a
point to form a cuspate bar.    Some maps of the region indicate

that a narrow inlet is
kept open across the
eastern embankment
near the former is-
land.    At Indian Har-
bor  (U. S.  Hydro-
graphic   Chart   No.
2355) on the southeast
coast of Nova Scotia,
Rude  Point  on  the
western side marks a
former island now tied
to the mainland by a
single tombolo, while
farther south a simi-
lar tombolo is form-
ing to connect Walter
Island with the main-
land.    On the eastern
side of the harbor are
tombolos   of   more
complex type, one of

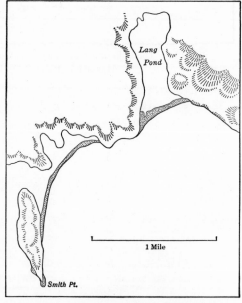

FIG. 137.    Tombolo and baymouth bar on
the coast of Nova Scotia.

which, known as the " Fiddler," connects at its base with what
appears to be a cuspate bar broken by a narrow inlet, while

the other seems to serve in part as a baymouth bar. A few miles to the southwest is a very narrow tombolo, associated with a beautiful example of a baymouth bar completely blocking the mouth of a drowned valley known as Lang Pond (Fig. 137). Near Country Harbor on this same coast are two islands united to form one by a small but typical example of a double tombolo (Fig. 120).

The complete erosion of an island which was tied to the mainland by a single or double tombolo may leave the former tombolo existing for a time as a simple spit or cuspate bar. Thus these forms may in certain cases represent the early stage of a tombolo, in others the ultimate stage. Furthermore, if one finds a spit or cuspate bar connecting with an outlying shoal, he may be in doubt whether it represents a tombolo which connected with an island, the remains of which are seen in the shoal, or whether the shoal alone influenced the location and development of the embankment. These and other problems connected with the various types of beaches and bars have been treated elsewhere.[12]

**Flying Bars.** — It remains here to point out that shoals as well as landmasses projecting above sealevel may determine the formation of various types of bars or embankments; and bars which from this cause, or because of the disappearance of a former landmass to which they were attached, are today seen isolated in the water, are called flying bars. On a coast so youthful as that of New England and Acadia one would not expect many cases in which hard-rock islands had been worn away, leaving tombolos, spits, or other types of bars, originally formed in connection with the islands, persisting as flying bars; although the occasional development of such forms about rocky shoals should not be regarded as impossible. What appears to be a remarkable example of a flying bar is found in Halifax Harbor, where it is known as Barrie Beach (Fig. 213a); but it apparently developed in connection with former islands or shoals of glacial débris, rather than in association with the bedrock topography; and it may temporarily be attached to the mainland at one end.

**Rôle of Weak-rock Formations and Glacial Deposits.** — It should be fully understood, in connection with all the preceding discussion of beaches and bars of various types, that it is not practicable to say in any given case just how much of the débris found in the embankment in question was derived from the rocks of the crystalline upland, and how much from weaker beds sometimes

associated with the older series, or from glacial débris or other unconsolidated deposits mantling over both types.   In some cases the
quantity of unconsolidated material within reach of the waves is
obviously great, and there can be no doubt that the neighboring
beaches and bars are in considerable measure composed of sand,
gravel or cobblestones derived from such deposits.   But even
where crystallines alone are present, and the rocks are bare, one
has no assurance that the beaches and bars are not in large part
derived from glacial or other loose deposits earlier washed off the
rocky slopes by waves and streams, or from similar material concealed beneath the sea but within easy reach of the waves.   Sometimes there is such a predominance of one type of material in a
cobblestone or gravel bar as to give one a safe indication of its
origin; but usually a reliable estimate of the proportion of material
of different origins is difficult to make, and in the case of sandy
beaches is generally not obtainable.

**Limited Development of Wave-Built Forms Bordering the
Resistant Uplands.** — Fortunately, for our purpose it is not necessary to be able to make the discrimination in question.   We need
to know two facts, which our examination of beaches and bars has
established: first, that the New England-Acadian shoreline exhibits
a variety of interesting wave-built forms, and is a fairly satisfactory storehouse for anyone seeking good illustrations of beach
and bar phenomena; and second (and far more important), that
despite a liberal assignment to the rocky upland coasts of forms
which probably are in no small measure the product of wave
action upon weak formations or glacial and similar débris rather
than upon hard rocks, the shoreline as a whole shows such a comparatively limited number of beaches and bars as to indicate an
extremely early stage in its development.   When one considers
the innumerable bays and islands of every conceivable form and
size which border this labyrinthine shore, he is amazed not at the
variety, but at the comparative paucity of beach and bar phenomena.   If this conclusion seems incredible in view of the
numerous examples cited in the preceding pages, let the reader
turn through the long series of detailed Coast Survey and Hydrographic charts of the New England and Acadian coasts, listing
the best examples of beaches, bay bars of different types, cuspate
bars and forelands, spits and tombolos.   Then let him eliminate
those which are obviously developed by wave attack on weak
Carboniferous or Triassic rocks, or on glacial or other unconsoli-

dated deposits. He will be surprised to find how small is the residue of forms which can be credited to wave action on hard-rock coasts; and particularly will he remark the extreme scarcity of baymouth bars, forms which become very abundant as rocky headlands are cut back during the advance of the waves into the land. He will be impressed with the little-changed raggedness of the initial shore; the unobstructed mouths of most of the bays; the countless rocky islands with no attachment to each other or to the mainland, or with only the beginnings of such attachments represented by submarine bars in an early stage of formation; and with the scarcity of good spits extending laterally from cliffed headlands. And when he remembers that this small residue would be still further reduced could he but make proper allowance for the proportion of the beaches and bars bordering hard-rock coasts which are really derived from much weaker deposits, especially glacial débris, he will be convinced from his studies that waves have accomplished very little erosion on the hard rocks at present sealevel.

**Résumé.** — We have found that the hard-rock shores of the New England-Acadian upland are bordered by an interesting variety of beaches, bars, and spits. But when we compare the total number of these forms with the enormous expanse of rocky shore presented to the action of the waves, and especially when we make allowance for the fact that a certain proportion of the forms in question found along the hard-rock shores are composed of débris derived from weaker deposits, we are profoundly impressed by the limited amount of work accomplished by the waves along the upland shores. This leads us to the same conclusion already reached as the result of other considerations: viz., that the sea came to rest against the land at the present level in a time relatively recent.

### BIBLIOGRAPHY

1. JOHNSON, DOUGLAS. "Shore Processes and Shoreline Development," 93, New York, 1917.
2. SHALER, N. S. "Beaches and Tidal Marshes of the Atlantic Coast." Nat. Geog. Mon. I, 144, 1896.
3. SHALER, N. S. "The Geology of Cape Ann, Massachusetts." U. S. Geol. Surv., 9th Ann. Rept., 563–565, 1889.
   SHALER, N. S. "Phenomena of Beach and Dune Sands." Bull. Geol. Soc. Amer., V, 210, 1894.

254 WAVE-BUILT FORMS — RESISTANT UPLANDS

4. JOHNSON, DOUGLAS. "Shore Processes and Shoreline Development," 283 et seq., New York, 1917.
5. CLARKE, JOHN M. "Boom Beach (Isle-au-Haut, Maine); a Sea-Mill." Geol. Soc. Amer., Abstracts of papers for 35th Annual Meeting (Ann Arbor), 1922.
6. BOLTON, H. C., and JULIEN, A. A. "The Singing Beach of Manchester, Massachusetts." Amer. Assoc. Adv. Sci., Proc., XXXII, 251–252, 1884.
BOLTON, H. C., and JULIEN, A. A. "Musical Sand, its Wide Distribution and Properties." Amer. Assoc. Adv. Sci., Proc., XXXIII, 408–413, 1885.
7. PENHALLOW, D. P. "A Blazing Beach." Sci., N. S., XXII, 794–796, 1905.
PENHALLOW, D. P. "A Blazing Beach." Pop. Sci. Mo., LXX, 557–564, 1907.
8. FARIBAULT, E. R. "Geology of the Port Mouton Map-Area, Queens County, Nova Scotia." Geol. Surv. Can., Summ. Rept. for 1913, 252, 1914.
9. BAILEY, L. W. "Some Nova Scotian Illustrations of Dynamical Geology." Nova Scotian Inst. Sci., Proc. and Trans., IX, 180–181, 1896.
10. JOHNSON, DOUGLAS. "Shore Processes and Shoreline Development," 306, New York, 1917.
11. SEARS, J. H. "The Physical Geography, Geology, Mineralogy, and Paleontology of Essex County, Massachusetts," 75, Salem, 1905.
12. JOHNSON, DOUGLAS. "Shore Processes and Shoreline Development," 584 pp., New York, 1917.

# CHAPTER VIII

## SUBMARINE FORMS BORDERING THE RESISTANT UPLANDS

**Advance Summary.** — A study of submarine profiles off the hard-rock coasts should offer convincing testimony as to whether or not the waves have accomplished a large amount of erosion at the present level. In the following pages we shall undertake such a study, first getting firmly in mind the general principles which must govern profile studies of this type, and a clear conception of the precise nature of the particular profiles to be employed. Since the form of the seafloor may offer precious testimony as to the physiographic history of the whole coastal border, we shall in some cases push our analysis of submarine profiles far seaward, to discover if possible the origin of such major features as the Grand Banks and the Gulf of Maine. If the solution of these major problems demands it, we shall not hesitate to examine briefly submarine profiles of the continental shelf from New England to Florida, in the search for evidence which may clarify or amplify that furnished by the submarine physiography of the regions here particularly under investigation. Finally, we shall revert to the more detailed problem of wave erosion upon the landmass the history of which is made clearer by the broader submarine studies, and shall ascertain whether or not the submarine profiles off hard-rock coasts indicate a long or a short stand of the sea at the present level.

## General Considerations Affecting Submarine Profile Studies

**Marine Profile of Equilibrium.** — When an irregularly dissected land area is submerged, the waves find that its contours, however nicely adjusted to streams working upon it, is unadjusted to wave action. The streams may have established their profiles of equilibrium, and the hillslopes may be smoothly graded; but the succession of valleys and hills represents, from the standpoint of wave action, a maze of unorganized irregularities which must be reduced

255

to an even surface sloping downward from the shore at a constantly decreasing angle, before the waves can operate with that nice balance between work to be done and ability to do work which characterizes the perfectly graded condition of either streams or waves. This fruitful conception of a graded profile or profile of equilibrium due to wave action we owe to Davis, who in 1896 elaborated the idea in connection with a discussion of the development of shore profiles forming part of his essay on " The Outline of Cape Cod." The reader will find more detailed analyses of the subject in a paper by Fenneman on the " Development of the Profile of Equilibrium of the Subaqueous Shore Terrace," published in the Journal of Geology for 1902, and in a chapter on the " Development of the Shore Profile " in the author's volume, " Shore Processes and Shoreline Development."

The fully graded marine profile of equilibrium, like the stream profile of equilibrium, is a curve convex upward and steepest in its upper part (Fig. 242). As soon as any irregular landmass is subjected to marine erosion the waves begin the task of planing down the hills and filling up the valleys, continuing the process until equilibrium is established. Thenceforward continued wave erosion advances the profile farther and farther into the land, and much more slowly cuts it deeper and deeper until at its outer end " wave base," the baselevel of wave erosion, is reached. It should be clear from this that " profile of equilibrium " and " wave base " are by no means synonomous terms. The former is curved, has a great vertical range (from sealevel at the shore to the maximum depth of wave erosion many miles out), and has a limited, though great, horizontal extent. Wave base is a plane, is everywhere at the same depth for a given type of wave, and has no horizontal limit since it is the projection of the plane of lowest wave action under the lands as well as in the oceans. To speak of a subaqueous wave-formed terrace as " wave base," as has not infrequently been done, is quite as misleading as it would be to say that a well-graded high mountain stream had reached baselevel.

If waves have operated for a long time on a partially submerged dissected landmass and have cut many miles into it, that fact should be evident in the profiles. Landward from the shore the irregular profiles of the hills and valleys formed under subaërial conditions remain unchanged except in so far as subaërial agents have progressed farther in their work of denudation. Far out in

deep water, if submergence brought the former land surface so
much below sealevel, the same irregular profiles of hills and valleys
persist unaltered, unless submergence was so extremely slow as to
permit their removal by wave erosion during the process, or deposition of sediments in deep water has more or less completely
filled the former valley depressions.   But between shore and deep
water, that is, within the zone of most effective wave action, the
record of extensive marine abrasion should easily be read in a
notable reduction of the irregularities and obvious progress toward
establishment of the marine profile of equilibrium.   Care must be
exercised not to mistake the effects of deposition (of river-brought
sediments, for example) in smoothing out seabottom contours as
an evidence of marine planation; but these effects can usually be
discriminated by studying the relation of the smoothed areas to
the rest of the profile.   Absence of any appreciable smoothing by
either erosion or deposition may constitute valuable evidence that
marine abrasion of a given coast is of slight amount.

**Comparison of Subaërial and Submarine Profiles.** — In comparing subaërial and submarine profiles, one must expect certain
strong dissimilarities due to a marked difference in the nature of
the available data.   Where contoured topographic quadrangles
are available for the land, the profiles may be made to reproduce
the form of that land with great fidelity, especially since those
contours were drawn with the land surface well exposed to the
topographer's view.   For the ocean floor such accurate data is
practically never available, and in the deeper waters one must
often consider himself fortunate if he has one or two approximate
elevations in areas of twenty-five or fifty square miles.   It is
therefore impossible to represent with great accuracy much of
the ocean floor, even near land where soundings are most essential
and therefore most abundant.   In general the best that can be
done is to show the *kind of topography* of the seabottom, and certain of the important elevations and depressions.   But in using
charts and profiles it must always be borne in mind that an unknown but undoubtedly great number of submerged hills and
valleys which actually exist in many of the charted areas are
entirely unrepresented, with the result that profiles will show a
relatively small number of broad hills and valleys with gentle
slopes, where numerous narrower, steeper sided hills and valleys
are really present.

For the same reason contours based on charts of submarine

surfaces must be used with extreme caution. The contours actually appearing on Hydrographic and Coast Survey charts are most frequently generalized with reference to the very practical matter of warning navigators from areas containing dangerous shoals. For this purpose they are often much simplified so as to separate safe from unsafe waters, and do not pretend to show the actual form of the seabottom with any approach to accuracy. Certain charts with contours indicating a very simple bottom topography have been found on examination to contain data sufficient to demonstrate the presence of a succession of hills and branching valleys, — facts significant to the physiographer, but for practical purposes hardly warranting the effort to draw more accurate contours, especially in view of the fact that the data is known to be inadequate for a correct representation of the bottom form.

Attempts are sometimes made to show the seafloor topography with a greater precision, as in certain of the topographic quadrangles issued by the U. S. Geological Survey and covering parts of the submarine surface near the land where data from soundings are most abundant. These represent an expert interpretation of the seabottom form in the light of a detailed knowledge of the adjacent land contours, and undoubtedly give as correct an idea of the kind of submarine topography present as it is possible to secure; but they are necessarily drawn on the basis of inadequate data and with the actual form effectively hidden from view. Hence, if critical points are at issue, the evidence of these maps must be accepted with reserve; and the student will do well to go back to the original data on file in the archives of the Coast and Geodetic Survey, which will often be found to permit considerable latitude in interpretation. The same area as contoured by different experts in the two government surveys on the basis of the same data, has given results significantly different as to details, minor ridges represented as running nearly north-south on one map appearing with an east-west trend on the other. This is an inevitable result of the inadequacy of submarine data, and is pertinent in connection with the discussion of the origin of the submarine scarp off Great Wass Island, Maine, and in certain other cases where the detailed form of the offshore bottom is of critical interest.

At present we are less concerned with details of actual seabottom form than with generalities regarding the kind of form, as represented by submarine profiles. Since proper comparison with land profiles is desirable, the disconcerting contrast between profiles based on sparse (submarine) and abundant (land) data may in part be overcome by using for the land areas only the same quantity of data as is available for the adjacent seafloor. This is accomplished by taking, more or less at random, elevations from the topographic quadrangles to the same number and with approximately the same spacing as soundings are shown on the charts used in constructing the profiles. It may at first thought appear undesirable to neglect to use the more accurate data available for the lands; but it is far more important for our present purpose to get a significant comparison of land and seabottom profiles; and for this it is essential to have profiles which are really comparable. Land profiles based on data inadequate to show the real form of the surface, but sufficient to show in a general way the kind of topography there existing, are alone properly comparable with submarine profiles based on the same kind of data; and such land profiles are secured in the manner indicated.

Another difficulty arises from the fact that inshore waters are charted in much greater detail than the deeper waters offshore. Hence a profile based on the most detailed Coast Survey charts is not comparable either with profiles constructed from land topographic quadrangles where all the topography is visible, nor with profiles made from charts of deep-water areas where scarcely any topographic details are recognizable. The best that can be done is to select, on the basis of experiment, the charts which give the best results for comparing inshore and offshore soundings, and to adapt the number of land elevations used to the number of soundings shown for inshore areas on the charts employed, checking conclusions where possible by profiles based on large scale charts with detailed soundings. Despite the difficulties which confront the use of charts for submarine profile studies, concerning which it was necessary to warn the reader in order that he may judge conclusions with a full knowledge of the nature of the evidence available, it is believed he will find the results of profile comparisons significant and decisive with respect to many problems of submarine physiography.

**Nature of Profiles Employed.** — The profiles used in this work are representative of a much larger number prepared in part by the author himself, but in much greater part under his direction by H. G. Bray, Research Assistant in Physiography at Columbia

University, and by several graduate students in physiography, especially M. A. Stolfus and E. A. Moon; to all of whom the author is deeply indebted for the valuable service performed by them.

Most of the profiles project on a single vertical plane all the soundings within a belt varying in different cases from half a mile to several miles in breadth. This avoids misconceptions due to abnormal minor features which might show in a single linear profile, and enables the student to judge the range of bottom inequalities over a considerable area. Where this range was small, and all soundings fell close to an average profile, the profile curve has been generalized to show the mean. Where bottom inequalities were pronounced (as was the case in a majority of the profiles studied), the belt under investigation was usually subdivided into three minor zones (sometimes two, sometimes four), and the soundings of each zone projected upon the common vertical plane in a special color. By this device the extent to which the bottom topography varied in closely adjacent zones could readily be determined by inspection. In a few cases the resulting subdivided or separate profiles are here reproduced; but for sake of simplicity the profile of the median zone alone, or of the central line of the median zone, is reproduced as a line, the departures from this profile in the remainder of the whole belt being sufficiently indicated by the range of the soundings as shown by the dots. Where a definite line of soundings offered more abundant and more accurate data than other parts of the belt, the linear profile has been drawn along this line instead of along the median line. Local shoals or deeps to one side of the linear profile are sometimes shown by a line broken into short segments. Lines broken into long segments indicate that little is known about that part of the profile because of lack of data.

### Submarine Profiles off the Acadian Shores

**Submarine Profiles off the Nova Scotian Coast.** — The exposed outer coast of Nova Scotia, where the upland peneplane slopes southeastward into the sea, seems a favorable place to test the amount of marine abrasion of resistant rocks as indicated by the submarine contours. At the northeastern extremity of this coast, near Cape Canso, the great depths of Chedabucto Bay on the north permit the development of large waves, which can then break with full force on the shallower areas south of the great

Chedabucto fault-line scarp.   Despite the presence of Cape Breton Island just north, exposure to northeast storms is fairly good, that to storms from the east and southeast excellent.   Figure 138 *A* is a projected profile running due east from Canso Harbor, parallel to and one or two miles south of the submarine scarp just mentioned, and following obliquely down the slope of the upland peneplane.   The slope of the dissected peneplane is well shown; and it is evident, despite the progressive decrease in number of soundings going seaward, with resulting greater apparent simplicity in the profile, that in this region the bottom is extremely rugged.   This is made all the more'evident by drawing separate profiles for the northern and southern halves of the belt.   There is little evidence in either profile of any planing away of the hills or filling of the valleys by marine agencies.

The same conclusion applies to profiles *B* and *C* (Fig. 138) drawn southeastward down the slope of the dissected peneplane where it passes under the sea near White Island Bay and Jeddore Harbor respectively.   In the latter profile, which combines the results for two subdivisions of the projected belt, the coincidence of sudden apparent greater simplicity of profile with the cessation of abundant soundings near shore is particularly noticeable.   Profiles *D* and *E* are likewise drawn down the slope of the peneplane, the first southeast from the Porter Lake region just east of Halifax, the second more southerly from near **Cape Sable** where the slope of the upland is changing toward the south.   Both profiles suggest the presence of a submarine scarp with its steep face seaward. In one case the " drop-off " is from 40 or 45 fathoms down to 70 or 80 fathoms; in the other from about 20 fathoms down to 35 fathoms.   The paucity of soundings makes it impossible to be sure of the bottom form in the vicinity of the supposed scarps. Additional profiles show some prolongation of the scarp in the Halifax region, while the one near Cape Sable can be traced northeastward to a point off Lockeport; but the charts at hand have not permitted a satisfactory tracing of their further extensions and relationships.

Both profile *D* and profile *E* show an irregular, ungraded sea-bottom from the shore out to the supposed scarp; and beyond that soundings are too few to permit generalizations.   That profile *D* shows some indications of an attempt to grade the seafloor to a more regular slope may be due to the fact that this profile traverses the great drumlin area east of Halifax; and doubtless

beneath the water, as above it, the rocky slopes are mantled with
weak glacial débris.   Nevertheless no contrast could be more
striking than that between these actual profiles, and the theoretical
profile of equilibrium, closely approached in Figs. 186 and 242.
And when it is remembered that the profiles as drawn off the
Nova Scotia hard-rock coast are softened not only fictitiously
due to scarcity of data, but actually by the presence of glacial
débris and doubtless also by the deposition of post-glacial sediments to be correlated with those represented in the narrow coastal
plain fringe of Maine, New Brunswick, the St. Lawrence Lowland,
and other parts of northeastern North America, the evidence of
extremely limited marine abrasion on this exposed coast, at or
near the present sealevel, seems most convincing.

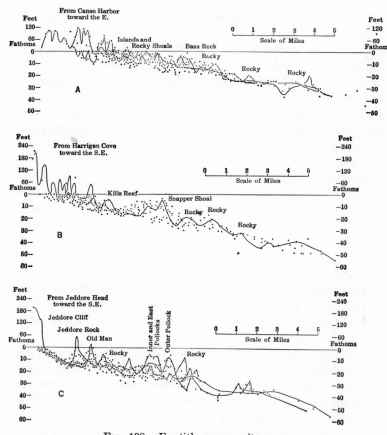

FIG. 138.   For title see opposite page.

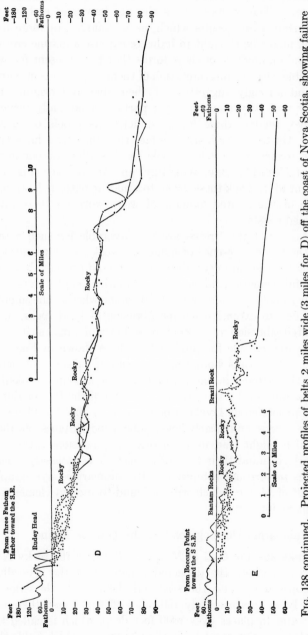

Fig. 138 continued. Projected profiles of belts 2 miles wide (3 miles for D) off the coast of Nova Scotia, showing failure of waves to reduce to grade the inequalities of the submerged portion of the dissected crystalline upland. Vertical exaggeration approximately × 50. Based on U. S. Hydrographic Charts Nos. 2126 to 2129 and 2132.

**Submarine Profiles across the St. Lawrence Embayment and Elsewhere.** — The profiles across the St. Lawrence embayment give in certain cases results which, as is pointed out more fully elsewhere, might be thought to indicate extensive marine erosion. But we find on analysis of these forms that they present features incompatible with the interpretation of them as products of marine forces, and strongly suggestive of their subaërial origin. The possibility that they may represent parts of a normally terraced river valley renders these forms valueless as proofs of marine abrasion. On the other hand, the fact that the waves have been unable to reduce to a graded profile the irregular seafloor in the vicinity of Kegashka Bay, Wolf Bay, and Wreck Bay (Fig. 111, *A, B, C*), or to cut back these shores to a mature pattern, is strongly indicative of the limited amount of wave work on these fairly well exposed coasts.

The coasts of Cape Breton are not favorable for such a test, because the known presence of numerous weak-rock lowland belts paralleling the resistant crystalline ridges would prevent the drawing of useful deductions in case the submarine profiles were comparatively smooth. One could not determine whether the smoothness was due to extensive marine abrasion of hard rocks, or to very limited abrasion of a weak-rock lowland area, such as is apparently responsible for profiles like those shown in Figs. 182 and 186. The coasts bordering the Gulf of Maine are better suited to the purpose in hand, providing due account is taken of those areas affected by the Triassic Lowland of the Bay of Fundy and the Carboniferous Lowland of the Boston Basin. There are submarine scarps and nearly level submarine surfaces off these coasts which might lead us to erroneous conclusions, unless we have clearly in mind their true relations. It is necessary, therefore, for us to turn our attention to the submarine physiography of the Gulf of Maine, which will be found to present elements of extraordinary interest.

## Submarine Physiography of the Gulf of Maine

**The Banks and the Gulf of Maine.** — Between the rocky New England coast where the dissected peneplane of the crystalline upland slopes down into the sea, and the remarkable series of " banks " lying approximately 150 miles off that coast, there is a body of water in places over 1000 feet deep, which is called the Gulf of Maine. The great basin-like depression which holds this water body is continued on the northeast by the Bay of Fundy lowland until the floor of the latter rises slightly above sealevel in the narrow Isthmus of Chignecto.   To the southwest it is cut off where its submerged southeastern rim, formed by the Banks, converges to meet the rocky northwestern rim at the base of Cape Cod.   The only effective outlet from the basin is a channel 800 or 900 feet deep between Georges Bank and Brown Bank.

**Theories of Origin of the Banks.** — The remarkable basin of the Gulf of Maine has attracted the attention of many students, and various suggestions have been made to explain its origin. The chief problem is the nature and origin of its outer or southeastern rim.   To account for the slightly submerged Banks extending from Nantucket Shoals through Georges Bank, Brown Bank, and others to the Grand Bank of Newfoundland, Maury[1] early suggested that they represent the accumulation of débris dropped from icebergs brought down by the Labrador Current and melted where this cold water comes in contact with the warm waters of the Gulf Stream.

The most serious study of the origin of the Banks is an essay by Thoulet[2] entitled " Considérations sur la Structure et la Genèse des Bancs de Terre-Neuve," published about thirty-five years ago. The well known French oceanographer, basing his opinion on a study of the ocean currents, the character of material dredged from the bottom, and the distribution of pebbles, shells, muds, and other deposits as shown by charts and maps, concluded that the Banks were composed of débris brought from the neighboring shores, especially the west coast of Newfoundland, instead of from the far north; that the conveying medium was shore ice instead of icebergs; and that the transporting agent was a current from the river and gulf of St. Lawrence issuing from Cabot Strait, and not the Labrador Current.   The form of the different Banks he explained as due to the courses followed by different branches of the " Cabot River," and to the angles at which these encounter the Gulf Stream; and he went so far as to predict the changes which the Banks would suffer in case Cabot River, " l'élément essentiel de l'existence des bancs," should diminish in volume or disappear, as well as the changes which he believed must follow a diminution of the power of the Gulf Stream.   The same theory of origin is very briefly restated by Thoulet in later works.[3]

Shaler,[4] Russell,[5] and others have regarded the Banks as in large part terminal deposits of the North American Pleistocene ice sheet. Rear-Admiral C. H. Davis, in his memoir on the geological action of tidal and other currents of the ocean,[6] seems to attribute the Banks, in considerable part at least, to the meeting of two tide waves which heap up sediment where they check each other; and this conception was apparently in some measure adopted by Alexander Agassiz.[7]  In his account of Sable Island, Patterson[8] says " there is reason to believe that the series of Banks . . . are based on an ancient ridge of rock parallel to the shore." Spencer[9] and others have considered them extensions of the Atlantic coastal plain of Cretaceous and Tertiary sediments; but no one, so far as I am aware, has systematically analyzed the form of the Banks and their associated features to learn what inferences might properly be drawn from such a study, although Upham[10] clearly recognized the subaërial character of the submerged topography.

**Basis of the Present Discussion.** — The present discussion of the submarine physiography of the Gulf of Maine is based upon a series of twenty-five projected profiles prepared by M. A. Stolfus in connection with a graduate course in physiography at Columbia University, and extending north-south and east-west across the Gulf and adjacent areas, in such manner as to cover effectively the whole region from a few miles within the New England landmass to beyond the limits of the continental shelf; supplemented by a large number of additional projected profiles prepared under the author's direction by H. G. Bray, these latter profiles being drawn northwest-southeast transverse to the submerged topographic belts, or northeast-southwest along the floor of the Gulf, parallel to the shore. The results here presented were in large measure made possible through the very heavy labor so efficiently performed by these two collaborators, to whom I am deeply indebted.

The north-south profiles (Fig. 139) show with sufficient clearness the essential elements of the submarine topography; and this direction has some advantage in facilitating the projection of soundings and elevations in selected belts specified. It is also the best direction to show the variable form of a topographic feature which changes its course from southeast to east, then northeast. The area to be covered was divided into belts of longitude 10 minutes broad, and all the soundings in each alternate belt were projected upon a single plane. For purposes of study each 10-minute belt was subdivided into 3 parallel zones, and the soundings in each zone plotted separately in a special color; but the separate profiles are presented here only when desirable to emphasize the extreme variability of the bottom contours within short distances. The east-west profiles (Fig. 140) serve as a useful check, since in places they cross obliquely certain of the significant features, and reveal others not so well shown on the north-south series. For the east-west profiles the area was divided into belts of latitude each 5 minutes broad, and alternate belts were treated in the same manner as explained above for the north-south series.

**The Submerged Banks Cuesta.** — The most striking feature brought out by these profiles is the beautifully developed cuesta and inner lowland bordering the oldland of New England. The steepness of the cuesta " inface " (profiles B, C, G, H, I, J, K, T, U, Y) and the gentle seaward inclination of the backslope are typical of such forms where well developed on a maturely dissected coastal plain. Both cuesta and inner lowland are drowned, the former to give the Banks, the latter the Gulf of Maine. Only at the west does the cuesta summit rise slightly above sealevel. Here the glacial deposits of Cape Cod and Nantucket rest upon it, with two morainal ridges (see profiles A and B), possibly the same found in a similar position on the summit of the Long Island cuesta farther west. To the northeast, off Nova Scotia and the lands beyond, the cuesta form of the Banks, although distinct in places, is less strikingly developed.

On the gentle backslope of the cuesta are found a number of longitudinal depressions, some of them nearly 100 feet deep, separated by long, parallel ridges. This system of topographic features trends roughly down the backslope, toward the southwest, south or southeast. While both hollows and ridges have been ascribed to the action of the tides, we may keep in mind the possibility that they represent, in part at least, the remnants of an old drainage system consequent on the backslope of the cuesta, now almost completely obliterated by marine erosion of the ridges and deposition in the valleys. Some of the profiles (C, E, I) suggest the presence of alternating resistant and non-resistant rock layers of minor importance, producing subordinate cuestas on the backslope. Other profiles (B, E, I, J) show especially well the fact that the backslope consists of a nearly level surface truncating one of more pronounced inclination, and suggests that we may have on the cuesta summit the remnants of a peneplane

(*Continued on page 281*)

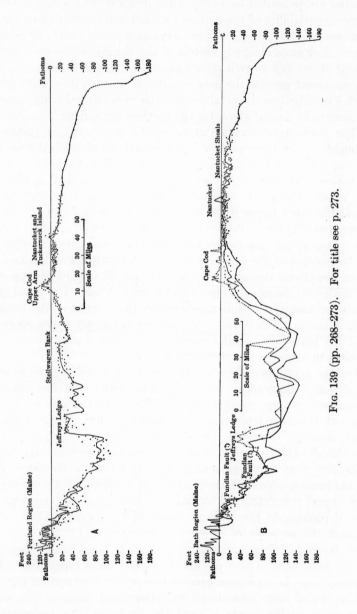

FIG. 139 (pp. 268–273).   For title see p. 273.

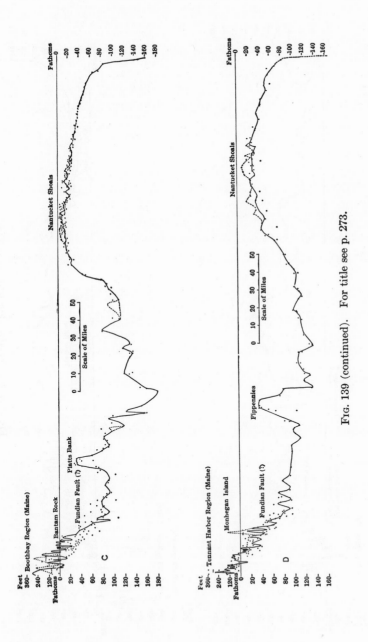

Fig. 139 (continued). For title see p. 273.

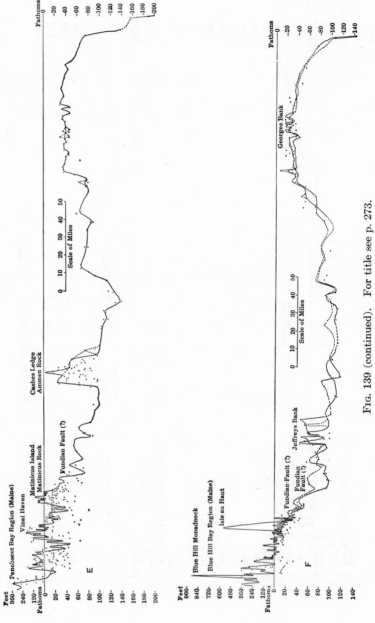

FIG. 139 (continued). For title see p. 273.

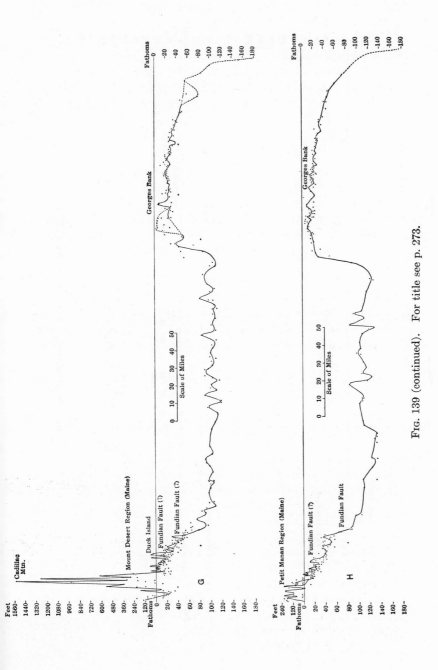

Fig. 139 (continued).   For title see p. 273.

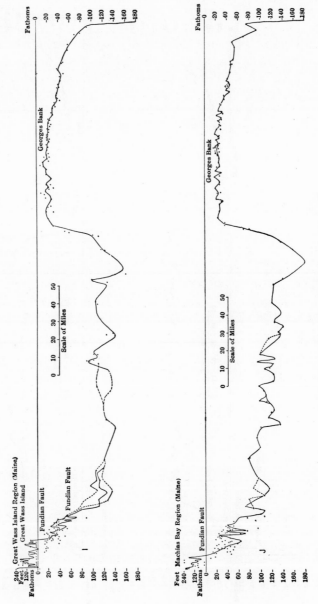

Fig. 139 (continued).    For title see page 273.

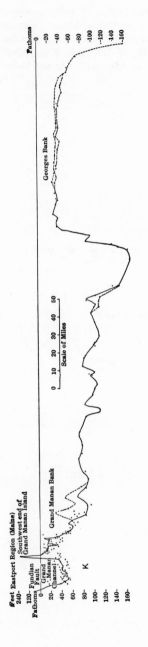

FIG. 139 (concluded). Projected profiles of belts approximately 9 miles broad, from north to south across the Gulf of Maine. Vertical exaggeration approximately × 300. Based on U. S. C. & G. S. Charts Nos. 1106 and 1107. The positions of the profiles (A to K inclusive) of this figure are indicated in the margins of Fig. 144. For east-west profiles see Fig. 140 following. Other projected profiles of this region, based on larger scale charts and showing less vertical exaggeration, will be found on later pages.

Fig. 140 (pp. 274–280). Projected profiles of belts approximately 6 miles broad, from east to west across the Gulf of Maine. Vertical exaggeration approximately × 300. Based on U. S. C. & G. S. Charts Nos. 1106 and 1107. The positions of the profiles (L to Y inclusive) of this figure are indicated in the margins of Fig. 144. For north-south profiles see Fig. 139 preceding.

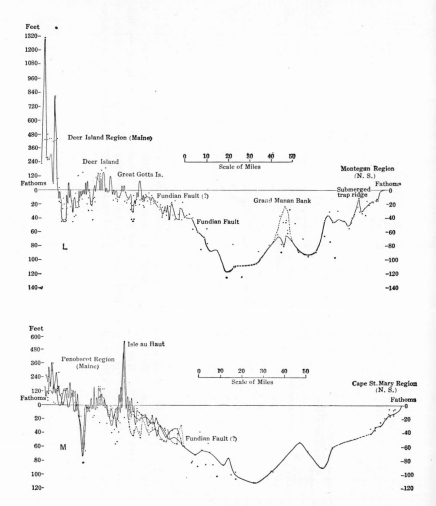

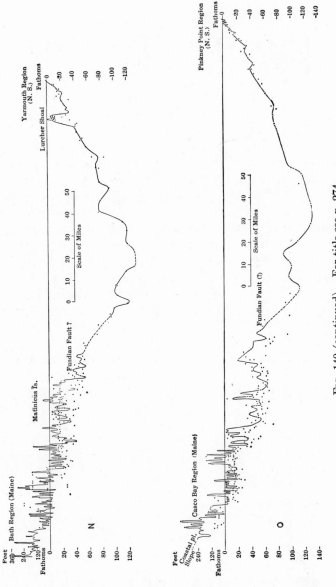

Fig. 140 (continued). For title see p. 274.

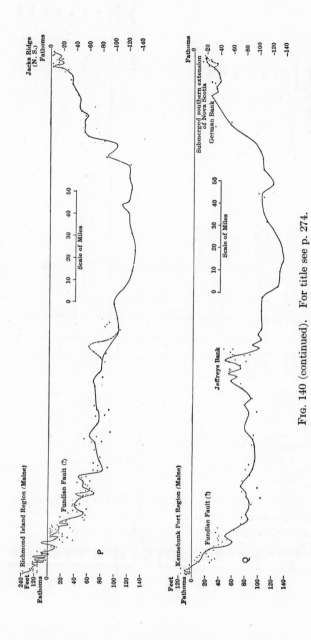

Fig. 140 (continued). For title see p. 274.

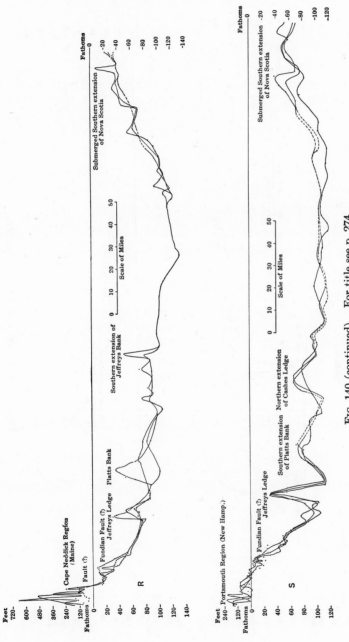

Fig. 140 (continued).   For title see p. 274.

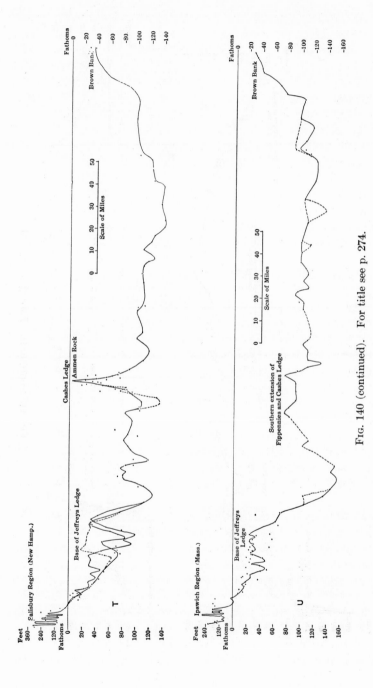

Fig. 140 (continued). For title see p. 274.

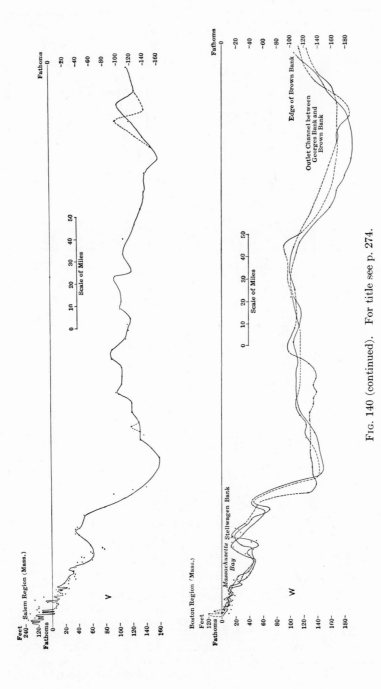

Fig. 140 (continued). For title see p. 274.

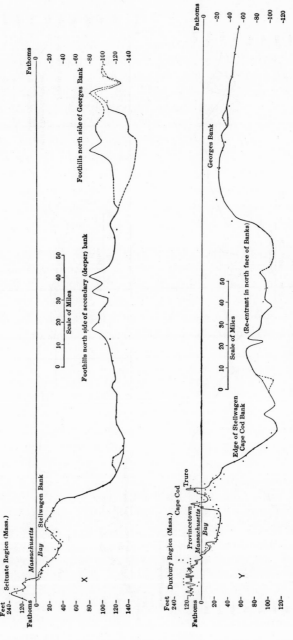

Fig. 140 (concluded).   For title see p. 274.

which beveled the coastal plain formations before the inner lowland was carved and the backslope of the cuesta was dissected in
a later cycle of erosion.   That the more nearly level surface cannot be ascribed to recent truncation of the cuesta summit by
marine erosion at or near present sealevel would seem to be indicated by the rather pronounced dissection of that surface, providing the hollows and ridges shown in the profiles are correctly
to be interpreted as remnants of a drainage system.

**Subordinate cuestas.** — In a normally dissected coastal plain
the inface or steep landward side of a cuesta, as well as the floor
of the inner lowland in front of it, frequently show benches or
minor cuestas, due to the outcropping of subordinate resistant
layers.   Such features apparently are represented in the remarkable drowned cuesta of the Gulf of Maine region, which for convenience I propose to call the " Banks cuesta."   Profiles E, F, H,
and I reveal, in the positions indicated, several benches which in
spite of more or less dissection show a steep face toward the oldland of New England and a more gentle backslope.   The east-
west profiles (Fig. 140) should cross any minor cuestas obliquely;
and on these profiles the features in question are shown more or
less distinctly, as in profiles T, U, V, X, and Y; while the contours of Platts Bank, Cashes Ledge (profile S) and the intervening Fippennies (profile D, Fig. 139), suggest that they also
may be erosion remnants of a subordinate cuesta.   Where soundings are so few and widely spaced as in the open waters of the Gulf
of Maine, one cannot afford to speak with too much assurance of
these minor forms, hidden deep under the sea and very imperfectly
revealed by profiles based on inadequate data.   But the fact that
the same feature, showing the same relation of slopes, is repeatedly
discovered in different parts of its extension by both the north-
south and the east-west profiles, and the further fact that when the
results of the several profiles are plotted on a map they show the
apparent minor cuestas curving more or less distinctly in conformity
with the pattern of the major cuesta, give one increasing confidence
in the opinion that at least two fairly extended minor cuestas, and
possibly two others of more limited development, are present under
the waters of the Gulf of Maine.   The approximate locations of
these minor forms are shown on the map (Fig. 144) representing
the reconstructed topography of the floor of the Gulf of Maine.

**Seaward Margin of the Banks Cuesta.** — The profiles of the
Banks cuesta here reproduced differ from cuesta profiles as ordi-

narily drawn, in that the seaward side of the coastal plain deposit, the steep seaward scarp of the continental shelf, is shown in many of them (Fig. 139).  In some cases the paucity of soundings or doubt as to their value makes the precise depth and location of the shelf margin uncertain; but in others the intersection of the gentle backslope with the precipitous " drop off " is clearly marked. One may explain the fact that the seaward portion of the back- slope, nearest the margin of the shelf, appears little dissected in some profiles and not at all dissected in others, partially on the ground that soundings are fewer for these outer areas; partially as the result of less pronounced elevation above sealevel with consequent shallower dissection when the higher parts of the cuesta were being more deeply trenched; and partially as the product of marine deposition after these portions were submerged and the higher areas still remained subject to subaërial denuda- tion.

**Floor of the Inner Lowland.** — When we turn our attention to the floor of the inner lowland, we find that while it is, for reasons which we shall consider later, much less uneven in certain parts than the adjacent land areas, nevertheless notable irregularities are to be observed.   Despite the limited number of the soundings, which gives to the profiles a fictitious appearance of much greater simplicity far out from land than actually exists there, the evidence is clear that hills and valleys carved by stream erosion on the floor of the lowland have been submerged by the sea, and not yet obliterated by erosion or sedimentation.   In other words, not only the broad feature of the lowland itself, but the detailed carving of its floor, are in a measure preserved at the bottom of the Gulf of Maine.   In part, especially on the landward side of the lowland, the drowned hills and valleys are those of the south- eastward sloping, maturely dissected New England upland pene- plane, continued under the sea.   Nearer the Banks cuesta they appear to be parts of the maturely dissected coastal plain which borders the upland; and we have already seen that some of them apparently represent erosion remnants of subordinate cuestas of that plain.

The exact significance of some of the prominent hills in the lowland must remain more or less in doubt.  Jeffreys Ledge, of which north-south profiles are shown in Fig. 139, A and B, and east-west profiles in Fig. 140, R, S, T, curves eastward and north- ward from Cape Ann in such manner as to be in alignment with the geological structure of the Cape Ann-Boston Basin region at the south and with that of the neighboring coast of Maine at the north.   This suggests that its foundation may be a resistant ridge of the Cape Ann granite, although Dr. Laurence LaForge of the United States Geological Survey informs me that at least part of the ledge is quartzite.   Locally the " ledge " shows a remarkably flat surface (Fig. 243, C);  the symbol for " rocky " is found only at occasional points on the detailed charts, while pebbles, sand, and mud are widely distributed over the ledge surface.   These facts raise the question whether glacial sandplains, similar to those on Cape Cod, may not rest on or against the ledge in places.   In this case the flatness of the surface may in large part be original; or we may consider whether removal of the soft material to a depth of from 25 to 30 fathoms by wave erosion will not equally well account for the feature observed.

Stellwagen Bank (Fig. 139 A, and Fig. 140 W and X) corresponds roughly in pattern and trend with the glacial sandplains of outer Cape Cod, and may represent a similar glacial deposit continuing the Cape Cod series northward under the sea toward Jeffreys Ledge.   A larger scale profile of this bank (Fig. 243 B) emphasizes the simplicity of its surface contours.   Jeffreys Bank (not to be confused with Jeffreys Ledge), located far out in the Gulf and some distance off the Maine coast (Fig. 139 F, and Fig. 140 Q and R), suggests by its position north of the innermost of the secondary cuestas of the submerged coastal plain, by the apparent steepness of its northern and southern sides as indicated in profile F, and by its relation to the great fault-line scarp discussed below, that it is a dissected monadnock mass on the submerged Triassic Lowland peneplane, consisting of an upfaulted block of resistant rock, similar in origin, geographic and geologic relationships, and erosion history to the Grand Manan Island block.   Profiles (Fig. 141) of the latter suggest that both on the northwest and the southeast it is bounded by precipitous fault or fault-line scarps descending into deep water, in one case visible in part as a lofty and inaccessible line of cliffs, in the other concealed under water beyond the shoals southeast of the island, but appearing on the profiles as a steep escarpment nearly 400 feet high.   It will be noted, however, that Jeffreys Bank is at the extreme western limit of the submarine Triassic area (Fig. 144), where the older crystallines begin to be exposed.   These last form the floor of the Gulf to the west and northwest, and it is quite possible

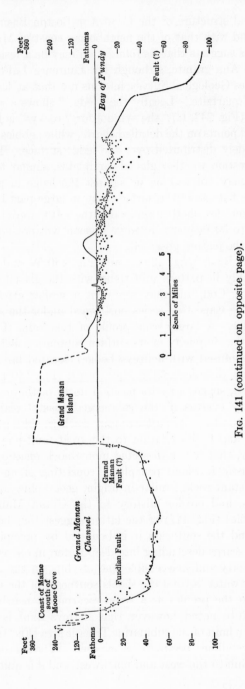

Fig. 141 (continued on opposite page).

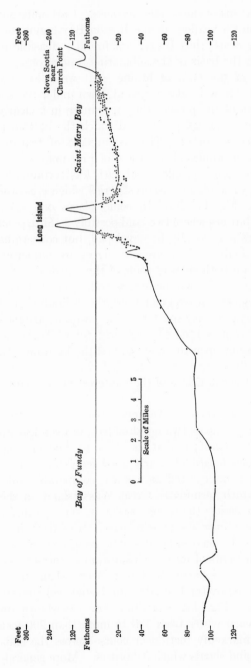

FIG. 141. Continuous projected profile of a belt nearly three miles broad, northwest-southeast across the Bay of Fundy, showing Grand Manan Channel, a submerged lowland apparently eroded on a downfaulted block of weak Triassic beds; the Grand Manan Island block apparently bounded by faults on both sides; the main Bay of Fundy lowland; and the gently inclined eastern wall of the lowland where the Triassic beds, including the main trap ridge and perhaps parts of the crystalline floor, slope down toward the northwest. Vertical exaggeration approximately × 50. Based on U. S. Hydrographic Charts Nos. 1057 and 2135.

that Jeffreys Bank is a part of the crystalline mass. Carboniferous beds certainly exist on the seafloor in the Boston Bay region and off part of the Maine coast; but I have not found it feasible to delimit these areas on the basis of the submarine topography.

**Submarine Scarps of the Gulf of Maine.** — If we follow the hills and valleys of the New England upland down under the sea we find that in certain of the profiles they terminate in a clearly marked submarine scarp, or scarps, beyond which the bottom is deeper and sometimes smoother. This assemblage of features is most clearly shown in profiles G, H, and I of Fig. 139, but can easily be recognized in other profiles, and with less certainty in still others, including some of the east-west series which cross the scarps obliquely (e.g., Fig. 140 N). In some places one scarp alone is in evidence; but elsewhere two, and possibly a third, seem to be present. Others may locally be developed, but concerning these there is more doubt. They are cut across by numerous drowned valleys, and on both sides of some of the scarps the bottom is extremely irregular. It will be understood, then, that with no guide but soundings on an irregular floor, the delimitation of the scarps is not always an easy matter. The positions assigned to them on Fig. 144 are presented with reserve; for while the existence of the scarps is not open to question, and the location is in some parts undoubtedly correct, more detailed studies may alter both the number and the extensions of these interesting submarine forms.

*Form of the Submarine Scarps.* — In height from base to summit the scarps vary from one or two hundred feet, or even less, to more than double that amount; and at one point, as shown in Fig. 139 I, have a combined height of nearly 1000 feet, if the steep lower slope is correctly interpreted as a scarp comparable with the one just above which terminates Great Wass Island on the south. At the latter point the upper scarp is very perfectly developed, and as soundings are here relatively abundant it is possible to represent it by contours with some assurance of portraying the broader elements of form with substantial correctness. This has admirably been done in the Great Wass Island topographic quadrangle issued by the United States Geological Survey, from which quadrangle Fig. 142 is reproduced. As shown on this map the upper scarp varies from 100 to more than 200 feet in height, and has a markedly rectilinear course across the ends of the various islands and shoals which it borders. More general-

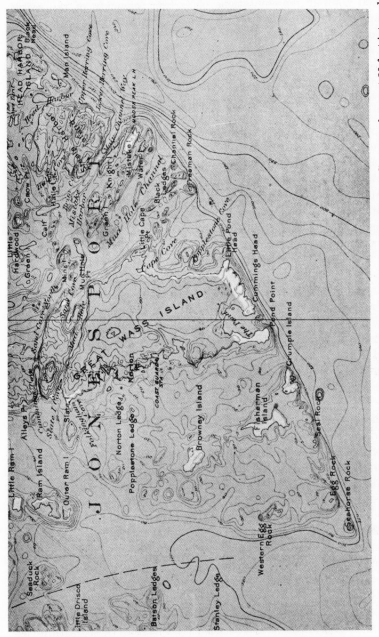

Fig. 142.  Rectilinear submarine fault-line scarp bordering part of the great Fundian Fault.    Contours drawn at 20-foot intervals upward and downward from the present shoreline.  From U. S. G. S. Topographic Atlas, Great Wass Island quadrangle.

ized contour representations of certain segments of the scarps
appear on the southeast corners of the Casco Bay and York
topographic quadrangles.

*Origin of the Submarine Scarps.* — Despite the striking character of the scarp as revealed on the Great Wass Island quadrangle,
and the presence of similar forms farther west as shown by the
Casco Bay and York quadrangles, these interesting submarine
forms seem to have attracted little attention; and so far as I am
aware, nothing has been published concerning them.   In response
to a letter addressed to the Director of the United States Geological Survey asking for information on the geology of the Great
Wass Island quadrangle, and particularly concerning the submarine scarp depicted on it, I learned that while little was known
about the region, Dr. Laurence LaForge, basing a tentative opinion
on a study of the contour maps, was inclined to regard the scarp
as a submerged wave-cut cliff.

Inasmuch as the marine abrasion theory of origin of the scarps
touches one of the fundamental elements of our discussion, it
is desirable to quote LaForge's statement somewhat fully: " At
first sight the regularity of the scarp and the complete absence of
islands or shallow reefs outside might be thought to indicate that
it is a fault scarp.   That it may be, however, simply the margin
of the granite mass (known to form some of the islands of the
group), in contact with much less resistant rocks on the southeast,
seems at least equally probable.   Another fact is the existence of
other scarps having other trends and at various depths.   Even
the main scarp, which is single northeast of Mistake Island, is
double southwest of that island, only the lower part continuing
the trend of the high single scarp, whereas the upper part has a
much more westerly trend.   Furthermore, a careful inspection of
the relief of the sea floor as shown on the Great Wass Island and
Columbia Falls maps seems to show the existence of several platforms at different depths, notably at about 5 feet, 20 to 30 feet,
120 to 140 feet, 220 to 240 feet, and 300 to 320 feet.   These are
separated in many places by slopes, but in others by fairly clear
scarps, especially between the depths of 5 and 20 feet, 30 and 120
feet, and 140 and 220 feet.   It is difficult to explain this relief
otherwise than by marine erosion on an intermittently sinking
coast, and I have reached the tentative conclusion that that is
the most probable explanation . . . I regard these features as
showing in a first rate manner what wave-cut scarps and plat-

forms are really like. . . . Somewhat similar features on the sea floor off other parts of the Maine coast are shown by the submarine contours on the Casco Bay and York topographic maps." The additional scarps mentioned by LaForge, with the exception of one shown on the Casco Bay and York quadrangles, are not among those described in preceding paragraphs. Those on the Columbia Falls quadrangle occupy positions which seem to me to preclude their interpretation as wave-cut features; and all of them, where sufficiently well developed to be clearly distinguished, appear to be normal subaërial forms carried under the water by a subsidence of the land or a rise of sealevel.

As regards the Great Wass Island scarp, there can be no doubt of its resemblance to a wave-cut cliff, and for a time I entertained the marine explanation as one of several working hypotheses to be tested by the facts as they developed in the course of investigation. These facts seem to exclude the marine theory of origin, and to point to a different but equally interesting explanation.

*Variation in Platform Levels.* — As shown by profiles, charts, and maps, the levels of the " platforms " or less steeply inclined areas between the scarps, vary widely and rapidly. There does not appear to be any such correlation between them, where found developed in different places, as should be expected if they were developed by marine erosion of an intermittently subsiding coast. The discrepancies observed do not seem to be of a nature reasonably to be explained by recent diastrophic movements following marine abrasion. On the Great Wass Island quadrangle the base of the cliff is 240 feet below sealevel at one point, and only 140 feet less than a mile away; while the topography in front of the scarp does not lend itself well to the interpretation that a single great cliff here divides into a higher and a lower, because the lower slope is extremely gentle and bears scant resemblance to a wave-carved form. The profiles record much greater discrepancies, all of which would be perfectly normal in a major fault or fault-line scarp with branch faults of varying displacement, but which it seems difficult to reconcile with the marine theory of their origin.

*Simplicity of Scarp Pattern and Irregularity of Platform Surfaces.* — The relative simplicity of pattern of the scarps, extending for great distances in gently curving or nearly straight lines, could only be acquired by wave erosion on a submerged, irregularly dissected, resistant landmass like the New England upland, after an enormous lapse of time had permitted the sea to cut far back into the mass to give a fully mature shoreline.  That so great an erosion as this did not occur once, much less several times, on the New England coast in recent geological time, seems to be indicated by the fact that enough débris has not been distributed in front of the scarps to bury the hills and valleys of the submerged land areas.  The " platforms " may locally be less irregular than the adjacent lands, especially where the seabottom is mantled by glacial débris or by post-glacial clays; and the seabottom is notably simpler when we pass to the Triassic Lowland south of the southernmost scarp.  The apparent simplicity of the bottom south of the Great Wass Island scarp, as shown on the topographic quadrangle, is undoubtedly due in part to the lack of sufficient soundings in the deeper waters to represent the true form.  Elsewhere, as shown by the profiles, the sharply dissected former land surface, still unobscured by marine deposition, is often found in front of the scarps.  Even on the Great Wass Island quadrangle there is represented, in front of the scarp and close to its base, a small unfilled depression apparently over 40 feet deep.  One may perhaps question whether the available soundings could safely be depended upon for the delineation of such a detail of the submarine surface; but if correctly shown, or if it should be drawn as a submerged channel continuing one in the face of the scarp just north, its presence as an unfilled depression would seem incompatible with the interpretation of the scarp as a product of wave erosion.  The only type of cliff which marine abrasion could produce on an irregular hard-rock coast still retaining much of its initial irregularity below sealevel, would be one which curved about submerged headlands to an extent sufficient to give it a markedly irregular pattern.  It would seem that the pattern of the scarps actually observed, and the presence of unfilled valleys in front of them, favor their interpretation as the direct or indirect product of faulting.

*Continuity of Scarp Base behind Outlying Hills.* — The marine theory seems further excluded by the fact that the scarp base appears to be equally well developed at exposed points and at others sheltered behind barriers which would prevent effective wave erosion.  This relation, as it appears on the profiles, might be explained by assuming that the base of the scarp was above the obstructing hills now seen in front of it, and that later uplift and erosion permitted streams to dissect the platform into hills and valleys, which have still later been again submerged. But it is hardly conceivable that waves could develop a cliff like that shown off Mistake Island on the Great Wass Island topographic sheet, while immediately in front of it there rose an island, approximately 100 feet high (160 feet below present sealevel) above the lowest part of the adjacent scarp base (260 feet below present sealevel). All the features noted are, however, compatible with the theory of recent faulting; or better yet, with the interpretation that parallel fault strips or splinters, related to one major fault but unequally displaced, and involving weaker beds overlying resistant crystallines, have been subjected to subaërial erosion long enough to remove the weak beds and dissect the crystallines below, and that the whole mass was then later submerged; or as otherwise more briefly phrased, with the interpretation of the scarps as submerged dissected fault-line scarps.

*Geographic Relations of the Submarine Scarps. The Fundian Fault.* — The fault-line scarp interpretation receives substantial support when the broader relations of the submarine features are considered. Inspection of the map shows that the scarp which abruptly terminates the Great Wass group of islands along a nearly straight line bordering their southeastern extremities (Great Wass Island topographic quadrangle), is directly in line with the remarkably rectilinear shore, so different from the rest of the Maine coast, which extends from Machias Bay to West Quoddy Head near Eastport. Submarine profiles of this part of the coast (Fig. 139 J, K; Fig. 143 A, B) show that it descends abruptly into deep water, and has the appearance of a rectilinear fault or fault-line scarp. In its turn this stretch of shore is but the continuation, after the local interruption of Passamaquoddy Bay, of the relatively straight shoreline, bordered in places by continuous rocky cliffs 200 to 400 feet high, which bounds the Bay of Fundy on the northwest. As we have already seen, analogy with the other great Triassic lowlands of Connecticut and New Jersey would prompt us to look for a fault terminating the lowland series as we follow them down the dip to the northwest; and concrete field evidence of faulting along this rectilinear coast, dropping (relatively) the Triassic beds to the southeast and raising the crystallines to the northwest, has actually been found.[11] There seems little room to doubt, then, that the submarine scarp off Great Wass Island is a fault-line scarp, formed by erosion along a major

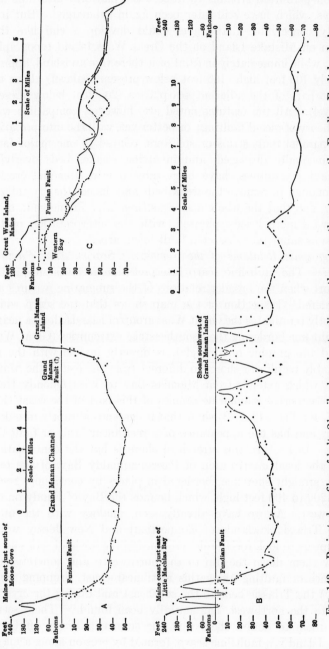

Fig. 143.  Projected profiles of belts 2½ miles broad extending northwest-southeast across the Fundian Fault bordering the Maine coast.  Vertical exaggeration approximately × 50.  Based on U. S. C. & G. S. Chart No. 1201.

displacement which may for convenience be called the " Fundian Fault."

*Westward Extension of the Fundian Fault.* — The case is distinctly less clear for the westward extension of the scarp and its branches. Here we have little to guide us save the imperfectly known submarine topography; and the fact that from the region of Casco Bay southwestward the trend of the scarp parallels that of the geological structure, increasing the danger of mistaking a differential erosion scarp wholly unrelated to faulting for a fault scarp or fault-line scarp, must be taken into consideration. One must also consider the possibility that Barrell's theory of ancient marine terraces on the surface of the New England peneplane, uplifted and profoundly dissected with that peneplane and later submerged beneath the sea, while apparently inapplicable to the clean-cut Great Wass Island scarp, might apply to the less perfect scarps and benches farther west. This would not affect our conclusion that marine erosion had cut no pronounced benches during the last principal submergence, but the westward extension of the Fundian Fault would be curtailed. I am inclined to the opinion, however, that the Fundian Fault, sometimes broken into branch faults, can be traced to the vicinity of Casco Bay, and possibly southwestward past the seaward margin of the Isles of Shoals. Woodworth[12] has considered the marked earthquakes at Plymouth in 1638, Newburyport in 1727, and the vicinity of Scituate in 1755 as " three valid symptoms of a fault existing along or off that coast"; and whether or not the Fundian Fault is ultimately traced with confidence so far, the submarine profiles certainly confirm in striking manner his conjecture of a southwestward continuation of the fault long known to separate Triassic and crystallines where the former are exposed on the northwest side of the Bay of Fundy. In the later edition of his lineament map Hobbs[13] prolongs the rectilinear northwestern shore of the Bay of Fundy as a lineament close to much of the Maine coast, but passing inland in the vicinity of Portland. The submarine profiles suggest rather a curving of the fracture belt to pass east of the Isles of Shoals.

*Length of the Fundian Fault.* — From near the head of the Bay of Fundy to the Isles of Shoals is a distance of more than 350 miles. One is tempted to speculate on the possible extension of this displacement farther southwestward to border Cape Ann on the southeast and the Boston Basin on the northwest, and on the consequent relation of the Carboniferous Lowland of the Narragansett and Boston Basins to the similar lowland at the head of the Bay of Fundy. But such speculations will be more profitable after the Fundian Fault has been more accurately traced and its extensions more fully determined. For the present we may limit ourselves to indicating the general character of what appears to be one of the great fracture lines of North America, and suggesting the importance of giving it more detailed study than has been possible in the present investigation.

**Southwestward Extension of the Submerged Bay of Fundy Triassic Lowland.** — If in the light of the foregoing interpretation we turn again to the profiles, we note certain apparently significant features. Profile G in Fig. 139 shows that south of the Fundian Fault the bottom is relatively simple for a distance of some 40 or 50 miles, when it again becomes somewhat more irregular, and so continues to the northern base of the Banks Cuesta. In other words, the floor of the Gulf of Maine between the fault-line scarp on the north, or better northwest, and the cuesta inface on the southeast, seems to consist of two somewhat unlike parts, the northern being the less irregular of the two. The same feature appears on profiles H and I in Fig. 139. I take this to mean that the gently undulating floor of the submerged Triassic Lowland, well shown in profiles A and B of Fig. 143, is present in its normal position on the down-dropped side of the Fundian Fault, but is overlapped somewhat obliquely on the south by the lower members of the Banks coastal plain, the dissected subordinate cuestas of which give a slightly more irregular surface. The Triassic Lowland can thus apparently be traced southwestward to the vicinity of Jeffreys Bank (Fig. 144), although much obscured by monadnock hills south and southwest of the upfaulted (?) crystallines of Grand Manan Island, and apparently rather deeply dissected in some places. Southwest of Jeffreys Bank the Triassic Lowland seems to disappear, in part because of further overlapping of the coastal plain deposits from the south, and possibly also in part because on the north the faulting did not drop the Triassic beds so low but that later erosion removed them, exposing and dissecting the crystalline basement.

**Analogous Forms of the Gulf of Maine and New Jersey Regions.** — On earlier pages attention has been called to the remarkable analogy between the shoreline features of the Bay of Fundy, Connecticut Valley, and New Jersey Triassic Lowlands. A

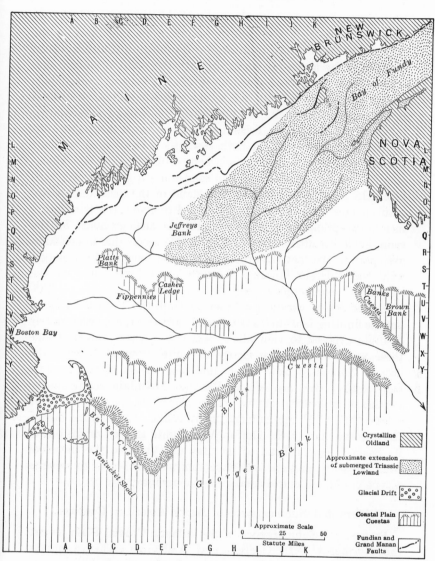

Fig. 144.  Sketch map of the floor of the Gulf of Maine and the adjacent
Banks, showing the New England oldland, the Gulf of Maine inner
lowland, the Triassic Lowland, the Banks cuesta and minor cuestas,
hypothetical pre-glacial drainage of the lowland, and the submarine
scarps of the Fundian fault.  The crystallines of the oldland continue
southeastward (across unshaded area) until they disappear under the
Triassic belt and the coastal plain cuestas.  The profiled belts of Figs.
139 and 140 are indicated by the appropriate letters.

broader analogy may now be pointed out between the physiographic provinces of the Gulf of Maine region and those of the
New Jersey region.  In both cases a crystalline oldland has been
overlapped by a coastal plain; in both the uplifted oldland and
coastal plain have been maturely dissected, to give rugged hills
and valleys in the oldland, and a typical cuesta and inner lowland
in the coastal plain belt.  In both cases the oldland contained an
infaulted wedge of weak Triassic sandstones, with the major fault
on the northwest; and in both cases the coastal plain at least
partially overlapped the Triassic belt, probably after peneplanation had reduced crystallines and sandstones to a fairly even surface.  In New Jersey the inner lowland of the dissected coastal
plain merges with the Triassic Lowland to give a low lying province of exceptional breadth.  Here too the analogy holds, for the
remarkable breadth of the Gulf of Maine seems due in considerable part to the fact that the coastal plain inner lowland merges
with the Triassic Lowland beneath its waters.  Only in the
element of submergence are the two regions radically unlike.
The New Jersey cuesta and inner lowland, the Triassic Lowland
and its limiting fault-line scarp on the northwest, are either nearly
or quite exposed to view above sealevel.  In the Gulf of Maine
these same features are nearly or quite drowned beneath the
ocean.  Submerge New Jersey until the waters of the Atlantic
beat against the face of the Ramapo Mountain scarp on the
northeast and overflow it toward the southwest, and one will have
a new Gulf of Maine hemmed in by a line of submarine banks.
Elevate the floor of the Gulf of Maine until the sea drains out of
its basin from the head of the Bay of Fundy to the shores of
Massachusetts, and one will have another New Jersey to serve as
a type of oldland and coastal plain topography.

### Differential Submergence of North American Continent

**Progressive Submergence of the Atlantic Coastal Plain toward
the Northeast.** — In Georgia and Alabama, exclusive of the
Florida projection, that part of the Atlantic coastal plain exposed
above sealevel has a breadth of 150 to 175 miles; in the Carolinas
and Virginia it narrows to 125 miles or less; in New Jersey it
declines from 65 to 25 miles; in Long Island, Marthas Vineyard,
and Nantucket it appears as narrow fragments only; and off the
coast of Maine is wholly lost to view.  At the same time the submerged portion of the coastal plain, forming the continental shelf,

which off southern Florida is only a few miles wide, broadens off
the Carolinas and Virginia to 50–80 miles, reaches a breadth of
100 miles off northern New Jersey, and where wholly submerged
off the coast of Maine has a width of 150 miles or more.   The
increase is not uniform, however, for the submerged part of the
plain is unusually broad opposite the bight where Florida and
Georgia meet, and unusually narrow in the Cape Hatteras region.
At the southwest the inner lowland, where well developed as in
Alabama, is far from the sea.   In the Virginia-New Jersey sector
it dips under the water in places, is slightly but continuously submerged in Long Island Sound, and deeply so in the Gulf of Maine.
Could we have a more striking picture of a single great topographic belt 150–200 miles broad, submerged progressively deeper
and deeper toward the northeast, one of its elements after another
disappearing from view, until all are completely buried under the
ocean?

**Progressive Deepening of the Margin of the Continental Shelf
toward the Northeast.** — If the progressively greater northward
submergence of the Atlantic side of the continent was a comparatively recent physiographic event, as all the evidence seems
clearly to indicate, the edge of the continental shelf, not yet being
redeveloped with respect to the new sealevel, should record the
fact by showing a progressively greater depth toward the northeast.   When we come to examine the seaward margin of the
cuesta-continental shelf to ascertain its present depth below sealevel, we find no little difficulty in determining the exact location
of the shelf edge.   It must be remembered that the profiles
in Fig. 139, particularly their seaward portions, do not pretend to represent the precise form of the seabottom, as the
data are not yet available to make possible such a representation.
That the larger features are shown with substantial correctness
seems certain;   but a little experimenting with the soundings
available will soon convince one that it is possible to draw profiles
over the margin of the continental shelf which will place the
margin either higher or lower than it appears in some of the profiles figured here.   In a number of cases the margin of the shelf
appears rounded, with no clearly defined edge;   or the profile may
follow down a re-entrant notch or ravine-like depression in the
shelf margin.   Both the present position of the edge of the shelf,
and the position it occupied when first formed, are somewhat
problematical.

To meet this difficulty I have adopted the device of projecting seaward the normal surface slope of the continental shelf, as shown on the profiles some distance back from the rounded or ragged edge, until it intersects a similar upward projection of the scarp face, as shown in Fig. 145. While these intersections do not accurately indicate the original position of the edge of the shelf, they give the best obtainable basis for a rough comparison of the relative positions of the shelf edge at widely separated points. We may be reasonably sure that if the elevation of these intersections increases or decreases from north to south, the edge of the continental shelf shows a similar change in elevation.

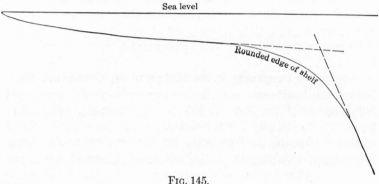

Fig. 145.

In the following table are listed the depths, in fathoms, of the plotted intersections, based on projected profiles of belts ten to fifteen miles broad off the Atlantic coast from southern Florida to the Banks. For the preparation of these profiles I am chiefly indebted to E. A. Moon, a graduate student in Columbia University, who performed the labor in connection with a physiographic study, further results of which will appear in a later volume. In addition a few of the profiles drawn by M. A. Stolfus and appearing in Fig. 139 were utilized, as well as supplementary profiles drawn by H. G. Bray, who also plotted all the intersections.

It will appear from this table that the margin of the Atlantic continental shelf (excluding the Bahama banks) is only a few fathoms below sealevel off Florida, is from 25 to 35 fathoms deep off Georgia and the Carolinas, 40 to 48 fathoms opposite Maryland, 48 to 55 off the New Jersey and Long Island coasts, and 60 to 70 fathoms deep at the outer edge of the Banks. There are some local departures from the gradual deepening toward the northeast;

APPROXIMATE RELATIVE DEPTHS BELOW SEALEVEL OF EDGE
OF CONTINENTAL SHELF FROM THE BANKS TO FLORIDA

| *Origin and Direction of*<br>*Profiled Belt* | *Depth of Intersection of*<br>*Shelf Surface and Scarp in*<br>*Fathoms* |
|---|---|
| From Grand Manan Channel s | 68 |
| " Cutler, Me., s | 64 |
| " Great Wass Island, Me., s | 60–62 |
| " Dyers Bay, Me., s | 64 |
| " Mt. Desert Island s | 68 |
| " Isle-au-Haut, Me., s | 66 |
| " Vinalhaven Island, Me., s | 71 |
| " Tennant Harbor, Me., s | 70 |
| " Portland, Me., s | 68 |
| " Nantucket Id., s.s.e | 54 |
| " Marthas Vineyard s | 54 |
| " Sagg and Wainscott, L. I., s.s.e | 47 |
| " Shinnecock Bay, L. I., s.s.e | 50 |
| " Beach Haven, N. J., s. e | 52 |
| " Intersection of 39° N–73° 30' W., e.s.e | 48 |
| " Atlantic City s.e | 53 |
| " Wildwood, Cape May, N. J., s.e | 50 |
| " Chincoteague Bay, Md., e.s.e | 42 |
| " Fishing Pt., Md., e.s.e | 44 |
| " Cedar Id., Md., e.s.e | 48 |
| " Cobbs Id., Md., e.s.e | 40 |
| " False Cape e.n.e | 25 |
| " Line of soundings e. from Currituck Sd. Light | 20 |
| " Roanoke Id., n.e | 25 |
| " Long Shoal Pt., Pamlico Sd., e | 30 |
| " Cape Hatteras s.e | 18 |
| " Portsmouth Id., s.s.e | 30 |
| " Cape Lookout s.s.e | 30 |
| " Stump Sound s.e | 30–36 |
| " Cape Fear s.s.e | 30 |
| " Little River s.s.e | 30 |
| " Cape Romain s.e | 24 |
| " Charleston, S. C., s.e | 25 |
| " St. Helena Id. (Beaufort) s.e | 28 |
| " Savannah s.e | 30 |
| " St. Simon Sd., e.s.e | 27 |
| " Pablo Beach, Fla., e | 24 |
| " Halifax R. (Daytona) n.e | 25 |
| " False Cape, Fla., n.e | 27 |
| " Sebastian, Fla., n.e | 21 |
| " Stuart n.e | 15 |
| " Card Sound s.e | $3\frac{1}{2}$ |
| " Up Matecumbe Key s.s.e | 4 |
| " Vaca and Fat Deer Keys s.s.e | 3 |

but the progressively greater submergence in this direction, indicated so clearly by the progressive drowning of the cuesta and
lowland topography and by the narrowing of the exposed coastal
plain toward the northeast, is strikingly confirmed by the attitude of the edge of the continental shelf. That this latter attitude has much significance in connection with the problem of

the origin and position of continental shelves will be shown when
in a later volume we come to study the Coastal Plain Shoreline.
Here we may simply remark that the margin of the shelf certainly pays scant attention to the 100-fathom depth at which it
is traditionally supposed to occur, and apparently was not developed at all with respect to the present relative positions of
land and sea.

**Contrasted Shoreline Provinces.** — It is this progressively
greater submergence toward the northeast which is responsible
for the major contrast in the shoreline topography of the Atlantic
Coastal Plain province and that of the New England-Acadian
province.   In the former the sea for the most part still rests
against the relatively weak coastal plain sediments; in the latter
it has reached clear across the coastal plain and submerges the
lower slopes of the rocky oldland of Appalachian structure.   No
two groups of shorelines could be more different, because progressive submergence has carried the sea border from the outer
edge of one province into the midst of another of utterly unlike
character.

**Depth of Submergence of the New England Region.** — It would
seem that the depth of the Gulf of Maine inner lowland offers
us the most reliable measure of the amount of submergence of
this coast that we thus far possess.   The unreliable character of
estimates based on depths of submarine channels, especially when
the subaërial origin of those channels is still open to question, has
been commented on in another connection.   But in the broad
inner lowland of a coastal plain, preserving on its floor features
characteristic of subaërial denudation operating on coastal plain
deposits of unequal resistance, we apparently have a safe basis
for calculation.   Unless tidal scour has been strongly operative, —
and both the form of the bottom and other considerations would
seem to dispose of the possibility of effective tidal erosion on the
broad open floor of the inner basin, — we have in the maximum
depth of the drowned lowland a minimum measure of submergence since the lowland was carved.   Several soundings between
180 and 200 fathoms are found along the deep channel at the
northern base of the main cuesta.   That these particular depths
cannot be ascribed to tidal scour is indicated by the fact that the
outlet channel farther east, between Georges Bank and Brown
Bank, is much shallower.   We must rather infer partial filling of
the former valleys in cuesta and lowland, due possibly to slumping

from the Banks and to material removed from their summits by waves and currents. Streams doubtless flowed from the deep areas in question through the outlet channel to the former sea margin many miles to the southeast; hence the apparent submergence calculated from the soundings must be increased by an allowance for the fall of the stream. It seems safe to say that since the inner lowland now forming the Gulf of Maine was carved, the land has been submerged to a depth of more than 1200 feet. If the land recently stood several thousand feet higher than now, as some have believed, it must have been for a very short period only; else the inner lowland, drained by a stream trenching comparatively weak coastal plain deposits, would have been graded to a much lower level. Farther to the southwest, as already noted, the submergence was progressively less than in the Gulf of Maine region, although there is evidence that the decrease was irregular, with local areas of increasing submergence, — facts which show that a subsidence of the land rather than a rise of sealevel was primarily responsible for the submergence.

**Former Position of the Continental Shelf Margin.** — An interesting corollary of the conclusion that the Banks coastal plain formerly stood more than 1200 feet higher than at present, is the presumption that at that time the seaward edge of the continental shelf may have been some hundreds of feet above the sea, the waves breaking on the face of the steep slope leading down to the oceanic abyss. It is interesting to speculate on the coastal scenery of that time. Even if the seaward slope of the coastal plain was then greater than now, so that its outer margin was less elevated than the inner border, it is at least possible that it rose above sealevel. The profiles show certain peculiarities near their outer ends, such as apparent rounding or steepening of slopes, lack of uniformity in position and elevation of margin, benching, and other abnormalities, which may represent the broken-down edge of the shelf where it was subjected to weathering, slumping, and gullying under subaërial conditions, as well as to wave erosion at the sealevel of that time.

**Age of Banks Cuesta and Date of Submergence.** — The interpretation of the Banks as a coastal plain cuesta receives support from the fact that in the course of their operations on the Banks fishermen bring to the surface fragments of fossiliferous sandstone and limestone. A series of these collected and described by Upham,[10] and determined by Verrill[14] to be of Tertiary age, (probably Miocene[14] or even Pliocene[10]) shows that the submergence must have occurred at the end of the Tertiary or still later in post-Tertiary time; for after the deposition of the late Tertiary sediments we must allow time for the erosion of the lowland prior to its submergence.   If the bevelled top of the cuesta is the remnant of a peneplane developed on the coastal plain beds (and perhaps also on the crystallines of the oldland), then since the deposition of the late Tertiary formations the land was uplifted, one cycle of erosion completed, another uplift occurred, and in the new cycle maturity was attained before subsidence drowned the resultant topography.   Thus we should expect the subsidence to be at least post-Miocene, and more probably post-Pliocene.   It should be observed that if the Banks Cuesta is composed in large part of late Tertiary deposits, it is not geologically the equivalent of the principal cuesta farther west.   It is, however, quite normal for an inner lowland to be bordered by a cuesta of resistant Tertiary beds in one place, and by a cuesta of resistant Cretaceous beds elsewhere, if the cuesta maker of one locality decreases in resistance at another, or is cut out by an unconformity or otherwise, in such manner as to give at most only a minor cuesta on the inface or backslope of the new major cuesta which replaces the first, due to increased resistance of higher or lower beds in the coastal plain series.

**Relation of Banks Cuesta to Former Plant Migrations.** — The conclusions here reached are not without interest in connection with an important problem of plant geography.   Fernald,[15] developing and extending a conception first stated by Hollick,[16] has shown that many species of plants characteristic of the Pine Barren and Coastal Plain floras of New Jersey and the south occur at various points along the New England and Acadian coasts, and even on Newfoundland.   After examining the means by which this coastal plain flora (believed to be incapable of migrating over the oldland which now reaches clear to the sea in New England and the lands northeast) could have reached the far northern localities, he reached the conclusion that the submerged Banks off these coasts must recently have projected far enough above sealevel to give a sandy land-bridge along which the flora could spread freely.   Following Daly[17] he appealed to a lowering of sealevel during the glacial epoch to lay bare the crests of the Banks.   Barrell[18] pointed out that this would require the migration of the flora during a cold period, whereas

the evidence indicates, and Fernald agrees, that such migration
must have taken place when the climate was as warm as, or
warmer than, that of the present; and he suggested a bulging up
of the Banks zone marginal to the ice sheet while the mainland
was weighted down by the ice, followed by further uplift as the
ice melted and the mainland rose, with a later settling back or
subsidence of the Banks as an after-effect of deglaciation.

The submarine physiography of the Gulf of Maine offers striking confirmation of the hypothesis that the Banks were formerly
much higher; but it throws no clear light on Barrell's theory of
an up-bulging during the glacial period.   The inner lowland and
cuesta represent a great work of erosion which must have been
practically completed before the ice invasion.   There seems to be
no reason, however, for placing the plant migration so late as
post-glacial time.   Fernald[19] recognizes the possibility that the
plants " migrated northward on the continental shelf prior to the
Wisconsin glaciation, and persisted outside the subsequently
glaciated area, finally taking possession of their present isolated
habitats on the receding of the ice"; and he finds evidence of the
existence of " some tract along the coast, especially of Acadia
and Newfoundland, which held this flora . . . continuously
through the Pleistocene."   In another connection[20] he definitely
places the date of migration as " late Tertiary"; and in a letter
to the author dated September 28, 1923, he writes: " In regard
to the possibility of the Coastal Plain flora migrating to Nova
Scotia and Newfoundland in pre-glacial times, there is absolutely no botanical reason, so far as I can see, why this might not
have been the case.   In fact, there are certain rather striking
points which would indicate that a migration in late Tertiary or
early Pleistocene times took place."   Some of the points referred
to in the last quotation are considered in Fernald's later contributions to the subject, published in 1918 and 1921[21]; and his
reference in the last paper[22] to an elevation of the continental
shelf " since the Pleistocene glaciation " must be read in the light
of his other clear statements that the plant migration in question
probably antedated the glacial period.

Whatever the later history of the region, the submarine physiography demonstrates the presence of a normal, maturely dissected coastal plain bordering the New England-Acadian oldland
at a period which would account for the very early migration
of the Pine Barrens flora contemplated in the foregoing quota-

tions.  There were then no such broad channels of open water as must have separated certain of the Banks on the theory of a more limited lowering of sealevel due to glaciation; while instead of a temporary land bridge due to bulging at the margin of the glacier there was a long-enduring coastal plain topography extending continuously from New Jersey and southward to beyond Newfoundland.  Thus the botanical problem of migration would seem to be measurably independent of changes of sealevel due to glaciation and of marginal bulging due to crustal readjustment under the weight of the ice; although we recognize the possibility that both these factors may have played a rôle in the later history of the Banks Cuesta.

**Coastal Plain Remnants on the New England Upland.** — Between the head of the subsequent river draining northeastward along the Gulf of Maine portion of the inner lowland, and the head of the subsequent flowing away in the opposite direction along the Long Island Sound portion, it would be normal to find the lowland imperfectly developed, and the cuesta coming close to the oldland.  Just at this point the crest of the cuesta does swing northwestward in Nantucket Shoals to touch or nearly touch the New England oldland, and the inner lowland locally nearly or quite pinches out.  It is precisely in this vicinity, also, that Hitchcock,[23] Bowman[24] and others have reported finding patches of the Tertiary coastal plain sediments still present on the southeastern margin of the New England upland.  The Cape Cod Canal is man's attempt to connect two parts of a drowned inner lowland which Nature unfortunately left unconnected; and it is cut close to where the meeting place of cuesta and oldland is obscured by glacial deposits, about where the inner lowland should have been developed.

### Limited Marine Erosion Indicated by Submarine Profiles

With the salient features of the submarine physiography of the Gulf of Maine fixed clearly in mind, we are in a position to answer the question as to whether or not the submarine profiles indicate extensive marine erosion of the rocky New England coast at present sealevel.  The answer appears to be in the negative.  We have already noted certain arguments against the marine origin of the submarine scarps found off Great Wass Island and elsewhere, which seem to apply with equal force against the conception of prolonged marine abrasion along the present shores.  As a rule the profiles show the hills and valleys of the New England upland descending well below sealevel with their essential characters unchanged. The profiles may be simplified, due to inadequate data in the form of soundings, and to the clay filling of the submerged valley bottoms, deposited when the sea was much higher than now, which filling, to judge from its uplifted portions, may be present in the drowned valleys to a thickness of 100 feet or more. We must recognize, also, that the dissected upland may cease rather abruptly at the Fundian Fault, and give place beyond to the lower and simpler topography of the Triassic Lowland, as is beautifully shown in profile G (Fig. 139). But despite these complications, the absence of a broad marine platform of abrasion bordering the coast, continued seaward in a terrace of deposition burying the former irregularities of the submerged land areas, is clearly apparent. Instead, we find that submarine data, incomplete though they may be, reveal beneath the sea, close to the land as well as far out in deeper water, the same kind of topography as above sealevel. Hills of varying height are abundant, and the valleys between them remain unfilled. How closely the seabottom form resembles that above sealevel is well indicated by contours on the Casco Bay topographic quadrangle, where the Appalachian topography of parallel ridges and valleys is scarcely less clear below sealevel than on the adjacent land; and profiles demonstrate that hills and valleys persist farther out to sea and deeper beneath its level. On the Nova Scotian side of the Gulf one may see the stripped surface of the pre-Triassic peneplane, or the inclined beds of the Triassic series, descending regularly northwestward without any marked wave-made bench interrupting the slope (Fig. 140, profiles N and O). The steep Fundian fault-line scarp and the seemingly similar scarp bounding Grand Manan Island on the northwest are not appreciably notched (Fig. 143 A, B), although here the exposure to storm waves and the steepness of the scarps are less favorable to rapid wave erosion. Projected profiles for parts of southwestern Maine, prepared by D. Houghton to show the character of the New England upland in that region, were prolonged under the sea with similar profiles drawn by H. G. Bray, with the result of showing a nearly uniform descent of the upland into the water, unbroken by any obvious marine benching at sealevel.

**Evidence from Larger Scale Charts.** — The data for the profiles cited above are insufficient to show a narrow wave-cut bench, although they should make known the existence of a broad one, were such present.  To check the results secured for large areas on the basis of the smaller scale charts, both linear and projected profiles with less vertical exaggeration were drawn for the more fully charted areas near shore, as represented on larger scale charts.   Such profiles constructed for exposed points on the northeast and southeast coasts of Cape Ann, for the islands off Bar Harbor showing steep southern slopes (Figs. 90 and 91) attributed by some to wave erosion, for the northwest side of the great North Mountain-Digby Neck trap ridge, and for other points on the hard-rock coasts of the Gulf of Maine, fail to discover any more pronounced indication of wave cutting than the probable removal from the present land margin of a small wedge of rock, never certainly attaining a mile in breadth, and usually but a small fraction of a mile broad.   Profiles parallel to the general trend of the Maine coast, and at different distances out to sea, demonstrate the presence of the hills and valleys shown by the small scale profiles, as far seaward as the larger scale charts extend, although the profiles have a simpler form in the deeper water, due in part to fewer soundings, and in part no doubt to glacial clay filling of the submerged valley bottoms.

*Submerged Hills and Valleys.* — Certain of the large scale projected profiles, while confirming the results already described, give additional data of some interest.   Such a profile running northwest-southeast off the mouth of Sheepscot Bay (Fig. 146 A) shows in greater detail than the small scale profiles the irregularities of the hill-and-valley topography down to depths of 250 feet. Profile B in the same figure, located a few miles east of profile A, shows that the hills and valleys are pronounced features of the seafloor down to depths of 400 or 500 feet.   Part of this compound profile, where farthest out from the land, seems to be located near a ridge crest, and part on a valley floor, giving very simple lines; while another part drops from the ridge into the valley and back again, emphasizing the relief that actually exists.

*Submarine Benches.* — Profile C (Fig. 146), farther to the southwest, shows to better advantage a feature which appears repeatedly on the smaller scale profiles.   This is an apparent benching or terracing at different levels.   That the upper terrace is not the result of wave erosion at present sealevel, nor of wave erosion at any level within recent time, seems sufficiently indicated by the typical subaërial hill and valley topography which characterizes it.  If a bench of marine origin, it has since its formation apparently been uplifted, maturely dissected by stream erosion, and again submerged.  The case of the lower bench is less clear.  It shows a fairly marked relief, but a strikingly less pronounced dissection which, although possibly in part fictitious, due to fewer soundings, cannot apparently be wholly thus explained.  The surface of this bench is about 250 feet below sealevel, even at its inner edge;  hence it cannot be ascribed to wave erosion at the present level.  Both its inner and its outer edge mark the position of what I have tentatively regarded as extensions of the Fundian Fault.  If this interpretation be correct, the included down-dropped block may have been less dissected than its higher neighbor on the west; or more extensive deposition of the glacial clays in quieter water, or less erosion of them during the period when the inner edge of the plain was raised higher than now and valleys now drowned were carved in the clay plain, may explain the smoother surface of the lower bench.  But we should not lose sight of another possibility.  Barrell[25] has reported from other parts of New England what he believes to be ancient marine terraces, long since badly dissected by stream erosion; while Katz and Keith[26] refer briefly to dissected rock terraces a short distance inland from the shoreline in the general region we are now considering.  Whether these ancient dissected terraces be of marine or some other origin, the features shown on the profiles may be a continuation of the same series of forms under the sea.  The lesser dissection of the lower terrace would still remain to be explained, perhaps reasonably in the same terms suggested above on the tentative assumption that the terraces represent the eroded tops of fault strips.

Profile D shows a bench which is both shallow and apparently but moderately dissected.  Were the Gulf of Maine margined by such a bench along much of its land border, one might argue in favor of sufficient wave erosion at present sealevel to carve an imperfectly developed marine bench.  But the evidence of the profiles as a whole strongly negatives such an interpretation; and the fact that we are here dealing with a part of the coast where the glacial clay coastal plain and glacial outwash plains are most strongly developed, and where the land contours are least irregular, offers adequate explanation for the relative simplicity of the inner part of the submarine profile; while scarcity of soundings is an added factor to be taken into consideration in the deeper

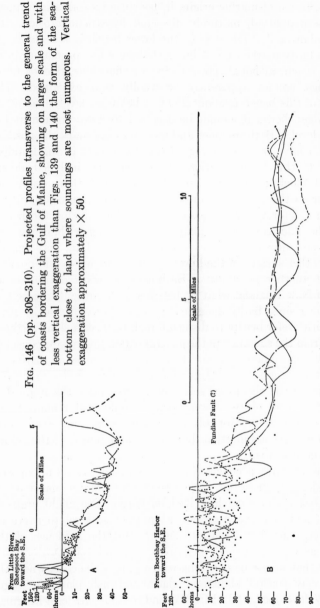

Fig. 146 (pp. 308–310). Projected profiles transverse to the general trend of coasts bordering the Gulf of Maine, showing on larger scale and with less vertical exaggeration than Figs. 139 and 140 the form of the sea-bottom close to land where soundings are most numerous. Vertical exaggeration approximately × 50.

A. Projected profile of a belt nearly 2 miles broad based on U. S. C. & G. S. Chart No. 314.
B. Projected profile of a belt over 4 miles broad based on U. S. C. & G. S. Chart No. 1204.

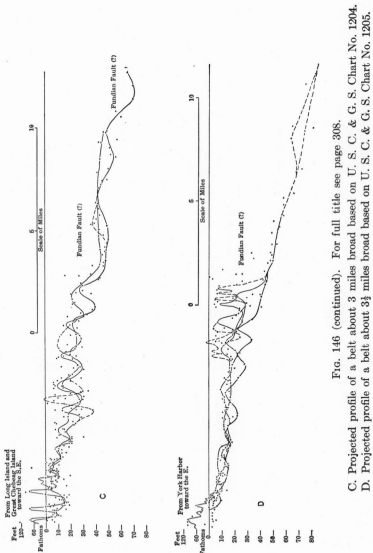

Fig. 146 (continued). For full title see page 308.

C. Projected profile of a belt about 3 miles broad based on U. S. C. & G. S. Chart No. 1204.
D. Projected profile of a belt about 3½ miles broad based on U. S. C. & G. S. Chart No. 1205.

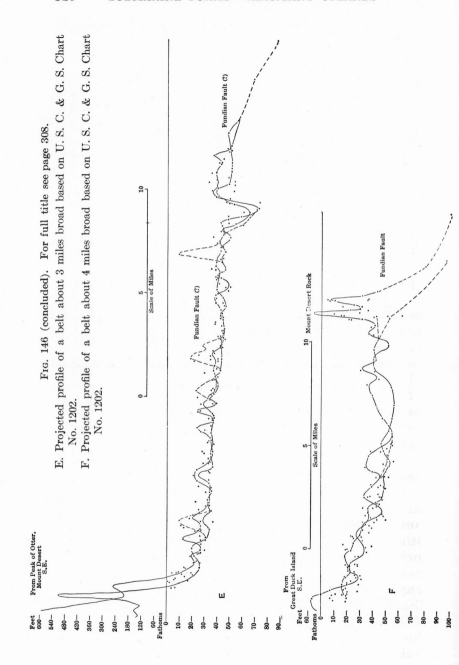

Fig. 146 (concluded). For full title see page 308.

E. Projected profile of a belt about 3 miles broad based on U. S. C. & G. S. Chart No. 1202.

F. Projected profile of a belt about 4 miles broad based on U. S. C. & G. S. Chart No. 1202.

areas, where the abundance of glacial deposits is doubtless still of importance in concealing the older topography. Profile E brings out clearly the strong contrast between the dissected and partially submerged New England upland peneplane, and the monadnocks of the Mount Desert Island range. If the upland levels indicated roughly by hill tops are considered, there seem to be two benches: one at a depth of 20 to 24 fathoms and a second nearer 40 fathoms deep, each deeply dissected and terminated seaward by a descent to deeper water. In profile F, a dozen miles to the west, the outer scarp borders Mount Desert Rock and is particularly pronounced.

**Conclusion.** — The study of the submarine profiles thus confirms our previous conclusion that marine forces have accomplished little in their attack at the present sealevel. We cannot attribute this fact to the protective influence of the Banks, for between this submerged cuesta and the Maine coast there is an expanse of deep water 150 miles broad, and storm waves break on the ragged mainland with great fury. Off the coast of Nova Scotia, in localities where the Banks do not rise so close to sealevel, the profiles are equally eloquent of the slight results of marine abrasion. It seems but reasonable to conclude that the waves have operated at the present level for a comparatively short time only.

**Nature of the Gulf of Maine Seafloor.** — In closing this discussion of the submarine physiography of the Gulf of Maine, it is desirable to emphasize once more the fact that the surface which underlies the waters of the Gulf is one of subdued topography, not very deeply trenched by stream erosion. The profiles so greatly exaggerate the ruggedness of the land that one does well to contemplate a view like that shown in Fig. 72, and to remember that the more irregular parts of the Gulf floor consist of this same type of surface declining very gradually under the water. Other parts consist of the drowned Triassic Lowland or other surfaces equally smooth, which surfaces were evidently uplifted and trenched by rivers before the submergence, but so far as one may judge from very imperfect data, not made so irregular as the dissected crystalline upland. Whether the northwestern portion of the Gulf floor is an earlier peneplane, formerly underlying the coastal plain deposits but revealed by stripping, while the main upland peneplane is to be correlated with the surface apparently truncating the beds in the Banks cuesta, is not yet clear.

There is some indication that a pre-coastal plain peneplane intersects a post-coastal plain peneplane at a very slight angle near
the present shoreline in southwestern Maine, as quite certainly is
the case in southern New England and farther south; but this
problem requires further study before a final statement can be
made.

**Résumé.** — Our study of submarine profiles off the New
England-Acadian coast has led us to a number of important
conclusions.  The famous series of " banks " enclosing the Gulf
of Maine on the southeast are shown to have all the characteristics
of a typical coastal plain cuesta completely submerged, while the
Gulf itself represents the more deeply submerged inner lowland
normally associated with such a cuesta.  Thus the long-discussed
question of the origin of the " banks " seems to find a reasonable
answer.  Subordinate cuestas parallel to the major " Banks
Cuesta " are recognized on the floor of the drowned lowland, and
far across this floor toward the southwest the continuation of the
Triassic basin of the Bay of Fundy region is traced by means of
the submerged topography, until the rocks of this formation disappear under the obliquely overlapping coastal plain deposits.
A great fault-line scarp, in places double or triple and apparently
350 miles in length, is traced under the waters of the Gulf, and
the relation of this " Fundian Fault " to the drowned extension
of the Triassic basin is made clear.  The Gulf of Maine region is,
in fact, found to be a duplication of the New Jersey coastal plain
and oldland topography, almost wholly concealed beneath the
waters of the sea.  This greater submergence of the North American continent toward the northeast is found to be confirmed by
a comparison of coastal plain and continental shelf breadths from
Florida to Maine, and by a progressive deepening of the outer
margin of the continental shelf in the same direction, as revealed
by submarine profiles.

To this progressively greater submergence northeastward we
owe the remarkable contrast in the two great shoreline provinces
of eastern North America: the shoreline of emergence southwest
of New York, and the shoreline of submergence to the northeast.
An apparently reliable minimum measure of the depth of submergence off New England, more than 1200 feet, is based on the
depth of the floor of the submerged Gulf of Maine Lowland.  As
the Banks Cuesta consists in part of late-Tertiary sediments, it
seems probable that the date of submergence of the present

drowned topography must be post-Tertiary. The physiographic history of the Banks Cuesta seems to offer a reasonable explanation of the northeastward migration of the Pine Barrens and Coastal Plain flora studied and described at length by the eminent student of plant geography, Fernald.

Finally, the submarine profiles support the conclusion already reached from a study of wave erosion and wave deposition, to the effect that the sea has operated on the hard-rock coasts of the New England-Acadian region for but a comparatively short time.

## BIBLIOGRAPHY

1. MAURY, M. F. "The Physical Geography of the Sea," 8th Ed., 38, New York, 1868.
2. THOULET, J. "Considérations sur la Structure et la Genèse des Bancs de Terre-Neuve." Bull. Soc. Géog., 7e Sér., X, 203–241, 1889.
3. THOULET, J. "Océanographie," 461, Paris, 1890.
   THOULET, J. "L'Océan, ses Lois et ses Problèmes," 285, Paris, 1904.
4. SHALER, N. S. "Remarks on the Geology of the Coast of Maine, New Hampshire, and that part of Massachusetts north of Boston." U. S. Coast Surv., Coast Pilot for the Atlantic Sea-Board: Gulf of Maine and its Coast from Eastport to Boston (1874), 885, 1875.
   SHALER, N. S. "The Geological History of Harbors." U. S. Geol. Surv., 13th Ann. Rept., Pt. 2, 163, 1893.
   SHALER, N. S. "Report on the Geology of Marthas Vineyard." U. S. Geol. Surv., 7th Ann. Rept., 304, 1888.
5. RUSSELL, I. C. "North America," 8, New York, 1904.
6. DAVIS, C. H. "A Memoir upon the Geological Action of Tidal and other Currents of the Ocean." Amer. Acad. Arts and Sci., Mem., N. S., IV, Pt. I, 117–156, 1849.
7. AGASSIZ, ALEXANDER. "Three Cruises of the United States Coast and Geodetic Survey Steamer Blake," I, 104, 1888.
8. PATTERSON, GEORGE. "Sable Island: Its History and Phenomena." Roy. Soc. Can., Proc. and Trans., XII, Sec. II, 41, 1894.
9. SPENCER, J. W. "Submarine Valleys off the American Coast and in the North Atlantic." Bull. Geol. Soc. Amer., XIV, 207–226, 1903.
10. UPHAM, WARREN. "The Fishing Banks between Cape Cod and Newfoundland." Amer. Jour. Sci., 3rd Ser., XLVII, 123–129, 1894. Bost. Soc. Nat. Hist., Proc., XXVI, 42–48, 1893.
11. POWERS, SIDNEY. "The Acadian Triassic." Jour. Geol., XXIV, 1–26, 105–122, 254–268, 1916.
12. WOODWORTH, J. B. "Cross-section of the Appalachians in Southern New England." Bull. Geol. Soc. Amer., XXXIV, 260, 1923.
13. HOBBS, W. H. "Earthquakes," 114, New York, 1907.
14. VERRILL, A. E. "Occurrence of Fossiliferous Tertiary Rocks on the Grand Bank and Georges Bank." Amer. Jour. Sci., 3rd Ser., XVI, 323–324, 1878.

15. FERNALD, M. L.   "A Botanical Expedition to Newfoundland and Southern Labrador."   Rhodora, XIII, 109–162, 1911.
    FERNALD, M. L.   "A Preliminary Statement of Results of Studies on
the Northeastward Distribution of the Coastal Plain Flora."   Amer.
Jour. Sci., 4th Ser., XL, 17–18, 1915.
    FERNALD, M. L.   "The Geographic Affinities of the Vascular Floras of
New England, the Maritime Provinces, and Newfoundland."   Amer.
Jour. Botany, V, 219–247, 1918.
    FERNALD, M. L.   "The Gray Herbarium Expedition to Nova Scotia,
1920."   Rhodora, XXIII, 89–111, 130–152, 153–171, 184–195, 223–245,
257–278, 284–300, 1921.
16. HOLLICK, ARTHUR.   "Plant Distribution as a Factor in the Interpretation of Geological Phenomena with Special Reference to Long
Island and Vicinity."   N. Y. Acad. Sci., Trans., XII, 189–202, 1893.
17. DALY, R. A.   "Pleistocene Glaciation and the Coral Reef Problem."
Amer. Jour. Sci., 4th Ser., XXX, 297–308, 1910.
18. BARRELL, JOSEPH.   "Factors in the Movements of the Strand Line and
their Results in the Pleistocene and Post-Pleistocene."   Amer. Jour.
Sci., 4th Ser., XL, 17, 1915.
19. FERNALD, M. L.   "A Preliminary Statement of Results of Studies on
the Northeastward Distribution of the Coastal Plain Flora."   Amer.
Jour. Sci., 4th Ser., XL, 17–18, 1915.
20. FERNALD, M. L.   "The Geographic Affinities of the Vascular Floras of
New England, the Maritime Provinces, and Newfoundland."   Amer.
Jour. Botany, V, 224, 1918.
21. FERNALD, M. L.   'The Geographic Affinities of the Vascular Floras of
New England, the Maritime Provinces, and Newfoundland."   Amer.
Jour. Botany, V, 219–247, 1918.
    FERNALD, M. L.   "The Gray Herbarium Expedition to Nova Scotia,
1920."   Rhodora, XXIII, 89–111, 130–152, 153–171, 184–195, 223–245,
257–278, 284–300, 1921.
22. FERNALD, M. L.   "The Gray Herbarium Expedition to Nova Scotia,
1920."   Rhodora, XXIII, 168, 1921.
23. HITCHCOCK, EDWARD.   "Final Report on the Geology of Massachusetts,"
91–95, Amherst, 1841.
24. BOWMAN, ISAIAH.   "Northward Extension of the Atlantic Preglacial
Deposits."   Amer. Jour. Sci., 4th Ser., XXII, 313–325, 1906.
25. BARRELL, JOSEPH.   "The Piedmont Terraces of the Northern Appalachians."   Amer. Jour. Sci., 4th Ser., XLIX, 227–258, 327–362, 407–
428, 1920.
26. KATZ, F. J. and KEITH, A.   "The Newington Moraine, Maine, New
Hampshire, and Massachusetts."   U. S. Geol. Surv., Prof. Paper 108,
11–29, 1918.

# CHAPTER IX

## EROSIONAL FORMS BORDERING WEAK-ROCK LOWLANDS

**Advance Summary.** — We have previously studied the work of wave erosion and wave deposition along the shores of the resistant uplands, and the submarine profiles off these shores. It now becomes our duty to prosecute similar studies of the shores of the weak-rock lowlands. In the present chapter we shall first note the obvious contrast in the stage of evolution reached by the weak-rock shores and those bordering the resistant uplands, especially when we consider those shores most exposed to vigorous wave attack. The present rate of wave erosion along the weak-rock shores will then be determined, and an effort will be made to ascertain the magnitude of the total work accomplished up to the present time. Thus may we arrive at a point where we can form some idea of the length of time during which the sea has operated at the present level.

**Contrast of Conditions on Hard-Rock and Weak-Rock Shores.** — It is reasonable to expect that regions in which the rock formations are so non-resistant as to fall a ready prey to the agents of subaërial denudation, would also yield readily to marine forces; both because the rapidity of marine erosion is in part determined by the readiness with which rock cliffs disintegrate under the influence of weathering, and because seacliffs bordering lowlands cannot be very high and hence cannot contribute a large amount of débris to embarrass wave action. On the other hand, it should be noted that following submergence the shorelines of lowlands are apt to lie along embayments in the shore, and hence to be more or less exempt from the most vigorous wave attack; and that where the crystalline upland slopes down into the sea, instead of meeting it along some fault-line scarp or resurrected peneplane scarp, or under other conditions which bring the sea close to high land, the cliffs bordering resistant rocks may be as low as any. That the balance of these conflicting considerations favors more rapid wave attack on the relatively non-resistant rocks of the Carboniferous Lowlands is obvious from a comparison of the physiographic features of the shorelines bordering these lowlands with the features which we have just found to be characteristic of the hard-rock shores.

Initial Character of the Weak-Rock Shores. — Let us first recall the presumable initial form of a typical lowland shoreline, as exemplified by the New Brunswick and Prince Edward Island shores. From the discussion of the sea margins of these weak-rock areas presented in Chapter III, it appears that the initial shoreline of the region was characterized by a succession of broad, low headlands alternating with shallow embayments, the former of which were presumably, as the latter were certainly, bordered by minor bays of dendritic pattern (Fig. 162), due to drowning of the dendritic drainage systems characteristic of nearly horizontal rocks. Thus the initial irregularity was comparable with that of the crystalline shores, although usually of a different pattern. Except where rectilinear due to structural controls, the shoreline bordering the crystalline upland is still typically irregular, forming a labyrinthine contour about islands, peninsulas, and bays. Headlands are cut back but little, baymouth bars are comparatively rare, and scarcely any progress has been made toward straightening out the shoreline to the simplicity of submaturity. It is still an extremely youthful shoreline.

Present Greater Simplicity of the Weak-Rock Shores. — What a contrast with the shoreline now bordering the Carboniferous Lowlands of New Brunswick and Prince Edward Island! Here the outer shoreline has attained, or nearly attained, the simplicity of submaturity. Headlands have obviously been cut back some distance and the embayments of the initial shoreline partially bridged across by a remarkable series of baymouth bars and spits. From Miscou Island to Buctouche Harbor (Fig. 147) the outer shoreline of the New Brunswick Lowland sweeps in a series of beautiful curves as a result of these changes, which have effectively transformed a coast initially of marked irregularity, as is evident from the complicated pattern of such parts of the initial shoreline as are more or less well preserved in the embayments back of the bars. On Prince Edward Island, from North Point to East Point (Fig. 148) the same simplicity of shoreline is found today, although the character of the embayments shows that the initial shoreline must here also have been extremely irregular. Both of these shores are exposed to the waves of the St. Lawrence

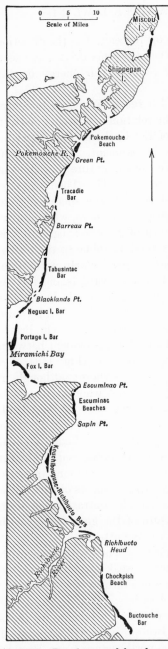

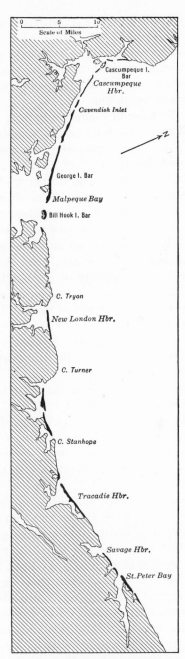

FIG. 147. Bay bars and beaches of the northeastern New Brunswick shore (modified after Ganong). A shoreline of submergence in late youth or submaturity bordering a partially submerged Carboniferous Lowland

FIG. 148. Bay bars of the northern shore of Prince Edward Island, a shoreline of submergence in late youth or submaturity, bordering a partially submerged Carboniferous (Permian) Lowland.

**(317)**

embayment, and not to those of the open ocean; but the direction of exposure is favorable, since northeast storms driving across a broad expanse of open water may expend their energy on the coasts in question.

**Relation of Shoreline Pattern to Degree of Exposure to Storm Waves.** — It is interesting to note the relation of shoreline pattern to degree of exposure in the case of the Carboniferous Lowland bordering the Gulf of St. Lawrence embayment. From Miscou Island to Buctouche Harbor we have the submature shorelines of comparatively simple form shown in Fig. 147. Then we pass under the lee of Prince Edward Island, and the shoreline from Buctouche River on eastward for 100 miles or more, while apparently simplified from an initial pattern of greater irregularity, is obviously more youthful than the exposed shoreline to the northwest. The scarcity of baymouth bars is particularly noticeable. Coming out from the protection of Prince Edward Island farther eastward, the shoreline again takes on a more simple form; but its continuation along the western side of Cape Breton may owe its simplicity, in part at least, to structural causes. On Prince Edward Island itself the same striking contrast is evident between the exposed northern shore of simple pattern (Fig. 148), and the much more irregular protected southern shore; although in this case the contrast may partially, but not wholly, be due to the somewhat higher elevation of the southern side of the island, which would involve slower retreat of headlands even if the vigor of wave attack were equal, instead of being so markedly unequal as in the present instance. In the contrasts observed we find a confirmation of the conclusion that a notable amount of wave work has been accomplished on fairly exposed shores of weak-rock lowlands; while the fact that no comparable contrast is found on hard-rock shores gives a rough measure of the greater ease with which the lowland rocks fall prey to marine attacks.

**Rate of Erosion of Weak-Rock Shores.** — The relative ease with which the Carboniferous and associated weak formations of the so-called Carboniferous Lowlands are cut into by the waves has attracted the attention of various observers. Dawson[1] and Gilpin[2] emphasize the rapid wasting of the Carboniferous rocks forming the western coast of Cape Breton, while Gilpin[3] says of coast erosion along the coal fields of northeastern Cape Breton: "The old French fort at Glace Bay has furnished a means of measuring the annual waste. From plans preserved in Paris of the position of the fort at the time of its erection, it would appear that the removal of the coast has been going on at the rate of two feet every year. At other points the annual waste has not exceeded six to ten inches." If the fort referred to is the famous one at Louisburg, the waves are not cutting in Carboniferous rocks there, but largely in unconsolidated débris resting on more resistant material, which latter only in places reaches above sealevel; and the rate of retreat is doubtless unusually rapid. Nichols[4] reports that at South Head or Cape Morien, where the sea has actually cut away parts of the coast in which mining for coal was carried on a few years ago, the retreat of the cliffs under wave attack has amounted to 1.5 feet per year.

*Northeastern Shore of Cape Breton.* — Mr. H. J. McCann, Assistant General Manager of the Dominion Coal Company, who gave me special facilities for seeing parts of this interesting coast, has generously granted permission to publish data gathered by him and placed at my disposal through the request of Mr. D. A. Nichols of the Geological Survey of Canada. The data include the results of accurate surveys of shoreline changes for that portion of the Cape Breton coast between Sydney Harbor and Morien Bay, where detailed studies are important because of the coal deposits which run out under the sea. West of Sydney Harbor, projecting points like Cranberry Head, Merrit Point, and Point Aconi (Fig. 149) are rapidly wearing away, a coal seam dipping toward the sea at Cranberry Head having been eroded at such a rate that whereas boats are said to have secured this coal at water level in the 60's, the seam now outcrops at the shore 30 feet above sealevel. On the eastern side of Sydney Harbor, just north of the entrance, the shore road has repeatedly been moved back on account of wave erosion, as the visitor can easily see (Fig. 150); and part of Low Point, farther out, is estimated to have been cut back 20 feet in ten years. To the east, near Indian Bay, the undermining action of the waves caused landslips extending a thousand feet along the coast which affected the upland to a maximum depth of 130 feet between 1885 and 1900, while the main highway running westward along the coast toward Sydney Harbor, which in 1907 was about 30 feet back from the top of the cliff, had been undermined by 1914. In Indian Bay itself, the midbay bar attached to the upland on the east was driven inward a maximum distance (in its central part) of 200 feet between 1907 and 1922, while an iron corner post which in

1893 was on the upland 85 feet back from the shore, in 1922 fell over the cliffs due to wave attack. Eastward the outer shore of Indian Bay retreated at the rate of 1 foot per year for some time prior to 1903, while one projecting headland was cut back 15 feet in the six years from 1902 to 1908. On the northern side of Table Head (Fig. 151) the crest of the seacliff was accurately surveyed in 1907 and again in 1919, and an irregular retreat averaging 20 feet, with a maximum of 30 feet, recorded for the twelve years. On the east side of the Head similar surveys show a maximum retreat of 20 feet between 1907 and 1913, and a

Fig. 149. Point Aconi, Cape Breton Island. An exposed point of the Carboniferous Lowland rapidly receding under wave attack. Note that the small island or stack in front of the point has its surface much lower than the grassy top of the point itself.

narrow point projecting out to sea (Fig. 152), photographed by Mr. B. A. L. Huntsman at frequent intervals, has receded 75 feet in twenty years. A third point on the shore of Glace Bay has lost 15 feet in fifteen years, while the headland of Cape Percy has been extensively cut back. As Mr. McCann points out, the data given above relate to places where the sea has advanced more rapidly than usual. He is inclined to believe that the average retreat of the coast in this region does not exceed 6 inches per year.

On the basis of thirty years' observations of cliff retreat near Sydney Mines on the western shore of Sydney Harbor, Brown[5]

FIG. 150.  Margin of the Carboniferous Lowland northeast of entrance to Sydney Harbor, showing rapid undermining of shore road by waves.  The newest position of road is farther back, where the auto and most of the houses are visible.  The man is standing in the abandoned road, where efforts at repairs were ineffectual.

determined the annual rate of erosion at this somewhat protected locality to be 5 inches. Hayes[6] has called attention to the importance of preserving a complete record of the positions of all coal seams along the coast, a matter earlier emphasized by Brown,[7] because seams now outcropping a short distance inland will soon be cut away, just as seams formerly exposed at Cape Morien are now lost to view, their outcrops being hidden beneath the waters of the Atlantic. Through comparison of surveys and the study of local records Hayes determined the rate of shore retreat on the extremities and along the sides of headlands to vary from .8 to 1.2 feet per year. Locally the rate is sufficiently rapid to leave the

Fig. 151.  Table Head, Glace Bay, Cape Breton Island, a Carboniferous Lowland coast suffering vigorous marine erosion.

matted roots of moss and grasses projecting over the cliff top and in a number of places (Figs. 150 and 153) to undermine roads which some few years ago were considered to be a safe distance back from the sea. The most striking evidence of active marine erosion observed by me was at Pt. Aconi, the northern end of Boularderie Island (Fig. 9). Here we have an excellent example of a cliff of diminishing height (Fig. 153), although the remnant of the headland forming an island-stack just beyond (Fig. 149) is so low as to indicate that the sea did not have to cut in far to reach the backslope of this hill. It should also be noted that we are here dealing with a narrow tongue of land attacked on both sides by the waves, so that moderate erosion all round produces an unusually marked retreat of the point. It is a large-scale example of the conditions found at the small tongue of land near Table Head, Glace Bay (Fig. 152). As at other localities along this coast, the rapidity of shore retreat in the Pt. Aconi region is attested by the remains of undermined roads (Fig. 153).

*New Brunswick Shores.* — Ganong[8] describes evidence of a considerable wearing back of headlands in the Miscou Island-Buctouche Harbor region of New Brunswick represented in Fig. 147, and the topography of this coast supports the opinion that some of the headlands must have suffered marked truncation. More precise data as to the rapid wearing away of the coast during historic times is given by Ganong for the northern part of Shippegan Island;[9] and for the Fort Moncton region on Bay Verte, where low shore cliffs have been cut back as much as 70 yards in a century and a half, judging from a comparison of careful surveys made in 1751 and 1897.[10] Ganong states in each case that it is the " upland " which has been worn away as described; but while the low " upland " or mainland is in general underlain by Carboniferous rocks, it is possible that the cliffs may be cut in whole or in part in glacial or other unconsolidated débris. Indeed, basing an opinion on his memory of the shore details, Ganong[11] is inclined to believe that the latter may be the case in both localities, although one of his more recent papers[12] implies that the waves have now reached the bedrock portion of the upland. Goldthwait[13] gives additional testimony demonstrating the rapid retreat of this shore under wave attack: " Lobster factories near Miscou Point, Point Escuminac (Fig. 147), and other places have been swept away by the recession of the cliffs, and rebuilt, farther inland, over and over again. According to Mr. Kenneth McClellan, light keeper at Point Escuminac, the lighthouse originally stood about 500 feet seaward from its present position, and was moved inland about eighty years ago, because of the rapid encroachment of the waves against the low cliffs of sandstone at that point. Since that time, the sea has advanced about 100 yards, and is now threatening to demolish a building where the fog horn is installed, unless the Government takes prompt measures to protect it." These and other cases are cited as " among the hundreds of illustrations which might be given " of the fact that in exposed localities this coast is being cut back at a rapid rate.

1900

1908

1916

FIG. 152.  Progressive marine erosion of Carboniferous Lowland coast near
(324)                                         by F. W. Gray;  last four photo-

1917

1918

1921

Table Head, Glace Bay, Cape Breton Island.   First two views from report
graphed by B. A. L. Huntsman.                                    (325)

FIG. 153.   In the distance Point Aconi, Cape Breton, shows a seacliff of progressively diminishing altitude, in front of which is a small island or stack detached by wave erosion.   In the centre foreground an abandoned road ends abruptly at the edge of the receding cliffs, while the new road replacing it is visible at the extreme left.

*Minor Shore Forms.* — The weak Carboniferous conglomerates and sandstones not only wear away with comparative rapidity, but their friable nature favors the development of interesting details of shore forms.   On the Carboniferous shores at the head of the Bay of Fundy are found " The Rocks " of Cape Demoiselle, marine stacks or chimneys carved into weird shapes by the waves.[14] Stacks of similar origin are found on the Cape Breton shores (Fig. 151), and in other places where these usually nearly horizontal red beds are exposed to the action of the sea.

**Extent of Marine Erosion of the Weak-Rock Shores.** — The impression left with one as a result of surveying the effects of marine erosion on the weak-rock coasts of the Carboniferous Lowlands is the expectable one that these coasts have suffered far more severely than the crystalline areas.   To one fresh from a study of the slightly cliffed shores of Maine or Nova Scotia, the contrast presented by the northeastern coast of Cape Breton, as seen from any of a dozen points of vantage, is profoundly impressive. Away to the southwest the low, gently rounded hills of the lowland peneplane, clothed with a wilderness of stunted spruce and alder, continue in seemingly endless succession.   On the southeast older and harder rocks rise as a barrier wall to the higher peneplane; while off to the northwest a more forbidding escarpment of crystallines presents a wonderfully even upland crest stretching far away northward to Cape Smokey, dim in the distance.   Between its border walls the broad lowland, open to the northeast, presents its seaward margin to the hungry waves.   Every view along this exposed coast tells eloquently of the ravages of the sea. Even within the mouth of the Sydney embayment cliffs 25 to 30 feet high (Fig. 154) show what the weaker waves are accomplishing.   The record is reinforced by the remnants of abandoned roads, ending abruptly where the scarp has undermined them. On the more exposed headlands cliffs 50 to 60 feet high are not uncommon, and a comparison of their profiles with those of the adjacent land areas indicates that the height is not the result of slight wave erosion of former steep slopes, but of a fairly extensive incision of the waves into a gently sloping coast.

No one can study the profiles of Lingan Head west of Indian Bay, of the Table Head region west of Glace Bay, of the seaward ends of Cape Percy and Cape Morien, or of the main coast east and west of Point Aconi, without reaching the conviction that here the indications of pronounced marine erosion

FIG. 154.   Eastern side of Sydney Harbor, Cape Breton, showing effects of active marine erosion.   In the distance is the irregularly cuspate bar known as Southeast Bar.

FIG. 155.   Red sandstones of the New Brunswick Lowland suffering active marine erosion at Cape Bald.

are real and not fictitious. Everywhere the cleared grassy fields or wooded slopes break off abruptly at the crest of a ragged scarp cut in cross-bedded red and grey friable sandstones and shales capped by glacial débris. The latter usually is not of great thickness, but locally extends well down toward the base of the scarp. The form of cliff and upland profiles, the freshness of the wave-cut scarps, the undermining of the roads, the disappearance of lease-corner iron posts and other carefully established landmarks, the loss of coal seams, the records of accurate surveys, and the evidence of comparative photographs of critical points, all combine to give an impressive record of the destructive power of the waves. Along the more sheltered waters of Northumberland Strait the bare red scarps of the New Brunswick coast (Fig. 155) and of the opposite shores of Prince Edward Island tell the same story; while residents whose summer homes border these picturesque waters have good reason to know that even in such sheltered localities as Shediac Bay they are not always immune from the toll which the waves levy upon their lands. The shores of the Bay of Chaleur exhibit many red sandstone cliffs of similar aspect, while the cliffed red conglomerates of Bonaventure Island (Fig. 104) and the neighboring mainland should perhaps also be mentioned in the present connection, although apparently of more resistant character. The formations of the Boston and Narragansett Lowlands are obviously still more resistant to wave erosion and less exposed to the sea than are the rocks of the northern lowlands, and show much less evidence of shore retreat.

Those who have studied most carefully, in connection with coal mining operations, the rate of coastal erosion along the Cape Breton shores, are in substantial agreement that the average figure is approximately 5 or 6 inches a year. If, as there is reason to believe, this coast has remained essentially stationary for the last few thousand years, this rate would allow for the waves cutting into the coast a distance of several thousand feet, providing due allowance is made for the faster rate which doubtless obtained in earlier stages of the process. It would seem that the total average incision of the waves into this coast is to be measured in some such terms, rather than in terms of many miles. Even Brown's more moderate estimate of two miles,[5] based on long and evidently careful study of the region, appears to be excessive; for this figure was obtained by projecting seaward, in a number of favorable localities, the observed upland slope " at the same angle of declination " until it intersected sealevel some two miles out (the straight line ABC, Fig. 156).  An inspection of the coast at a large number of points between Point Aconi and Mira Bay shows that the upland surfaces are characteristically convex, and that their angles of slope gradually increase toward sealevel. Hence a more plausible restoration of the typical upland profile would be that of the curved line ABD, Fig. 156, in which the restored surface is seen to intersect sealevel much closer to the present shoreline.  One who in the field mentally projects many of these slopes seaward gains the impression that something like five or six thousand feet might be a fair figure for the average extent of shoreline retreat along this coast.

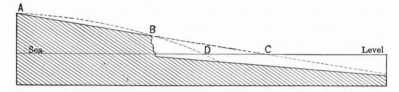

FIG. 156.    Projection of upland slopes of a cliffed coast to determine approximate position of the former shoreline.

### Supposed Extensive Marine Erosion of the Magdalen Islands. —

In contrast with the evidence of moderate marine incision of the weak-rock shores described above, there are certain features which have been interpreted to indicate a far greater work accomplished by the waves.  In a report on observations on the Magdalen Islands, Clarke[15] infers an enormous amount of marine erosion of the weak Permo-Carboniferous rocks there exposed, and considers the islands as mere remnants of a much greater mass almost destroyed by the sea.  " If the eye will follow the 20-fathom line on the chart, it will be seen what a tremendous platform has been carried away by the waves in the gradual wasting of the land to this slight depth and what slender broken remnants of it now remain above the water line."[15]    As the 20-fathom line is in places from 15 to 20 miles, or even more distant from the island cliffs, this would mean a very impressive exhibition of marine abrasion at or near the present sealevel.  There is, however, no clear indication of a platform edge at the 20-fathom line.  A northwest-southeast profile (Fig. 157) across the islands transverse to the major axis of the low anticlinal arch which is believed to be represented by the Magdalens, shows the best submarine terraces at depths of 36 and 50 fathoms. These are 45 and 50 miles out from the island shore, and only 15 and 10 miles respectively from the coast of Cape Breton. This geographical relationship would appear to eliminate the terraces in question from the class of wave-made platforms; and the facts that they occur on the wall of a deep channel bordering the northwestern coast of Cape Breton, and that the opposite wall of this channel shows a minor terrace at a third and different level, seem to indicate that they represent the subaërially terraced walls of a valley now deeply drowned, and are therefore to be classed with the prominent terraces which characterize the submerged valley of the lower St. Lawrence (Figs. 110, 111 and 112).

Additional profiles (Fig. 158) outward from the Magdalen Islands in various directions fail to show the presence of a graded platform sloping outward to the 20-fathom line, then descending more steeply into deeper water. They show instead an undulating surface descending more or less irregularly to greater and greater depths with occasional flats of considerable breadth which might be interpreted either as imperfect wave-cut benches, or as subaërial forms normally developed by stream action on nearly horizontal rocks, later submerged and more or less modified by marine erosion and deposition. The most pronounced of these flats are found off the south side of the islands at depths of 18, 16, and 12–14 fathoms (profiles B, C, and D,

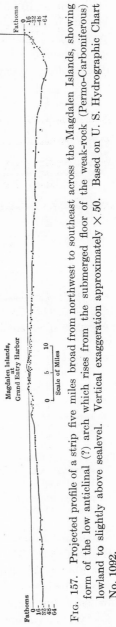

Fig. 157.  Projected profile of a strip five miles broad from northwest to southeast across the Magdalen Islands, showing form of the low anticlinal (?) arch which rises from the submerged floor of the weak-rock (Permo-Carboniferous) lowland to slightly above sealevel.  Vertical exaggeration approximately × 50.  Based on U. S. Hydrographic Chart No. 1092.

Fig. 158); off the east side at 20 fathoms (profile G); and off the north side at 10 fathoms (profile I). Other fairly well developed flats are found at depths of 30 fathoms (profile E) and 32 fathoms (profile J). There are more or less abrupt steepenings of slope or " drop-offs," such as usually mark the outer margins of terraces, at the following depths: 12 fathoms (profile I), 16 fathoms (C),

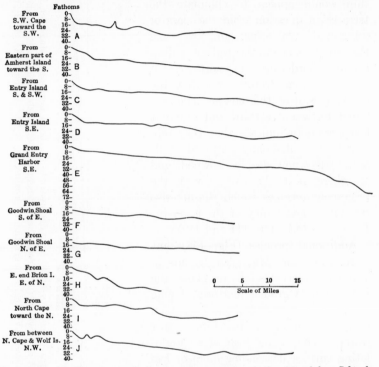

FIG. 158. Profiles seaward from various parts of the Magdalen Islands showing form of seafloor. Vertical exaggeration approximately × 100. Based on U. S. Hydrographic Chart No. 1092. E and J are projected profiles of strips 5 miles broad (see Fig. 157); the others are simple linear profiles, following continuous lines of soundings where feasible.

18 fathoms (A and D), 20 fathoms (E), 26 fathoms (A), 30 fathoms (B and C), 36 fathoms (E), and 50 fathoms (E). The last two have already been discussed.

As is the case with all profiles of inclined undulating surfaces of low relief, one may suspect terrace levels and margins at a great variety of elevations, and one is therefore in doubt where to draw the line between those sufficiently distinct to be significant of the origin of the forms in question, and those which have no particular significance. Possibly other levels should be included in the above list as of potential significance; or possibly some of those given should be excluded as without meaning. In any case it would seem that the submarine contours afford no clear evidence of extensive marine planation. The irregularity of the profiles, the fact that certain of the nearly flat areas are shallower on their seaward than on their landward margins, the variable elevations, widths, and degrees of imperfection of these flats, all point to the conclusion that the submarine plain surrounding the Magdalen Islands is primarily of subaërial origin. Wave erosion has undoubtedly reduced parts of the undulating plain to lower levels; and deposition of débris has doubtless filled or partially filled some of the shallow valleys. The result was the production of more perfect flats wherever the depths below sealevel or the distances from land were not too great, and the topography submerged was favorable to the levelling process. The most pronounced suggestion of wave erosion is seen in the sudden steepening of the submarine slope in the vicinity of the shore, a feature characteristic of practically all of the profiles, except F and G which are not extended to the land.

I have not found anything in the submarine physiography giving us a definite clue as to where the original shoreline of the Magdalen Islands was located. That it was not very far out from its present position is suggested by the evidence of the profiles that profound modification of the submerged land surface has not yet been accomplished. On the other hand, comparatively rapid erosion of the weak rocks of the lowlands has been shown to be the rule along the lowland coasts. In the relatively short period during which the sea has maintained its present level, we should therefore expect a considerable but not an excessive retreat of the shoreline,— a retreat measured at most by a very few miles, and more probably to be expressed in thousands of feet. The form of islands and seabottom appears to accord best with the interpretation that the shallows about the islands represent a faint elevation left by subaërial denudation on the floor of the St. Lawrence Lowland, while the islands themselves are the highest knolls crowning this elevation, left unsubmerged when the lower land was drowned. Since the islands were first formed by this partial submergence, they have been reduced in size a limited but unknown amount by wave erosion, and more or less extensively connected by wave-built bars (Fig. 169); while the subaërial contours of the surrounding shallows have been more or less modified by marine deposition and abrasion.

**Cliffs of Diminishing Altitude are Rare.** — That the retreat of the shore bordering the weak-rock lowlands has not been very great is indicated by the scarcity of cliffs of diminishing altitude. The case at Pt. Aconi (Fig. 153) is exceptional, and apparently due in part at least to exceptional circumstances already discussed.    As a rule the cliffs are mainly those of increasing altitude, while those of the reverse type are of limited number and of small magnitude.    Even in the Pt. Aconi region, whether one looks west or east, he cannot doubt that the cliffs are for the most part of the type associated with coasts which have suffered only moderate marine abrasion.    The same is true where the waves are cutting into the coast just outside Sydney Harbor (Fig. 150), and where occasional apparent exceptions are of minor dimensions; both east and west of the New Waterford district, where the cliffs are low, and on either side of the entrance to Indian Bay where on the east they show heights of 25 or 30 feet; around the shores of Glace Bay (Fig. 151) where the cliffs vary in height from 15 or 20 up to 30 or more feet; and in general all along this coast is one impressed with the prevalence of cliffs of increasing height and the scarcity of good examples of the opposite type. The same rule holds good for the New Brunswick and Prince Edward Island shores, and even on capes where the results of wave work are unusually prominent one generally finds cliffs of increasing altitude (Fig. 155).    Here, however, the inroads of the sea are obviously less extensive than on the more exposed coasts of Cape Breton; for along the south side of Northumberland Strait the low-lying land slopes gently down into the water, to the distant view seemingly devoid of cliffs for long stretches, although a closer inspection reveals small scarps where none were first suspected, and fairly high cliffs on some of the salient headlands.    Nevertheless the contrast with the Cape Breton coast is most striking and in considerable measure is an expression of the difference in exposure to wave action between the two places.

Parts of the Chaleur Bay lowland coast more closely resemble the cliffed Cape Breton shores, and the excellent views which one obtains in the course of a day's journey along the crest of the ragged scarp, which in places is so close under the railway line as to constitute a distinct menace to the safety of the travelling

public, are sufficient to establish the overwhelming predominance
of cliffs of increasing altitude.   At Cape d'Espoir there is a fine
cliff of diminishing altitude, perhaps 60 feet high at present, cut
in the nearly horizontal red sandstones; but this exposed point
is one of a very limited number of exceptions   In strong contrast
with the wooded highlands, which usually rise more or less abruptly
some distance inland but occasionally reach the sea to give
stretches of rugged coast of irregular pattern, the grassy lowland
belt characteristically slopes southward to the sea, to end abruptly
in cliffs which must get higher as the waves cut farther inland.
Projecting the lowland slope till it intersects sealevel, one secures
confirmation of the moderate amount of wave erosion suffered by
these shores.   Everywhere one finds abundant evidence that
despite the comparatively rapid encroachment of the sea upon the
margins of the weak-rock lowlands, the process has not yet gone
very far.   In other words, the evidence seems clearly to indicate
that the work began not very long ago.

**Triassic Lowland Shores.** — The almost complete submergence
of the Triassic Lowland which produced the Bay of Fundy left few
areas of Triassic rocks exposed to vigorous wave attack.   The only
large Triassic areas are found about the head of the Bay (Fig.
13), exposed to relatively weak waves developed in the Basin of
Minas.   Smaller areas at isolated points, subject to more effective
marine erosion, give a better measure of the inroads of the sea on
the weak Triassic sediments.   Thus at Quaco, New Brunswick,
the waves have cut steep cliffs in soft Triassic sandstones and conglomerates, the latter beds being so little consolidated that the
pebbles are easily separated from one another with the hands.
Whittle[16] emphasizes the relatively incoherent character of the
conglomerate, the readiness with which it yields material to the
waves in such abundance as to embarrass them, and the beauty
of the cliffs which " in many places present mural faces three
hundred feet high."   I have not seen the Quaco cliffs, but their
position along the Fundian Fault zone makes it seem possible that
the region presented steep slopes to the sea when the waves first
began their work upon this shore.   In any case, Whittle's description
makes clear the small resistance which the rocks here oppose to
wave attack; and the rapidity with which the waves are eating into
exposed shores of the Triassic and Carboniferous Lowlands renders
all the more impressive the evidence, equally strong, that the total
erosive work accomplished at the present level is not great.

**Résumé.** — Our examination of wave work along the shores of the weak-rock lowlands has revealed the fact that these shores are being cut back with a rapidity quite unknown along the hard-rock coasts studied in earlier chapters. A loss of land amounting to one foot or even several feet per year in exposed localities is not unknown, while long stretches of coast seem to be cut back at an average annual rate of about six inches. Yet despite this rapid incision of the waves, the total amount of erosion accomplished at the present level does not appear to be very great. Headlands have been cut back and bays bridged across by baymouth bars to give relatively simple outer shorelines bordering exposed low coasts; but the total breadth of the zone thus lost to the sea is apparently to be measured in a few thousands of feet rather than in miles. Accordingly we are led to conclude that the time during which the sea has operated at the present level cannot have been great, probably a matter of some few thousand years at most.

## BIBLIOGRAPHY

1. DAWSON, J. W. "Acadian Geology," 2nd Ed., 401, London, 1868.
2. GILPIN, EDWIN. "The Submarine Coal of Cape Breton, N. S." North of England Inst. Min. and Mech. Eng., Trans., XXIV, 182, 1875.
3. GILPIN, EDWIN. "The Submarine Coal of Cape Breton, N. S." North of England Inst. Min. and Mech. Eng., Trans., XXIV, 174, 1875.
4. NICHOLS, D. A. Personal communication.
5. BROWN, RICHARD. "The Coal Fields and Coal Trade of the Island of Cape Breton," 12, London, 1871.
6. HAYES, A. O. Unpublished notes on coast erosion bordering the Sydney coal field, Geological Survey of Canada.
7. BROWN, RICHARD. "The Coal Fields and Coal Trade of the Island of Cape Breton," 41, London, 1871.
8. GANONG, W. F. "The Physical Geography of the North Shore Sand Islands." Nat. Hist. Soc. New Brunswick, Bull., VI, No. XXVI, 26, 1908.
9. GANONG, W. F. ("The Site of Denys' Establishment at Miscou.") Footnote on page 203 of Ganong's translation of "The Description and Natural History of the Coasts of North America" by Nicolas Denys, 625 pp., Toronto, 1908.
   GANONG, W. F. "Additions and Corrections to Monographs on the Place-Nomenclature, Cartography, Historic Sites, Boundaries, and Settlement-Origins of the Province of New Brunswick." Roy. Soc. Can., Proc. and Trans., 2nd Ser., XII, Sec. II, 133, 1906.
10. GANONG, W. F. "A Monograph of Historic Sites in the Province of New Brunswick." Roy. Soc. Can., Proc. and Trans., 2nd Ser., V, Sec. II, 289–290, 1899.
    GANONG, W. F. "Evidences of the Sinking of the Coast of New Brunswick." Nat. Hist. Soc. New Brunswick, Bull., IV, No. XIX, 340, 1901.

11. GANONG, W. F.  Personal communication.
12. GANONG, W. F.  "Further Data upon the Rate of Recession of the Coast Line of New Brunswick."  Nat. Hist. Soc. New Brunswick, Bull., VII, No. XXXI, 1-5, 1913.
13. GOLDTHWAIT, J. W.  "Supposed Evidences of Subsidence of the Coast of New Brunswick Within Modern Time."  Geol. Surv. Can., Mus. Bull. No. 2, 48, 1914.
14. WRIGHT, W. J.  "Geology of the Moncton Map Area."  Geol. Surv. Can., Mem. 129, plate II, 1922.
15. CLARKE, JOHN M.  "Observations on the Magdalen Islands."  N. Y. State Mus. Bull. No. 149, 134-155, 1910.
16. WHITTLE, C. L.  "The Beach Phenomena at Quaco, N. B."  Amer. Geol., VII, 183-187, 1891.

# CHAPTER X

## WAVE-BUILT FORMS BORDERING THE WEAK-ROCK LOWLANDS

**Advance Summary.** — Rapid marine abrasion of irregular weak-rock lowland shores should produce a wealth of wave-built beaches and bars of various types. In the present chapter we shall examine the shores of the Carboniferous and Triassic Lowlands of the New England-Acadian province to determine what light a study of these wave-built forms may throw upon the physiography of the shoreline under investigation, especially with reference to the progress made in the present cycle of shoreline development since the sea attained its present level. Incidentally this will confirm or refute our previous conclusion as to the relative recency of the submergence which initiated the present marine cycle.

**Baymouth Bars of the Northeastern New Brunswick Shore.** — The conclusion in favor of more vigorous marine erosion of the lowland formations is supported by an examination of the features due to wave deposition bordering the lowland coasts. The most significant forms in this connection are the baymouth bars, the extensive development of which in the Miscou Island-Buctouche Harbor section of the New Brunswick coast (Fig. 147), and on the northern coast of Prince Edward Island (Fig. 148) has previously been mentioned. The characteristics of the first series and the changeable nature of the inlets or " gullies " which break the continuity of parts of the series, are briefly described by Ganong.[1] That author's contention that the bars indicate a subsidence of the coast will be discussed in a later volume. That these spits and bars are the product of littoral drift or beach drifting under the influence of wave action, rather than of tidal or other currents, was recognized by Stead[2] in his brief account of the New Brunswick shores. The sandspits which nearly unite Miscou Island with Shippegan Island, and the latter with the mainland, may be considered as baymouth bars, notwithstanding that the bays behind them have openings to the west. If completed to close the bay mouths, they would also be tombolos.

*Tabusintac Bar.* — The fact that Tabusintac Bar is convex toward the sea, especially in its southern half, is explained by Ganong as due to the rapid retreat of the headland near its southern extremity, which, consisting of peat (the " Blacklands "), is rapidly being cut away by the waves; but it may be observed that the free end of a spit or bar is frequently deflected landward, whether mildly to give a gentle convexity toward the sea or strongly to produce a recurved spit, for reasons which I have explained elsewhere,[3] and which have to do with the relations of conflicting currents and with current direction as affected by the outline of the mainland shore.   A further word may be added here.   If spits or bars lie landward of a straight line connecting the adjacent headlands, their general pattern will normally be concave toward the sea, the two extremities curving seaward to connect with the headlands.   This results from the fact that the ultimate tendency of onshore wave action is to drive a bar landward during or after its development, or both, a process which is partially checked when the waves encounter shallow water or the mainland.   This they do well seaward near the headlands, but not until they have reached farther in along the axis of the embayment.   Hence the concave pattern.   But where inlets interrupt the continuity of growing spits or bars which are in general concave toward the sea, the free ends of the embankments in the vicinity of the inlets are commonly deflected landward by the force of landward moving currents caused by tides and waves; and this may give a convex pattern to a significant part of each section of the embankment, as is obvious, for example, in several of the bars forming the concave festoon across the mouth of Miramichi Bay (Fig. 159).

Where longshore current action is pronounced, a spit may grow straight across the mouth of a bay to the opposite headland, to form a straight baymouth bar; or if the opposite headland is set back some distance, " offset " so to speak, from the general trend of the coast which has given to the longshore current its " set " or direction, then the spit will begin to deflect toward the land as the longshore current becomes dissipated and weakened in deeper and deeper water, with consequent formation of a bar convex toward the sea.   This seems to offer a satisfactory explanation for the Tabusintac Bar, the Blacklands headland being set far back of the line along which the southward moving current naturally endeavored to extend the growing spit (Fig. 147).   Convex bars also result where a shoal in front of the coast retards the retrogression of the central part of the embankment, while the ends are deflected landward during growth, or driven landward later.

*Form of the Miramichi Embayment.* — The great Miramichi embayment (Fig. 159), with its relatively simple northwestern shore and its far more irregular southeastern shore, reminds one

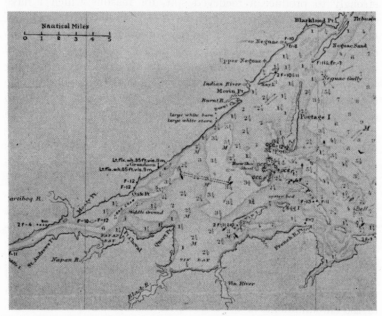

FIG. 159. Miramichi Bay, New Brunswick, showing contrast between rectilinear northwestern, and irregular southeastern shores. The former is probably determined, directly or indirectly, by some structural control, possibly faulting. The mouth of the bay is partially closed by a series of bars interrupted by inlets. From U. S. Hydrographic Chart No. 1067.

of the Aspy embayment (Fig. 21); and the query suggests itself as to whether in the Miramichi case, as in the Aspy Bay region, a fault line may not have determined the rectilinear northwestern shoreline. Certainly some structural control, if not faulting then folding or warping sufficiently pronounced and involving beds sufficiently contrasted in resistance to give, after erosion, a distinct slope (whether scarp or dip slope is immaterial) into the embayment along a northeast-southwest line, seems the most plausible explanation of this marked contrast in shoreline pattern. Such a structural trend is in harmony with the chief tectonic lines of the Acadian region, and with known folding in this immediate district, as has been shown in an earlier chapter.

*Portage Island and Fox Island Bars.* — But we are here chiefly concerned with the beautiful series of bars festooned across the mouth of the bay in a line concave to the sea. The largest of these, Portage Island and Fox Island, have been made the subject of a special paper by Ganong[4] from which Fig. 160 is reproduced because, while it makes no claim to accuracy, it shows the essential physiographic features of Portage Island far better than do the charts. As is clear from the figure, the structure of the island is identical with that of a compound recurved spit, showing on the inner side the series of landward deflected points which represent successive recurved southern termini of the growing embankment and which demonstrate the correctness of Ganong's conclusion that this island is "rolling southward." The truncation of the parallel ridges and swales by the outer shoreline shows that there has also been a landward movement of the embankment, such as is most frequently characteristic of a compound recurved spit.[5] Since Portage Island is not a true spit, we may perhaps best call it a "compound recurved bar." The descent of the recurved points beneath the waters of the

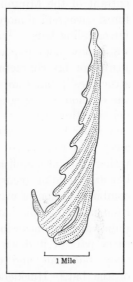

FIG. 160. Portage Island, at mouth of Miramichi Bay, New Brunswick. (After Ganong.)

bay, and the position of the bars some distance out from the mainland, are interpreted by Ganong as proofs of subsidence. It seems to me that such an interpretation must be based on a misapprehension of the physical conditions controlling spit and bar formations, a subject which I have already treated elsewhere,[6] and will discuss more at length in a later volume.

Fox Island is similar to Portage, although apparently more complex in that the truncation of an earlier set of ridges and swales has in places been followed by the prograding of the shore to give a new series of ridges and swales in front of, and at a marked angle to, the older series, a phenomenon manifested on a grand scale at Cape Canaveral.  Whether the westward trending ridges ever had any great extension in that direction may be regarded as doubtful.  They probably declined into the bay at no great distance, like the recurved points along the western side of Portage Island.  Both Fox and Portage Islands are partially covered with trees, which suggests that they have been retreating westward more slowly than the bars to the north and south.  The latter are perhaps somewhat more exposed than those in the reentrant of the Miramichi embayment, and are generally free of forest cover and of more youthful aspect, a characteristic of rapidly retrograding bars.  There can be no doubt of the gradual landward movement of the bars recognized by Ganong, and of the justice of his characterization of them as " remarkably mobile structures"; but I am not able to agree with his interpretation of the method of retrograding[7] in which shoals and islands on tidal deltas within the inlets are believed by him to form the nuclei of a new inner line of beaches or bars, leaving the old bar to be cut away and reduced to a submarine shoal.  Retrogression seems rather to be accomplished partly by cutting from the front of the bar and building recurved spits at the inlets, and partly by the combined action of waves and winds in taking material from the front margin of the bar and casting it farther up the beach slope (landward), whence wind, rain, spray, and overwash of storm waves carry part of it down the backslope into the marsh or lagoon.  Only abnormally and temporarily do the waves prograde the front of the bar.[8]  Huckleberry Island is a remnant of the upland bordered by beaches, but Chalmer's idea that the island bars were also formed about resistant nuclei[9] seems to have been based on an erroneous idea of the origin and evolution of the forms in question.

*Buctouche Bar.* — The beautiful series of bars which sweep in a graceful curve from Sapin Point to Richibucto Head (Fig. 147) might be regarded as a bayhead bar with respect to the embayment as a whole, or as baymouth bars across the individual drowned valleys.  Buctouche Bar (Fig. 161) developed into a remarkably fine example of a compound recurved spit, showing a whole series of recurved points along the inner margin of its southern half.  It reveals in clearest manner the truncation by the outer shoreline of the ridges and swales of the distal portion, and the narrowness of the bar and scarcity of recurved points

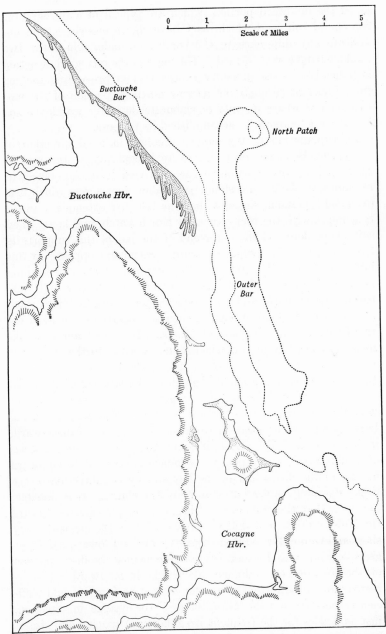

FIG. 161.  Buctouche and Cocagne Harbors, showing remarkable compound recurved spit across mouth of former, and series of spits and forelands near entrance to latter.

along the landward portion, which are typical of a retrograding compound spit, and which, as I have shown elsewhere,[10] do not indicate any difference in the conditions under which the two unlike portions were formed.   The vigor of the retrograding action is indicated by the difficulty experienced in preventing the sea from breaking through the narrow northern portion of the embankment,[11] where in spite of elaborate defensive works the sea has at least temporarily accomplished its purpose.

An explanation of the sudden changes in axial direction of Buctouche Bar may be found in an irregularity of the rate of retreat of different portions influenced possibly by differences in resistance of the uneven submerged valley floor across which it is extended.   Ganong suggests that the bar first extended seaward to connect with the rocky shoal of North Patch, and later, when subsidence deprived the outer end of the bar of this support, its free end gradually swung landward.   Seemingly opposed to this interpretation is the fact that the pronounced channel running north and south between the subaqueous Outer Bar and Buctouche Bar is simple and continuously open except for a rock shoal in one place, instead of being irregularly obstructed or even extinguished as would probably be the case if a great sand embankment had recently migrated across it;  and the further fact that the recurved points on the inner side of the Buctouche Bar show that from a beginning slightly north of the latitude of the shoal the bar must have been built progressively southeastward but very little in front of its present position.   Had the bar swung back to its present location from one far to the northeastward, in line with the North Patch, it could hardly possess such a series of recurved points as appear to be indicated both by the landward margin of the distal half of the bar and by the direction of the ridges obscurely indicated on some of the charts.   It is possible, however, that the embankment began as a spit directed toward the North Patch;  and that as wave erosion on the exposed rocky shoal and Outer Bar reduced them to lower and lower levels, progressively larger and larger waves broke against the distal portion of the growing embankment, deflecting it landward.   The irregular and intermittent character of marine forces would sufficiently account for the abruptness of the change in direction, just as it does for the frequent irregularity in spacing and size of beach ridges, and in the direction of sandspit extension.   It is also possible that irregularities in tidal and other conflicting currents moving in and out of the Buctouche embayment, south-eastward along the coast, and perhaps both north and south through the channel between the mainland and the Outer Bar, are responsible for the serpentine form of the Buctouche Bar, just as they have been for other serpentine embankments.  Whatever the correct explanation, it is not necessary to regard the Outer Bar as a former bay bar rising above the water, later carried below sealevel by recent submergence and erosion.  It seems more probable that it is a former subaërial rock ridge continuing north-ward the ridge which partially encloses Cocagne Harbor on the east, an interpretation which receives some support from the in-dications of " rock " on several parts of the bar as represented on the hydrographic charts.

**Bars of Northern Prince Edward Island.** — Cascumpeque Har-bor and Malpeque (or Richmond) Bay in the western half of Prince Edward Island (Fig. 148) have already been cited as beautiful examples of bays formed by the partial submergence of a dendritic drainage system.  The mouths of these bays are blocked by a series of bars extending in a faintly curved arc from the Cape Kildare headland to that of Cape Aylesbury, a distance of from twenty-five to thirty miles.  Between the two bays is a low, broad headland; and although the waves appear to be push-ing the line of bars gradually landward, it has not yet touched this part of the mainland at any point, a long strip of shallow water known as " The Narrows " connecting the two bays (Fig. 162). Here, more than is usually the case, the bay bars partake of the character of a single offshore bar broken by numerous tidal inlets.

*Changeable Inlets.* — The variability in the number, size, and position of the inlets which interrupt the continuity of this bar, is typical of others along the New England-Acadian shore, and may justify a further word.  The present aspect of the barrier is strongly suggestive of past changes in the position of inlets.  In places the barrier consists of successive dune ridges, the back ones being well forested and representing a relatively ancient part of the bar.  Elsewhere the barrier is covered with grass only, while in still other places it consists of a low, sandy flat, barren of vegetation.  Judging from experience gained on other bars, the low bare patches probably represent old inlets which have been filled up at a comparatively recent period.

The testimony of old inhabitants of the region confirms the physiographic evidence of changeable inlets.  According to a citizen of Alberton, whose knowledge of the barrier beach dates back fifty years, there have been times when several of the inlets now open have been closed.  He gave dates for the opening and closing of certain of these, and called attention to the present existence of inlets not shown on any map of the region.  At the time of my visit there was an inlet through the barrier some distance southeast of the Black Bank cliffs.  This inlet had been opened about five years before, according to the fisherman who

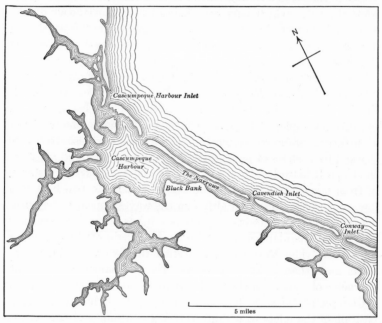

Fig. 162.  Cascumpeque Harbor, Prince Edward Island, a partially submerged dendritic drainage system in nearly horizontal weak rocks.  The strip of water known as The Narrows extends southeastward to connect with Malpeque Bay, partially visible in the lower right-hand corner.

accompanied me, and who stated that prior to its opening there was a continuous stretch of unbroken beach for 5 miles northwest from Cavendish Inlet.  On a " Plan of the Island of St. John " (Prince Edward Island), based on surveys by Captain Holland, and dated 1765, no inlets are shown between Cavendish Inlet and the main entrance to " Holland Bay " (Cascumpeque Harbor), north of Savage Island.  This doubtless correctly represents the conditions at that time, for the map is quite detailed as to shore features, gives many soundings, and appears to be reasonably accurate. The "Hydrographic Chart of Prince Edward Island and Adjacent Coasts," published by the U. S. Navy Department in 1888, shows two additional inlets between these same points. On the other hand, one inlet into the northern part of the harbor, and another into the Narrows, east of Conway Inlet, prominently shown by the Holland map, do not appear on the Hydrographic Chart. Mr. Lawrence W. Watson, of the Canadian Department of Marine and Fisheries and a resident of Charlottetown, Prince Edward Island, has informed me that since my visit to the Island Cavendish Inlet has closed and a new one opened some distance away. All the evidence agrees in indicating that the inlets are temporary and changeable features. The importance of this fact in connection with the problem of coastal subsidence will fully appear in a later volume.

*Shoreline Changes at Cascumpeque Harbor.* — On the southeast side of the main entrance to Cascumpeque Harbor, the adjacent portion of the bar terminates in a poorly formed spit curving into the harbor. On this spit are a series of dune ridges separated by low swales, indicating successive additions to its area. Some of the ridges and swales are sharply truncated by a newer set, and these in turn are themselves cut across by the present shoreline. Evidently there have been considerable changes in the form and position of this part of the bar and consequently in the adjacent inlet. Still more interesting, however, is the devastation wrought among the trees on the seaward side of the barrier as a result of normal shoreline retreat under continued wave attack. Of the ridges and swales truncated by the present shoreline, the north-westerly or later ones are covered with grass, while the south-easterly or older ones are forested. The fact that these ridges and swales are abruptly cut off by the present shore is sufficient proof that the waves have been driving the shoreline landward. That this process is actively going on is shown in a most interesting manner. Where the forested ridges approach the outer shore their form is destroyed or masked by quantities of the red beach sand which the waves have driven into the edge of the forest, burying the bases of the trees and partially filling up the seaward ends of the swales. Salt water not only saturates the sand at every storm, but passes into the swales to form salt ponds which may stand for some time in the depressions. Trees that were formerly protected from salt water by the ridges and swales in

front of them, are now succumbing to the " flank attack " of the
sea. A more desolate scene can scarcely be imagined than that
afforded by the ghostly trunks of the dead trees standing in the
barren waste of red sand under a stormy sky (Fig. 163).

*Tidal Deltas.* — The two principal inlets into Cascumpeque
Harbor have associated with them fairly pronounced tidal deltas
of the usual type[12]; and the same is true of the two chief inlets
into Malpeque Bay, that of West Gully (Fig. 164) being the smaller
but more typically formed of the two. Similar tidal deltas, the
channels across which are constantly shifting, are found at a
number of points along the New England-Acadian coast. Eastward from Malpeque Bay there is a succession of smaller bays

Fig. 163. Baymouth bar partially closing Cascumpeque Harbor, Prince
Edward Island, showing effects of retrograding shore. The forest is
being invaded and the trees killed by sand cut from the outer beach
and thrown backward on older part of bar, and by salt-water pools
occupying swales blocked by the sand.

with mouths partially blocked by bars interrupted by narrow
inlets, while between the bays are significant stretches of cliffed
rocky headlands, the whole making a remarkably simple shoreline
of submergence in a submature stage of development (Fig. 148).

**Spits and Bars of the Southern Shore of Prince Edward Island.** —
Nothing comparable to the simple outer shorelines of northeastern
New Brunswick and northern Prince Edward Island with their
frequent alternations of cliffed headlands and baymouth bars is
to be found along the New England-Acadian coast until we reach
the borders of the glacial outwash plains of southern New England,
to be discussed in a later chapter. The southern shoreline of

Prince Edward Island is obviously in an earlier stage of development. The chief re-entrant, Hillsborough Bay, like all the bays of any size on this protected shore, is not only open to the sea, but shows a surprisingly small number of minor wave-built forms, among which the double tombolo of Buchanan Point (U. S. Hydro-

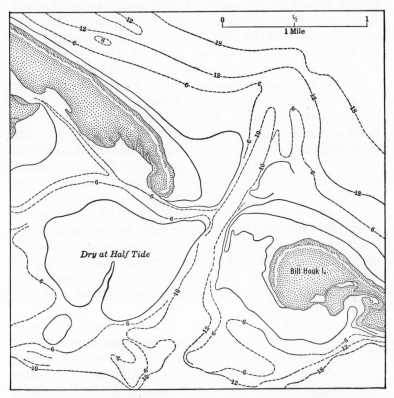

FIG. 164. West Gully, a tidal inlet into Malpeque Bay, Prince Edward Island, and its associated tidal delta of typical double form, the seaward portion characteristically of smaller size and more simple pattern, the lagoonward portion larger and more irregularly lobate. Note the compound recurved bars on either side of the inlet. Based on U. S. Hydrographic Chart No. 2695.

graphic Chart No. 1068), apparently attached to a small island and perhaps originally to a larger island or shoal immediately in front, is the most interesting. Bedeque Harbor to the west is similar in character, but shows a good example of two spits growing toward each other, under the influence of converging currents, to form a bay bar (Fig. 165), and very excellent cases of bifurcated and trifurcated sandspits, apparently the product of variable wave and current action between the mainland and a neighboring island. These two spits may soon unite to form a tombolo. The northwest side of Egmont Bay, the last large reentrant toward the west, shows a very good example of a spit, apparently of the compound recurved type, enclosing a long lagoon known as Wolfe Inlet, and being continued eastward by the bar known as Brae Island. Together these two might be considered as forming a fair example of a bayhead bar.

**Western and Eastern Shores of Prince Edward Island.** — The simple western shoreline of Prince Edward Island exhibits minor examples of baymouth bars, but is believed to owe its fairly rectilinear pattern to some tectonic cause rather than to a maturity of development which would seem incompatible with its limited exposure to wave action. It has been noted that this shoreline trends with the shallow folds known to exist in this region, and that Dawson and Harrington[13] show an anticlinal axis parallel to and but a short distance out from the shore. This is the structure which Ells[14] calls the Miminegash anticline, and as this authority reports the presence of limestone visible at low tide at one point on the coast, it is possible that erosion of limestone exposed along the arch of the anticline, or faulting, gave a rectilinear termination to the sandstone series along a low scarp facing northwest from Cape Wolfe to North Point.

The eastern shore of the island is intermediate in character between the northern and southern. The great development of bay bars and consequent simplicity of the former are lacking; but spits and bars are a more pronounced feature of the shore than along Northumberland Strait. Murray Harbor is partially closed by two spits, one of which, Old Store Point (U. S. Hydrographic Chart No. 1150), is sharply recurved and seems to be in process of forming a cuspate bar. Very pretty examples of minor spits, cuspate bars and forelands, and tombolos are found about the island and mainland shores within the harbor. Cardigan Bay, next north, is partially closed by two typical long, narrow tombolos, that on the north joining Boughton Island to the mainland, while a short double tombolo connects this island with Boughton Point. In this same area there are a good serpentine spit and other wave-built forms, while the shores of the bay abound in illustrations of simple spits, recurved spits (Billhook

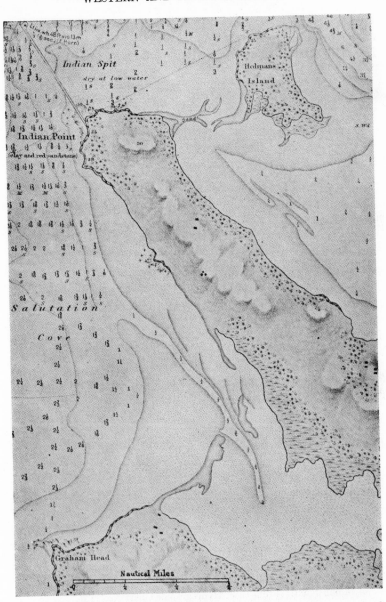

FIG. 165. Indian Point region, Bedeque Harbor, Prince Edward Island, showing at south two sandspits growing toward each other across the mouth of a small bay; and at the north trifurcated and bifurcated spits growing toward each other to form a tombolo uniting Holman's Island to mainland. Small cuspate bar on northeast corner of island. From U. S. Hydrographic Chart No. 1080.

Point), cuspate bars (Aitkins Point), and other similar forms, all of small size, but admirably shown on U. S. Hydrographic Chart No. 1077. Still farther north the Boughton River embayment is

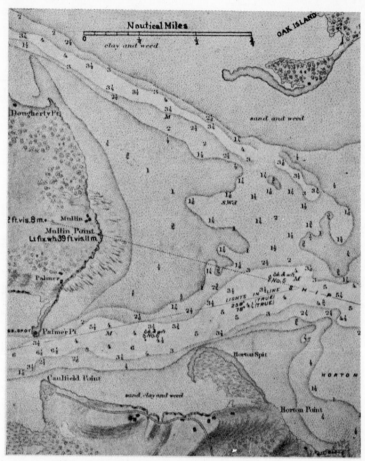

FIG. 166. Entrance to Wallace Harbor, Nova Scotia, showing serpentine spit extending west from Oak Island, the cuspate bar of Caulfield Point, Horton Spit recurving as if to form a larger cuspate bar, and two minor spits at Dougherty Point and Palmer Point flanking the winged headland of Mullin Point. From U. S. Hydrographic Chart No. 1151.

nearly closed by a spit or baymouth bar, while on either side of the entrance minor drowned valleys are more or less completely blocked by baymouth bars (U. S. Hydrographic Chart No. 2696). Near East Point the shore becomes fairly straight, probably due to structural control, and is bordered for several miles by a long narrow spit or offshore bar, behind which is a narrow lagoon.

**Spits, Forelands and Tombolos of the Protected New Brunswick-Nova Scotian Shore.** — The fairly sheltered shores of New Brunswick and Nova Scotia, under the lee of Prince Edward Island, show features comparable to those of the southern side of the island. Baymouth bars are rare, but the spits, forelands, and tombolos associated with an irregular shore are well developed. Projecting from an island in the mouth of Cocagne Harbor (Fig. 161) are two examples of cuspate bars, the apex of one of which is prolonged to form a Y-tombolo connecting with the fast disappearing sandstone islet at Pacquet Point (U. S. Hydrographic Chart No. 2692). From one side of this bar a subsidiary spit projects backward into the harbor entrance, while on the opposite shore are two small cuspate forelands.

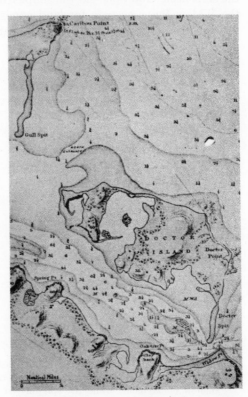

Fig. 167. Entrance to Caribou Harbor, Nova Scotia, showing variety of shore forms, among which the serpentine Gull Spit, the simpler Doctor Spit, and the Widow Point cuspate foreland, deserve special mention. From U. S. Hydrographic Chart No. 1140.

Two typical spits help enclose Shediac Harbor, while about the entrance of Wallace Harbor (Fig. 166), across the boundary in Nova Scotia, we find a good serpentine spit, cuspate bar (Caulfield Point), strongly recurved spit (Horton Spit) approaching the cuspate bar type, and two minor spits extending north and south to make a winged headland[15] of Mullin Point.   The region of Caribou Harbor is a perfect· paradise for the student of minor shore forms, for spits and tombolos of all types, small baymouth bars, and cuspate forelands occur in great variety.   Most interesting of the series are the serpentine Gull Spit and the simpler form of Doctor Spit with the Widow Point cuspate foreland opposite (Fig. 167);  and the Y-tombolo connecting Caribou Island farther west with a small

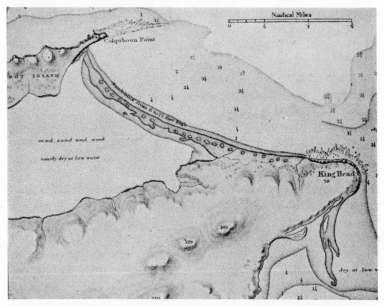

Fig. 168.   King Head at entrance to Merigomish Harbor, Nova Scotia.   A winged headland, the spit or bar on the west blocking the mouth of a shallow embayment, while the spit on the south shows a hooked end and distinct evidence of prograding, indicative of a rapid supply of débris.   From U. S. Hydrographic Chart No. 1099.

outlying island.   Well within the embayment of Pictou Road, at the narrow entrance to Pictou Harbor (U. S. Hydrographic Chart No. 1076) we find two spits developed at right angles to each other, the larger resembling a bayhead bar at the inner end of the Road, and showing the beginnings of a second bar in front of and parallel to the present one;  the smaller growing into the harbor entrance, parallel to the shore but close to the edge of the main channel.

**Increased Development of Baymouth Bars with Increased Exposure.** — East and west of Merigomish Harbor there are long spits or tombolos, sometimes represented as nearly, at other times as completely connecting islands with the mainland. Both of these are practically baymouth bars across bays which have other connections with the sea, and the marked development here of this type of bar is probably related to the greater expanse

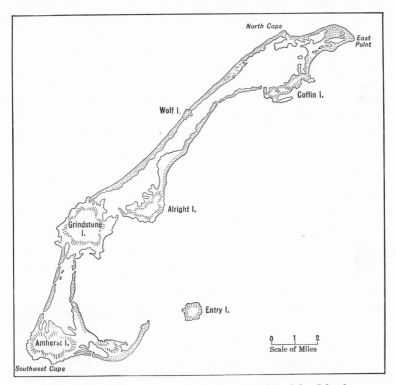

Fig. 169.   Tombolos, bars, and spits of the Magdalen Islands.

of open water toward the northeast; for in our progress eastward we have now passed out from under the lee of Prince Edward Island.   The smaller of the two bars in question, together with a spit on the opposite side of King Head (Fig. 168), makes of this projecting point a good winged headland.   The rectilinear east and west sides of George Bay (Fig. 31) suggest a structural control, which on the east may be a fault prolonged through the Gut of Canso, the latter having some of the features of a partially submerged fault-line valley.  At the head of the bay there is an increased development of baymouth bars, the beginning of which we noticed about Merigomish Harbor.

Antigonish Harbor is nearly blocked by two spits which almost meet, while smaller bays on either side are nearly or completely closed.  The shoreline is, however, decidedly less regular than that bordering the more exposed coast of New Brunswick between Miscou Island and Buctouche Harbor, or the northern coast of Prince Edward Island.  The rectilinear west shores of Cape George and Cape Breton Island, probably dependent indirectly on fault control (fault-line-scarp shorelines?), show occasional baymouth bars but, like most exposed rectilinear shores, are poor in wave-built forms.  According to Dawson[16] a tombolo which formerly connected Port Hood Island to the west coast of Cape Breton has recently been destroyed by the waves.  The Magdalen Islands, a group elongated in a southwest-northeast direction conformable to the shallow folds of Prince Edward Island and adjacent parts of New Brunswick, and situated in the central portion of the great southern embayment of the Gulf of St. Lawrence where they are fairly well exposed to wave attack from all directions, are with few exceptions more or less closely connected with each other by a remarkable series of tombolos, spits, and bars (Fig. 169) which unite to give a fairly simple shoreline on the northwest, but one less simple on the southeast facing the nearest coast, Cape Breton.

**Shore Forms of Chaleur Bay.** — If we pass beyond the present limits of the great Carboniferous Lowland which we have been considering, we find a number of minor weak-rock basins, developed on beds which were either deposited in older depressions, or inwarped, infolded, or infaulted into older rocks, later reduced to lowlands by subaërial erosion, and finally more or less completely submerged to give pronounced embayments in the coast.  Bordering the embayments the lowland rocks may persist as fringes of greater or less breadth.  The shores often show wave-built forms comparable with those on the lowland coasts just studied, and in some of the cases at least there can be no doubt that Carboniferous or other weak rocks along the shores and perhaps on the floor of the embayment have contributed largely to the building of the forms in question.

*Chaleur Bay.* — To the northwest one of the largest of these minor basins is apparently responsible for Chaleur Bay, along the south side of which we find a continuation of the New Brunswick Lowland; while bordering the northern margin is a lowland fringe, in places extremely narrow, occasionally altogether lacking. The lowland is underlain by red sandstones and conglomerates, generally more or less nearly horizontal, but tilted up in places, sometimes very steeply, especially where in contact with the steep border of certain parts of the crystalline upland, usually a short distance inland. The form of the upland border in some places suggests a resurrected sloping peneplane, which may give a resurrected peneplane shoreline just east of Port Daniel; while elsewhere, especially east and west of Cascapediac Bay, the topography leads one to suspect block faulting of ancient date, followed by peneplanation and later removal of the weaker sandstones from the downthrown side of the

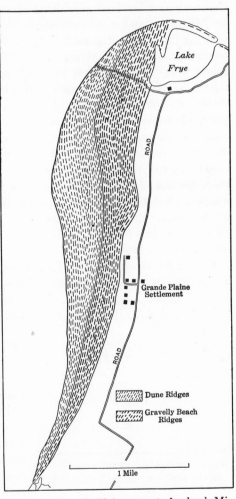

Fig. 170.   Grande Plaine cuspate foreland, Miscou Island, New Brunswick, showing successive beach ridges or "lines of growth," the later series being covered with dune sands. (After Ganong and Goldthwait.)

fault contacts.  The author, however, had no opportunity to verify these impressions, based on views obtained from a passing train.

*Miscou Island Foreland.* — Just at the entrance to Chaleur Bay, on the south side and still within the limits of the greater Carboniferous Lowland considered above, we find facing the bay on Miscou Island a good example of a blunt cuspate foreland showing its " lines of growth " in the form of a beautifully preserved series of beach ridges (Fig. 170). This foreland and its ridges were early described by Chalmers,[9] and later much more fully by Ganong,[17] who distinguished thirty or more parallel beach ridges, the older ones forested, the later covered with beach grass. Because the inner ridge crests were lower on the average than were the outer, Ganong believed that the foreland was formed during a subsidence of the coast; but Goldthwait[18] after a detailed study of the foreland concluded that the older ridges were lower because they lacked the cover of dune sands added by the winds to the later ridges, and that the beach phenomena afforded no support for the subsidence theory. We will return to the consideration of this foreland when discussing the problem of coastal subsidence in a later volume.

*Spits and Cuspate Bars.* — The shores of Chaleur Bay between Shippegan Island and the mainland show a great variety of simple, hooked, compound recurved, and serpentine spits (U. S. Hydrographic Chart No. 1217). Farther up Chaleur Bay to the west, Bathurst Harbor, near the junction of the Carboniferous and older series, is almost closed by two recurved spits growing obliquely into the harbor entrance, toward each other, due to the convergent direction of beach drifting resulting from the general pattern of the shore. To the northeast, across Chaleur Bay, is the beautiful cuspate bar of Paspebiac Point (Fig. 171), the graceful westward curving apex of which is not adequately represented on the charts. Clarke[19] attributes this and other cuspate bars to interfering current action. The narrower and more youthful appearance of one side of a cuspate bar, which is a prominent feature of the Paspebiac example as seen from the upland just north, is a normal

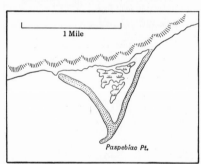

1 Mile

Paspebiao Pt.

Fig. 171. Paspebiac Point, a cuspate bar on the northern side of Chaleur Bay.

feature of cusps built by wave action, the side facing the more vigorous wave impact being forced to retrograde, with the result that it is usually narrower and fresher in appearance than the opposite arm.   Deposition of material carried around the point and added to the opposite side of the bar by weaker waves causes prograding there.   Hence this arm is broader and its older parts obviously of greater age.   As the continuation of this process will transform a cuspate bar into a cuspate foreland eroded on one side and added to on the other, the prevalence of cuspate bars is one indication of the extreme youth of a shoreline.   The fine cuspate bar forming Tracadigash Point at Carleton seems to border a narrow lowland remnant at the base of the great scarp here leading up to the higher peneplane.

**Bayhead Bar of Mal Bay.** — At the eastern end of the Gaspé Peninsula, Mal Bay seems to represent another drowned basin, formerly occupied in part at least by weak red sandstones, near the inner end of which occurs a long, faintly concave gravel bayhead bar (Fig. 81) enclosing the usual lagoon.   The latter feature is known to the inhabitants of the Gaspé country as a " barachois," and connects with the open sea by a narrow inlet or " tickle." Clarke[20] explains the bayhead bar of Mal Bay, as he does other bay bars and cuspate bars, as a product of the interfering action of currents, in this particular case tidal currents.   In another connection I have set forth somewhat fully my reasons for believing that in simple wave action and wave-made currents we find a more potent cause of the forms under discussion than in the impact of river currents against marine waters, the interference of opposing tidal currents, or the interaction of paired tidal, eddy, or other types of currents.[21]   There is, however, much difference of opinion on this point, as the reader who cares to follow the subject further will soon discover.

**Wave-Built Forms of the Cape Breton Island Lowlands.** — On Cape Breton Island we find well-developed bayhead bars near the inner ends of Aspy Bay (Fig. 21) and South Bay, Ingonish (See Geological Survey of Canada, Cape Breton sheet No. 4), these bars in both cases serving also to block the mouths of minor bays behind them.   The extremely irregular Carboniferous Lowland of southeastern Cape Breton shows a truly remarkable series of wave-built forms.   The Saint Ann embayment is separated into two parts, Saint Ann Bay and Saint Ann Harbor, by a compound recurved spit which occupies the position of a midbay bar

(Fig. 172).   Despite its simple outline it shows, both above and below water, the successive recurving beach ridges characteristic of a compound recurved spit, and the angle of deflection from the shore is that of a spit, rather than that of a midbay bar.

In the long narrow arms of the Bras d'Or Lakes ideal conditions exist for the development of cuspate bars and forelands, since vigorous wave attack is limited to two directions, opposed to each

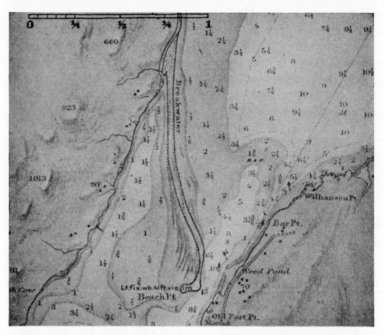

Fig. 172.   Spit separating Saint Ann Bay from Saint Ann Harbor, Cape Breton Island.   Nearly opposite its point is a cuspate bar partially enclosing a shallow pond.   From U. S. Hydrographic Chart No. 1134.

other, with the result that beach drifting is from opposite directions toward inequalities in the shore, shoals, or protected areas back of islands or in the lee of points projecting from the other shore. Accordingly hooked spits, cuspate bars in all stages of development, and forelands in a variety of shapes and sizes abound. The traveler en route to Sydney by rail has fleeting glimpses from the car window of a wonderful series of tombolos, spits, and cuspate bars and forelands bordering the shores of the southeastern side of St. Andrews Channel. Some of these have been described by Tarr,[22] who found in the abundant development of these forms in waters free from strong oceanic or tidal currents convincing evidence that they were produced by waves, and not by such currents as had been supposed by Gulliver.[23] On the basis of more detailed study in this same region Woodman[24] supported Tarr's conclusion as to the wave-formed character of the cuspate bars and forelands, and described briefly and classified a large number of the Bras d'Or forms. The reader is referred to the papers by Tarr and Woodman for a more extended account than space here permits of one of the most remarkable assemblages of detailed shore features to be found anywhere along the New England-Acadian coast. I content myself with calling attention to the profusion with which the cuspate bars are sometimes developed, especially on the southeastern shores of St. Andrews Channel (Fig. 173) and East Bay; to examples of a class of cuspate bars which because of their position in the lee of islands are sometimes called "loop bars" (Fig. 174); and to the extensive development of tombolos, of which Fig. 174 shows a good illustration. The shores of Sydney Harbor (U. S. Hydrographic Chart No. 1061) exhibit beautiful cases of cobblestone and gravel spits and cuspate bars, two of which, Northwest Bar and Southeast Bar (Fig. 154) guard the entrance to the inner harbor.

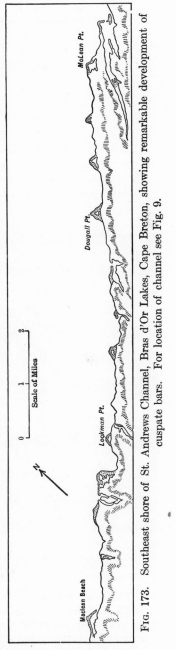

Fig. 173. Southeast shore of St. Andrews Channel, Bras d'Or Lakes, Cape Breton, showing remarkable development of cuspate bars. For location of channel see Fig. 9.

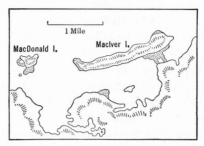

FIG. 174. Loop bars at western ends of MacDonald and MacIver Islands, in western end of St. Patrick Channel, Bras d'Or Lakes. A double tombolo connects MacIver Island with the mainland.

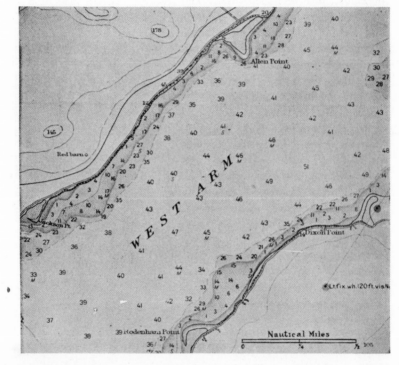

FIG. 175. West Arm of Sydney Harbor, Cape Breton, showing two hooked spits (Jackson and Rodenham Points) recurving to form cuspate bars; a practically completed cuspate bar with opening into lagoon (Allen Point); and cuspate bar with closed lagoon (northeast of Dixon Point). From U. S. Hydrographic Chart No. 1061.

The west arm of the harbor shows examples of cuspate bars in three stages of development (Fig. 175). Some of the latter are well seen along the road from Sydney to North Sydney. Farther east Indian Bay and Glace Bay have their headward portions shut off by bars which are perhaps far enough within the re-entrants to deserve the appelation of midbay bars.

The long, narrow passage of the Gut of Canso, representing a drowned valley the course of which was probably determined either by faulting or by the southeastward slope of the upland peneplane or its coastal plain covering, shows a variety of interesting shore forms among which are two long spits extending southward parallel to the Cape Breton shore to make bars across the broad mouths of two shallow embayments, Heffernan Pond and Long Pond (U. S. Hydrographic Chart No. 2276). The rocks here are believed to be of Devonian age, but Carboniferous beds are close at hand on the mainland, and perhaps even closer on the sea-floor. Eddy Point, at the southeast end of the Gut, is a cuspate bar with lagoon enclosed; while the northern shores of Chedabucto Bay, where the rocks are also considered to be Devonian but are apparently of a weakness comparable to that of the Carboniferous Lowland formations, exhibit a beautiful series of spits,

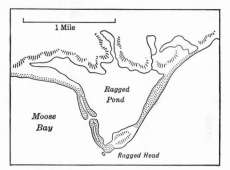

FIG. 176. Ragged Point tombolo, north shore of Chedabucto Bay, apparently showing prograding on west to give double bar or spits. Later maps indicate the partial destruction of the west bar.

tombolos, baymouth bars, and cuspate bars, among which the Ragged Point tombolo (Fig. 176) is of particular interest because it apparently shows double parallel spits on the west due to a prograding of the shore at this point. The approach toward a graded outer shoreline which marine forces have here already been able to accomplish by cutting back headlands and bridging across embayments by bars, is sufficiently noticeable to recall the pattern of the New Brunswick shoreline from Miscou Island to Buctouche Harbor (Fig. 147). Guysborough Harbor is nearly closed by a baymouth bar, and the occurrence of Carboniferous rocks in this

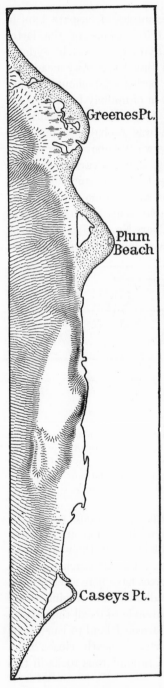

Greenes Pt.

Plum
Beach

Caseys Pt.

vicinity, at the very head of Chedabucto Bay, suggests that the whole
bay is a drowned Carboniferous Lowland, probably developed on an infaulted block of weak Carboniferous
sediments, like Aspy Bay.

**Bay of Fundy Carboniferous Low-
land Shores.** — About the head of
the Bay of Fundy, the Carboniferous
Lowland shores bordering parts of
Chignecto Bay and the Basin of
Minas, show a number of small spits
and baymouth bars, including one
interesting example of a midbay bar
at Apple River (Geol. Survey of
Canada, Apple River sheet, No. 100),
which seems related less to the shallow-
ing floor of the bay than to a marked
salient of the shore from which it has
grown northward as a spit under the
influence of beach drifting.

**Wave-Built Forms of the Narra-
gansett Bay Shores.** — The next important Carboniferous Lowland is that
of Narragansett Bay (Fig. 28). From
its general resemblance to the Bras
d'Or Lowland, of similar physiographic history, we should expect to
find cuspate bars and forelands, as
well as spits and tombolos, bordering
the narrow arms of the bay, while
baymouth bars would be either small
in size or relatively few in number.
These expectations are realized, and
the succession of cuspate bars (Fig.
177) bordering the west shore of the
Western Passage strangely reminds
one of conditions on the southeast

Fig. 177.  Cuspate bars on the west shore
of Western Passage, Narragansett Bay.
Compare with Fig. 173.

shore of St. Andrews Channel in the Bras d'Or region.   Farther south Westquage Beach (U. S. Coast Survey Chart No. 353) offers a fair example of a midbay bar, while on the east side of this same passage the two parts of Conanicut Island are united by a tombolo which with respect to Mackerel Cove might be considered a bayhead bar.   Still farther to the east are found other midbay bars and the fine double tombolo connecting the former island of Sachuest Neck with the mainland.   Coggeshall Point (U. S. Coast Survey Chart No. 262) is a good example of two spits grown toward each other to form a cuspate bar.   It was from the shores of Narragansett Bay that Gulliver[25] selected his type of a cuspate bar which was formerly a cuspate tombolo connecting with the mainland an island now entirely destroyed (Sandy Point, U. S. Coast Survey Chart No. 262), and a typical example of his so-called " lagoon-marsh stage of a tidal cuspate fore-land," Gaspee Point (Fig. 178).

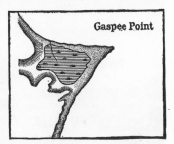

FIG. 178.   Gaspee Point near Providence, Rhode Island, a cuspate bar showing enclosed marsh.

*Origin of Gaspee Point.* — Brown[26] has given a very interesting de-tailed account of Gaspee Point, in which he supports Gulliver's con-tention that tidal, continental, and wind-driven currents rather than waves or wave currents are mainly responsible for cuspate bars and forelands, (although he admits wave action as a contributing factor), and quotes Gilbert[27] in support of assign-ing a minor rôle to waves.   The arguments by which Brown reaches his conclusion in favor of the current origin of cusps do not seem to me convincing, and I have elsewhere[21] stated with some full-ness the grounds for not accepting Gilbert's interpretation of the inefficiency of wave action.   The most abundant development of cuspate bars and forelands on the Atlantic coast is in the Bras d'Or Lakes, where tidal currents are negligible and wave action alone is important; and where the materials composing many of the bars and forelands not only are obviously brought from adja-cent cliffs by the wave-generated process of beach drifting,[28] but are far too heavy for tidal or other longshore currents to move.[29] It may be added that Gaspee Point, like some of the other wave-built forms about the Narragansett shores, is probably composed largely of débris removed from glacial deposits.

**Bay of Fundy Triassic Lowland Shores.** — As has already been noted, the Bay of Fundy Triassic Lowland has been so extensively submerged that only a few scattered areas of the weak Triassic sandstones occur along the more exposed shores near the mouth of the bay, whereas the larger areas near its head are not open to the attack of big storm waves sweeping across a broad expanse of deep water.   Under these circumstances there is little of importance to record concerning wave-built shore forms along the Fundy coast.   Much of the more protected shore retains something of its initial form (Fig. 179), or shows but a minor development of cliffing on the headlands with associated minor spits and

Fig. 179.   Partially submerged Triassic Lowland viewed from the Lookoff,
near Canning, Nova Scotia.   Photo by J. W. Goldthwait, Geol. Surv.
Canada.

bars.   The greatest change is in the embayments which, about the head of the bay, have been extensively silted up with deposits brought by tidal currents.   These will be considered later. The eastern shore, bordering the backslope of the North Mountain-Digby Neck trap ridge, is not greatly altered;  and it is doubtful if the trap shores of Grand Manan Island, where only occasionally do the weak red sandstones show beneath the massive covering of resistant igneous rock, have undergone much modification due to wave attack.   A baymouth bar, like the beautiful example which almost closes Dark Harbor (Fig. 180) is a rare exception along this fairly rectilinear coast.   Its form, convex to the sea, is probably due to the influence of deposits at the mouth of the small embayment, brought in part by stream and in part by wave and current action. At Quaco, New Brunswick, where a small remnant of Triassic sandstones and conglomerates remain, one finds, in addition to the cliffs previously described, an interesting double bar, one ridge at high tide and one at low, the peculiar features of which are ascribed by Whittle[30] to the great range of tides in the bay. Whether the bars are actually the product of tidal currents, as believed by Whittle, rather than of wave action, seems more doubtful. Advocate Harbor (Fig. 181) just west of Cape d'Or, exposed to the attack of waves sweeping up the bay from the southwest, shows two converging spits, which some maps represent as connected to form a completed baymouth bar.

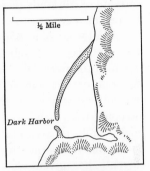

FIG. 180. Dark Harbor, west coast of Grand Manan Island, showing baymouth bar convex to sea.

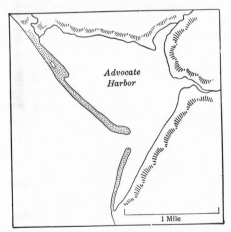

FIG. 181. Advocate Harbor, Nova Scotia, showing two slightly recurved, converging spits which practically form a baymouth bar.

The Triassic Lowlands of Connecticut and New Jersey are so slightly submerged in the one case, and so remote from the open sea in the other, that little opportunity has been afforded for the development of wave-built forms along the shores of either.

General Conclusions. — Our hasty survey of the low, weak - rock coasts of the Carboniferous and Triassic Lowlands, more particularly the former, has demonstrated the fact that the shorelines of these lowlands are extremely rich in spits, bars, and forelands of all types. Especially noticeable is the development of baymouth bars and the truncation of headlands on certain of the more exposed shores, where the stage of early youth is passed, and late youth or submaturity attained. Here the disorganized currents of all kinds (especially tidal currents and the still more important wave currents that generate beach drifting), which in the initial stage of a shoreline of submergence split on the numberless headlands and islands, and flow in the numberless directions to which the irregular shores constrain them, have been simplified into one or but few systems which with remarkable constancy pursue their way along the outer shoreline, where baymouth bars sweeping from one retrograded headland to another give a simplicity of form favorable to a unity of direction of flow. The outer shoreline is nearly or quite graded, and disorganization of currents has given place to organization. On no part of the initially irregular crystalline shores has so advanced a stage of shoreline development been attained.

As in the case of the shorelines bordering the crystalline uplands, so in that of the Carboniferous and Triassic Lowland shores, it is often difficult or impossible to determine to what extent the material composing spits, bars, and forelands has been derived from unconsolidated glacial débris and not from the bedrock. If the glacial débris were far more abundant in the lowlands than on the uplands, a not improbable assumption, the greater development of wave-built forms along the lowland shores, and the advanced stage of development of the more exposed parts of such shores, might be attributed to this fact rather than to a contrast in the resistance of bedrock. It is difficult to get a reliable measure of the relative amounts of glacial débris on the uplands and in the lowlands; but while there may be a marked contrast in thickness of glacial deposits where the contrast in elevation is great, it is doubtful whether there is a great difference when we compare weak-rock lowland shores with the low parts of the uplands where the latter decline to sealevel and pass under the water. Certainly there is an abundance of glacial débris on the low, seaward border of the Nova Scotian upland; and while Stone[31] has noted that there is less of such material along the Maine sea-border than farther inland, this is believed to be the result of special conditions which need not have affected upland shores either generally or exclusively.

The active cliffing of the weak rocks which has been noted at various points bordering the Carboniferous and Triassic Lowlands,

and the apparent derivation of the material of spits, bars, and forelands from adjacent cliffed headlands which has repeatedly been
noted by field observers, leaves little doubt that weakness of
bedrock, rather than abundance of glacial débris, is primarily
responsible for the greater development of wave-built forms
along the lowland shores. My own field observations have
led me to agree substantially with Ganong's statement that the
spits and bars of the northern New Brunswick shore are composed of material " derived from the wear of the sandstone headlands, but with some intermingled gravel, small cobbles, shells
and sea-drift."[32] Locally, however, glacial débris has provided a
large part, sometimes by far the largest part, of the material; but
so far as practicable these cases are segregated in a later chapter,
and do not affect the validity of our main conclusion. This conclusion may be stated in the following terms: The remarkable
number and variety of wave-built forms bordering the shores of
weak-rock lowlands confirm the direct evidence that these shores
are developing much more rapidly than those bordering the hard-
rock uplands; but the fact that the most exposed of these shores
have only reached the stage of late youth or submaturity, while
those less exposed are still in early youth, confirms the evidence
found along the upland shores that the sea has stood at its present
level for a comparatively short time.

**Résumé.** — We have described the remarkable series of baymouth bars bordering the lowland shores of northeastern New
Brunswick and northern Prince Edward Island, the cuspate forelands and cuspate bars of the Bras d'Or and Narragansett Lowland shores, and the great variety of spits, tombolos and other
wave-built features characteristic of these and the other lowland
coastal borders. Our study has demonstrated the more advanced
stage of development attained by these shores, in contrast with the
extreme youth of the sea margin of the crystalline uplands; but
has at the same time convinced us that the stage of development
is still so early, despite the rapidity of wave action on the weak-
rock lowlands, as to imply a relatively short stand of the sea at
the present level.

## BIBLIOGRAPHY

1. GANONG, W. F. "The Physical Geography of the North Shore Sand Islands." Nat. Hist. Soc. New Brunswick, Bull., VI, No. XXVI, 22–29, 1908.
2. STEAD, GEOFFREY. "Notes on Surface Geology of New Brunswick." Nat. Hist. Soc. New Brunswick, Bull., V, No. XXI, 5-13, 1903.
3. JOHNSON, DOUGLAS. "Shore Processes and Shoreline Development," 289 et seq., New York, 1917.
4. GANONG, W. F. "On the Physiographic Characteristics of Portage and Fox Islands, Miramichi." Nat. Hist. Soc. New Brunswick, Bull., VI, No. XXVI, 17–22, 1908.
5. JOHNSON, DOUGLAS. "Shore Processes and Shoreline Development," 290–300, New York, 1917.
6. JOHNSON, DOUGLAS. "Shore Processes and Shoreline Development," 297, 386, New York, 1917.
7. GANONG, W. F. "The Physical Geography of the North Shore Sand Islands." Nat. Hist. Soc. New Brunswick, Bull., VI, No. XXVI, 27, 1908.
8. JOHNSON, DOUGLAS. "Shore Processes and Shoreline Development," 304, 380, New York, 1917.
9. CHALMERS, R. "Report on the Surface Geology of Northeastern New Brunswick." Geol. Surv. Can., Ann. Rept., N. Ser., III, Pt. II, 27N, 1889.
10. JOHNSON, DOUGLAS. "Shore Processes and Shoreline Development," 292, New York, 1917.
11. GANONG, W. F. "The Physical Geography of the North Shore Sand Islands." Nat. Hist. Soc. New Brunswick, Bull., VI, No. XXVI, 25, 1908.
12. JOHNSON, DOUGLAS. "Shore Processes and Shoreline Development," 374, New York, 1917.
13. DAWSON, J. W., and HARRINGTON, B. J. "Report on the Geological Structure and Mineral Resources of Prince Edward Island," 51 pp., Montreal, 1871. See map.
14. ELLS, R. W. "Report on the Geology of Prince Edward Island with Reference to Proposed Borings for Coal." Geol. Surv. Can., Summ. Rept. for 1902, 372, 1903.
15. JOHNSON, DOUGLAS. "Shore Processes and Shoreline Development," 303, New York, 1917.
16. DAWSON, J. W. "Acadian Geology," 2nd Ed., 401, London, 1868.
17. GANONG, W. F. "On the Physical Geography of Miscou." Nat. Hist. Soc. New Brunswick, Bull., V, No. XXIV, 447–462, 1906.
18. GOLDTHWAIT, J. W. "Supposed Evidences of Subsidence of the Coast of New Brunswick Within Modern Time." Geol. Surv. Can., Mus. Bull. No. 2, 61–66, 1914.
19. CLARKE, JOHN M. "L'Ile Percée," 62, New Haven, 1923.
20. CLARKE, JOHN M. "L'Île Percée," 61, 134, New Haven, 1923.
21. JOHNSON, DOUGLAS. "Shore Processes and Shoreline Development," 333–339, New York, 1917.

22. TARR, R. S. "Wave-Formed Cuspate Forelands." Amer. Geol., XXII, 1–12, 1898.
23. GULLIVER, F. P. "Cuspate Forelands." Bull. Geol. Soc. Amer., VII, 399–422, 1896.
24. WOODMAN, J. E. "Shore Development in the Bras D'Or Lakes." Amer. Geol., XXIV, 329–342, 1899.
25. GULLIVER, F. P. "Shoreline Topography." Amer. Acad. Arts and Sci., Proc., XXXIV, 199, 217, 1899.
26. BROWN, R. M. "Gaspee Point: A Type of Cuspate Foreland." Jour. Geog., I, 343–352, 1902.
27. GILBERT, G. K. "The Topographic Features of Lake Shores." U. S. Geol. Surv., 5th Ann. Rept., 75, 1883.
28. JOHNSON, DOUGLAS. "Shore Processes and Shoreline Development," 94–103, New York, 1917.
29. TARR, R. S. "Wave-Formed Cuspate Forelands." Amer. Geol., XXII, 1–12, 1898.
    WOODMAN, J. E. "Shore Development in the Bras D'Or Lakes." Amer. Geol., XXIV, 329–342, 1899.
30. WHITTLE, C. L. "The Beach Phenomena at Quaco, N. B." Amer. Geol., VII, 183–187, 1891.
31. STONE, G. H. "The Glacial Gravels of Maine and their Associated Deposits." U. S. Geol. Surv., Mon. XXXIV, 54–58, 1899.
32. GANONG, W. F. "The Physical Geography of the North Shore Sand Islands." Nat. Hist. Soc. New Brunswick, Bull., VI, No. XXVI, 22, 1908.

# CHAPTER XI

## SUBMARINE FORMS BORDERING THE WEAK-ROCK LOWLANDS

**Advance Summary.** — It is our purpose in the present chapter to examine the character of the submarine forms bordering the weak-rock lowlands, with special reference to the question as to the progress made by waves in establishing the marine' profile of equilibrium off the lowland coasts. Incidentally we shall note the evidence furnished by submarine forms regarding the possible existence of one or more earlier profiles of equilibrium established by the waves when the sealevel was materially lower than now. The answer to the first question may confirm or correct our previous conclusions as to the length of time the sea has stood at the present level; while the answer to the second may enlighten us as to whether or not at a relatively recent period there was a pronounced halt of the sea at some particular level below the present.

**More Rapid Attainment of Marine Profile of Equilibrium off Weak-Rock Coasts.** — We have seen in an earlier chapter that practically no advance has been made by the waves toward establishing a marine profile of equilibrium bordering the resistant crystalline coasts. The evidence of more effective wave attack on the weak-rock coasts leads us to anticipate there a closer approach to the profile of equilibrium on the offshore slope. Two factors favor more rapid attainment of the profile of equilibrium along the less resistant coasts: the waves remove weak rocks with comparative rapidity, and thus sooner adjust the seabottom contours to their activity; and just as the weak rocks are usually represented by lowlands of faint relief on the land, so on the seabottom the gentle slopes and the relative scarcity of high hills forming islands or shoals which must be planed down, reduce to a minimum the work that the waves must do before the submarine contours are perfectly adjusted to their activity.

**Development of Marine Profile of Equilibrium without Extensive Marine Erosion.** — Due consideration of the last point should place us on guard against the fallacy of considering a well-developed profile of equilibrium off weak-rock coasts as an indication of long-continued or extensive wave erosion. It is obvious that if subaërially formed contours (Fig. 109) more or less closely approximate the shape demanded by the waves for their maximum efficiency of action, the minor re-adjustments necessary may be completed very soon after submergence brings such a land surface into the zone of wave action.

*Region of Prince Edward Island.* — A profile (Fig. 182, A) northward from the north side of Prince Edward Island, near its eastern end, follows obliquely down the gentle backslope of this partially submerged cuesta, toward the centre of the broad shallow syncline into which the rocks of the region appear to be warped. Conditions presumably were here highly favorable to the attainment of a profile of equilibrium with a minimum of wave work; and the profile in question, while showing departures from the normal curvature, represents in its landward two-thirds a fair approximation to the typical marine profile of equilibrium. The outer third shows a broad shoal, rocky in places, some 35 to 40 miles from land, representing the submarine extension of the low northeast-southwest ridge, probably a minor anticlinal arch, the summit of which rises above sealevel in places to form the Magdalen Islands.

*Shippegan Island Region.* — A similar profile is that drawn southeastward from the south-

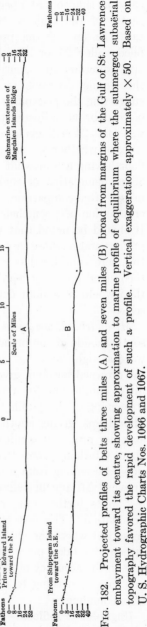

Fig. 182. Projected profiles of belts three miles (A) and seven miles (B) broad from margins of the Gulf of St. Lawrence embayment toward its centre, showing approximation to marine profile of equilibrium where the submerged subaërial topography favored the rapid development of such a profile. Vertical exaggeration approximately × 50. Based on U. S. Hydrographic Charts Nos. 1066 and 1067.

eastern side of Shippegan Island (Fig. 182, B) toward the centre of the Gulf of St. Lawrence synclinal basin. In this case the line of the profile appears to cross an incompletely filled valley 25 or 30 miles out, but up to this point is a fair approximation to a marine profile of equilibrium. Farther out the profile descends more steeply from the 24-fathom level, suggesting the possibility that we may have here an older profile of equilibrium adjusted to conditions existing when the sealevel was some 24 fathoms lower than at present. Whether such is the case, or whether the steeper slope represents part of the lowland floor having a somewhat steeper inclination as the result of sub-aërial denudation of slightly dipping rocks, can only be determined after comparison of many profiles has made possible discrimination between their significant and non-significant features. It should be noted that while the vertical exaggeration of these profiles and of those discussed below is the same, the scale of the two here considered is much smaller; hence departures from a theoretical profile of equilibrium are less noticeable on these two than would be similar departures on the profiles drawn to larger scale.

*Miramichi Embayment.* — A profile (Fig. 183, A) from the southern side of the broad, shallow Miramichi embayment northward at right angles to the shore but obliquely across the axis of the drowned lowland, gives a fairly good representation of a profile of equilibrium for about 3 miles out. Beyond this there is a steepening of the profile from the $5\frac{3}{4}$-fathom level down to 10 or 11 fathoms, giving another curve which might be interpreted as an older profile of equilibrium established when the sealevel was about 6 fathoms lower than at present, or as a subaërially formed slope descending from a higher to a lower (terrace?) level of the drowned Miramichi valley. An apparent reversal of the slope a few miles farther out certainly cannot be credited to marine denudation. The fact that soundings in fractions of a fathom cease just where the change in curvature of the profile at the $5\frac{3}{4}$-fathom line takes place raises the question as to whether a difference in the accuracy of depth measurements in the two zones may not have something to do with the change in profile as plotted from soundings.

**Ungraded Profiles.** — In the Buctouche Harbor region the profile of a belt extending seaward from north of Cocagne Harbor across Buctouche Outer Bar shows irregularities (Fig. 183, B) sufficiently pronounced to indicate notable failure of wave erosion to attain a profile of equilibrium in a locality where the initial topography of the submerged land was probably favorable to such action. The Outer Bar (Fig. 161) shows rock on its surface in places, and is probably a rocky ridge as yet imperfectly reduced by wave erosion. This locality is under the lee of Prince Edward Island, protected from the greatest storm waves; yet northeast winds sweep across a 25-mile stretch of open water, and one should expect to find a well developed profile of equilibrium, but graded to a shallower depth than on more exposed coasts, had wave attack persisted for a long time at the present level. Off Shediac Point, farther south and likewise protected from the most violent storm waves, a rocky shoal interrupts a curve which might otherwise be nearly normal for a profile of equilibrium at very shallow depths (Fig. 183, C). In the Caribou Harbor region, another moderately protected locality, the profile from Gull Island northward (Fig. 183, D) for at least 2½ miles shows a typically ungraded condition.

**Comparison of Subaërial and Submarine Profiles.** — It is desirable when practicable to compare submarine profiles with profiles of the adjacent land areas. It is true that such comparison is often negative in its result, due to the fact that what appear as marine-formed profiles in strong contrast with adjacent land profiles may in reality be subaërially produced profiles slightly or not at all modified by marine agencies (Fig. 109). On the other hand, where the former seaward continuation of the land profile can be determined with some assurance, its restoration may demonstrate with reasonable certainty that the present submarine contours could have been produced only as the result of extensive wave erosion. This is usually most feasible in regions of low relief developed on horizontal rocks of fairly uniform resistance, where abrupt and strongly marked variations in the surface form are uncommon. Thus appreciable wave erosion of the seaward margins of certain coastal plains is clearly indicated by profile studies undertaken by Merrill[1] to determine the origin of offshore bars. The case is less simple with the profiles discussed above, in part because we lack adequate topographic maps for the adjacent land areas, and time has not been available to prepare suitable land profiles by special field work. There exist, however, data as to land elevations which permit a partial comparison with the submarine profiles; and such comparison indicates that no

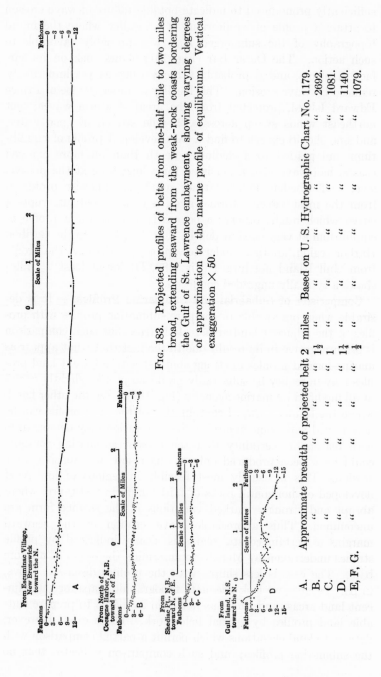

FIG. 183. Projected profiles of belts from one-half mile to two miles broad, extending seaward from the weak-rock coasts bordering the Gulf of St. Lawrence embayment, showing varying degrees of approximation to the marine profile of equilibrium. Vertical exaggeration × 50.

Approximate breadth of projected belt  Based on U. S. Hydrographic Chart No.

| | | | |
|---|---|---|---|
| A. | 2 miles | " " 1179. | 2692. |
| B. | " 1½ " | " " | 1081. |
| C. | " 1 " | " " | 1140. |
| D. | " 1¼ " | " " | 1079. |
| E, F, G. | " ½ " | " " | |

one of the latter thus far described requires the assumption of extensive marine erosion, while certain of them seem to be the continuation of adjacent land profiles practically unmodified.

*Port Hood Region, Cape Breton.* — In this connection the three profiles off the west coast of Cape Breton Island in the vicinity of Port Hood (Fig. 183, E, F, G) are of interest, for while they show but a few miles of the submarine slopes, they permit comparison with land elevations to an extent sufficient to demonstrate but a moderate amount of wave erosion. The normal hillslopes of the islands and mainland are shown by the chart to be sharply

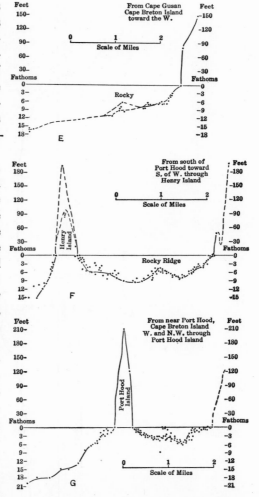

FIG. 183 (continued). For title see opposite page.

truncated at the base by steep wave-cut cliffs usually 20 to 30, but sometimes 60 or even 80 feet high. The projection of the normal slopes seaward, even if we materially decrease the angle of these slopes and so increase the former land area, indicates that but a limited wedge of the land can have been removed by the waves. The submarine contours are such as we should expect if a subaërial surface consisting of outlying hills separated from an adjacent highland by a rather shallow valley 2 to 3 miles broad, was sub-

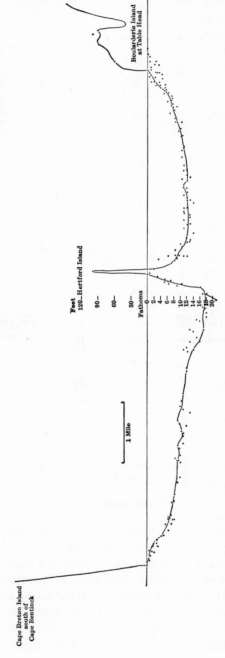

FIG. 184. Projected profile of a belt a little more than a mile in breadth across part of the submerged Bras d'Or lowland, showing limited modification of former subaërial contours by marine agencies. Vertical exaggeration approximately × 50. Based on U. S. Hydrographic Chart No. 1134.

merged until the valley floor became flooded and the hills converted into islands; and this so recently that the irregularities of the submerged surface have not yet been planed down, and the lower slopes alone of the hills have been cut away by the sea. Even if we assume that the irregularities in part represent temporary bars of loose débris, and that the greater depth and smoother curves on the more exposed outer coasts of the islands and at Cape Susan are due largely to wave action, the evidence of these profiles is still strongly indicative of limited marine abrasion.

*Northeastern Cape Breton.* — The same conclusion is indicated by the profile from Table Head on Boularderie Island across the open ends of Great Bras d'Or and Saint Ann Bays to the steep coast of northern Cape Breton (Fig. 184). Here the exposure to wave attack is quite good; yet the former subaërial topography of ridges and valleys is well preserved, with lower slopes of hills alone moderately cliffed, and the submerged portion of the land contours little altered by marine agencies. Extensive marine abrasion of the exposed Hertford Island seems incompatible with the persistence of a deep channel or drowned valley close to the northwestern side of the island.

**Ungraded Profiles off the Magdalen Islands and the Boston Basin.** — The series of profiles off the Magdalen Islands (Figs. 157 and 158), described at length on earlier pages, seems clearly to demonstrate the failure of the waves to establish the marine profile of equilibrium about this exposed rocky mass in the very midst of the Gulf of St. Lawrence. The same is true of the profiles across portions of the submerged floor of the Boston Basin lowland (Fig. 185), where the Atlantic waves have not yet planed down the many irregularities of a floor exposed in one case (A) to fairly vigorous marine action, in the other (B) to storm waves from the open sea. It should be noted, however, that the resistant conglomerates and igneous rocks of the Boston Basin oppose more frequent and more serious obstacles to wave erosion than are usually encountered in the submerged lowlands.

**Submarine Profiles off Bay Bars.** — We may compare with the foregoing profiles two or three which extend outward, not from cliffed rocky shores, but from bay bars more or less distant from the mainland. At least the landward ends of these profiles should show a normal marine curve of equilibrium, since the seaward faces of the bars must be graded to the wave action which was largely instrumental in forming them. A profile (Fig. 186, A)

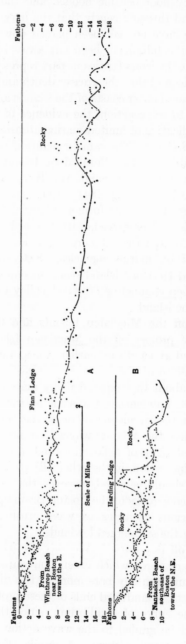

FIG. 185. Projected profiles of belts approximately 1½ miles in breadth across portions of the submerged floor of the Boston Basin lowland. Both profiles terminate landward on wave-built bars (tombolos) connecting eroded drumlins, but for the most part they show failure of the waves to attain the profile of equilibrium on a fairly well exposed lowland coast. The roughness of the bottom is further indicated by the wide range of the soundings (dots) from the median profile (line). Vertical exaggeration approximately × 50.    Based on U. S. C. & G. S. Chart No. 246.

from Malpeque Bay, near the western end of Prince Edward Island, northeastward down the gentle backslope of the low Prince Edward Island cuesta, shows the typical curve of a marine profile of equilibrium for about 15 miles out. Twenty miles out and at a depth of 20 fathoms, there is a low elevation rising perhaps a dozen feet above the general plane, beyond which elevation the bottom declines somewhat more steeply downward. This last characteristic might imply the presence of an older profile of equilibrium graded with reference to a stand of the sealevel some 20 fathoms lower than at present; or it might be interpreted as an inherited subaërial feature of the submerged plain; as a change from a wave-worn and flattened portion of the submerged plain to a portion maintaining its original somewhat steeper slope; as the product of the greatest storm waves, which, breaking far out from land, have there begun a steepening of the seabottom and the construction of an offshore bar on the landward side of the steepened zone; or possibly in other ways which need not now claim our attention. A profile (Fig. 186, B), from Portage Island bar at the mouth of the Miramichi embayment, eastward across the continuation of the submerged floor of the embayed lowland, gives

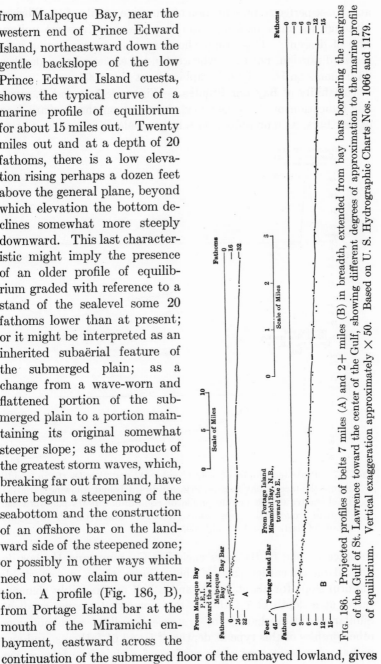

Fig. 186. Projected profiles of belts 7 miles (A) and 2+ miles (B) in breadth, extended from bay bars bordering the margins of the Gulf of St. Lawrence toward the center of the Gulf, showing different degrees of approximation to the marine profile of equilibrium. Vertical exaggeration approximately × 50. Based on U. S. Hydrographic Charts Nos. 1066 and 1179.

an almost perfect representation of a marine profile of equilibrium, although its outer part may too long preserve the same uniform rate of descent.   This profile shows no trace of steepening in its seaward portion, not even when extended eastward to a depth of 26 fathoms on U. S. Hydrographic Chart No. 1067.

**Variability of Bay Bar Profiles.** — Figure 187, A and B, give a fair indication of the variability of profiles on the seaward faces of bay bars, as represented on a larger scale.   The profile (A), on

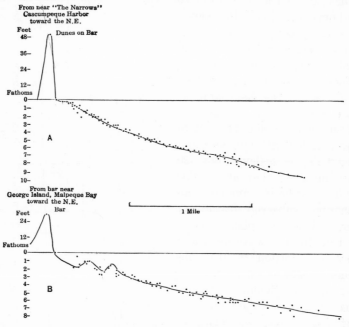

FIG. 187.   Projected profiles of belts 1½ miles (A) and 2½ miles (B) in breadth across the face of bay bars on Prince Edward Island, showing variations in character of the marine profile of equilibrium at its landward end. Vertical exaggeration approximately × 50.   Based on U. S. Hydrographic Charts Nos. 2694 and 2695.

the face of one of the bars enclosing Cascumpeque Harbor described on an earlier page of this volume, shows a remarkably uniform slope for about a mile and a half out, possibly changing there, at a depth of 7 fathoms, to a somewhat steeper gradient. Similar doubtful changes to a steeper gradient were noted on other profiles of this type at depths of 5 and 6½ fathoms, and may perhaps represent temporary profiles of a shoreface terrace constantly changing under varying intensity of wave attack, after the manner which I have elsewhere described in some detail.[2] It is hardly conceivable that the lower-level steeper angle of slope should represent part of an old profile of equilibrium established when the sealevel was 5 to 7 fathoms lower if, as seems likely, the seabottom at the point in question is composed of shifting sands constituting the seaward extension of a bay bar. Southeast of Cascumpeque Harbor a profile (Fig. 187, B) on the face of the main bar enclosing Malpeque Bay shows a curve of gradually decreasing gradient, diversified near the shore by what appear to be two parallel minor bars only locally developed. These are doubtless temporary features, such as frequently mark the seaward faces of beaches and bars, sometimes vanishing with heavy storms only to reappear later, sometimes being incorporated in the beach by its seaward advance.

**Résumé.** — Our study of submarine profiles off weak-rock coasts leads us to conclude that where the submerged subaërial topography left comparatively little work for the waves to do in order to adjust the seafloor to their activities, and the exposure to vigorous wave action was relatively favorable, the marine profile of equilibrium with reference to the present position of sealevel has been more or less nearly attained. But where the submerged topography imposed considerable work upon the waves, or the shores were more or less protected from the most vigorous wave action, or the rocks of the submerged lowlands were locally of unusual resistance, little progress toward the establishment of a profile of equilibrium has been made, except of course in the loose sands of wave-built structures. Inasmuch as the marine profile of equilibrium, like the fluvial, is established at an early stage in the cycle of development, and that stage is quickly reached in weak-rock areas, it follows that the submarine profiles confirm other evidence already given to the effect that the waves have worked at the present sealevel for a very short time only.

The question as to whether the submarine profiles afford reliable evidence of a former long stand of the sea at a lower level than the present, seems to require a negative answer. There are occasional steepenings and flattenings of the profiles which in individual cases might be interpreted as remnants of ancient profiles of equilibrium established when the sealevel was lower than now; but, as shown in the preceding paragraphs and in the discussion on earlier pages of the submarine profiles off the Magdalen Islands, the irregularity of form of the sections of profiles in question, the variability of their depths below sealevel, and the complete absence of such terrace-like forms in many areas, are opposed to their interpretation as remnants of earlier graded marine profiles.   They appear to find a more reasonable explanation in one of the several other interpretations to which they are open; and perhaps best as remnants of subaërial profiles, submerged and partially modified by marine agencies.   If one or more of them do represent remnants of earlier profiles graded with reference to one or more earlier sealevels, we can only say that in the New England-Acadian area the fact is effectively obscured by other elements of the profiles. In a later volume we shall return to this problem when we analyze the submarine profiles off the coastal plain shoreline.

## BIBLIOGRAPHY

1.  MERRILL, B., in "Shore Processes and Shoreline Development," (Johnson) 355–365, New York, 1917.
2.  JOHNSON, DOUGLAS.   "Shore Processes and Shoreline Development," 217–222, New York, 1917.

# CHAPTER XII

## EROSIONAL FORMS BORDERING UNCON-
## SOLIDATED DEPOSITS

**Advance Summary.** — We have found that the shoreline bordering resistant crystalline uplands is extremely youthful, practically in its initial stage; while that bordering weak-rock lowlands, if exposed to the full force of the waves, has advanced to a late-young or submature stage of development. We are accordingly prepared to find that the shoreline bordering exposed coasts formed of unconsolidated deposits has progressed still farther in its evolutionary history, and attained early or full maturity. The remarkably simple shorelines bordering the glacial outwash plain of Marthas Vineyard on the south (Fig. 51), and the glacial sandplains of Cape Cod on the east (Fig. 58), fully justify our expectations. Just as there is nothing on the crystalline upland shores to compare with the relative simplicity of the weak-rock lowland shores of northeastern New Brunswick and northern Prince Edward Island, so, also, is there nothing on these latter shores to compare with the absolute simplicity of the glacial débris shores of Marthas Vineyard and Cape Cod.

In the present chapter we shall first investigate the rapidity of wave erosion on coasts of unconsolidated débris, noting incidentally some legal problems consequent upon such erosion. We shall next review the oft-cited studies made by Edmund Andrews of coast erosion on the Great Lakes, and ascertain in how far they afford a basis for comparison with the rate of coast erosion bordering the sea. Finally, attention will be directed to the very important subject of map studies of shoreline changes; and the precautionary measures which should surround such studies, whether made for scientific purposes or for the solution of practical problems, will be set forth. Here again we shall have occasion to note the manner in which the principles of shoreline physiography may be applied in the settlement of legal controversies.

**Rapidity of Marine Erosion of Glacial Deposits.** — If the rate of cliff erosion in the sedimentary rocks of the lowlands has been noticeable, as pointed out on earlier pages, the retreat of the glacial coasts has been so rapid as to astonish man, and even to disconcert him in no small measure.   Roorbach[1] quotes from the Massachusetts Colony Records for September 8, 1636, the following entry in regard to one of the many glacial drumlins forming islands in Boston Harbor: " There is 12 acres of land granted to John Galop upon Nixes Island to enjoy to him and to his heirs forever."   Unfortunately for Galop's heirs and assigns the whole island has been completely swept away by the waves, and a bouldery shoal alone marks its former position.   That it was still of some size in 1726 is evidenced by the Boston News Letter, July 14 of that year, which records the execution of three pirates and states that " their bodies were carried in a boat to a small Island called Nick's Mate, about 2 leagues from the town, where Fly (one of the pirates) was hung up in Irons as a Spectacle for the Warning of others, especially seafaring men; the other Two were buried there."   The Des Barres chart of 1775 still shows the gradually disappearing island, which had a low bluff, doubtless a wave-cut cliff, along its northern side.   Cherry Island Bar, in the Winthrop area (Fig. 188), is another shoal marking the position of a former drumlin known as Cherry Island, now completely destroyed by the waves.   It is said that there are records on file in the State House at Boston of permits granted to certain individuals to pasture cows on Cherry Island in the early days of the Massachusetts Colony.

That many other drumlin islands in the Boston region, as well as along parts of the Nova Scotian coast, have been removed by marine erosion, will be demonstrated in a later section.   The process is still active, as is evident from the form of Winthrop Great Head (Fig. 189), Little Allerton Hill (Fig. 236), and other drumlins in various stages of erosion.   Extensive engineering works for the protection of these shores have been constructed. At Third Cliff (Fig. 190) near Scituate, Massachusetts, drumlin-shaped hills of till with other unconsolidated deposits at the base are being so actively eroded that the road along the top of the bluff has been cut away, fences have been undermined, and the houses farther back are in danger of destruction unless adequate protective measures are undertaken.

Mitchell[2] reports that the site of a row of houses which in 1838 stood on a glacial upland well above sealevel on the southeast coast of Nantucket Island, was forty years later out beyond the

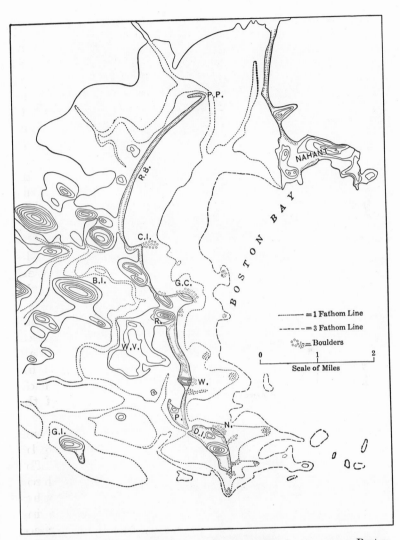

FIG. 188. Complex tombolo of the Winthrop Beach area, near Boston, uniting partially eroded drumlins to the mainland. (After Roorbach.) P.P., Point of Pines; R.B., Revere Beach; C.I., Cherry Island Bar; G.C., Grovers Cliff; W.V., Winthrop Village; W., Winthrop Great Head.

Fig. 189.  Winthrop Great Head, a drumlin near Boston being rapidly cut back by wave erosion.  In the foreground is a wave-built tombolo composed of material removed from the drumlin, and connecting the Head with another partially eroded drumlin.  For location see Fig. 188.

Fig. 190. Third Cliff near Scituate, Massachusetts, showing rapid undermining of drumloidal hill by the waves. The road in front of the house has been completely cut away, and the fence in the foreground left hanging in the air.

breaker line, with a broad stretch of beach between it and the face of the retreating cliff.   The same writer quotes Koppmann, an engineer of the Massachusetts Harbor Commission, as authority for the statement that at Chatham the crest of the glacial bluff on which the lighthouse stands was cut back 46 feet in a single year.   Marindin in a report to Henry Mitchell[3] of the Coast Survey says he was informed by the keeper of Chatham lights that nearly 100 feet of cliff recession occurred in another year, both instances apparently due to fresh exposure of the mainland to wave attack following the breaching of a protecting bar in front

FIG. 191.   Part of northern coast of Long Island, here composed of glacial sands and gravels with occasional boulders.   Oak Neck Point in the foreground, being undermined by the waves; the peninsula of Lloyd Neck in distance, with Oyster Bay between.   See Fig. 193.

of the cliffs.   Ram Island, near Chatham, which in 1606 may have contained something like 100 acres, but in 1847 had been reduced to 13 acres, was still used as a pasture in 1851, when all but traces of it were washed away during the great Minot's storm;  these traces in turn had disappeared by 1888.[4]

**Erosion in More Protected Localities.** — Even on relatively unexposed shores, like those of Long Island Sound, the rate of marine erosion is exceedingly rapid.   The northern coast of Long Island (Fig. 191) consists almost wholly of glacial deposits, in part sands and gravels, with occasional clayey layers and numerous large boulders; and in part of till or boulder clay, the former being more easily removed by the waves. That practically this whole coast is yielding rapidly to wave attack has long been recognized by geologists. In his report on the geology of the First Geological District of New York, published more than three-quarters of a century ago, Mather[5] devotes much attention to the encroachments of the sea, which greatly impressed him, and estimates that at least one thousand tons of débris are removed daily from the north side of the Island. Landslips are a not uncommon feature of this coast, the undermining action of the waves causing the over-

Fig. 192.  The "Broken Ground," northeast of Northport, Long Island. A landslip due to wave attack on glacial sands underlain by clay. The sea is to the left of the view. Photo by G. N. Knapp for U. S. Geol. Surv.

lying beds to slump down, sometimes on a large scale as at the "Broken Ground" northeast of Northport (Fig. 192). The larger slips seem to occur where the glacial deposits overlie clay beds, the weight of the upper beds sometimes squeezing the clay out upon the shore, as explained by Fuller[6] for the Broken Ground and other cases.

*Oak Neck Region, Long Island.* — In 1833 Edmund Blunt of the United States Coast and Geodetic Survey established a series of triangulation stations along this coast, among other places at Oak Neck Point, East Fort Point, Matinicock Point, and Peacock Point (Fig. 193). Fifty years later or in 1883, the Coast Survey,

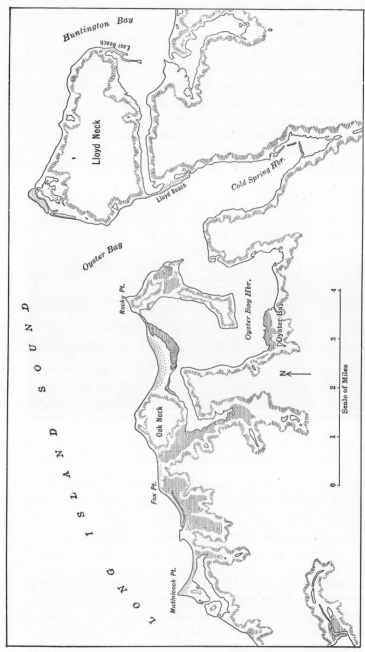

Fig. 193.   Part of northern coast of western Long Island, showing approach to submature stage of shoreline bordering uncon-solidated glacial deposits, even where exposure to wave action is limited.   The projecting headlands are suffering rapid erosion.   East Fort Point is at the eastern end of Lloyd Neck, while Peacock Point is the unnamed point between Fox Point (Fox Island Point) and Matinicock Point.

having learned of extensive changes of the shoreline due to wave erosion, sent F. H. Gerdes to recover the triangulation stations, and re-mark them if necessary. From an examination of Gerdes' manuscript " recovery notes " on file in the archives of the Survey at Washington, it appears that he made a somewhat doubtful recovery of the station at Oak Neck Point, but that the other three had been undermined and destroyed by the sea. At East Fort Point, where the " signal " was erected on the north corner of a fort said to have been built in 1812, not only the signal but the entire fort and a portion of the high land on which it was built, had been undermined and swept away some twenty or twenty-five years before. The crest of the cliffs here stands 60 to 70 feet above sealevel, and there is partial protection from northeast storms; but the form of the shore favors rapid removal of débris from the headland on which the cliff is located. From an examination of the local conditions, and an inspection of the size of a companion fort still partially preserved on a neighboring part of the coast, I concluded that the rate of cliff recession at East Fort Point must have averaged at least 3 feet per year during the fifty years from 1833 to 1883. The signal placed a few feet back from the edge of the wave-cut cliff on Matinicock Point had been undermined about 1870, and the earthenware cone buried under the signal pole as a security for the Coast Survey triangulation point, washed up on the shore. The spot where the signal was supposed to stand Gerdes found to be 40 or 50 feet out in front of the shore under a depth of 5 or 6 feet of water. At Peacock Point the signal and the point of land on which it stood, together with the houses of fishermen, were all swept away by the waves.

At Oak Neck Point the cliff is cut in a hill 45 to 50 feet high, and an unknown distance back from the edge of the cliff Gerdes in 1883 established a triangulation station, called Oak Neck No. 2, in what was believed to be approximately the same position as the original station of Blunt. In 1915 a Coast Survey party under Forney was unable to recover Gerdes' station, so in turn established a new one, called Oak Neck No. 3, six meters back from the edge of the cliff. A few years later, 1922, another Coast Survey party found that the cliff had receded about two meters, the station then being only four meters back. Mr. K. T. Adams, in charge of this last party, reported: " The bank is being worn away by the action of the sea and it is probable that the station mark will disappear in the course of time." Such is the lack of permanence of important triangulation points established near the sea on a rapidly receding coast; and hence the importance of placing such points at a safe distance from the shore, and of providing for their easy recovery by recording an ample number of both directions and distances to suitable reference marks, subject of course to the practical necessities of securing intervisibility of points, and of keeping within the limit of funds available for the work.

At my suggestion Mr. Adams made a series of accurate measurements from the top of the wave-cut cliff and from the estimated position of mean high water line to certain fixed objects in the vicinity, to serve as a basis at some future time for more accurate data as to the rate of cliff and beach recession between Oak Neck Point and Fox Island than is usually available. These measurements are on file in the offices of the Coast Survey at Washington, but are here recorded as an example of the kind of data desired for many parts of our coast, and also for the convenient use of any who may from time to time desire to determine the extent of shoreline changes, whether retreat or advance, at any of the points mentioned.

### LIST OF ACTUAL MEASURED DISTANCES, OAK NECK — FOX POINT REGION

*Taped Distances*

The top edge of the bank is

    6.41 meters    N (true) from △ Oak Neck No. 3.
    11.83 meters NW (true) from △ Oak Neck No. 3.
    4.47 meters NE (true) from △ Oak Neck No. 3.
    20.35 meters NW (true) from flagpole (150 meters west of △ Windmill.)
    17.43 meters    N (true) from flagpole (150 meters west of △ Windmill.)

The mean H.W. line is

    22.8  meters    N (true) from N.W. corner of group of concrete bath houses 200 meters east of Fox Point.
    22.5  meters    N (true) from N.E. corner of group of concrete bath houses 200 meters east of Fox Point.
    17.0   meters    S (true) from Boulder No. 1 Fox Point.
    30.9   meters    N (true) from N.W. corner of Bayville concrete bath house.

The top edge of the bank is

    13.7   meters  NE (mag) from Flagpole near △ Oak Neck No. 3.
    16.25 meters    N (mag) from Flagpole near △ Oak Neck No. 3.
    22.75 meters    E (mag) from Flagpole near △ Oak Neck No. 3.
    8.4   meters    N (true) from Flagpole Fox Pt.
    6.3   meters NW (true) from Flagpole Fox Pt.
    10.15 meters    W (true) from Flagpole Fox Pt.

*Stadia Distances*

The mean H.W. line is

35½  meters NW (true) from N.W. corner of Bayville Bath House.
52¼  meters NE (true) from N.W. corner of Bayville Bath House.
30   meters  W (true) from Flagpole Fox Point.
18   meters NW (true) from Flagpole Fox Point.
21½  meters  N (true) from Flagpole Fox Point.
57   meters NE (true) from Flagpole Fox Point.

The top edge of the bank is

31¼  meters NE (true) from Flagpole (Fox Point).
23½  meters  E (mag) from N.W. corner of house (540 meters west of
                 Bayville Bath House).
25¼  meters  N (mag) from N.W. corner of house (450 meters west of
                 Bayville Bath House).
86   meters  N   4°E(mag) from first telephone pole on eastern
                 end of straight stretch of macadam road
                 which parallels the beach in the vicinity of the
                 Bayville Bath House.
78   meters      from seaward edge of macadam road on same
                 line as above.

*Taped Distance*

The flagpole (Oak Neck Point) is

19. 16 meters N52°E (true) from △ Oak Neck No. 3.

**Need of Accurate Measurements.** — One must hope that such a valuable list of accurate and authentic measurements as that by Mr. Adams will be made for many points along our changing coast, for the shoreline student of today is seriously hampered by the scarcity of trustworthy data on which to base reliable estimates of the rate of marine erosion under varying conditions. Had the survey parties of 50 or 100 years ago left such records for a large number of points these would today have a very high scientific and practical value; for not only does the student of shoreline physiography require a large quantity of precise data of the type in question in order to solve certain difficult problems in his special field, but the value of coastal property, and in some cases even the title to ownership of such property, may depend on a knowledge of the direction and rate of past shore changes, and of the probabilities as to future changes.

**Legal Complications: Oak Neck Case.** — A detailed study of the Oak Neck-Fox Point section of the Long Island shore has convinced me that this part of the coast has been cut back a minimum distance of 500 feet in the last 250 years; that the cutting was most rapid prior to the erection of strong seawalls and other coast defenses, dating probably from about the 80's of the last century; that wave attack is so vigorous the artificial defenses are broken down and cliff erosion continues, although at a diminished rate (Figs. 194 and 195); and that the retreat of adjacent headlands has carried back with it a bar connecting Oak Neck Point with Fox Point (Fig. 196), with resulting legal complications, since the bar has thus " by an act of God " been moved bodily out of the property lines of one claimant to the beach, and deposited upon the salt marsh in the rear, within the property lines of another claimant.   That the bar has been driven in over the marsh admits of no doubt, as by a large number of borings it

Fɪɢ. 194.    Base of cliff at Oak Neck Point, showing destruction of concrete seawall and active erosion of cliff by wave attack.

was possible to establish the presence of the marsh under all parts of the bar in dispute; but the time within which the retreat took place, while a proper subject of expert opinion, could be demonstrated with an approach to mathematical certainty only on the basis of precise measurements such as have recently been made for this locality, thanks to the work of the Coast Survey here executed by Mr. Adams, but which unfortunately were not made in connection with the earlier surveys of this shoreline.   The encroachment of the bar upon the marsh since a fence separating the two was erected in 1886, is clearly visible in Fig. 197.

A maximum measure of the time involved in the retreat of a bar over a marsh may be secured where examination (microscopic if necessary) reveals in the marsh deposits under the bar particles of any plant imported into America by the European settlers. Since the marsh must have been open to receive such a plant fragment, and since fragments of imported plants could not have reached the marsh earlier than the date of their importation, all that portion of a retrograding bar landward of the point where the plant is found, must have moved over the marsh since the date in question.

Fig. 195.  Low seacliff cut in glacial sands and gravels at Bayville, west of Oak Neck Point, Long Island.  The houses are rapidly being undermined despite attempts to protect them.  Note ruins of concrete seawall in front of temporary wooden structures.

*Bradley Beach Case, New Jersey.* — In condemnation proceedings instituted by the Borough of Bradley Beach, near Asbury Park, New Jersey, in order to acquire for public purposes a strip of shore front valued at from one to several hundred thousand dollars, the value as finally determined by the Commissioners depended in part on the probable future rate of shore retreat under wave attack at the locality in question, since only thus could the probable life of the threatened area, or the need of protecting it by costly defense works, be estimated.  The calcula-

Fig. 196.   Aeroplane view of the Oak Neck-Fox Point region, north coast of Long Island.   In the right foreground one sees the low hill of former Fox Island covered with grass (light grey in photograph), surmounted by a house and several trees, and exposing its cliffed end to the sea, with great boulders on the beach and in the water indicating the former seaward extension of the island.   The beach or bar stretching straight to Oak Neck in the background has migrated southward (right) over the salt marsh as the headland cliffs have been cut back, thereby giving rise to important legal complications.   The irregular strip of white along south side of the beach is a road marking approximately the present contact between beach and marsh.   Photo by Fairchild Aërial Camera Corporation.

tions of the physiographer based on general geological and other considerations were strengthened and checked in this case by actual figures for shore retreat in a neighboring area of similar character, prepared by the state geologist of New Jersey on the basis of a comparison of successive surveys; although the survey data (being for charting purposes only) were not as precise and accurate as is desirable for such comparative studies.

Ganong[7] has rendered a valuable service in putting on record certain detailed surveys of limited areas on the New Brunswick coast; but these would gain in usefulness for future students of

Fig. 197.   Back side of bay bar near Fox Island Point, Long Island, showing encroachment of bar upon the salt marsh at left.   In 1886 the back (south) margin of the beach was marked by the fence at right.   In 1922 the southward encroachment of the beach had brought it to the line indicated by the camera case.   The trees in center distance are on Fox Island, now attached to the mainland by the bar.   (Cf. Fig. 196.) The edge of the marsh bordering the white sand and gravel of the beach shows a narrow "Juncus zone" or "Black grass zone," with *Juncus gerardi* and other characteristic plants.

coast recession if he would publish fully the precise figures, with accurate descriptions of the features (parts of artificial objects, crest of bluff, mean high water line, etc.) from and to which each measurement is made; for reproductions of plats of surveys made on a scale given only in words cannot be satisfactory because smallness of scale, warping or shrinking of paper, possible reduction or enlargement in reproduction, and other factors may introduce very significant errors into future computations of supposed shore changes.

**Measured Rates of Cliff Retreat in Glacial Débris.** — It may be useful to note here some calculated rates of cliff recession in unconsolidated glacial débris, based on more or less accurate surveys.

*Boston Harbor Region.* — Whitman and Howard, civil engineers of Boston, on the basis of a comparison of charts and surveys of the Massachusetts Harbor and Land Commission from 1860 to 1908, verified by surveys of their own at intervals, found that the cliff cut by the waves in the seaward face of Winthrop Head (Fig. 189), Boston Harbor, had receded 36 feet in 48 years, or at the average rate of 9 inches per year.   For Grovers Cliff (Fig. 188) the U. S. Army Engineers have compiled records and maps covering the periods 1891–1898, and October 1903–August 1905. These show an average recession of 9 inches per year along 1000 feet of cliff for the first period, and 12 inches per year for the second period.[8]   Certain of these surveys give accurate measurements for both crest and base of cliff, from which it appears that in some places the crest retreated most rapidly for a given period, in others the base; but that the average for the two was nearly the same.   Both cliffs are from 60 to 70 feet high near the centre, decreasing in altitude on either side due to the fact that they are cut in drumlins; and the material is a compact glacial till or boulder clay, with numerous large boulders imbedded in the mass. Exposure to wave attack is moderate, the cliffs being partially sheltered from northeast storms, and receiving the effect of waves from the open ocean through a gap four miles wide.   Prominent shoals still further interfere with wave attack on both cliffs.

*Outer Coast of Cape Cod.* — We may compare the above with the rate of cliff retreat on the outer coast of Cape Cod from Highland Light (Fig. 198) southward to Nausett Lights, where the cliff averages from 50 to 100 feet in height, with a height of 140 feet along much of its course; the material is fluvio-glacial sand and clay with some boulders; the exposure is to the main waves of the Atlantic; and important shoals are usually absent.   The greater cliff height favors less rapid retreat than in the Winthrop Head-Grovers Cliff area; but the other elements of the situation strongly favor more rapid retreat.   This part of the coast was surveyed in 1848 and again in 1888 by the U. S. Coast and Geodetic Survey, and on the basis of a comparison of these two surveys Marindin[9] calculates a mean recession of 128 feet in the 40 years, or an average of 3.2 feet per year.   This involved the removal of more than thirty million cubic yards of débris from this stretch of coast, or approximately 54,000 cubic yards per annum for every mile of shore.   I have not critically examined the charts used by Marindin, to see how carefully he guarded against possible sources of error in making his comparison; but the facts that he himself conducted the second survey, that he was fully acquainted with the character of the shore cliffs, that he determined the slope of the cliff face at a number of points, and that he specifically states: " The high-water line and the bluff line, where it exists, give reliable data for comparison," justify one in believing that he exercised much care in his study of the problem, and

FIG. 198.   Marine cliff cut in glacial clay overlain by glacial sands
at Highland Light, outer side of Cape Cod.

hence that in so great a retreat as 128 feet the percentage of error is probably not large.   The calculated rate of retreat is, furthermore, about what one would expect under the physical conditions controlling wave action along the outer shore of Cape Cod.   The comparative regularity in the amount of cliff recession along the section of the coast specified is brought out in a striking manner by the plate accompanying Marindin's report, and is a normal feature in view of the remarkable uniformity of conditions there existing.   Farther south the nature of the coast changes entirely, and rates of retreat are more variable, in one section averaging as high as 8 feet per year, but elsewhere giving place to a forward building which at one point reached a maximum of 58 feet per year.

*Mature Aspect of the Outer Shoreline of Cape Cod.* — While the ordinary observer is most impressed by the detailed character of the cliffs (Fig. 198) cut by the waves in the fluvio-glacial deposits of Cape Cod, and by the rapidity with which the cliff is retreating under wave attack, the student of shoreline physiography sees in the remarkably simple pattern of the shoreline bordering the outer coast (Fig. 58) a phenomenon of broader significance. This shoreline marks one of the rare places on the New England-Acadian coast where the cycle of shore development has advanced to the stage of maturity. Nowhere else, indeed, has so long a stretch of shore progressed so far in its evolutionary history; for nowhere else in the province has an unconsolidated coast of such uniform composition been subjected to the full force of the Atlantic storm waves. It will be convenient to defer a more complete consideration of the evolution of this coast until the following chapter, where it may best be discussed in connection with the associated depositional forms which enable us to reconstruct the past physiographic history of the region.

*Time Required for the Complete Destruction of Cape Cod.* — It is of some interest to calculate the probable " lease of life " of the forearm of Cape Cod in view of the vigor of wave attack on its unconsolidated materials. At Highland Light and some distance south of Wellfleet the breadth of the Cape is about 10,000 feet. In the wider section north of Wellfleet it averages nearer 20,000, with a maximum of something over 25,000. With a rate of recession of 3.2 feet per year the narrow parts should be cut through in a little more than 3000 years, the broader parts in from 6000 to 8000 years. There are, however, factors tending to alter the rate. As the waves cut farther into the land the rate tends to decrease, due to the increasing breadth of submarine platform over which the wave-eroded débris must be transported to deep water, and the progressive decrease in the cutting power of waves which traverse an increasing breadth of platform. Such decrease is most noticeable in the early stages of coast erosion, and it seems probable that at present the tendency in this direction is very slight. The land slopes downward toward the west, and becomes more broken there, both conditions favorable to a marked increase in the rate of cliff recession because the waves will have progressively less and less material to remove. When the narrower areas are cut through a further increase in rate of cliff recession of the broader areas may result from a more ready disposal of débris by longshore current action. When these and other factors of less importance are balanced, it seems probable that the net result will be a distinct increase in the rate of cliff recession in the future. If we take account of the further fact that waves in Cape Cod Bay will contribute appreciably to the destruction of the land, it does not seem unreasonable to suppose that the outer part of Cape Cod, the " forearm," may be reduced to fragmentary remnants of its present form within the next two thousand years, and that it may all have disappeared within four or five thousand years, provided that man does not retard the rate of destruction by elaborate coast defenses. These figures may seem unduly small in view of Davis' more liberal estimate of eight to ten thousand years, from which he would, however, subtract something to allow for wave cutting by the waves of Cape Cod Bay[10]; but so far as I can analyze the problem, probabilities seem to favor the smaller figures. Davis estimates that the waves have cut into the glacial sands and clays of the outer side of Cape Cod a distance of something like two or two and a half miles since the sea reached approximately its present position; and thinks 3000 or 4000 years, or even less, would suffice for the accomplishment of this part of the total task.

*Marthas Vineyard.* — The rate of coast recession, where the terminal moraine of Marthas Vineyard underlain by sands and clays of the coastal plain is attacked by the waves of the Atlantic at Nashaquitsa Cliffs, appears to be even more rapid than on the outer shore of Cape Cod. The point in question is near the western end of the south shore of the island, and numerous large boulders occur in the unconsolidated drift of the moraine. Thus the exposure is toward less violent storm waves, and the composition of the land less favorable to rapid erosion, than in the case of Cape Cod. The cliffs have a maximum elevation of 152 feet above sealevel near the centre of the section, and here Whiting[11] found a retreat of 220 feet shown by a comparison of surveys made by him for the Coast and Geodetic Survey, presumably in the years 1846 and 1886. Whiting's account is obscure in places, but as he clearly states that his first mapping of the island was in 1845–46, and writes (in 1888) of his " last survey " in 1886, the interpretation here given seems to be correct. Shaler[12] so interpreted it at the time, as he says Whiting " ascertained that in forty years, i. e., from 1846 to 1886, the shore in the central part of Nashaquitsa Cliffs moved into the land 220 feet, or at the average rate of about five and one-half feet per annum." Ten years later, however, Shaler[13] writes that Whiting " fixed the rate of erosion of the Nashaquitsa cliffs by very careful observation for a period of fifty years at 3 feet per annum," and refers the reader to the same account on the basis of which he earlier figured the rate of $5\frac{1}{2}$ feet per annum. As fifty years had not elapsed from the date of his earliest survey when Whiting wrote his account, and as there are no figures in that account which would give a rate of 3 feet on the basis of either a 40- or a 50-year interval, Shaler's later statement is apparently erroneous. We may accept the rate of $5\frac{1}{2}$ feet per year as the one determined by Whiting for the Nashaquitsa locality, without knowing how much care was used by him in making his comparisons. It should not be surprising, however, to find so great a rate of cliff recession in unconsolidated glacial drift where, as in the present case, the extent of the cliffs yielding abundant waste under marine attack is very limited.

Shaler,[14] by projecting the present slope of the glacial outwash plain of Marthas Vineyard southward till it cuts the plane of sealevel, estimates that the original position of the south shore of the island, assuming no change of sealevel, must have been about three miles south of its present position; but he does not imply that the much higher terminal moraine has been cut back so far. Even for the outwash plain the figure may be excessive, for if the contours of the Marthas Vineyard topographic quadrangle correctly represent the slope of that surface, it should intersect the plane of sealevel not more than a mile and a half south of the present shoreline.

*Submature Aspect of the Southern Shore of Marthas Vineyard.* — While the initial form of this shoreline exhibited the lobate or scalloped pattern (Fig. 50) due to the coalescing alluvial fans which constitute the plain, and the numerous embayments resulting from partial submergence of shallow valleys cut in the surface of the plain, the most remarkable characteristic of the present shoreline is its rectilinear pattern. The headlands have been cut back and the bay mouths bridged by bars to give an excellent example of a submature shoreline of submergence (Fig. 51).

At Gay Head, which has a western exposure, Shaler thinks the waves have cut a mile into the moraine and its underlying clays and sands of the coastal plain since the sea reached approximately its present level; and he describes a wave-cut bench extending a mile seaward just below high tide, to plunge abruptly into deeper

water beyond.[15]  The Coast Survey chart (No. 112) shows a
narrow submarine ridge, called the " Devil's Bridge," extending
northwestward from the Gay Head cliffs for nearly a mile; but
on either side the descent, both from the ridge and from the cliff
base, seems to be steeper and less terrace-like than Shaler's
description would imply (See also Fig. 245, C, D).  The average
rate of cliff recession at Gay Head Shaler estimates at 2 feet per
annum, diminishing to one foot recently; but he makes clear that
the estimate does not rest on accurate measurements.  Where the
moraine (here perhaps best called a kame moraine) reaches the
north shore east of Vineyard Haven, and exposure is to the waves
of Nantucket Sound driven by east and northeast storms, Whiting[16]
found that a cliff 40 feet high extending nearly a mile along the
shore had retreated 75 feet between his surveys of 1845 and 1871,
or at the rate of about 3 feet per annum; while a cliff only 20 feet
high on the exposed salient of Cape Poge (Fig. 212) had yielded
under the attack of northeast and southeast storms at the yearly
rate of $10\frac{1}{2}$ feet during the period 1846–1886.[11]

## Andrews' Studies of the Great Lakes Shores

The shores of the Great Lakes offer opportunity for an interesting comparison of the annual rate of cliff retreat in unconsolidated
drift under the attack of lake waves.  In his highly suggestive
essay on " The North American Lakes considered as Chronometers of Post-Glacial Time "[17] Edmund Andrews, a professor of
surgery in Chicago Medical College, more than half a century ago
presented the results of many years' study of the lake shores,
especially the western shore of Lake Michigan.  He found that
the waves cut into the unconsolidated " drift clay " between
Manitowoc and Evanston, where the crest of the cliffs rises from
20 to 100 feet above the water, at an average rate of more than 5
feet a year.  This he compares with rates of 6 feet or more on
shores better exposed to waves driven by onshore winds.  On the
basis of profile studies Andrews described a subaqueous terrace
or bench, bordering the shores in a number of places, which he
attributed to wave erosion.  This bench was reported as having
its outer edge at a depth of 60 feet below the lake surface, and as
attaining breadths of from two to six miles, or occasionally more,
where the shores are of drift; a thousand or fifteen hundred feet
off rock shores of moderate resistance; and scarcely two hundred
feet where developed in some of the hard rocks bordering Lake

Superior. On the west shore of Lake Michigan the average breadth was believed to be approximately four miles. To get the former position of the shoreline Andrews projected "the steepest part of the slope, just outside of the edge of the terrace, . . . upward till it (met) the surface of the water " (Fig. 199); and thus calculated the average total recession of the western shoreline of Lake Michigan to be 2.72 miles. Dividing the total recession of the shoreline by the average annual rate of recession he obtained a figure (2720 years) for the time required to form the terrace; and, by adding the time required to produce shore forms at higher elevations, an approximate measure of 5290 years (or 7491 years as calculated from data secured on Lake Huron) for the whole of post-glacial time. Andrews realized that his calcu-

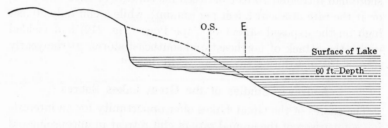

Fig. 199. Andrews' average profile of western shore of Lake Michigan, showing supposed wave-cut bench cut in post-glacial time, and that author's method of determining position of the original shoreline (O.S.). E, edge of subaqueous terrace or bench.

lations could give approximate results only, but he was inclined to believe " the exact truth lies somewhere between the results of the Lake Huron and the Lake Michigan calculations; that is, between about 5300 and 7500 years."

**Possible Sources of Error in Methods Employed.** — One may suggest several possible sources of error in Andrews' methods which would affect his results to a significant degree. His calculations all rest on the very doubtful assumption that the subaqueous terrace is wholly a wave-cut bench, whereas it may well be that a large but unknown proportion of its outer part is a built terrace, composed of débris washed lakeward from the wasting cliffs. The normal section of a wave-cut cliff and its associated cut-and-built terrace is more like Fig. 200, even where longshore beach drifting transports much of the débris to distant localities. It is impossible to say in any given case what proportion of such a terrace is built.    If the coastal lands are low and the water near the shore deep, the terrace may be largely wave-cut, with only a marginal fringe of submarine talus.    But if the coastal lands are high in comparison with the original water depth, most of the terrace may be constructed of débris.    Removal of wave-eroded débris by longshore current action of any type tends to restrict the extent of terrace building;  but importation of débris from cliffs on either side acts to increase it.

If the front of the terrace is a slope at the subaqueous angle of repose of the débris of which it is built, there is a double objection to the method by which Andrews determines the position of the original shoreline: first, such a slope is unrelated to the original contour of the land, and hence cannot be used to reconstitute any portion of that contour;  and, secondly, the slope is an unknown

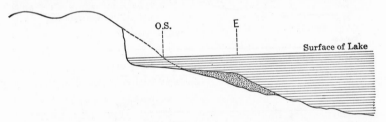

FIG. 200.   Modification of Fig. 199, making it conform to normal section of wave-cut cliff and associated cut-and-built terrace, and showing that original shoreline (O.S.) may have been much closer to the present shore cliffs than indicated in Fig. 199.   E, edge of subaqueous terrace.

and possibly great distance lakeward of the original surface which was cut into by the waves.

Andrews assumes that the rate of wave cutting remained the same throughout the whole period of terrace formation, whereas on the basis of a constant water level we are compelled to postulate a very pronounced decrease, due both to the weakening of wave attack as the terrace broadened, and to the increasing amount of débris to be disposed of as the height of the cliffs increased with further advance into the land.   The decrease in the rate of shore retreat for these causes may have been so great as to make the present rate of shore retreat but a faint indication of the rate in earlier times.   The net result of applying the corrections indicated above would be to reduce heavily Andrews' figures for post-glacial time, figures already comparatively low.

**Profile Studies of the Great Lakes Shores.** — Andrews' investigation was hampered by the fact that for some of the areas most important in his studies no reliable charts existed, while for other areas the data available in his day was doubtless far less satisfactory than that now at the disposal of students of lake shore erosion. Profile studies undertaken in association with the writer by H. G. Bray and D. A. Nichols, and based on charts by the U. S. Army Engineers and in a few cases on U. S. Hydrographic charts from surveys made by the Canadian Government, give results of interest in the present connection.

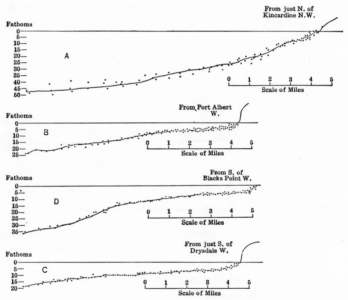

Fig. 201. Projected profiles of belts approximately two miles broad off the east shore of Lake Huron. Vertical exaggeration approximately × 50. Based on U. S. Hydrographic Charts Nos. 2672 and 2673.

Along the straight north-south section of the eastern shore of Lake Huron, between Point Clark and Brewster's Mill, Andrews reports a well-developed subaqueous terrace with its outer edge at a depth of 60 feet below lake surface. Our profiles, (based on all soundings within a strip of lakebottom two miles wide in order to eliminate the effect of local irregularities), show such a terrace; but while its outer edge is at a depth of 60 feet just south of Drysdale (Fig. 201, C), it appears to be only 40 feet deep fifteen miles farther north (D), although the terrace margin is here rounded and obscure; while thirty miles to the northward the depth is about 35 feet (B).  In other words, the terrace seems to slope southward at a variable rate averaging about 1 foot per mile.  The outer edge of the terrace is about 3 miles from shore at the north, near Goderich and Blacks Point, and 7 miles near Drysdale farther south.  North of Point Clark a profile (A) near Kincardine descends to a depth of 300 feet 14 miles out, without discovering any clear indication of a terrace; while off Blacks Point (D) the most pronounced change of slope in the region takes

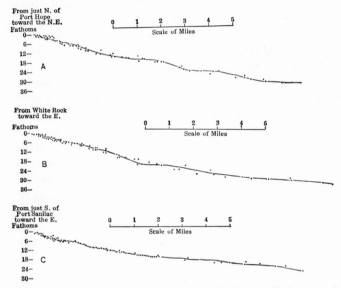

Fig. 202.  Projected profiles of belts three miles broad off the west shore of Lake Huron showing apparent absence of Andrews' subaqueous 60-foot terrace.  Vertical exaggeration approximately × 50.  Based on U. S. War Department Coast Charts Nos. 1 and 2, Catalogue Nos. 51 and 52.

place at a depth of 100 feet.  Obscure suggestions of terraces at the same and at a slightly greater depth appear off Port Albert (B).

On the opposite shore, where Andrews reports a similar terrace only half as wide, our profiles (projected profiles of strips 3 miles broad) are less convincing.  They show no terrace at the 60-foot level, and only moderately clear indications of such forms at 110 feet and 155 feet off Port Hope (Fig. 202, A), at 110 to 125 feet off White Rock Point (B), and uncertain indications at about 135 feet off Port Sanilac. A much better terrace is shown at a depth of 36 feet a mile and a half from shore in the locality last mentioned.

Andrews states that the 60-foot subaqueous terrace is well shown among the islands and shores of the northern part of Lake Michigan, and in illustration he gives a profile described as extending " from north to south across North and South Manitou Islands, and thence to the mainland near Sleeping Bear." Presumably his profile ran from northeast to southwest, thence southeast, in order to include the points mentioned; and it appears to be largely conventional, showing at five points a steep-faced terrace always with sharp edge precisely at the 60-foot level. A projected profile (Fig. 203, A) of a belt two miles broad extending northeast-southwest across the two islands in question shows the terraces described by Andrews, but indicates for them a less regular form than that author's account would lead one to expect. The most extensive development of the terrace form is off the southwest side of South Manitou Island, where it attains a breadth of three miles, but has an extremely irregular surface and seems to be continued farther southwest in the sloping surface found beyond a clearly marked submerged valley. Altogether this shelf has an extension in the direction indicated of eight or nine miles, whereas no form of comparable breadth is found off other parts of the island. The nearest approach to a similar form is an extremely irregular shelf three and a half miles broad off the southeast side of North Manitou, where the exposure to wave action is relatively poor. The irregularity of these broad shelves, their restriction to narrow belts at occasional localities only, their occurrence where wave action is comparatively weak and their absence off more exposed shores, and the fact that they are trenched by unfilled drowned valleys, suggest that they are subaërial forms drowned by the waters of the lake and subsequently but moderately affected by wave action. The submarine valley between the two islands is clearly shown, but the terrace form is here poorly developed. Off the northeast shore of North Manitou Island there is a terrace or shelf only three-fourths of a mile broad with its outer edge at a depth of 40 feet. Elsewhere on this profile the outer edges of the supposed terraces, where distinct enough to be clearly indicated, appear to vary from 55 to 80 feet in depth.

The profile (B) from South Manitou Island to Sleeping Bear Point reveals a deep and fairly broad submerged valley with shelves three-fourths of a mile wide at the top of the valley walls having a depth of 30 or 40 feet on one side, and 20 or 25 feet on the other.  Off the west shore of South Manitou Island, where the cliffing by waves seems to have been most pronounced and the form most clearly suggests a wave origin for the shelf there encountered, the breadth of the terrace is about $1\frac{1}{4}$ miles, and the

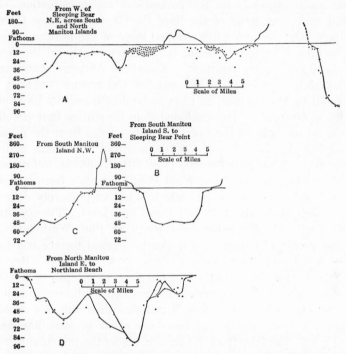

FIG. 203.  Projected profiles of belts approximately two miles wide (except B, which is a linear profile) in the region of North and South Manitou Islands, Lake Michigan, showing submerged valleys presumably of subaërial origin, and subaqueous terraces apparently due in part to subaërial forces and in part to wave action following submergence.  Vertical exaggeration approximately × 50.  Based on U. S. War Department Coast Chart No. 8, Catalogue No. 78.

outer edge has a depth of 35 feet (C).  A profile (D) from the east shore of North Manitou eastward to the mainland is particularly interesting because of the clearness with which it reveals the hills and valleys typical of a subaërial surface; and also because it shows what appear to be wave-formed terraces along both shores, that bordering the mainland being three-fourths of a mile broad with an outer edge 20 to 25 feet below the lake surface, while the one bordering the island is both narrower and shallower.

For the west shore of Lake Michigan, where Andrews possessed special facilities for determining the rate of shoreline retreat under wave attack, he unfortunately had no reliable charts, and was compelled to depend upon occasional lines of soundings, some of them made expressly for the purposes of his investigation. He found that " on some of the lines the (60-foot) terrace is very distinct, while in others the gradual slope of the bottom beyond it obscured the edge, rendering it necessary to rely on the depth as the guide to its position." Elsewhere Andrews states that under such circumstances the edge of the terrace " cannot be detected by the contour, and has to be determined by its known depth of 60 feet."[18]  He concluded from his studies that the edge of the terrace was on the average about 4 miles from the present shore, but that it was much broader south of Milwaukee than to the north.  A projected profile (Fig. 204, B) fifteen miles south of Milwaukee, not far from Wind Point, reveals a terrace 7 or 8 miles broad, the outer edge of which is not very sharply defined, but is apparently about 70 feet below lake level.  Twenty-three miles north of Milwaukee, just south of Port Washington, a similar profile (A) shows a less clearly marked terrace one mile and a half broad, with its outer edge only 40 feet deep.  Beyond that the bottom has a fairly uniform slope to a depth of 300 feet or more, except for an occasional isolated shallower sounding. On the other hand, some 45 or 50 miles south of the city of Milwaukee, a linear profile (C) based on a line of soundings eastward across the lake from Waukegan, shows the principal terrace to be 9 or 10 miles broad, with its outer edge 130 feet below the surface of the lake.  There is some suggestion of a minor terrace close inshore with its outer edge 25 feet or less in depth.  On the opposite side of the lake the major terrace is a prominent feature, and here also the depth of the outer margin is approximately 130 feet.  Between the western and eastern terraces the bottom of Lake Michigan occupies a broad lowland bordered by another obscure terrace on either side at a depth of 240 feet, while apparently two stream valleys are incised in the eastern part of the lowland floor.  It will be noted that if the major terrace in each of the three profiles off the west shore of Lake Michigan represents one and the same topographic feature, then here as off the eastern shore of Lake Huron the terrace shows an increase both in breadth and in the depth of its outer margin as one goes south.  Since the foregoing was written I have discovered that in a letter addressed to Goldthwait in 1906 Leverett reported doubtful evidence of terrace-like stretches along the western shore of Lake Michigan which seemed to increase in depth toward the south.  Goldthwait[19] himself found difficulty in identifying Andrews' 60-foot terrace, and acutely observed that " if a ten-fathom terrace does exist over a wide area, it is often discontinuous and not of uniform height."

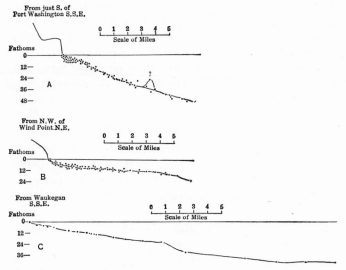

Fig. 204.   Projected profiles (A and B) of belts three miles broad off the western shore of Lake Michigan north and south of Milwaukee, and a linear profile (C) still farther south, showing subaqueous terraces at markedly different levels.  Vertical exaggeration approximately × 50.  Based on U. S. War Department Coast Charts Nos. 4 (New) and 5, Catalogue Nos. 74 and 75.

## Significance of the Subaqueous Terraces Bordering the Great Lakes Shores.

— We are not prepared to express a final opinion as to the significance of the subaqueous terraces of the Great Lakes, for it has not seemed possible to turn from the main problems of the Atlantic shoreline long enough to complete such studies of this collateral issue as alone would justify conclusions. But the facts presented above are sufficient, perhaps, to serve as a basis for the following tentative observations: The subaqueous terraces of Lakes Huron and Michigan seem to be greater in number, more irregular in form, and far more variable in depth than Andrews suspected. There are some indications that they fall into two distinct groups of diverse origin. One group consists of narrow terraces, usually not more than a mile or so in breadth and having their outer margins from 20 to 40 feet below the lake surface, which it seems probable may be the result of wave action on the present lake shores. The second group includes terraces of much greater breadth which in some places at least seem to slope southward at a rate of one or two feet per mile, which therefore have varying depths for the outer margins, and which appear to be associated with lowlands and valleys of subaërial origin. These terraces would seem to be of earlier date than the first group, and to be genetically unrelated to the present lake level. The possibility that they represent wave cut-and-built terraces formed when the lake levels had other positions than those of the present, a possibility suggested by Goldthwait[20] and apparently also entertained for a time by Taylor[21] for the supposed 60-foot terrace, should receive careful consideration; but I am inclined to think it more probable that they represent forms which characterized the old inter-cuesta lowland before it was drowned. Whether such lowland terraces were due to differential erosion of nearly horizontal rocks, to normal stream terracing, to fluvio-glacial action, or to combinations of these and possibly other agencies, remains to be demonstrated. In any case there seems to be no clear evidence of a wide-spread 60-foot terrace, and no reliable indication that wave-base on the lakes in question is located 60 feet below the water surface. The terraces actually due to wave action presumably still have their outer margins well above wave-base. The whole problem of the subaqueous terraces of the Great Lakes deserves more study, especially in the light of the principle that submerged land areas are apt to show many such terraces wholly unrelated to wave action at the present or any other level. Whether or not such study supports the hypothesis here tentatively advanced on the basis of a very brief examination of the problem, it will place our knowledge of the extent and character of wave action on the Great Lakes in post-glacial time upon a much firmer basis than that on which it now rests.

**Rate of Lake Shore Erosion.** — It should be observed that whatever view one may hold with respect to the nature and origin of the subaqueous terraces, the figures presented by Andrews regarding the rate of erosion along different parts of the lake shores are not affected. His figures are extremely variable, however, and his average of about $5\frac{1}{4}$ feet a year may be too high. Leverett[22] gives the results of more careful measurements of cliff recession along the shores of Lake Michigan in Racine, Milwaukee, and Berrien counties, determined by comparison of detailed government land surveys in 1829, 1835, or 1836 on the one hand, and on the other hand special surveys for the purpose made at dates ranging from 1870 to 1886. The mean results show a rate of recession little more than half that calculated by Andrews, and are as follows:

*Feet*

Mean annual recession of shore in Racine County.................... 3.33
Mean annual recession of shore in Milwaukee County............... 2.77
Mean annual recession of shore in Berrien County.................. 3.30

These figures differ but slightly from that for the rate of coast erosion on Cape Cod (3.2 feet per annum) where the average altitude of the cliffs is decidedly greater, but where the waves are also more vigorous; or from that of the terminal moraine on the north shore of Marthas Vineyard where material possibly somewhat more resistant than borders Lake Michigan forms cliffs forty feet high which retreat at the rate of about 3 feet per annum under wave attack from Nantucket Sound.

**Sequential Forms Bordering Coasts of Unconsolidated Débris.** — The initial forms of the shorelines bordering coasts of unconsolidated débris have been described in Chapters IV and V, and the comparison of the restored initial shore pattern with that of the present shows the progress made in shoreline evolution during the last marine cycle. In the case of Cape Cod we have already seen that a large section of the outer shoreline, well exposed to storm waves of the Atlantic, has advanced to the stage of maturity, while the southern shoreline of Marthas Vineyard has only attained submaturity. The southern shoreline of Nantucket Island, bordering an outwash plain similar to that of Marthas Vineyard, occupies a place, in respect to its development, somewhere between the two shorelines just cited. A large proportion of the shorelines bordering the unconsolidated coasts are in a still earlier stage of development; but as the erosional forms characteristic of these shores are closely associated with the depositional forms fashioned from the eroded débris, under conditions which make it possible to decipher the history of the whole shoreline with exceptional facility, it will be most convenient to defer further consideration of these shores to the following chapter. In the meantime we may profitably turn our attention for a moment to certain practical considerations of importance to those who would for any reason trace the sequence of shoreline changes as recorded on successive maps or charts of the same region.

### Map Studies of Shoreline Changes

Those who attempt to compute amounts of shore recession or advance on the basis of charts or maps must exercise great care not only to guard against such sources of errors as those mentioned in earlier sections of this chapter, but also to take into account certain inevitable limitations of the method. If these limitations are adequately recognized it is usually possible to make a comparison of two or more successive surveys with an accuracy equal to that inherent in the survey plots themselves. Conversely, failure to recognize these limitations may result in the introduction of errors of such magnitude as to make the comparison valueless. The following suggestions may be found helpful to those who have to deal with problems of map and chart comparison.

**Possible Errors due to Distortion of Medium on which Maps and Charts are Printed.**\* — Fundamentally, a comparison of maps or charts must consist of the determination of distances, as ascertained by the various surveys, from known, unchangeable points to the changeable feature studied. It is not, however, sufficient to rely on such distances as scaled directly from the map, particularly if the only available information regarding the scale consists merely of a statement of it in words or figures. Even though that scale may have been correct at the time the map was drawn, it must not be assumed that it has remained so, as the paper on which the map is printed is subject to changes of dimensions, both during the printing process due to alternate wetting and drying, and to other technical operations which need not be enumerated; and subsequently as a result of varying atmospheric conditions. It is also important to remember that these changes of dimensions are usually unequal in amount in the two directions with and across the grain of the paper, with intermediate values in other directions. These changes, usually referred to as distortions, must be anticipated in maps reproduced either by photography or by printing.

\* Based on information supplied by Commander R. S. Patton, Chief of the Division of Charts of the United States Coast and Geodetic Survey.

**Correction Factors to be Applied.**\* — The first step in any comparative study is, therefore, to ascertain the correction factors to be applied to measurements scaled along various directions on each map. This is true whether the measurement be made by direct scaling of distance, or indirectly, as through the medium of a composite tracing. The latter method should be adopted only after it has been positively ascertained, as the tracings from the different sheets progress, that they can be reduced to one common scale.

If the surveys have been based on a geodetic control referred to, or susceptible of reference to, one common geodetic datum, the task of comparison becomes greatly simplified. In this case the actual distances between the points which control the survey have been determined with great precision and by such methods that the values are not affected by the paper changes referred to. A comparison of the computed distance between points with the distances scaled from the map will result in the ready determination of the scale of the latter. If, in addition, as is usually the case, the map carries a projection based on the geodetic datum, the problem is still further simplified. These coördinates are usually drawn with great precision, from tabular values of the actual dimensions computed to the nearest centimeter. The field within which distances must be considered is thus limited initially to the smallest rectangle formed by adjacent meridians and parallels, and may be still further reduced by subdivision of that rectangle into any number of equal parts. By such subdivision even those maps on which the distortion is material and variable may readily be utilized in the production of a composite drawing, to any scale approximating that of the original, by first constructing a projection in its true dimensions with the same subdivisions as on the maps to be compared, and then tracing directly from the latter, frequently shifting the tracing minute distances so as to distribute the error throughout each rectangle. If the rectangles be made small enough, the amount by which the tracing paper is shifted each time can be so reduced that no part of the feature traced need be in error by more than the width of the line drawn; and the errors inherent in the method will be negligible in comparison with those of the plotted field surveys from which the maps were originally produced.

\* Based on a memorandum prepared by Commander R. S. Patton, Chief of the Division of Charts of the United States Coast and Geodetic Survey.

If it is considered preferable to determine actual distances to the shoreline from fixed points on the map, that process is equally facilitated. It is not even necessary to know which points on the map have been determined by geodetic methods. The intersections of latitudes and longitudes themselves become fixed points. The distance between any two of them is known, and in consequence these points, or in fact any point situated anywhere on the map, can be made the origin of measurements. The scale error in any direction can be determined by scaling a distance from the map and comparing it with the distance as computed from the geographic positions of the ends of the line. If the distance is measured along any meridian or parallel, the actual distance can be taken from published tables.

Before the foregoing method can be applied, it is necessary to ascertain the geodetic datum on which each map is constructed, as any differences between two or more datums would result in corresponding displacements of the shoreline. Such information can usually be obtained by writing to the organization which compiled the map. This may not be necessary, however, if a sufficient number of definite points can be found to permit proper comparison of any map of the series with each of the others. The comparison may be direct where two sheets have the same points. Where direct comparison is not possible, the result may be obtained indirectly by comparing these sheets with a third, which has points common to each of the other two. If the surveys have been accurately made, any difference in the datums can be ascertained by a careful scaling of the latitudes and longitudes of such points. In order to be reasonably certain of the results, the comparison should include at least three such points on each map. Having ascertained the corrections necessary to reduce all maps to a common geodetic datum, a corrected projection can then be drawn on each map.

If it is proposed to utilize surveys not based on geodetic control, it becomes necessary to select a number of definite points, of the kind described in the preceding paragraph, and by a careful measurement of the distances between them, to ascertain the relation between the scales of the two maps. In this case the problem is complicated by the fact that the highly accurate framework furnished by the geodetic control is here lacking. We have no positive knowledge of the true distance between any of the selected points. Inherent in the distances scaled from the maps are not only the errors due to paper distortion, but also those due to both the systematic and the accidental errors of the survey itself.   Therefore, in ascertaining the correction factor for a map of this character, not less than three distances should be measured, some with and others across the grain of the paper, and between not less than four common points.   A variation in the individual correction factors thus obtained, so radical as to result in material differences in the values obtained by applying them separately to the scaled distance between fixed point and shoreline, should result in the rejection of the map.   In other words, where the fixed point is closely adjacent to the shoreline, a greater uncertainty in the correction factor is allowable than would be permissible if fixed point and shoreline were widely separated. The best possible results will be obtained if the correction factors are determined from the longest distances which it is possible to measure from the map, and if those factors be then applied to the shortest possible measurement between fixed point and shoreline.

**Possible Errors Inherent in Original Surveys.** — A more serious difficulty arises from inaccuracies in the original surveys.   It must be remembered that no chart or map is a precise copy, in miniature, of the original features on the earth.   Even the best cartographic work is but an " abstract " of a part of the earth's surface, professing nothing more than to show, with a greater or less degree of accuracy according to the nature and purpose of the survey, the major features on that surface.   The remarkably high standard of work maintained by the United States Coast and Geodetic Survey, and the great precision of the surveys executed by this bureau, have justly earned for it an enviable reputation both at home and abroad.   Not unnaturally, perhaps, this reputation has led more than one layman to attribute to the Survey's charts an infallibility, even as to minute details, to which the best cartographic work makes no pretension.   In legal proceedings involving shore changes I have heard it sincerely maintained by counsel, and apparently accepted by the court, that the accuracy of a chart surveyed on a small scale is equal to that of one surveyed on a large scale, so that photographic enlargement of the small scale chart to the same size as the larger one, must give an accurate basis for comparison of shore changes; the argument being based on the erroneous assumption that surveys are precise copies of the original features, reduced in various degrees.   On this same erroneous assumption it has similarly been argued that charts made nearly a century ago, in the early days of the Coast Survey, must be as accurate as those made recently; and also that a Coast Survey Chart on the scale 1 inch = 833 feet was comparable with a local engineer's survey on the scale 1 inch = 100 feet.

If maps or charts were precise copies of the original features represented, regardless of the scale on which they are represented, these arguments would be valid.  But since maps and charts are never copies, it is obvious that the degree of accuracy must depend on many factors; and he who would compute shore changes from comparisons of maps or charts must remember that in earlier years there was no such need for great precision as there is to-day; that the standard of survey work then, while high for its period, was much lower than it is today; that then, as now, the degree of accuracy varied greatly with the individuality of the men executing the surveys; that the degree of accuracy attained depended upon the purpose of the survey; that the degree of accuracy likewise varied with the scale of the map or chart, it being possible to show the true outline of the shore far more correctly when a given amount of time was devoted to making a large scale map of a limited part of the coast, than when in the same time a great stretch of coast had to be represented on a smaller scale.

In actual practice I have found it impossible to compare, for example, certain charts prepared in the thirties with charts of more recent date, because two of the earlier charts representing the same shore at the same period showed, when superposed, discrepancies of 40 to 50 feet in the position of the shoreline. Comparison of two recent charts made seven years apart, was obviously impracticable, in part because they showed a discrepancy of 20 feet in the location of a fixed pier or breakwater. In the first instance the difficulty was that the older charts were too inaccurate to serve as a basis of comparison; in the second the charts were more accurate, but the scale hardly permitted the degree of accuracy necessary for the desired comparison; in both cases the errors were of the same order of magnitude as the figures for the supposed rate of coast recession at the locality under investigation.

**Possible Errors due to Difficulty of Locating Certain Shoreline Elements or to Changeability of Such Elements.** — Another very important and inescapable source of error lies in the difficulty of determining the position of the shoreline with any great degree of precision. It most frequently happens that the sole basis for determining shore changes is a comparison of the position of the shoreline at different periods as shown on successive charts. But the shoreline is the very element of the coastal border most difficult to locate accurately. It is the intersection of a water plane which everywhere is constantly changing, with a shore which is itself most frequently the ever changing inclined plane of a beach. The height of the water varies with the state of the tide, the direction of the wind, the conditions of barometric pressure, and other factors; and a very slight vertical change in the sealevel will, on a gently sloping beach, shift the shoreline backward or forward to a much greater distance. The average tidal heights can be accurately calculated, and foretold for any given day and hour; but the actual height at the time in question, due to variable factors, may be from one foot to several feet higher or lower; and while some allowance may be made for such variations, it is not practicable to locate the high water shoreline, low water shoreline, mean high water shoreline, or any other water line with great precision by direct observation at the time of a given survey.

It would, of course, be possible to run a line of levels from some bench mark established at a definite altitude on the basis of a long series of tide gauge readings, in cases where such a bench mark was available, and thus to determine the precise intersection of the plane of mean high water, let us say, with the beach slope. But where the beach itself is a constantly changing slope, such precision of methods would merely involve a waste of time and money; for while the surveyor might locate the mean high water line within a fraction of an inch of its true position on the actual beach at a given moment, a few hours later, after the tide had risen and fallen, and waves had altered the slope of the beach, the same line might lie several feet farther forward or farther back. In days or weeks the change may be even more pronounced, especially as storm waves not only alter the beach slope, but temporarily remove so much material from the upper part of the beach to deposit it farther out on the shoreface terrace, or subtract so much from the latter area to build forward the top of the beach,[23] that pronounced variations in position of the shoreline are constantly taking place; and from season to season and year to year a shifting of the shoreline back and forth over a zone 20,

30, or even more feet in breadth, independently of any progressive change in the average position of the shoreline, is quite expectable under favorable conditions.

It is, therefore, customary to estimate the probable position on a beach of the water line during the higher tides (somewhat above mean high water line) by observing the lines of driftwood, seaweed, and other débris left by different tides, and on such a basis to draw the shoreline. Skilled surveyors experienced in the latest and most precise methods, such as those engaged in the work of the United States Coast and Geodetic Survey, do not claim to locate, in practice, the line of high water with a greater accuracy than within 10 feet either way of its true position. Yet I have heard testimony and arguments, in legal cases involving title to valuable coastal lands as affected by shore changes, based on a comparison of maps on which it was claimed a local surveyor had plotted the high water line, simply by inspection of lines of drift, within 2 feet of its true position; and that this line varied so little that reliable comparisons were possible after a lapse of some years.

**Possible Errors in Measurements from Cliff Crest or Base.** — A more reliable basis for computing shore retreat is found where maps or charts accurately represent the position of the crest or base of a wave-cut cliff at successive periods. It must be known, however, that either the cliff crest or base is in fact correctly located; for vertical cliffs are commonly represented by a symbol which occupies a significant horizontal space on map or chart, with the result that if the crest be correctly located the base must be some distance from its true position, whereas if the base be accurately placed, the crest must be incorrectly represented. Even when successive positions of the cliff crest are correctly shown on maps or charts of a scale suitable to serve as a basis for accurate comparisons, it does not necessarily follow that a retreat of the crest amounting to twenty feet means a corresponding retreat of the shoreline; for slumping from the upper part of the cliff, causing retreat of the crest, may be accompanied by an accumulation of the débris at the cliff base, causing an actual advance of the shoreline at that point. So, also, a shoreline may retreat for a limited distance, causing a steepening of the cliff face, but no retreat of the crest. These are simple relations, familiar to every observer of shore forms, but sometimes ignored by those making computations of shore retreat or advance. Errors in computations arising from failure to consider the points noted will be appreciable only where the total shore retreat is small and the coast high; and will usually be negligible where the coast is low or the total retreat large.  One may usually guard against such errors, or at least determine the limits of their possible magnitude, by giving careful attention to the nature of the cliff as at present observed and as indicated by past descriptions, photographs, or other sources of information; to the angle of repose of its constituent materials where these are unconsolidated; and to any other available data affecting the problem.

**High Water Line vs. Mean High Water Line.** — In a preceding paragraph it was stated that the shoreline, usually plotted as a solid line on the charts of the Coast Survey, represents the line reached by the higher tides.  It is important to remember, especially in legal controversies of certain types, that it is the high tide line, and not the mean high water line, which usually appears on the charts.  Commander R. S. Patton, for twenty years connected with the United States Coast and Geodetic Survey and now Chief of the Division of Charts of that service, has thus described the method of determining the high water line in actual practice: " The topographer sets up his instrument at some commanding point where he can see the beach for 400 or 500 yards.  The rodman walks along the beach, holding up his rod at frequent intervals along the high water line.  The topographer determines the direction and distance to the rod, plots them on the map, and draws the high water line through the series of points thus located.  The markings delineated are the lines of drift left by the ordinary high tides as distinguished from the drift cast up by high tides during storms when the water level may be appreciably raised.  The tendency is for the high water line as determined by our topographical surveys to indicate the limit reached by the highest tide which has occurred within a reasonable period of time, exclusive of exceptional storm tides."[24]

**High Water Line not Indicated on Charts of Tidal Marshes.** — An important exception to the foregoing generalization occurs where tidal marshes are represented on the charts.  Here two lines are usually shown, one bounding the outer or seaward edge of the marsh, and the other the inner edge, where the marsh is in contact with the upland; and neither line is the line of high water.  In other words, where on the charts marshes appear the high water line is not indicated.  Furthermore, its actual position is highly problematical. On this point Commander Patton describes the practice of the Coast Survey as follows: " As a rule, in the case of marsh lands, the line of high water is not definitely located on the charts. In general one may assume that it lies somewhere between the lines limiting the seaward and landward edges of the marsh. One cannot, however, be sure that the outer line, or seaward limit of the marsh, is below high water, because ultimately salt marsh grows upward to a level approximately even with, or slightly above, high water. All one can say is that in general the higher tides penetrate to a line somewhere between the inner and outer limits of the marsh."[24] One might amplify Commander Patton's caution against too positive conclusions by pointing out that there may also be cases where the inner edge of the marsh is below high water, although this is a less common condition, and is best seen after a recent local change in the amplitude of the tidal range, consequent upon some change in the form of the shoreline. ᵛA more frequent condition is that in which the portions of the marsh bordering the sea or tidal channels are built higher than the central areas, due either to greater deposition of sediment there, or to other causes discussed later. I have seen grass cut from that part of a marsh near the sea, when the central and even the landward belts were too wet for such an undertaking. Under these conditions the high water line might be anything but simple.

**Legal Problems Involving the High Water Line.** — The practical importance of the foregoing considerations may be very real. Ownership of the land between high water mark and low water mark may rest with a state, a municipality, or an individual, according to the terms of legislative acts or of deeds by virtue of which title has passed from one owner to another. Such lands are often in litigation. Along the water fronts of our large coastal cities, where land is very valuable and where artificial filling has in many cases completely buried the old high water line and the lands on either side of it, the disposition of property worth many thousands of dollars may depend upon relocating the proper position of the high water line. In one such case before the Supreme Court of New York, where the testimony of maps and charts was most conflicting, the author was able to demonstrate that a brick building erected by one party projected beyond the high water line, which was his property boundary, and trespassed upon the lands of another. In this case the original surface features had long been buried under artificial filling; but by excavations the former beach slope was revealed with certain of its characteristic features, shells of forms which attach themselves to rocks at the high water level were discovered in the position in which they were living when buried, and instrumental levelling to known high water marks demonstrated that the contact between beach sand and artificial filling was below the plane of high water.  In this instance a dispute of many years' standing, involving much costly litigation, was quickly decided by the physical and faunal evidence.

Where marsh lands and adjacent uplands have been buried by fill, the problem may be less simple.  Suits have been brought to recover valuable filled-in water-front lands of this type, in connection with which it has been claimed that the inner edge of the marsh, as shown on old maps or charts, marks the high water line, seaward of which the ownership of lands usually rests with the people, through their government, unless alienated by deed or otherwise.  Since, as has been shown above, the inner edge of the marsh very commonly, and the outer edge sometimes, rises above high water, and the high water line may lie anywhere between the inner and outer limits of the marsh, the contention is clearly invalid.  It may be possible, however, to determine within reasonable limits what are the decisive facts in such a case, by a suitable series of soundings made on the ground, through the filling, into the original surface deposits.  Not only may upland be distinguished from marshland in this manner, but the different levels of the marsh as they originally existed may be discriminated, notwithstanding any amount of compression of the marsh deposits and unequal depression of its surface under the weight of the overlying fill.  The possibility of such discrimination results from the well-known fact that different types of salt marsh plants require different amounts of submergence by salt water, and hence grow at different levels above and below mean tide, as will later be more fully explained.  One who has made many sections through typical salt marshes becomes familiar with the characteristic appearance of the matted roots of different salt marsh vegetation; and his judgment may be checked by detailed examination of the plant remains.  Such studies may enable one to locate within certain limits, not too narrow, the position of the high water line; and so enable the expert to say, with reasonable certainty, whether a given piece of property is situated upon land

which formerly was above or below high water. In one case a
series of excavations, revealing in every instance either wash from
the upland or salt marsh deposits characteristic of the very highest
marsh levels, enabled the physiographer to determine that the line
of high water lay an unknown distance seaward of its alleged position on lands in litigation.    Greater precision will be possible when
the botanists have prosecuted further investigations of the exact
vertical ranges of different salt marsh plants, and associations
of plants, under varying conditions of tidal range, similar to the
valuable work of Johnson and York[25] on the Cold Spring Harbor
marsh.

**Résumé.** — In the preceding pages we have considered the fact
that marine erosion of coasts composed of unconsolidated débris
proceeds at a rate many times faster than erosion of the weak-
rock lowland coasts.    In the course of a few generations whole
islands are swept away, survey monuments and signals are undermined and destroyed, and the detailed aspect of the coast materially altered.    These rapid shore changes give rise to legal problems of considerable importance, for not only the value of coastal
property, but even the ownership of such property, may depend
upon a knowledge of the probable future rate and the total past
extent of such changes.    We have briefly reviewed certain of
these problems, and have emphasized the great need of more
accurate data than we now possess for calculating changes in the
position of the shoreline, some of which we have found to involve
a retreat of the shore cliffs amounting to 3, 5, and even 10 feet
per annum.    On the basis of the present rate of wave erosion of
Cape Cod, but making due allowance for changing conditions in
the future, we have calculated that the outer part, or forearm,
of the Cape should disappear within the next four or five thousand
years.    The annual rate and total extent of wave erosion on
other portions of the unconsolidated coasts have been discussed.
Andrews' studies of wave erosion along the Great Lakes shores
have been analyzed, and the difficulties in the way of accepting
certain of his conclusions have been set forth.    In particular it
has been shown that his conception of a subaqueous terrace 60
feet below lake level, accepted by some writers as indicating a
depth of 60 feet for wave base on the lakes, is not substantiated
by the character of the terraces as revealed by profile studies,
but seems to depend upon an erroneous interpretation of forms
which apparently are for the most part of non-lacustrine origin.

The average annual rate of coast erosion along the lakes as calculated by Andrews (5¼ feet) has been found to be somewhat larger than the figure derived from more recent studies (2.77 feet to 3.33 feet). Finally, we have considered somewhat fully the precautions which must be observed by those who would study shoreline changes by comparing maps and charts of the same area made at successive periods, and have found that mechanical distortions of the media upon which maps and charts are printed, errors inherent in original surveys, the difficulty of locating accurately certain elements of the shore, and other factors introduce into such calculations of shore changes significant errors which must be recognized and if possible corrected before the results of the calculations are accepted. Special attention has been directed to the employment of such calculations in legal controversies, and to other uses of maps and charts in connection with legal problems involving shoreline phenomena.

## BIBLIOGRAPHY

1. ROORBACH, G. B. "Shoreline Changes in the Winthrop Area, Massachusetts." Phil. Geog. Soc., VIII, 172–190, 1910.
2. MITCHELL, HENRY. "Physical Hydrography of the Gulf of Maine." U. S. Coast and Geod. Surv., Rept. for 1879, 176, 1881.
3. MITCHELL, HENRY. "Report Concerning Nauset Beach and the Peninsula of Monomoy." Mass. Board of Harbor Comm., 7th Ann. Rept., 106, 1873.
4. MITCHELL, HENRY. "Report Concerning Nauset Beach and the Peninsula of Monomoy." Mass. Board of Harbor Comm., 7th Ann. Rept., 102, 1873.
5. MATHER, W. W. "Geology of New York, Part I, Geology of the First Geological District," 653 pp., Albany, 1843.
6. FULLER, M. L. "The Geology of Long Island, New York." U. S. Geol. Surv., Prof. Paper No. 82, 56, 1914.
7. GANONG, W. F. "Further Data upon the Rate of Recession of the Coast Line of New Brunswick." Nat. Hist. Soc. New Brunswick, Bull., VII, No. XXXI, 1–5, 1913.
8. ROORBACH, G. B. "Shoreline Changes in the Winthrop Area, Massachusetts." Phil. Geog. Soc., VIII, 177, 1910.
9. MARINDIN, H. L. "Encroachment of the Sea upon the Coast of Cape Cod, Massachusetts, as shown by Comparative Surveys." U. S. Coast and Geod. Surv., Rept. of Supt. for 1889, Appendix 12, 403–407, 1890.
10. DAVIS, W. M. "The Outline of Cape Cod." Amer. Acad. Arts and Sci., Proc., XXXI, 331, 1896.
11. WHITING, H. L. (Results of successive surveys on Marthas Vineyard.) U. S. Geol. Surv., 7th Ann. Rept., 361–363, 1888.

12. SHALER, N. S. "Report on the Geology of Marthas Vineyard." U. S. Geol. Surv., 7th Ann. Rept., 348, 1888.
13. SHALER, N. S. "Geology of the Cape Cod District." U. S. Geol. Surv., 18th Ann. Rept., Pt. 2, 525, 1898.
14. SHALER, N. S. "Report on the Geology of Marthas Vineyard." U. S. Geol. Surv., 7th Ann. Rept., 349, 1888.
15. SHALER, N. S. "Report on the Geology of Marthas Vineyard." U. S. Geol. Surv., 7th Ann. Rept., 350, 1888.
16. WHITING, H. L. "Report on Vineyard Haven." Mass. Board of Harbor Comm., 7th Ann. Rept., 111–117, 1873.
17. ANDREWS, EDMUND. "The North American Lakes Considered as Chronometers of Post-Glacial Time." Chicago Acad. Sci., Trans., II, 1–23, 1870.
18. ANDREWS, EDMUND. "The North American Lakes Considered as Chronometers of Post-Glacial Time." Chicago Acad. Sci., Trans., II, 4, 6, 1870.
19. ATWOOD, W. W., and GOLDTHWAIT, J. W. "Physical Geography of the Evanston-Waukegan Region." Geol. Surv. Illinois, Bull. 7, 50, 1908.
20. ATWOOD, W. W., and GOLDTHWAIT, J. W. "Physical Geography of the Evanston-Waukegan Region." Geol Surv. Illinois, Bull. 7, 49, 1908.
21. TAYLOR, F. B. Personal communication. See also his paper on "The Second Lake Algonquin." Amer. Geol., XV, 107–108, 1895.
22. LEVERETT, FRANK. "The Illinois Glacial Lobe." U. S. Geol. Surv., Mon. XXXVIII, 457–459, 1899.
23. JOHNSON, DOUGLAS. "Shore Processes and Shoreline Development," 217–220, New York, 1917.
24. PATTON, R. S. Personal communication, by permission of the Director of the U. S. Coast and Geodetic Survey.
25. JOHNSON, D. S., and YORK, H. H. "The Relation of Plants to Tide Levels." Carnegie Institution of Washington, Pub. No. 206, 162 pp., Washington, 1915.

# CHAPTER XIII

## WAVE-BUILT FORMS BORDERING UNCON-SOLIDATED DEPOSITS

**Advance Summary.** — Obviously those shorelines bordering glacial débris so non-resistant that the waves cut into it at the rates indicated in the preceding chapter, should be richly adorned with bars, spits and forelands of various types; unless, indeed, erosion has gone so far that the shoreline has passed through the stage of youth, when such forms are most abundant, and has attained the simplicity of full maturity. Limited sections of the glacial drift coasts do present the nearly straight or simply curved outline and the practically continuous marine cliff which are the most striking characteristics of the mature stage of shoreline development; the best example being the outer coast of Cape Cod, previously mentioned and more fully described on a later page. But for the most part even these weakest of coast lands are still young or submature, and present to the student of coastal physiography a bewildering wealth of interesting forms. They have a further value to the investigator because of the fidelity with which former positions of the sea margin against them are sometimes recorded. The material of drumlins, moraines, and fluvioglacial sandplains registered plainly even brief attacks of the waves, often in positions now far removed from the sea; and the abandoned cliffs, grassed over or forested but still sharply defined, when studied in connection with associated wave-built forms, tell with remarkable clearness the successive episodes in the development of the shoreline. Seldom if ever do rocky coasts present evidence of such rapid changes in shore pattern, or evidence so clearly indicated, as that recorded in the outlines of Cape Cod, Nantasket Beach, and other parts of our glacial drift coasts. It will be our task in the present chapter to pass in brief review some examples of the varied forms due to wave deposition bordering the coasts of unconsolidated débris, and to trace more fully the physiographic history of certain sections of the coast where the depositional forms

FIG. 205.   Landward side of cobblestone pocket beach near Rye, New Hampshire.

enable us to follow the shoreline evolution with exceptional facility.

**Bayhead Beaches and Bars.** — Bayhead or pocket beaches and bayhead bars are so common along the New England-Acadian coast as to render scarcely necessary the mention of specific cases. Countless little coves in the irregular terminal moraine shorelines, and similar embayments in irregular patches of ground moraine, particularly on the less exposed coasts, contain beautiful examples of these forms on a small scale. The coast of New Hampshire, from Little Boars Head northward, where bedrock ledges protrude in places from a thin covering of glacial drift, presents a number of small but remarkably fine cobblestone pocket beaches (Fig. 205), the crests of which rise 15 to 20 feet or more above high tide level. Larger examples are found along the drift-strewn Connecticut shore, as

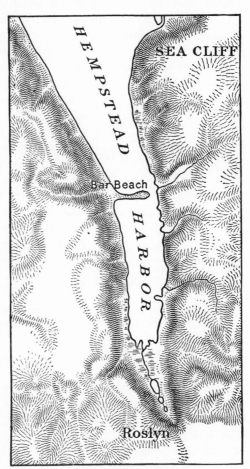

Fig. 206.    Midbay bar in Hempstead Harbor, north shore of Long Island.

southeast of Milford (U. S. Coast Survey Chart No. 263), and in the beach and bar at the head of Centerville Harbor, a reentrant in the southern margin of the pitted outwash plain of upper Cape Cod (U. S. Coast Survey Chart No. 247). This last case has special interest because back of it are earlier bayhead bars and spits, and back of them ancient marine cliffs, which deserve special attention in connection with the problem of modern coastal subsidence.  Together these furnish an excellent example of the normal features of a prograding shore.  Of midbay bars the most beautiful illustration is Bar Beach, which cuts in twain the Hempstead Harbor drowned valley in the fluvio-glacial plain of northern Long Island (Fig. 206).

**Baymouth Bars.** — Baymouth bars are as abundant on the glacial drift shores as they are rare on those bordered by hard

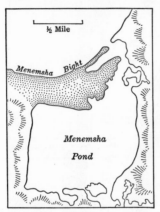

rock.  The small bays of the drowned irregular margins of the terminal moraines are sometimes blocked by bars of this type, an example of larger size than usual being the bar which nearly closes the broad northern mouth of Menemsha Pond in the Ronkonkoma moraine near Gay Head (Fig. 207), while smaller illustrations in the Harbor Hill moraine are found in the Elizabeth Islands.  Menemsha Pond owes its comparatively large size not so much to a normal irregularity of the morainal knob and kettle topography, as to a major irregularity in the distribution of the morainal mass as a whole, influenced perhaps by antecedent inequalities of the disturbed coastal plain beds upon which

Fig. 207.  Broad baymouth bar nearly closing mouth of Menemsha Pond, a submerged depression in the Ronkonkoma moraine of Marthas Vineyard.

the moraine is deposited in the Gay Head region.  James Pond and Chappaquonsett Pond, or Lake Tashmoo, farther to the northeast on Marthas Vineyard, may belong in the same class as Menemsha Pond, and like it are nearly closed by baymouth bars of somewhat irregular form; while the Vineyard Haven embayment (U. S. Coast Survey Chart No. 347) is divided into two parts by a midbay bar running obliquely across the depression.  Where the ice-contact side of a moraine shows concave scallops, larger embayments are enclosed by more extended baymouth bars, as in the case of the bar enclosing Sengekontacket Pond, Marthas Vineyard (Fig. 208).  The Sandy Neck sandspit is growing eastward in an attempt to close Barnstable Harbor, a similar embayment in the north side of the Harbor Hill moraine on upper

Cape Cod (U. S. G. S. Barnstable quadrangle). Although this broad spit is largely obscured by dunes more or less irregularly distributed as a result of migration since they first formed on successive beach ridges of the growing spit, the incurving lines of growth are nevertheless distinctly recognizable on the ground, and show it to belong to the compound recurved variety (U. S. Coast Survey Chart No. 339). Blowouts among the dunes show pebbles and boulders far back from the present shore, thus indicating the composition of the early ridges. West of Sandy Neck a succession of narrow baymouth bars enclosing salt marshes continues the simple, slightly concave shore which here records a sub-

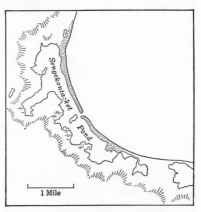

FIG. 208. Sengekontacket Pond, a partially submerged concave scallop along the ice-contact side of the Ronkonkoma moraine on Marthas Vineyard, nearly closed by a baymouth bar.

mature stage of shoreline development. Salt Pond is separated from the sea by a small baymouth bar which also serves as a tombolo uniting several small islands to the northern headland. About the shores of this pond are excellent examples of abandoned marine cliffs, the bases of which are just above high tide level, indicating that there has been no change of level since the formation of the baymouth bar.

The northern coast of Long Island, where a submaturely dissected fluvio-glacial sandplain has been partially submerged to give an irregular shore with many bays, furnishes excellent illustrations of baymouth bars. East Beach enclosing Mt. Sinai Harbor, Setauket Beach enclosing Port Jefferson Harbor, and the beaches enclosing Stony Brook Harbor and Nissequogue River, all in the vicinity of Port Jefferson (Fig. 209), are typical of many others which might be named. Between Stony Brook Harbor and Nissequogue River is a good illustration of a " winged headland,"[1] with the two spits so far extended as to become baymouth bars.

By far the most remarkable series of baymouth bars are those blocking the mouths of partially submerged shallow valleys in

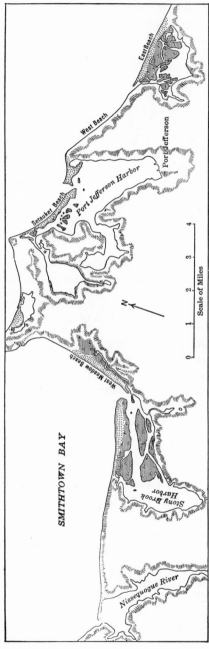

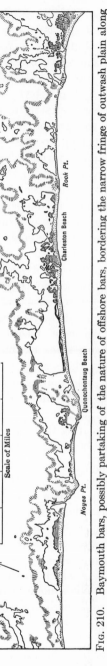

Fig. 209. Baymouth bars on the northern shore of Long Island, nearly closing drowned valleys in a submaturely dissected fluvio-glacial sandplain. Between Stony Brook Harbor and Nissequogue River is a good example of a winged headland.

Fig. 210. Baymouth bars, possibly partaking of the nature of offshore bars, bordering the narrow fringe of outwash plain along the south side of the Harbor Hill moraine in Rhode Island.

the southern margins of the outwash plains south of the moraines. The valleys in question are often unoccupied by streams at present, and were apparently carved when distributary streams from the melting ice flowed southward down the gentle slopes of the plains. In the absence of upland waters to help keep inlets open through the bars, some of the latter completely and more or less permanently separate the bays from the ocean. To this class belong the beautiful series of baymouth bars which characterize the straight submature shoreline along the south side of Marthas Vineyard (Fig. 51), and several on the south side of Nantucket. Those along the south side of the outwash plain east of Woods Hole are less evenly developed as yet, in part because here the plain topography is complicated by outlying bits of moraine or older glacial deposits. In Rhode Island little of the outwash plain associated with the Harbor Hill moraine is left above sealevel, and the waters often set back into irregular depressions between the morainal hills; but a whole succession of bays or " ponds " are enclosed by long, straight baymouth bars, which may partake of the nature of offshore bars developed by wave action on the smooth seaward slope of the outwash plain (Fig. 210). Occasionally the normal landward migration of the bars is checked by a hill of the old crystalline surface projecting through the mantle of glacial deposits. A good example is found at Quonochontaug Beach, where the waves break against crystalline ledges.

**Spits.** — Of bars developed but a short distance across the mouths of bays, or in other positions ending with a free point in open water so as to belong properly in the class of spits, the glacial drift shores of New England and Acadia furnish countless examples. Long Beach helping to enclose Plymouth Harbor (U. S. Coast Survey Chart No. 245) is a straight spit of the simplest type. The remarkably straight spit extending northwestward from Tuckernuck Island (Fig. 211), noted for its extreme variability in form and position, partakes of the character of an offshore bar. Monomoy spit, at the southeast point of Cape Cod, is a larger example, somewhat recurved at its distal point, much studied because of the rapid and important changes in its form and position. Cape Poge Bay (Fig. 212) is enclosed by a long simply recurved spit or bar which overlaps North Neck, an extension into the bay which looks like an earlier formed spit, but which, as is well shown on U. S. Coast Survey Chart No. 346, is a combination of double tombolo and minor spit interrupted by a remnant of upland which the double tombolo unites to the mainland of Chappaquiddick Island. The larger spit or bar itself depends from a complex tombolo united to Chappaquiddick farther to the southeast. Long Point and Race Point (Fig. 229) are recurved spits, the former complex near its eastern terminus, and both depending from the extensively prograded spit of somewhat complex history forming the Provincetown district of Cape Cod. Revere

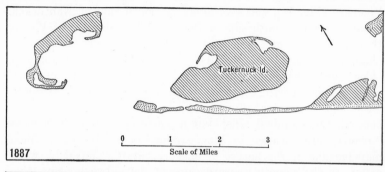

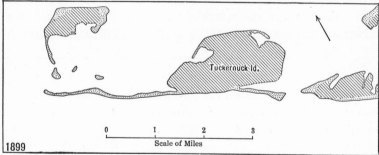

Fig. 211. Spits of the Tuckernuck Island region, near Nantucket, subject to rapid changes in form and position. The long spit partakes of the character of an offshore bar.

Beach, Massachusetts (Fig. 188), and Old Orchard Beach, Maine, are baymouth bars occupying very similar positions and ending in compound recurved spits known in the first case as Point of Pines, in the second as Pine Point. The former has been carefully mapped and studied by students in the Department of Geology at Tufts College, under the direction of Professor A. C. Lane, and will deserve special attention when in a later volume we come to discuss evidences of modern coastal subsidence.

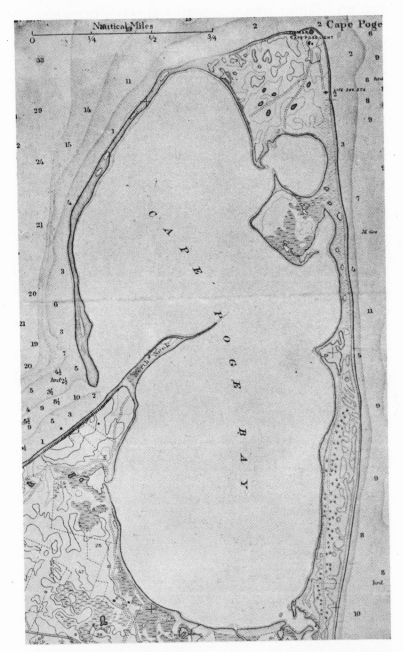

FIG. 212. Cape Poge Bay, bordered on the east by a complex tombolo, on the northwest by a simple recurved spit or bar, and partly divided near the centre by the double tombolo of North Neck from which a simple spit is growing eastward. From U. S. C. & G. S. Chart No. 346. (437)

Goulet Beach (Fig. 213) is a peculiarly irregular spit at the eastern end of Madame Island, Nova Scotia, while the southeastern shore of Nova Scotia, particularly where the sea is cliffing drumlins and other glacial débris, as for example east and west of Chezzetcook Inlet (Chezzetcook sheet, Canadian Department of Militia and Defence), furnishes illustrations of minor spits showing a variety of forms. The drumlin islands and other glacial forms in Halifax Harbor are adorned with a remarkable series of spits, bars, and

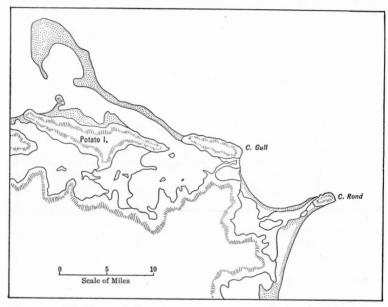

Fig. 213. Double tombolo of Cape Rond and irregularly recurved spit of Goulet Beach (northwest corner of map), both at eastern end of Madame Island, Nova Scotia.

forelands (Fig. 213a), including the flying bar known as Barrie Beach, probably developed as a complex tombolo attached to former islands now represented by rocky shoals. As one should expect, the Acadian shores, with their more numerous rocky headlands and less abundant glacial débris, are not so rich in bars and spits as the shores of southern New England, where for vast stretches the coast presents to the waves nothing but unconsolidated glacial deposits.

**Cuspate Bars and Forelands.** — Cuspate bars and forelands are well represented along the glacial drift shores. On the coast of

Connecticut near Milford there is a fairly well developed cuspate bar enclosing a marsh, and pointing seaward toward a gradually wasting island. From the island a submerged bar reaches back to the apex of the cusp, suggesting that a Y-tombolo may be in process of forming (U. S. Coast Survey Charts Nos. 265 and 266). Near Bridgeport, Connecticut, Shoal Point and

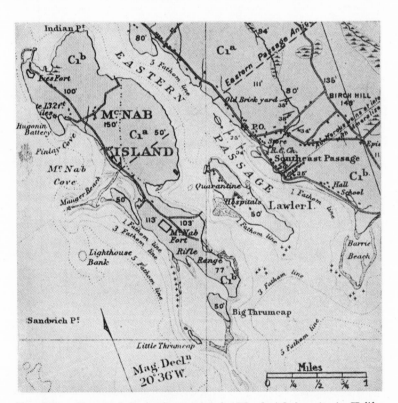

FIG. 213a. Bars and forelands associated with glacial deposits in Halifax Harbor. Barrie Beach appears to be a complex flying bar developed in connection with a former island or shoal of glacial débris. From Halifax Sheet, No. 68, Geol. Surv. Canada.

Pine Creek Point are similar cuspate bars. Both cusps point seaward toward shoals which appear to represent former islands now vanished under wave attack (Fig. 214): the first toward The Cows, from which a very perfect long, narrow, submarine bar, Fairfield Bar, stretches back to the apex of the cusp; the second toward minor shoals near its apex, beyond which lie the

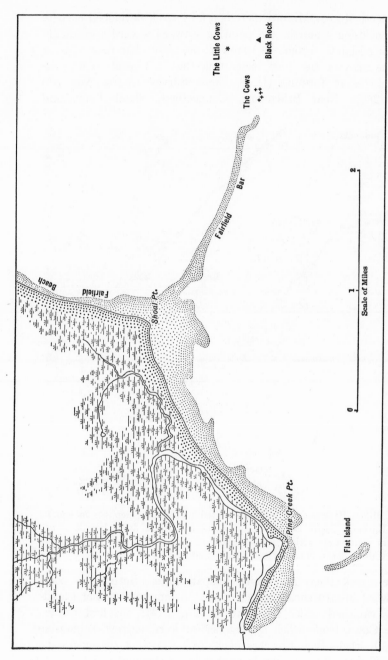

Fig. 214.  Cuspate bars near Bridgeport, Connecticut, which apparently owe their form to islands now vanished under wave attack.  They may represent portions of unfinished or partially destroyed Y-tombolos.  Based on U. S. C. & G. S. Chart No. 220.

remains of Flat Island, with a bar trailing landward, but at present at least, toward one side of the cusp instead of its apex. These cusps may represent either uncompleted Y-tombolos, or parts of such tombolos which existed for a time, but which were soon destroyed after the former islands were removed by the waves. Cedar Point near Saugatuck on this same coast is a very acute cuspate bar one side of which is as yet uncompleted, while the apex is prolonged seaward in a slender spit connecting with a shoal or former island. The chart (U. S. Coast Survey Chart No. 267) portraying this interesting example shows other cuspate bars and a great variety of small spits and tombolos. Gaspee Point (Fig. 178), the type of Gulliver's " lagoon-marsh " stage of a tidal cuspate foreland[2] and the subject of an interesting paper by Brown,[3] is composed of débris removed from glacial drift mantling the shores of Narragansett Bay, and apparently is independent of any shoal or former island. Additional examples of both bars and forelands adorn these shores. The objections to the tidal theory of cuspate bars and forelands, and to the idea that other currents than those generated by wave action are necessary to the development of these forms, have been briefly treated on an earlier page, and more at length in another volume.[4] The northern and southern extremities of Gardiners Island afford unusually pretty illustrations of cuspate bars enclosing lagoons (U. S. Coast Survey Chart No. 298). The one at the north shows particularly well the narrow arm on the side of more vigorous wave attack, and the broad arm, preserving its older, inner portions, on the more protected side, a contrast quite characteristic of cuspate bars subjected to unequal marine action on the two sides.

*Coskata Cusps.* — A broad blunt cuspate foreland projects seaward from the abandoned marine cliff, Tom Nevers Head, at the southeastern point of Nantucket Island, while the most superb illustration of a cuspate bar on the New England-Acadian shores is the great Coskata triangle, prolonged as a spit to Great Point, forming the northern projection of Nantucket (Fig. 215). This cuspate bar represents an uncompleted double tombolo, for at the apex is found the remains of an island of glacial débris[5] which doubtless in part determined the form and development of the bar. The more exposed and narrower eastern arm is sometimes broken through at Haulover Beach, while the southwestern extension of the broader western arm is fringed on its inner or lagoon side with a series of six minor cuspate points, the origin of which has puzzled more than one investigator. Shaler[6] tentatively invoked the theory, since become a favorite with other writers, that tidal currents, or series of eddy currents generated by them,

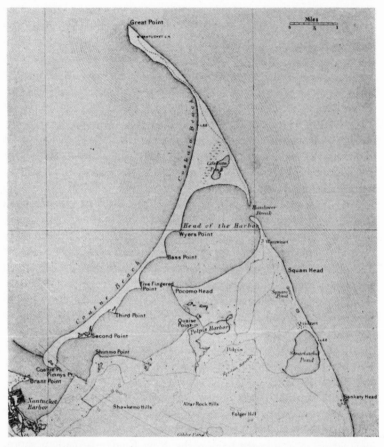

Fig. 215. Coskata cuspate bar, Nantucket Island, showing series of six cusps on inner side of Coatue Beach, and the temporary opening (Haulover Break) through Haulover Beach. From U. S. G. S. Topographic Atlas, Nantucket quadrangle.

scoured the concavities and deposited the salients. "The cause of these peculiar projections," wrote Shaler, "is not plain. They are possibly due in some way to the action of the tidal currents, which sweep up the bay with much speed and move the fine-grained sands with considerable ease. From a superficial inspection it appears that the tidal waters are thrown into a series of whirlpools, which excavate the shore between these salients and accumulate the sand on the spits." Gulliver[7] likewise believed that the form of the cusps indicated the presence of a small eddy current between each pair. Shaler represents by diagram (Fig. 216) a structure for the cusps in which successive beach ridges, in general parallel to the axis of the spit but becoming shorter

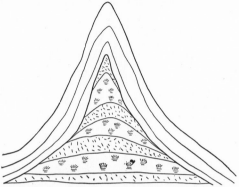

FIG. 216.   Structure of small cuspate forelands on inner side of Coatue Beach, Nantucket, as interpreted by Shaler.

and more convex as they advance into the lagoon, are added until the cuspate form is completed.

Inasmuch as the successive recurved points of a compound recurved spit may give cuspate forms without the intervention of any special series of tidal currents or whirlpool eddies, and there was thus offered the possibility of a more simple explanation of the Coatue cusps, I requested one of my field assistants, Mr. (now Dr.) Donald Barton to make a special examination of Coatue Beach to determine whether the beach ridges curved inward in the vicinity of the cusps in the manner shown in Fig. 217. This was a matter of some importance in connection with the problem of coastal subsidence; for if Shaler's theory were correct, the cusps might all be of the same age, whereas if they represented recurved points of a growing spit they must be progressively younger from northeast to southwest, and so should by their levels record either essential coastal stability during the time required for the growth of the spit, or marked changes of sealevel if such had occurred in that interval. Dr. Barton accordingly visited Nantucket, and reported that the beach ridges parallel to the outer shore distinctly curved southward on First and Second Points; but farther east he could find no evidence of ridge curvature related to the cusps, and was inclined for this reason to think that the easterly cusps were formed independently at a later date.

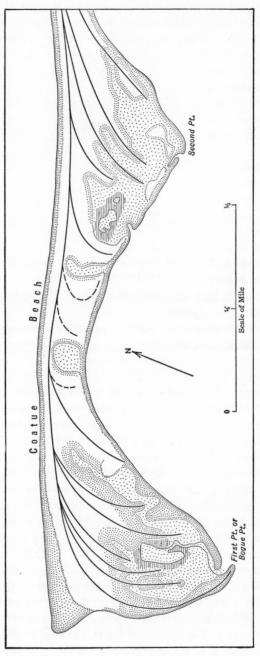

FIG. 217. The two most recently formed cuspate points on the inner side of Coatue Beach, showing successive curved beach ridges indicated on the Nantucket Harbor hydrographic chart, and proving that the cusps represent successive recurved points of a growing sandspit. The lines show apparent axes of the curved ridges.

He noted, however, that on these cusps the southwestern side was bordered by a dune-covered beach ridge much higher than that margining the east side, a circumstance which would normally result from exposure to more vigorous waves on the western, open-water side than on the eastern, lagoon side, if the cusps represent successive recurved points of a southwestward growing spit later modified by the lagoon waves; although it is also possible to explain this feature as due to the action of prevailing southwest winds in blowing more sand from the beach to the adjacent ridge on the southwest side. The curvature of the older ridges toward the older points would not appear in any case, if the front of the spit had suffered retrogression prior to the formation of the beach ridges now parallel to the outer shore and curving southward to Second and First Points. Barton's sketches do not indicate the succession of ridges and swales in the heart of the cusp represented in Shaler's diagram, and he reports that the inner part of the cusp " is in all cases low, and in some cases flooded at high tide."

The detailed chart of Nantucket Harbor (U. S. Coast Survey Chart No. 343) shows the three younger cuspate forelands of the Coatue series, known as First, Second, and Third Points. The structure of Third Point as shown by the map is inconclusive, and might result from cusp formation according to Shaler's theory, or according to the theory that they represent the recurved points, slightly modified by the action of small waves in the lagoon, of a normally developing compound recurved spit. First and Second Points, however, clearly show the structure (Fig. 217) required by the latter theory. The successive recurving of the southwestern end of the spit, constantly growing farther toward the southwest but each new ridge being bent landward in the manner typical of such spits,[3] is very evident, despite the minor alterations of outline later effected by the lagoon waves. There seems to be no good reason to doubt that all the cusps have the same origin; and hence it appears most probable that these cuspate forms merely represent successive stages in the growth of the recurving spit forming the western arm of the Coskata cuspate bar.

Such forms are fairly common, but the present case more readily attracts attention because the cusps happen to be unusually prominent, and spaced with what appears to be some approach to regularity, although First and Second Points are nearly twice as far apart as Bass and Wyers Points, and the latter two about three-quarters the distance of the next adjoining interval to the southwest, between Bass and Five Fingered Points. Since the Coatue spit has grown from northeast to southwest, and the cusps are therefore progressively younger in the latter direction, it is obvious that if the coast had suffered any marked subsidence or elevation during the period required for their formation, the older cusps should be notably lower or higher than the younger members of the series. Barton finds no significant, systematic difference in their elevations; hence we must conclude that during the formation of Coatue Beach no marked change in the relative elevation of land and sea occurred. That the time required for Coatue to develop may have been appreciable, is suggested by the fact that a map published by Des Barres in 1776 also shows 6 cusps, the last one being apparently less perfectly developed than now. But such spits often grow with comparative rapidity, and Coatue may possibly have formed within a few centuries. The most we can say, therefore, is that apparently no great change of level has occurred here within the last few centuries.

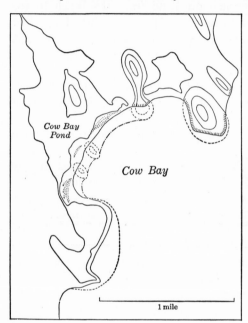

Fig. 218.   Cow Bay Beach, Nova Scotia, a complex tombolo uniting several eroded drumlin remnants.   Based on two sketch maps by McIntosh.

**Tombolos.** — The partial submergence of a drumlin area affords ideal conditions for the development of tombolos, or island-tying bars, and the drumlin shorelines of the New England-Acadian province present some of the most interesting examples of tombolos to be found anywhere in the world.   In the remarkable drumlin area of Mahone Bay (Fig. 56), Nova Scotia, there are

cases of drumlins united by tombolos, but here the waters are so
sheltered that for the most part the shorelines are too young to
show the best development of these forms.   On the more exposed
outer coast east of Halifax conditions are more favorable;  and at
Cow Bay is an interesting complex tombolo (Fig. 218) developed
in connection with drumlins, some of which have been consumed
by the waves.   The physiographic development of the Cow Bay
tombolo (Fig. 219) has been well described by McIntosh.[9]   The
Chezzetcook topographic map, issued by the Canadian Department
of Militia and Defense, shows not only the Cow Bay tombolo, but

FIG. 219.  Succession of cobblestone beach ridges with intervening grassy
    swales, showing prograding of part of the Cow Bay Beach complex tom-
    bolo, Nova Scotia.  Cf. Fig. 218.  Photo by J. W. Goldthwait, Geol.
    Surv. Canada.

a whole series of beautiful examples farther east, especially the
complex group blocking the seaward end of Porter Lake (Fig. 220).
At the northeastern extremity of Nova Scotia is the double tombolo (Fig. 221) uniting the Glasgow Head drumlin and its rocky
base to an island just behind, and a similar double tombolo (Fig.
213) ties the Cape Rond drumlin to the mainland of Madame
Island, Cape Breton.   Winthrop Beach (Fig. 188) in the vicinity
of Boston is a complex tombolo strongly reminding one of the
Cow Bay example.   Its history has been traced in a valuable
paper by Roorbach,[10] which explains how the present form of
the tombolo has been affected by drumlins long since removed

by waves.   It is in Nantasket Beach (Fig. 234), however, that
we find the most highly instructive example of a complex tombolo uniting remnants of eroded drumlins to the mainland.   This
beach, also near Boston, is so important to the student of shore

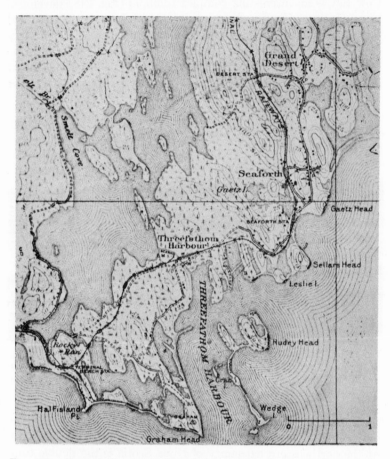

Fig. 220.   Remarkable series of tombolos and bay bars near Porter Lake,
    Nova Scotia.   From Chezzetcook topographic quadrangle, Canadian
    Department of Militia and Defense.

forms that it will be more fully described when we come to consider the extensive changes which have taken place in the outline
of the shores bordering glacial deposits.

Tombolos uniting isolated portions of a partially submerged
terminal moraine may be found in the Elizabeth Islands (U. S.

Coast Survey Chart No. 297), and in the Watch Hill region of
Connecticut (U. S. Coast Survey Chart No. 358) where Napatree
Point shows cliffs in a very bouldery till, and is united to the main
part of the moraine at Watch Hill by the long and slender Napatree Beach.

Remnants of fluvio-glacial sandplains united by tombolos are
common along the north shore of Long Island, an exceptionally
good series being found in the bars uniting Eaton Neck, Lloyd
Neck, the Center Island group, Oak Neck, Fox Point and
East Island to the mainland in the region of Oyster Bay (Fig.
193). Similar relations exist in the Wellfleet Harbor district
of Cape Cod, where Griffin Island, Great Island, Great Beach
Hill, and Little Beach Hill, sandplain remnants, are united by

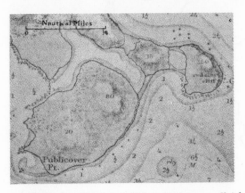

FIG. 221.   Glasgow Head drumlin (at right) united to small island to west
by a double tombolo.   From U. S. Hydrographic Chart No. 1074.

very slender tombolos (U. S. Coast Survey Chart No. 340). The
very striking tombolo of Duxbury Beach-Saquish Neck, enclosing
Duxbury Bay near Plymouth (Fig. 222), is also worthy of special
mention.

**Abundance of Wave-Built Forms Indicates Short Stand of Sea
at Present Level.** — The foregoing review of detailed shore forms
bordering the glacial drift shores, while relatively more brief than
will justly emphasize the far greater abundance of such forms
on the drift coasts as compared with the number on coasts of
either resistant or non-resistant rocks, is nevertheless sufficient to
make clear the fact that rapid marine erosion of unconsolidated
débris from the vast number of exposed points presented by
partially submerged drumlins, morainal hills, sandplain remnants

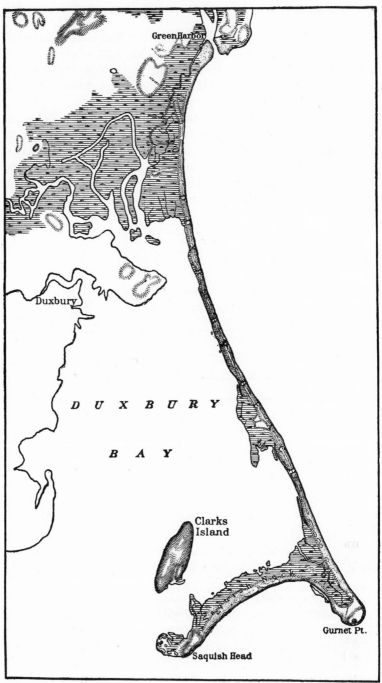

FIG. 222.  Duxbury Beach-Saquish Neck tombolo, uniting the former islands
of Gurnet Point and Saquish Head to the Massachusetts coast near
Plymouth.                                                          (450)

and other glacial features has resulted in an endless variety of spits and bars of every description.   On the hard-rock coasts the relative scarcity of these forms impressed us as an evidence of the short time during which the waves have worked at the present level.   Sufficient time has not yet elapsed for the waves to re-move large quantities of material from resistant shores to build into spits and bars.   Paradoxical as it may seem, the very abun-dance of such forms on the glacial drift coasts is likewise an evi-dence of the short stand of the sea at its present level.   Rapidly as the waves work in loose débris, sufficient time has not yet elapsed for them to cut these coasts back to a simple shore un-adorned by anything save a cliff and beach.   Only in exceptional cases has the shoreline bordering a fluvio-glacial plain reached the stage of submaturity (e. g., the south shore of Marthas Vine-yard) or maturity (outer Cape Cod), and then only where ex-posure to vigorous wave attack and also, in some cases at least, the initial outline of the shore, favored rapid attainment of simple contours.   In general one is impressed with the extent to which the irregularities of youth persist along the drift shores, and hence with the added testimony to the short stand of the sea at the level where we now find it.

**Rapid Changes in Wave-Built Forms.** — The rapidity with which the waves cut into unconsolidated glacial deposits, suffi-ciently evidenced by figures for rates of erosion under different conditions given on earlier pages, should be paralleled by rapid changes in the spits and bars dependent from such weak and easily eroded uplands; for where the upland is cut back quickly, differences in rates of erosion due to variations in direction and force of wave attack, to differences in height of upland, to altera-tions in the average composition of the glacial débris, and to other causes, are more rapidly developed.   We are quite prepared, therefore, to find that frequent and rapid changes in spits, bars, and inlets along the glacial débris coasts are a cause of serious anxiety to the navigator, an occasion for much labor by the coast surveyor, and a source of great interest to the physiographer.

*Edgartown Harbor Bar.* — The Coast Survey chart for Edgar-town Harbor (No. 346) shows the narrow baymouth bar across the entrance to Katama (or Cotamy) Bay with this significant inscription: " Shoreline and hydrography subject to frequent changes " (Fig. 223).   The changes in this bar and in the inlet to the bay proved so important in their effects on Edgartown Harbor at the head of the bay, that they were early made the subject of special studies by Henry Mitchell, H. L. Whiting, and other members of the Coast Survey. In the annual report of the Superintendent of the United States Coast Survey for 1871 the reader will find an interesting map of " Edgartown Harbor and Cotamy Bay " prepared by Mitchell, Whiting, and Marindin to accompany a report on shore changes in this region, forming Appendix 15 of the Report for 1869, but delayed and printed separately because the original was destroyed in the great Boston fire.

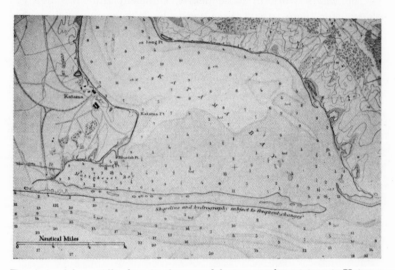

FIG. 223.   The rapidly changing baymouth bar across the entrance to Katama Bay, Marthas Vineyard.   Parallel to the shore is an excellent example of the "ball" or submerged bar (with only 3 to 5 feet of water over it) which is a normal feature of many shores, and which is separated from the shoreline by a "low" or channel of deeper water.   From U. S. C. & G. S. Chart No. 346.

This map shows the position of the bar and of the inlet at different periods, and thus makes clear the extensive variations which this part of the shoreline suffers.   The map is reproduced in the Sixth Annual Report (1872) of the Board of Harbor Commissioners of Massachusetts in which also appear two reports on the shore changes of the so-called " Cotamy Beach," one by Whiting[11] and another by Mitchell.[12]   The first is of special value because it gives a résumé of the changes in beach and inlet, from which it appears that there was an inlet through the eastern end of the bar in 1776; that in the early part of the next century the inlet was closed and no opening existed for a short period; that at the time of the first accurate survey, in 1846, there was again an opening in the eastern end of the bar (Fig. 224); that by 1856 this inlet had moved a mile farther eastward and had become much narrower, while a new inlet had opened near the centre of the bar; that soon afterward the old inlet closed, and the new one moved gradually eastward until it was opposite the extreme eastern shore of Chappaquiddick Island; and that by 1869 the beach was driven in against the island, the inlet closed, and the bay left without a southern opening.

From later reports by Whiting[13] it appears that the bar remained practically without inlets for nearly twenty years, when in 1886 an inlet was broken through near the position of the opening of 1856, and for a time moved westward, contrary to the usual direction of inlet migration on this part of the coast. Accompanying these reports is a sketch map showing the different openings since 1846, and also the successive positions of the general outer shoreline in 1846, 1856, 1871, and 1886, each demonstrating an appreciable advance of the sea into the land near the western end of the bar where it is attached to the mainland of Marthas Vineyard. Another report by Whiting,[14] accompanied by a map of recent changes only, shows that by 1889 the newly developed inlet had migrated eastward, and a second subsidiary opening had formed. The chart of this region (Fig. 223) shows a beautiful example of a " ball " or submarine bar parallel to the shore and separated from it by a " low " or channel. Peaked Hill Bar and another nearer the shore on the northeast side of the Provincelands (Fig. 229) may be of this same type. The ball is sometimes mistaken for a remnant of a former baymouth bar or beach, originally projecting above sealevel but later destroyed by the waves;[15] observation seems to show, however, that balls may be normal features of a stationary or prograding shore.[16] Whiting's reports give valuable data on other changes in bars and inlets along the shores of Marthas Vineyard.

*Nauset Beach and Monomoy Point.* — As an illustration of a rapidly changing sandspit we may take the famous case of Monomoy Point and its continuation in the so-called Chatham Bar or Nauset Beach (Fig. 225), dependent from the southeastern extremity of the outwash plain of upper Cape Cod which is here apparently complicated by remnants of older fluvio-glacial de-

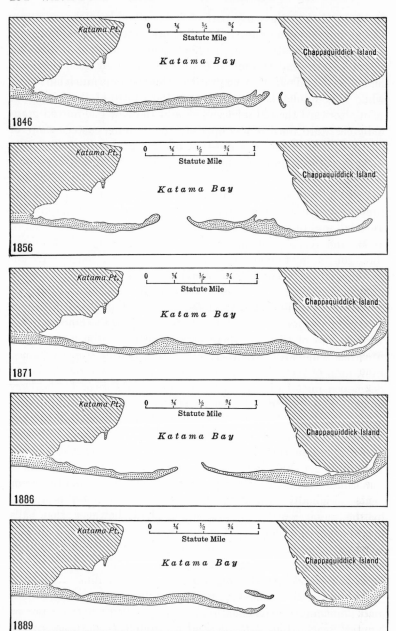

Fig. 224.   Changes in the position of the Katama (Marthas Vineyard) baymouth bar and its inlets as recorded in successive surveys by the U. S.
C. & G. S., 1846–1889.

posits protruding through it.    In 1871 the waves broke through
the bar and attacked the water-front of the town of Chatham.
Shortly thereafter the Superintendent of the Coast Survey,
Benjamin Peirce, directed Rear-Admiral Charles H. Davis, Professor H. L. Whiting and Professor Henry Mitchell, members of
the Coast Survey, to meet him at Chatham for a consultation on
the behavior of the marine forces at this changeable part of the
shore.    Out of the conference there issued instructions to Henry
Mitchell to make surveys of the region from time to time, and to
report the results of his studies to the Superintendent of the
Survey.

Mitchell's first report[17] appeared a couple of years later, and
traced the history of Monomoy spit and Nauset Beach from the
time of the accounts given in Champlain's narratives (1606) up
to the date of the investigation.    In particular this report showed
the changes in size and position of spit, bar, and inlets, in so far
as these could be determined from earlier maps and writings, and
from more recent surveys conducted in part by H. L. Marindin
for the special purpose then in hand.    Mitchell concluded that
while the upland back of Nauset Beach (or bar) had not been
greatly changed in two and a half centuries, " the ocean has
swept away, and re-formed the beach in front repeatedly."    Monomoy Point grew southward two miles within a century, extending into Nantucket Sound at the average rate of 138 feet a year
from 1853 to 1856, and at the rate of 157 feet a year from 1856 to
1868.    On the other hand certain parts of Nauset or Chatham
Beach had lost 319 acres from 1847 to 1872, or 63 per cent of the
area existing in 1847.

In later reports[18] Mitchell continues to set forth his studies of
the ever-changing shores, bar, spit, inlets, and shoals, and presents comparative maps prepared by Marindin and other to
illustrate the changes, some of which appear in Fig. 225.    The
reader who would follow more in detail the history of these changes
is referred to Mitchell's papers, and to a summary of some of the
more important early events by Edward Hitchcock.[19]    Suffice it
to say here that the rate of the southward extension of Monomoy
spit is shown to have varied from 12 feet a year up to 175 feet and
back to 22 feet, between 1840 and 1886, and that the form and
position of bar, inlets and shoals have been quite as variable.

Haulover Beach, the eastern side of the Coskata cuspate bar,
and its extension in Great Point (Fig. 215), afford a good example

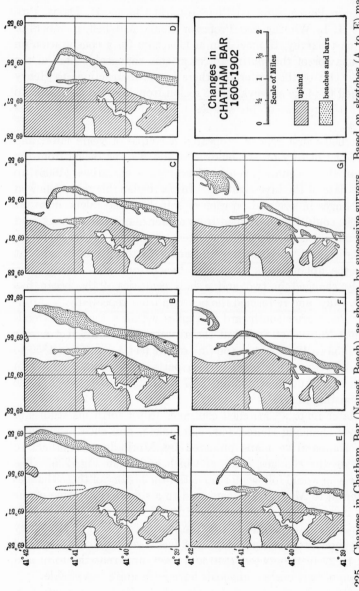

Fig. 225. Changes in Chatham Bar (Nauset Beach), as shown by successive surveys. Based on sketches (A to E) made by H. L. Marindin for Henry Mitchell, and photostat copies of later surveys (F and G) furnished by U. S. C. & G. S. To facilitate comparison with Marindin's published sketches, the projection used by him is retained. A, 1606; B, 1847; C, 1868; D, 1872; E, 1873; F, 1886; G, 1902.

of a tombolo subject to frequent changes. H. L. Whiting[20] reported in 1873 that since 1846 Haulover Beach, the eastern arm of the cuspate bar, had been cut back and reduced in width about 100 feet on an average. Comparison of surveys made from 1784 to 1874 later showed that the Great Point spit had lost, " by fits and starts," 1400 feet during the time that Monomoy was growing southward toward it.[21] In 1896 Haulover Beach was broken through by the sea, and an inlet a mile in width soon developed.[22] The variations of this inlet and of the bar on either side of it have been described in some detail in a series of brief papers by Gulliver.[23]

For a careful study of moderate variations in outline and submarine contours of a complex spit, partially protected by artificial works, the reader should consult Marindin's report on the changes in shorelines and anchorage areas of Provincetown Harbor, as shown by a comparison of surveys made in 1835, 1867, and 1890.[24] To this report is attached a comparative map showing in great detail the gains and losses of land for much of the wave-built portion of the outer terminus of Cape Cod.

*Sable Island Bar.* — Extensive and remarkably rapid variations, less accurately recorded, characterize the isolated bar of Sable Island, a strip of sand resting on the submerged coastal plain of the Banks, with part of its summit just above water. Whether this bar, which has a double crest enclosing a long narrow strip of water, is the product of wave action directly on a slightly submerged portion of the coastal plain cuesta, or represents a flying bar formerly attached to a drift island now consumed by the waves, as suggested by Gulliver,[25] is not clear; but its development without relation to any island, either of drift or of coastal plain deposits, seems quite possible.

The history of shoreline changes on Sable Island may be gleaned from valuable accounts by McDonald,[26] Patterson,[27] Macoun[28] and others, and a summary by Goldthwait.[29] From these records it would appear that during one four-year period 4 miles were cut away from the western end of the island, requiring the removal inland of the signal station there. During a single gale in 1813 a strip 3 miles long by 40 feet wide was carried away. In another thirty-year period, 11 miles of the western end disappeared and the signal station was moved three times. About 1830 storm waves broke an opening through one side of the bar into the central lake, which thus became a harbor for small vessels;

but not long after, another storm sealed up the opening, enclosing
two American vessels which had taken refuge there.  In 1881
three successive storms removed strips 70 feet wide and half a
mile long, 33 feet wide the entire length of the beach, and 48 feet
wide and a quarter of a mile long.  A lighthouse built near West
Point in 1873 had to be moved eastward a quarter of a mile in
1881, a mile and a half farther east in 1888, and in 1915 was again
in danger of being washed away.  As the island was 26 miles long
in 1767 according to the Des Barres chart, and now has a length
but 5 miles less, it would seem that some of the length removed
must have been recovered from time to time, or else part of the
washings away referred to the submarine extensions of the bar, —
this assuming the substantial accuracy of the records.  Modern
surveys give the length of the island as about 21 miles, with the
two ends continuing as submerged bars for 17 miles at the west
and 13 miles at the east.

## The Development of Cape Cod

The marked changes in shore outline which have taken place
in the last century or two as described above, are typical of even
more extensive changes along these glacial drift coasts during an
indefinite but long period covering part of post-glacial time.
Fortunately for the student of shore physiography parts of these
coast preserve, in abandoned marine cliffs and old beach ridges,
decipherable records of certain such changes.  An example is the
" forearm " and " hand " of Cape Cod, made classic by Davis in
his essay on " The Outline of Cape Cod."[30]  As this essay contains the first adequate statement of the fundamental principles
to be employed in reconstructing the development of a complex
recurved spit of the Provincetown type, its salient features are
here summarized in slightly altered form to make them applicable
to the general as well as to the specific case.

*Principles of Reconstruction.* — After eliminating the possibility
of extensive changes in the relative level of land and sea during
the development of the spit, the first problem is to reconstruct
the initial form of the mainland from which it grew.  This is
done on the basis of five guiding principles: (1) all areas consisting of materials deposited by marine agencies, such as beaches,
bars, forelands, spits, and marshes, must be removed as the first
step in getting back to the original form of the mainland shore;
(2) restoration of the mainland form takes into account the fact

that subaërial denudation has not effected significant changes in
its topography during post-glacial time, even where the mainland
consists of loose glacial deposits; (3) the restored outline should
possess irregularities of pattern comparable to those in the protected bays of today, advancing from the headlands and retreating toward the troughs or valleys in the high ground; (4) the
amount of land restored should be much less on protected shores
than on exposed shores; (5) cliffs that are now protected by fore-

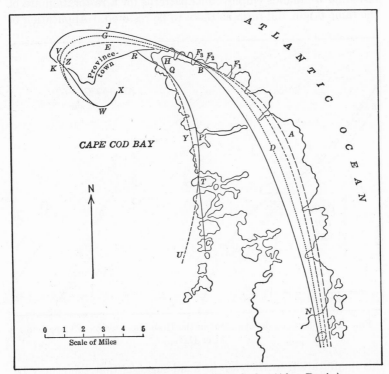

FIG. 226.  The development of Cape Cod.  (After Davis.)

lands of marine deposits must not, in the restoration, be extended
so far that their recession could not have been accomplished before the bars began to grow in front of them.

  *Initial Shoreline of the Truro Mainland.* — Applying these
principles to the case of the Provincetown spit, Davis draws for
the initial outline of the Truro mainland the irregular solid-line
part of Fig. 226.  The nature of the eastern shore as restored
will depend in some measure upon one's conception of the origin

of the deposits composing the mainland of Truro, for in this case
neither the protected bays on the inner or western side of the
Cape, representing the distal portion of the sandplains, nor the
ones farther south on the outer shore, where the terminal moraine
reaches the sea, were necessarily comparable with those which
indented the seaward edge of the Truro plains, where it possibly
formed an ice-contact margin of special pattern.   Thus in applying the third principle given above it is essential to know that the
bays and headlands employed as patterns for a restoration are of
the same origin and form as those to be restored.   Application of

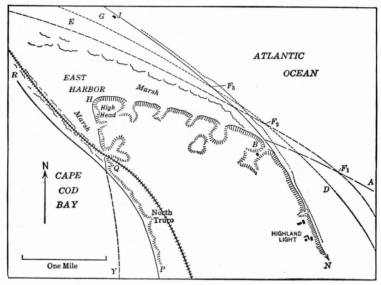

FIG. 227.   Shoreline development in the High Head region of Cape Cod.
(After Davis.)

this qualification to the case in hand suggests that there may be
considerable latitude for one's judgment in restoring the eastern
shore of the Truro mainland, as has already been indicated (Fig.
58), but the fundamental principle involved remains unaffected.

*Initial Shoreline in the High Head Region.* — In restoring the
initial shoreline for the High Head portion of Truro, (Fig. 226, H),
the fifth of the principles as listed above comes into play in a
manner which is especially significant.   Both the western and
the northern sides of the upland plain are abandoned marine
cliffs (Fig. 227), which are now protected by outlying bars or

spits (Fig. 228) springing tangent from later cliffs farther south or southeast. Areas of marsh lie between the bars and the abandoned cliffs. The bar on the west (Fig. 226, QR) is part of a long concave shoreline, TPQR, — for convenience called by Davis " the west concave shore," — which manifestly was not cut until after the peninsula of Provinceland to the northwest had come into existence. Before that time there was a " west straight shore," CTYQH, as is clearly indicated by its remnants still to be observed in the abandoned cliff QH, and in the nearly straight western shore of Bound Brook, Griffin, and other islands (C). But when the growth of the Provinceland spit toward the west began partially to protect the northern end (QH) of the west straight shore from wave attack, and to change the regime of wave and current action, the central part of that shore was excavated more rapidly to form the west concave shore, TPQ. Soon a spit or bar, QR, springing tangent from this concave shore, completed the protection of the northern remnant of the west straight cliff, QH.

Inasmuch as it was the westward growth of the spit BJ (or of its representative in former days) to make the Provinceland peninsula, which interfered with the cutting of the straight west shore, thus leading to excavation of the concave shore and hence to the final protection of the west cliff, QH, by a bar tangent to the concave shore, it is obvious that the north cliff, BH, lying behind the very base of the spit BJ, must have been protected long before the final protection of the west cliff, QH, was accomplished. In other words, a shorter time was allowed for the cutting of the north cliff of High Head than for cutting its west cliff; but since wave energy was greater on the north than on the west, the combined factors of time and energy may be regarded as roughly equivalent in the two cases, and an equal amount of land may be added to each cliff to effect the restoration of the initial shoreline. Whether to add a small or a large amount of land in both cases depends on whether the beginnings of the spit BJ were formed early or late in the erosion history of the Truro mainland. From our knowledge of the principles of shoreline development we may be sure that on a coast of unconsolidated glacial débris, the shoreline would be simplified and the growth of a tangent spit or bar would be initiated very early in the cycle of marine erosion. Hence the amount of land to be added on the two sides of High Head is small, and Davis gives an extension of little over half a mile.

*Initial Shoreline Southeast of High Head.* — Further aid in the restoration of the initial shoreline of the Truro mainland is secured from a critical examination of the relation of the northern abandoned cliff (Fig. 228) to the inner or first stage of the Province-town spit (Fig. 229). This relation is made clear in Fig. 227, from which it is evident that the earliest part of the spit did not spring from any part of the cliff still preserved, but from its extension eastward into the present domain of the sea. The approximate point is found by prolonging eastward or southeastward the faint curves of the northern cliff, HB, and of the inner ridge of the spit, EF, until they intersect at $F_1$, some 4000 feet off the present shore. The line HBA then, gives us the gently curved,

Fig. 228. Abandoned marine cliff (right middle ground) on north side of Truro mainland, Cape Cod, now separated from the sea by a salt marsh and a bar covered with dunes (in the background).

well graded shoreline of an early stage of erosion of the mainland, all along which the irregular peninsulas of the initial shoreline must be projected seaward to an extent similar to that at High Head, as shown in Fig. 226. This carries the initial shoreline a maximum of two and a half miles outside (east) of the present shore.

*Development of the Shifting Fulcrum.* — After the graded shoreline HBA was attained, further cutting back of the coast so changed the curvature that longshore current action (growing stronger as the shoreline became graded to a simple line and transporting more débris as the bays were blocked and the cliffs became higher) could no longer follow the shore curve around toward the west, but departed from it at a slight angle so as to build the bar EF.  Continued excessive retrogression of the coast to the southeast caused the longshore currents to deflect more and more toward the north, with consequent addition of new bars to the face of the first one along the lines GD and JB, so as to maintain at all times a well graded, gently curving shore, successive positions of which would be $EF_2F_1$, $GF_3D$, and JBN (the present shoreline).  As the waves in cutting back the exposed cliff on the outer shore also trim off the seaward extremities of the abandoned cliff and of bars previously formed, the fulcrum point between the section of shore to the southeast where erosion is in progress, and the section toward the northwest where prograding is taking place, shifts constantly toward the northwest, through the successive positions $F_1$, $F_2$, $F_3$.

*Conclusions.* — Thus does Davis analyze the major significant features of outer Cape Cod, and enable us to reconstruct, step by step, the orderly development of the complex spit of the Provinceland.  The submarine bars (Fig. 229) off the northeast side of the Provinceland may represent the beginnings of new ridges to be added in the next stages of the spit's development.  The formation of a subsidiary spit at Race Point, and of a somewhat complex recurved spit at Long Point, both dependent from the western extremity of the main spit, offers no problem of any difficulty.  Davis estimates that 3000 or 4000 years may suffice for the accomplishment of the changes on the mainland recorded by these shores.  If, during that period, marked subsidence of the coast had occurred, the bases of the old abandoned cliffs should be deep below the marsh deposits now found out in front of the cliffs (Fig. 228).  If marked elevation had taken place, the abandoned cliffs should appear as elevated shorelines.  The bases of the abandoned cliffs are close to present sealevel, and soundings in the marsh show that the marsh depths farther out are those normally to be expected offshore from such a wave-cut cliff. Hence we must conclude that no marked change in the relative level of land and sea has occurred in the Cape Cod region during the last few thousand years.  For the future, Davis estimates that eight or ten thousand years will be required for the removal of all that is left of the mainland of Truro, if no account is taken of the work done by the waves of Cape Cod Bay.  On an earlier page I have considered additional phases of the problem, and have suggested a smaller figure, four or five thousand years,

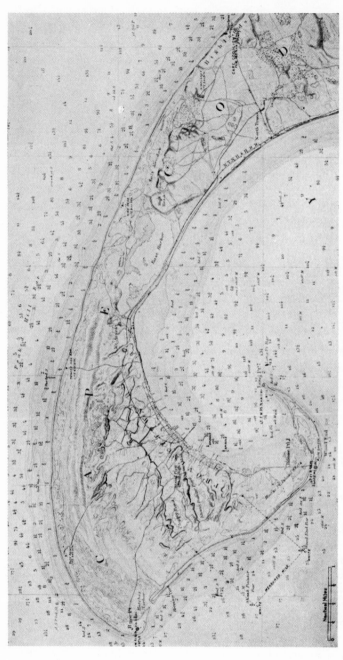

FIG. 229.   The Provinceland complex spit and part of the Truro mainland (lower right-hand corner).   Note the two submarine bars nearly parallel to the shore on the northeast, which may represent the early stages of new beach ridges to be added to the prograding spit, or more temporary bars of the "low and ball" type.   From U. S. C. & G. S. Chart No. 341.

as possibly a sufficient time allowance for the removal of the mainland.

## The Development of Nantasket Beach

A remarkable record of past shoreline changes is preserved in the abandoned marine cliffs and beach ridges of Nantasket Beach, a complex tombolo near Boston uniting to the mainland several former drumlin islands. This beach was the subject of a joint study by one of my former students, Mr. William Gardner Reed, Jr., and myself,[31] and undoubtedly represents one of the most interesting and complicated illustrations of shoreline evolution to be found on any coast. The principles involved in deciphering the record of the changes, and in restoring lands long ago vanished under wave attack, are applicable to all similar cases, and were used in later studies of other drumlin shorelines at Winthrop, Massachusetts, by Roorbach,[10] another of my former students, and at Cow Bay, Nova Scotia, by McIntosh.[9] Hence it seems desirable to present somewhat fully the facts of the Nantasket case.

*Character of the Nantasket Tombolo.* — The principal topographic features of Nantasket Beach are shown on the accompanying map (Fig. 234). The irregular hills in the southern part of the map are composed of much altered sedimentary and igneous rocks which are very resistant and yield but slowly to the attack of waves and weather. All other elevations on the map represented by contours are drumlins more or less eroded by wave action. The lower areas, including the ridges indicated by short hachures or dots, are practically all of beach material; the exceptions consist of low areas of till between certain drumlins located close to each other, beach sand gathered into small dunes by the wind, and some deposits in swampy areas to be considered later. If we except the rocky area first mentioned, we may say that the features of the Nantasket region are due to marine action upon drumlins; for the effects of stream action and wind action are so slight as to be negligible.

*Cliffed Drumlins of the Nantasket Region.* — In describing the present form of the Nantasket drumlins it will be convenient to consider them in the order of their preservation from marine erosion. The letters in parentheses refer to the respective drumlins on the map (Fig. 234). The best preserved is a small drumlin called Hampton Hill (H), located in the southern part of the region, back of the beach. It has been slightly cliffed by the harbor waves, on the southwest, but is otherwise practically in the same condition as when the ice left it. Nantasket Hill (N) at Hull, also called Telegraph Hill, is another drumlin which has suffered but little erosion; it is slightly cliffed on the south. Thornbush Hill (T), just west of Nantasket Hill, is somewhat more strongly cliffed, but retains its initial form to a marked degree. Some erosion has taken place at the southwest side. Sagamore Head (Sa), near Hampton Hill, preserves a nearly perfect outline except for a pronounced cliff on the northeast side and a minor cliff on the north and west. The main cliff is well back from the present shoreline, and has evidently not been touched by the waves for many years.

North of Sagamore Head is White Head (W), a drumlin which retains its initial form fairly well on the south, although a slight cliffing is noticeable there; but which has a remarkable strongly curved cliff cut into its northern side (Fig. 238), and smaller cliffs on the northeast and east. Like the northeast cliff on Sagamore Head, the cliffs on the north and east sides of White Head are well back from the present shoreline and have long remained untouched by the waves. West of White Head are several low drumloidal hills, connected by lower areas of till and cliffed on both the north and south sides. Great Hill (G), at Allerton, has a strongly marked cliff on the eastern end where the waves are still cutting into the hill, although not so effectively as formerly. There has apparently been a slight cliffing on the western end of Great Hill, also. Strawberry Hill (St), about halfway between Allerton and Sagamore Head, is in many respects the most remarkable drumlin in the district. Except for a short distance along the northwest side, it has been cliffed throughout its entire circumference; a rather inconspicuous cliff is developed along the north side, more prominent cliffs on the south and west sides, while the southeast face is a splendid marine cliff long ago abandoned by the waves (Fig. 237). In fact the only point where the sea still reaches the drumlin is along its southwest side. There is a marked escarpment on the northeast corner of the cliffed drumlin, but much of this is due to the removal of till for roadbuilding. Dr. Isaiah Bowman is authority for the statement that a small nip existed there before the excavations by man obscured the relations. It should be noted that the abandoned cliffs of Sagamore Head, White Head, and Strawberry Hill do not face

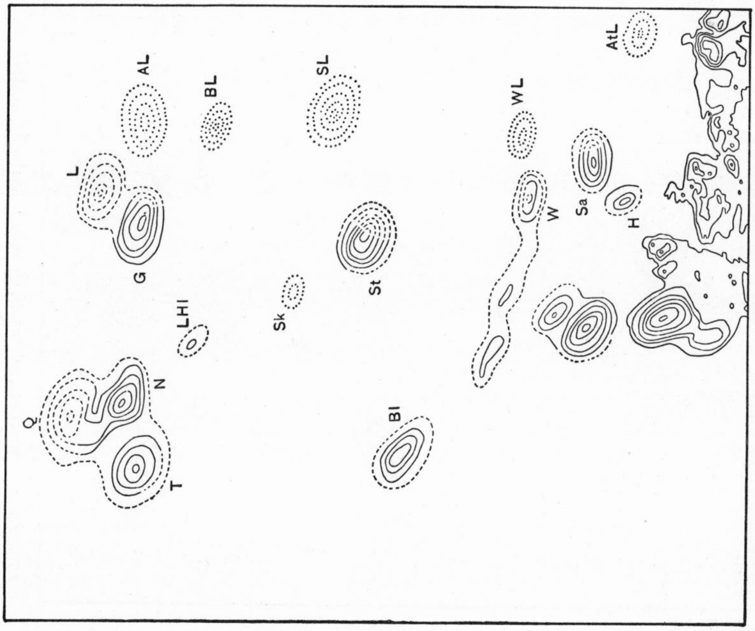

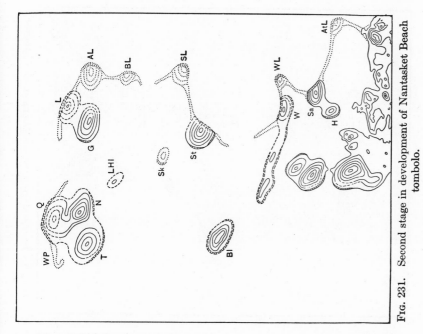

Fig. 231.   Second stage in development of Nantasket Beach tombolo.

Fig. 230.   Initial stage of Nantasket Beach complex tombolo.

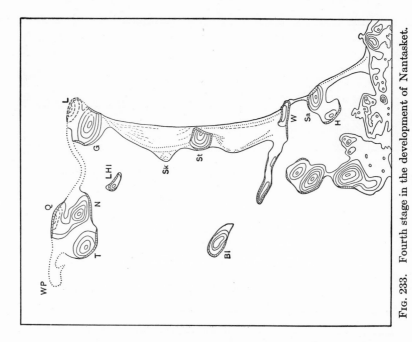

FIG. 233.   Fourth stage in the development of Nantasket.

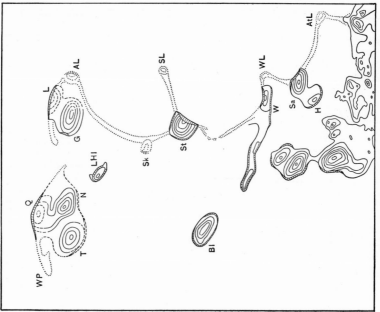

FIG. 232.   Third stage in the development of Nantasket.

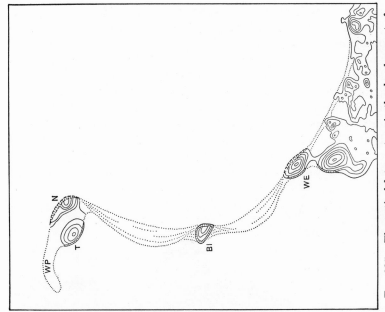

FIG. 235. Theoretical future stage in the development of Nantasket.

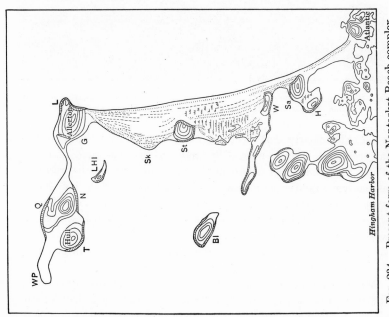

FIG. 234. Present form of the Nantasket Beach complex tombolo.

in the direction of the present shoreline, but make pronounced angles with that shoreline, as shown by the map.

Quarter Ledge (Q) at Hull is a more than half-consumed drumlin, the marine cliff facing northward. Little Hill (L) at Allerton is of special interest because it is evidently but a small remnant (Fig. 236) of a drumlin on the northeast of Great Hill. It would doubtless have been completely removed by the waves ere this but for the protection afforded by a stone sea-wall constructed north and east of it to check the progress of destruction. Skull Head (Sk) represents the final stage in the series, having been completely destroyed. This drumlin was situated to the northwest of Strawberry Hill, and was probably of small size. It was

Fig. 236. Little Allerton Hill, last remnant of a drumlin near Nantasket Beach, Massachusetts, almost completely eroded by the waves.

apparently nearly destroyed by wave action from the west, the last remnant being removed by man and used as road material. Those who remember this drumlin remnant agree in describing it as having a gentle slope toward the east and a steep cliff facing west. The presence of great boulders near the supposed former site of this drumlin, the shape of the associated beaches, and the westward protuberance of the shoreline northwest of Strawberry Hill, confirm the descriptions and location of the drumlin given by the inhabitants.

West of Nantasket Beach there are many drumlins more or less cliffed by marine erosion. On Nantasket Beach are drumlins in all stages of marine erosion, from slight cliffing to almost complete destruction.  East of Nantasket Beach no drumlins are encountered.  The suggestion is very strong that the sudden cessation of drumlins to the east is due to the complete removal of formerly existing drumlins by marine erosion.  As will appear later there is strong evidence in favor of this interpretation.

*Spits, Bars and Beaches of the Nantasket Region.* — Let us next consider the various spits, connecting bars, and beaches, both ancient and recent, which make up the composite feature called Nantasket Beach.

The beaches at Hull present no striking characteristics.  The cliffed drumlins of Nantasket Hill, Thornbush Hill, and Quarter Ledge are close together, connected by lowland areas of till, and the cliffed portions are bordered by a narrow, sometimes bouldery beach.  A sandspit, called Windmill Point, is built out toward the west, probably under the influence of tidal currents passing through Nantasket Roads.  This group is connected with Allerton by a bar believed to be the result of simple backward tying from Great Hill and Little Hill.  The resemblance to a Y-bar is due to a railroad embankment built across the end of the bay back of Great Hill in order that the track would not have to be placed in the very exposed position on the seaward side of the Allerton drumlins.  The protuberance of beach material from the northwest side of Great Hill is explained later.

From Allerton Great Hill on the northwest to the rock hills of Cohasset on the southeast a relatively straight beach borders the present shoreline (Fig. 234).  Back of this modern beach one observes parallel ridges of sand, gravel, and cobbles, in all respects similar to the higher part of the present beach which is still being acted upon by the waves.  Still farther back the ridges become less prominent, until in the central areas of the Nantasket lowland they are scarcely perceptible.  Moreover, they are no longer parallel to the modern beach, but are strongly curved, concave toward the east.  At the extreme west, however, these curved ridges become prominent features once more, and are as high in places as the modern beach.

If we examine the older beaches more carefully, we note several significant points.  Just south of Allerton Great Hill the high and prominent westernmost beach, which we may call West Beach, is intersected by the modern beach.  West Beach does not touch Great Hill, and from the curvature of the beach it seems hardly probable that it connected with the former seaward extension of

Great Hill. At its southern end West Beach ties to the northwest side of Strawberry Hill, just in front of the only part of the hill which has no bordering marine cliff. From the western side of the beach projects the protuberance of the Skull Head area, which destroys the otherwise symmetrical curve given to this portion of the harbor shoreline. Of the beaches which intervene between West Beach and the modern beach, a few connect with Strawberry Hill, others curve eastward as if to connect with something formerly situated in front of Strawberry Hill, and still others pass in front of the hill to connect with White Head or Sagamore Head farther south; while at the north all converge toward the intersection of West Beach with the modern beach, merging with the former or being cut off by the latter. The waves from the harbor are now attacking West Beach north of Skull Head, giving it a steeper western face, cutting off part of the western convexity, and building a small subsidiary beach toward the north. This attack of the harbor waves upon a beach formerly constructed by the powerful Atlantic waves has become so effective that sea-walls have been built in places to prevent its further destruction.

South of Strawberry Hill the relations are much the same, except that the beaches are less distinct and less regular in outline. The equivalent of West Beach does not connect directly with Strawberry Hill, but is truncated by a more recent beach or spit which extends southward from the southwest end of the great cliff on Strawberry Hill. The older main beach curves rather strongly southwest, continues south and southeast in much broken and complicated ridges, and finally spreads out in a broad, indefinite plain of beach material near the western end of White Head. The most prominent beach in this vicinity is one which extends from the eastern point of Strawberry Hill to the eastern end of White Head, and on which the County Road is located for much of the distance between the two hills. Both east and west of the County Road beach are some fairly well-marked beaches, more or less obscured by sand dunes, especially toward the east. Two of the older beaches between White Head and Sagamore Head are especially prominent, and are practically straight. Both north and south of Strawberry Hill the beaches in the central areas, midway between the drumlin hills, are often so low and indistinct as to be nearly or quite imperceptible. In places the detection of the beaches is made easier by a difference in the grass and other

FIG. 237.   Strawberry Hill, as seen from the south, showing abandoned marine cliffs; the higher cliff faces southeast.

vegetation growing on the beach ridges and in the intervening depressions.

*Data for Reconstruction of Initial Shoreline.* — In the attempt to reconstruct the initial form of Nantasket Beach, three sources of information were appealed to: (1) some of the older inhabitants who recalled the appearance of the beach in earlier days; (2) old maps and charts of the region; (3) the principles of shoreline development as applied to the interpretation of the present forms.

As shoreline changes on glacial drift coasts sometimes take place with comparative rapidity, a man may live to see profound alterations in the outline of the shore on which he lives. Certain residents of Nantasket told of a time when the sea used to come in to the present location of the County Road. It must be remembered, however, that people are apt to be impressed by the unusual, and that some long-past transgression of exceptional storm waves far across the present beach may be responsible for the impression that the sea is now farther removed from the road than it was fifty years ago. As late as 1898, during the " Portland Storm," breakers crossed the railroad track, which is well back from the present beach. In regard to the former location and general appearance of the remnant of Skull Head drumlin, now completely lost, the descriptions of the older inhabitants agree fairly well, and are corroborated by the physiographic evidence.

The old maps and charts of the region afforded some evidence as to the general outline of the beach in earlier years, but proved to be too inaccurate to justify any important conclusions as to recent changes in outline. A chart prepared by the United States Coast and Geodetic Survey in 1846 indicates a shoreline so nearly like that of the present as to warrant the belief that the sea has not been materially closer to the County Road in the last sixty years than it is today, except during unusual storms. Indeed, a chart of Boston Harbor published in the fourth part of The English Pilot in 1709, while not accurate in details, seems to show that no radical changes in the shoreline of Nantasket Beach have occurred in the last two hundred years.

The application of the principles of shoreline development to the interpretation of the present form of Nantasket Beach offers the only means of reconstructing the initial form of the beach. By this means it is possible to determine with a fair degree of certainty the geography of the Nantasket region before the present beach came into existence. The problem involves the restoration of the lost drumlins of this portion of Boston Harbor.

*Restoration of Cliffed Drumlins.* — There is little difficulty in the restoration of those drumlins which retain their initial form to a considerable degree. The existing drumlins of the Boston district are of the same general type, none of them resembling the greatly elongated type found in some parts of New York. It is possible, therefore, to complete the outlines of Thornbush Hill (T), and Nantasket Hill (N) at Hull, Great Hill (G), Strawberry Hill (St), White Head (W), Sagamore Head (Sa), and Hampton Hill (H) without danger of appreciable error. This has been done in Fig. 230, the restored portions being indicated by broken lines. Where more than half of a drumlin has been destroyed, the restoration cannot be made with the same degree of certainty, and we must recognize that the location and size of such drumlins cannot be determined with absolute precision. The margin of error is not so large as materially to affect the problem, and the restorations of Quarter Ledge drumlin (Q) and Allerton Little Hill (L) in Fig. 230, are believed to be essentially correct. The position of Little Hill will account for the peculiar protuberance of beach material northwest of Great Hill, if we agree that a spit trailing back from Little Hill by the action of waves and currents through Nantasket Roads would have a form somewhat similar to that of Windmill Point (WP) in Fig. 234. The restoration of the drumlins which are wholly destroyed involves a larger chance for error, and each individual restoration of this kind must be carefully considered.

*Restoration of Lost Drumlins.* — The first restoration of a drumlin completely destroyed (complete restorations in dotted lines) is that of Allerton Lost Drumlin (Fig. 230, AL). That this drumlin formerly existed is shown by the relations of West Beach. The beach does not connect with Great Hill at the present time, but is abruptly cut off by the present shoreline a short distance south of Great Hill. That this beach formerly continued toward the east seems clear. It is equally clear that the seaward continuation of the beach would not connect with the seaward continuation of Great Hill, unless we imagine the beach to have been bent sharply northward. This last assumption is contrary to what we should expect in a beach as well developed as West Beach, has no evidence to support it, and is one which we are not permitted to make arbitrarily. The precise location of the drumlin with which West Beach must have connected cannot be determined with certainty, nor can its size be inferred; but that it occupied some such position as is indicated in Fig. 230, there would seem to be little doubt. It is not permissible to consider West Beach connected with the eastward extension of Little Hill, for this would require a marked northward bend in the beach, or the reconstruction of Little Hill on too large a scale.

It will be convenient to consider the restoration of Skull Head drumlin (Sk) next, as certain features connected with it will aid us in other reconstructions. The location of this drumlin is made clear, as already noted, by the peculiar protuberance back of West Beach northwest of Strawberry Hill, by the occurrence of large boulders along the shoreline at this point, and by the historical evidence. That the drumlin was small is indicated by the fact that it has been completely removed, although in a relatively sheltered position, and by the further evidence that this removal was accomplished mainly by the harbor waves, it being stated by those who remember the drumlin that the eastern slope was not cliffed, while the western face was a distinct marine cliff. The last remnant of this drumlin was removed by man in recent years. The location and size of Skull Head drumlin are believed to be essentially correct.

An examination of the great southeast cliff on Strawberry Hill shows that the cliff was formed by waves coming from the southeast, and not from the northeast, the present direction of main wave attack. The fact that a sharp angle on the cliffed drumlin projects forward on that part of the hill which would be most exposed to the direct attack of the waves, had no other drumlin existed in front of it to protect it, confirms the opinion that the restoration of a drumlin must be made in the vicinity of the shallow area offshore known as Strawberry Ledge. This we may call the Strawberry Lost Drumlin (SL). As will appear later, the former presence of a drumlin at this point accounts for the northeastern angle (recently blunted by excavations for road material) of Strawberry Hill, the small amount of cliffing on the north side of the hill, the eastward curve of the beaches northeast of the hill, the direction of the imposing southeast cliff, and a certain feature of West Beach to be considered in the next paragraph. Whether the shallow area at Strawberry Ledge has any connection with the Strawberry Lost Drumlin is uncertain, but that the drumlin must have been located near this spot seems clear.

As has already been noted, Skull Head drumlin (Sk) was apparently not cliffed on the east, or was so slightly cliffed as not to attract the attention of persons who did notice the cliffing on the west.   Yet this drumlin must have occupied a position fairly well exposed to the waves of the Atlantic, unless some protection from those waves was afforded by drumlins or beaches farther east.   It should be noted also that West Beach is unusually high and broad, the modern beach at the east alone showing the same strength of development.   In order that the waves should build a beach so extensive and so well developed, they must either have acted on the ancient West Beach shoreline for a long period of time, or must have been rapidly supplied with an immense amount of material previously reduced to a condition ready for beach construction.   That the waves did not act for a long period of time in the vicinity of the ancient West Beach shoreline is shown by the absence of any considerable cliffing on the east end of Skull Head drumlin and the north side of Strawberry Hill. It is evident, moreover, that the large amount of material in West Beach could not have been supplied by the cliffed portions of the existing drumlins in that vicinity, so it must have come from drumlins long ago destroyed, or from the seabottom.   It is believed that the most probable condition which will account for all the facts is the former existence of a beach or series of spits more or less completely closing the space of open water between Strawberry Lost Drumlin and Allerton Lost Drumlin, thus forming a barrier which protected Skull Head drumlin and Strawberry Hill from wave action.   The construction of this barrier was probably facilitated by the existence of another drumlin in the vicinity of the shallow area east of Bayside, and we may call the restoration of this drumlin (Fig. 230) the Bayside Lost Drumlin (BL).   As will appear in the next section, the present relation of beaches and cliffs strongly suggests that a drumlin located in the vicinity of the Bayside shallow maintained the barrier so long as any part of the drumlin remained; but that with the complete removal of the drumlin the barrier was broken through, the accumulated débris swept rapidly back to the present position of West Beach, still protecting the east end of Skull Head drumlin but exposing a large part of the north side of Strawberry Hill to the waves which formed the low cliff we observe today.

The highly peculiar character of the cliffing on the north and northeast sides of White Head drumlin can be explained only by the restoration of a drumlin northeast of White Head. This we will call the White Head Lost Drumlin (WL). Its precise location cannot be determined, but it must have been close enough to White Head to control the marked curvature of the White Head cliff and the less marked but distinctly curved cliff on the northeast side of Sagamore Head. The position assigned to it in Fig. 230 cannot be far from correct. The character of the Sagamore Head cliff, just referred to, necessitates the restoration of another drumlin to the southeast. Unless this drumlin existed somewhere in that region, affording protection to the southeast corner of Sagamore Head, it is difficult to understand why the latter was not cliffed directly from the east, and why the cliff is concave

Fig. 238. White Head drumlin showing concave marine cliff on north side, and road built on curving beach ridge tangent to cliff.

instead of convex. A shallow area north of Atlantic Head may have been the location of this drumlin as shown in Fig. 230. It is possible, however, that it may have been nearer Sagamore Head. We will call this restoration the Atlantic Lost Drumlin (At L).

*Initial Stage of the Nantasket Shoreline.* — This completes the restorations which seem required by the present forms of cliffs and beaches. That other drumlins may have existed in the region is, of course, possible; although the former existence of many more in the immediate vicinity of the Nantasket area would doubtless be indicated by peculiar alignments of cliffs on the remaining drumlins, or by the relations of the beaches. That additional drumlins may have existed still farther east is quite possible, but the data necessary for the reconstruction of such

easternmost drumlins would be recorded only on drumlins and in
beaches since completely destroyed.  So far as the present problem is concerned the conditions shown in Fig. 230 may fairly be
taken to represent the initial one of a series of developmental
stages which we will now endeavor to follow until the present form
of Nantasket Beach is reached.

*Sequential Stages of the Nantasket Shoreline.* — Figure 231 represents an endeavor to show the conditions which probably existed
in the Nantasket region at a much later stage than Fig. 230.  The
Allerton, Bayside, and Strawberry Lost drumlins have been much
eroded by the waves and the material removed from them has
been built into spits or connecting bars, which together with the
remaining portions of the drumlins form a barrier to protect the
east end of Skull Head drumlin and the north side of Strawberry
Hill from any appreciable erosion.  From Strawberry Lost Drumlin a bar ties backward to Strawberry Hill, protecting the northeast corner of the hill and helping to determine the direction of the
wave attack which is producing the southeast-facing cliff.  That
Strawberry Hill and White Head were exposed to strong wave
action while Skull Head and Great Hill were well protected is
evident from the remarkable development of the ancient marine
cliff on the two former.  White Head Lost Drumlin is much
eroded, but still serves to determine the character of the cliff on
the north side of White Head, and at the same time effectually
to protect the eastern end of the same.  Sagamore Head has been
cliffed on the northeast, the character of the cliff being determined by the position of White Head Lost Drumlin and Atlantic
Lost Drumlin, and the bars tying back from them.  Atlantic Lost
Drumlin is much eroded, and in addition to being connected with
Sagamore Head has a short bar connecting with the rock cliffs
just south.  Allerton Little Hill and Quarter Ledge drumlin,
facing the main channel to the north, have been considerably
eroded, while even the better-protected drumlins have, as a rule,
been cliffed slightly, especially on their more exposed sides.

It is evident that some latitude is allowable in the restoration
of certain of the features shown in the figure, without affecting
the validity of the general interpretation here set forth.  For example, the precise shape and location of the sandspits cannot be
ascertained; and Atlantic Lost Drumlin might be nearer Sagamore Head, in which case the long bar connecting the two might
be altogether absent or represented by short spits or a short bar.

The figure indicates, however, those conditions considered as most probable and the main features of the drawing are believed to be essentially correct.

Figure 232 represents a later stage than Fig. 231. The complete destruction of Bayside Lost Drumlin has allowed the material formerly accumulated in its vicinity to be swept back to the Strawberry Hill-Skull Head region, and to be rapidly constructed into the prominent West Beach. At the north this beach still connects with the remaining portion of Allerton Lost Drumlin, thus accounting for the failure of this beach to touch Allerton Great Hill, a relation which is very distinct at the present time. At the south the connection with Strawberry Hill was far enough west to allow a slight cliffing along much of the north side of the hill. The absence of a pronounced cliff at the northeast corner of Strawberry Hill previous to recent excavations, and the eastward curve of some of the old beaches northeast of the hill (Fig. 234) indicate that a remnant of Strawberry Lost Drumlin still survived at the period represented by Fig. 232 and even later, preserving the backward-tying bar until West Beach was considerably prograded. Between Strawberry Hill and White Head spits or a curved bar nearly or quite closed the space of open water, although the irregular character of the gravel ridges now observable at this point suggests that the bar may have been repeatedly broken through during heavy storms. The retreat of the shoreline on the southwest side of Strawberry Hill has caused the older beach ridge to be truncated by a sandspit now forming. Other minor developments are indicated, including the continued cliffing of various hills, and the growth of Windmill Point and other smaller spits.

In the stage represented by Fig. 233 the present characteristics of Nantasket Beach begin to be more easily recognizable. Allerton, Strawberry, White Head, and Atlantic Lost drumlins have all been completely removed. Prograding has gone on actively in the two re-entrant curves north and south of Strawberry Hill, the shorelines thus migrating eastward until a single beach describes a very gently concave curve from Allerton Little Hill to White Head. That the process of prograding was relatively rapid is indicated by the small size of the beaches in the inland areas north and south of Strawberry Hill. In places these beaches are almost imperceptible, and south of the hill it seems probable that the change in the position of the eastern shoreline from the westernmost beach to the County Road beach was made without the formation of complete intermediate beaches. That the prograding had proceeded quite far, in the northern re-entrant at least, before the removal of the bar connecting Strawberry Hill with Strawberry Lost Drumlin, is shown by the development of faint beaches just north of the hill, curving eastward so strongly that they would pass in front of the restored portion of the hill if they were prolonged. These beaches must have been formed before the bar was destroyed. After the complete removal of Strawberry Lost Drumlin and the destruction of the bar, the ends of these beaches were eroded, as shown in Fig. 233, and the eastern angle of Strawberry Hill was slightly cliffed by the waves. In

Fig. 239.   Ancient beach ridge (right center) connecting abandoned marine cliff on Sagamore Head drumlin with similar cliff on White Head drumlin (in foreground). A later beach ridge to the left. Note that a road has been built on the crest of each ridge, and that the intervening swale is spanned by foot bridges.

this manner the portion of the shoreline which had been prograded with reference to the Strawberry Lost Drumlin and bar, was retrograded until brought into harmony with the conditions existing after the destruction of drumlin and bar. Before the waves could seriously affect the corner of Strawberry Hill the prograding of the entire beach (from Allerton Little Hill to White Head) as a single unit carried the shoreline eastward beyond the base of the hill. The prograding of the beach appears to have been connected with the retrograding of the headlands at Allerton and the removal of White Head and Atlantic Lost drumlins. As Allerton Lost Drumlin, Little Hill, and Great Hill have been cut back, the beaches to the south have been built forward, the point of no change, or fulcrum, being just south of the east end of Allerton Great Hill. The lack of a complete series of beaches south of Strawberry Hill may be connected with a more sudden westward migration of the southern end of the shoreline upon the disappearance of White Head and Atlantic Lost drumlins, and a consequent sudden eastward movement of the zone of wave building just north of White Head drumlin. As soon as the eastward migration of the beaches allowed the shoreline to clear the hill, the successive beaches appear to be more or less continuous from Allerton to White Head. The remaining changes indicated on the drawing need but little comment. The removal of White Head Lost Drumlin, together with the formation of the County Road beach, has resulted in the cliffing of White Head on the east and northeast, while the removal of the Atlantic Lost Drumlin has allowed the connecting bars to swing back and form a single bar which unites with the rock cliffs at Atlantic Head.

The next stage in the development of Nantasket Beach is that of the present, represented in Fig. 234. The principal change from the preceding stage consists in the prograding of the beach until it makes an unbroken, gently curved shoreline from Great Hill to Atlantic Head; the further cliffing of White Head at the eastern end, followed by the abandoning of the cliffs on White Head and Sagamore Head by the waves as the shoreline migrated eastward, leaving parallel beach ridges and swales to mark its former positions (Fig. 239); the complete removal of the Skull Head drumlin, partly within recent years; the filling-in of the small bay on the south side of Windmill Point, largely within historic times; and further erosion of all the drumlins still exposed to wave action.

In Fig. 235 is represented a possible future stage in the development of Nantasket Beach. At the present time the most effective wave erosion is concentrated upon Great Hill and the small remnant of Little Hill. But these hills control the future of the beach, the erosion of the rocky mainland at the southern end being so slow as to be practically negligible. Heretofore the retrograding of these hills has caused the prograding of the beach; at the present time, however, a condition of equilibrium prevails, and a further cutting-back of the hills must result in a cutting of the beach also. With Great Hill gone, the beach would connect Nantasket Hill, Little Hog Island, Strawberry Hill, White Head, and Sagamore Head.   Strawberry Hill would be at an exposed angle of this beach and would soon be destroyed.   Little Hog Island and White Head would be more exposed than before, providing the former had outlasted Strawberry Hill.   Sagamore Head and Hampton Hill would take their turns in controlling the position of the beach until completely reduced by wave attack. The drumloidal extensions west of White Head and the Hull district at the north will be the last remnants of Nantasket Beach to survive, and of these two the Hull district will probably last much longer.   If this interpretation is essentially correct, the relations in the Nantasket region will, in the remote future, resemble those indicated in Fig. 235.   It is possible that the connecting bars may be broken through by the sea in one or more places, and that sandspits may replace the bars here shown. This will depend on local conditions of water depth and other factors which cannot be predicted.   At present the area in question is shallow, and favors the building of bars as indicated.

The protection of Great Hill is the key to the preservation of the entire Nantasket Beach district.   A sea-wall has been constructed for the preservation of Little Hill, and this, of course, means protection to the adjacent areas of Great Hill.   By such protective measures man may indefinitely postpone the normal changes which Nature would effect in the Nantasket area.   It is interesting to note that man has begun his work in controlling the development of Nantasket Beach just at the time the beach has reached the greatest size which Nature could probably give it. Heretofore the beach has been increasing in area.   Hereafter the normal development of the beach, unless arrested, must result in decreasing its area.

**Conclusions.** — It appears from the foregoing analysis that the present form of Nantasket Beach is not due to the accidental tying together of a few islands without system, but represents one stage in a long series of evolutionary changes which have occurred in orderly sequence and in accordance with definite physiographic laws.   The order of magnitude of the time required for the evolution in question can roughly be determined.   Judging from old maps, there has been no great change in the width of Nantasket Beach during the last two hundred years.   Judging from the rate of cliff cutting in various drumlins in the vicinity of Boston as determined by surveys extending over forty years or more and discussed in an earlier chapter, the length of time required for the removal of those portions of drumlins which have disappeared since the early cliffing of Strawberry Hill and White Head, and the formation of West Beach, with liberal allowance for relatively rapid cutting of drumlins well exposed to the sea, could scarcely have been less than one thousand years, and was probably two or three thousand years. Had there been any marked subsidence of this coast during the last one to three thousand years, West Beach should be very low, possibly completely submerged. Had marked elevation occurred, West Beach should be relatively high, and the abandoned marine cliffs should appear as elevated shorelines. As a matter of fact West Beach is similar in size and elevation to the beaches being formed along the present eastern shore of the Nantasket area, and the bases of the abandoned cliffs are not elevated. Hence we must conclude that there has been no marked change in the relative level of land and sea in the Nantasket area during the last thousand years at least, and probably none during the last two or three thousand years.

**Other Drumlin Shorelines.** — Further consideration of the evolution of complex tombolos uniting drumlin islands to the mainland, and involving the restoration of lost drumlins, will be found in the papers by Roorbach[10] on the Winthrop area and by McIntosh[9] on the Cow Beach area, previously cited. The essential relations in the Winthrop region may be gleaned from an inspection of Figs. 54 and 188, and in the Cow Bay region from Fig. 218. Both cases are simpler than that of Nantasket, and need not be presented here in detail. East of Cow Bay the Nova Scotian coast presents other cases of drumlin shoreline development which would well repay detailed study.

**Shorelines of the Narrow Coastal Plain.** — We may now direct our attention briefly to the development of those shorelines which border the narrow and irregular coastal plain (Fig. 240) fringing the rocky coast of Maine and other portions of New England and Acadia. As already noted, the marine clays and sands of late-glacial and post-glacial age were insufficient in quantity to bury the marked irregularities of the previously submerged land surface upon which they were deposited, with the result that post-glacial emergence of the inner margin of these deposits gave a shoreline still markedly irregular in its general pattern, although less so in detail than was the earlier shoreline due to submergence of the resistant but much dissected landmass (Fig. 66). Just as the land contours were softened by the partial filling of drowned valleys and the mantling over of some hills by sand and clay, so the irregularities of the initial shoreline were reduced in the simpler contact of the somewhat smoother coastal plain with the sea.

*Influence of Underlying Bedrock.* — Notwithstanding the obvious weakness of the post-glacial marine coastal plain deposits, we should not expect an extensive cliffing of these shores for the reason that, the coastal plain deposits being generally thin, the waves in cutting back the shores must soon have their progress arrested by encountering the underlying hard rock. This is the

Fig. 240. Looking across the narrow post-glacial coastal plain (middle distance) southwest of Portland, Maine, from the edge of the rocky oldland (foreground).

case with much of the coastal plain shoreline under discussion, as has been made clear by Davis[32] for the Maine example, both in his diagrammatic representation of the shoreline, and in his effective description of the rocky hills of islands or peninsulas, bordered below by a rim of clay, at the base of which the hard rock again outcrops along the shores where waves are active. The result of wave action, supplemented possibly in some degree by the aid of tidal currents in removing clay from between islands where current action is accelerated, must be to increase the irregularities of the shoreline, causing them to approach more closely to the earlier irregularities of the hard-rock shores resulting from the first submergence. Stone[33] gives a map showing the distribution of the marine clays and sands bordering the Maine coast, from which one may infer that the differences in the general shoreline pattern of today, as compared with the initial hard-rock shoreline, must be of minor importance. One possible difference which should perhaps be noted consists in what appear to be drowned valleys in the coastal plain itself, indicating a slight submergence following the uplift and partial dissection of the marine clays and sands. Such drowned-valley shorelines belong to a different generation from those produced earlier by the major submergence of the hard-rock topography.

*Hanging Valleys Bordering the Sea.* — Streams cutting through the weak coastal plain deposits must often be superposed upon buried rock ledges, developing waterfalls as the clays and sands below the barrier are rapidly removed. Retreat of the clay coast under wave attack, or renewed submergence permitting the sea to enter the lower valleys carved in the clays, may give waterfalls at the shoreline, — " hanging valleys " from which the streams descend abruptly into the sea. Davis[34] was the first to point out the physiographic significance of such waterfalls at the seaward margin of the Maine coastal plain.

*Phenomena of Shorelines of Emergence.* — Katz and Keith[35] have shown that the marine clays in part merge with the outwash plain from an ice front which stood in the sea along the coastal district of southwestern Maine, southeastern New Hampshire, and northeastern Massachusetts, in late Wisconsin time. The combination of outwash plain and coastal plain, together with the fact that this part of the coast trends more nearly parallel with the geological structure of the crystalline mainland, give us a shore of relative simplicity (Fig. 67), more like the coastal plain margins of the St. Lawrence embayment than like those of most of Maine. Here then we should expect to find shoreline phenomena similar to those characteristic of a typical coastal plain shoreline, a shoreline of emergence. We are not disappointed in this expectation. From southwestern Maine to northeastern Massachusetts the shore repeatedly presents the aspect of a young shoreline of emergence, with offshore bar enclosing a belt of salt marsh, back of which the upland plain slopes gently down to disappear under the marsh deposits. The best development of this feature is shown in the vicinity of the Massachusetts-New Hampshire boundary (U. S.

Geological Survey, New-
buryport    topographic
quadrangle), where the
offshore bar is represented
by Salisbury Beach and
Plum Island Beach, with
a tidal inlet between them
bordered  on  either  side
by  the  repeatedly  re-
curved  ends  of  the  two
sections of the bar (Fig.
241).    The    Hampton
Harbor end of Salisbury
Beach also has the form
of a compound recurved
spit, showing three par-
ticularly  good  recurved
points  when  I  saw  it.
These  features,  and  the
rock  and  glacial  drift
islands  rising  out  of  the
marshes,  are  not  well
shown on the topographic
map.

Hampton Beach par-
takes more of the charac-
ter  of  a  tombolo,  being
tied  to  Bound  Rock  on
the  south  when  seen  in
1911, and connecting bed-
rock  and  glacial  drift
islands, at Great Boars
Head and two miles to the
north, with the glacial till

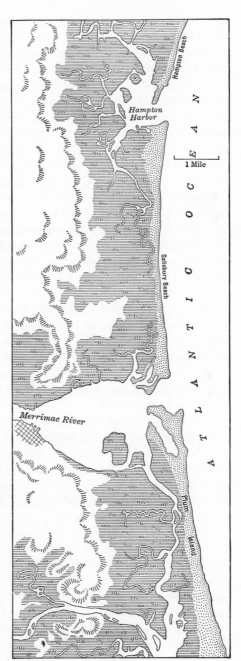

Fig. 241.  Young shoreline of
emergence bordering post-
glacial marine coastal plain
(merged with outwash plain
and other glacial deposits)
in southeastern New Hamp-
shire and n o r t h e a s t e r n
Massachusetts.

and rock ledge mainland at Little Boars Head. The inlet south of the latter was closed at the time of my visit. In this locality gravel and cobblestones are naturally more in evidence, sand and sand dunes less so, than on the Plum Island and Salisbury Beaches; and Dr. John K. Wright reports evidence of the former existence farther seaward of glacial drift islands, apparently drumloidal in form, the consumption of which by the waves no doubt contributed to the material of the present beaches. On Plum Island the dunes are especially striking, steep sided, and of considerable height, and give a picturesque shore where their seaward sides have been truncated by the waves.

**Résumé.** — From the considerations set forth in the preceding pages it appears that the coasts composed of unconsolidated débris, particularly glacial and fluvio-glacial deposits, are characteristically bordered by a wealth of wave-built forms, including beaches and bars of various types, spits, cuspate forelands and tombolos. Many of these features we have classified and described, and the origin of some problematical forms, like the Coskata cusps of Nantucket, have been discussed. Occasionally an offshore bar, a form characteristic of shorelines of emergence, borders the narrow post-glacial coastal plain, as in the Newburyport region of Massachusetts. The rapid changes in shape, size, and position of the wave-built forms bordering unconsolidated débris coasts have commanded our attention, and we have traced some of these variations as recorded for the baymouth bar of Edgartown Harbor, for the Monomoy sandspit and its continuation in Nauset Beach or Chatham Bar, and for Sable Island bar. Only in rare cases has the shoreline advanced to the mature stage in which the variety of wave-built forms is replaced by a simple, more or less continuous line of wave-cut cliffs. Even here the adjacent areas may show an exceptional development of wave-built forms, which enable us to reconstruct with assurance the past physiographic history of whole sections of the shoreline. It is thus that it has been found possible to trace the development of the shorelines bordering Cape Cod and Nantasket Beach, two types of glacial débris coasts in which the records of the past are preserved in remarkable fashion. The physiographic forms associated with these and certain other areas appear to present clear evidence that the relative levels of land and sea have not greatly changed, if they have changed at all, during the period covered by the development of these shores, a period which must be measured in terms of one to several thousand years. On the other hand, the youth of much of the shoreline bordering coasts of unconsolidated débris, where wave-built forms are still extremely abundant, shows that the sea has not stood at its present level long enough for the waves to cut far into the weak material. In other words, it would seem that a few thousand years must cover the duration of the present marine cycle.

## BIBLIOGRAPHY

1. JOHNSON, DOUGLAS. "Shore Processes and Shoreline Development," 303, New York, 1917.
2. GULLIVER, F. P. "Shoreline Topography." Amer. Acad. Arts and Sci., Proc., XXXIV, 151–258, 1899.
3. BROWN, R. M. "Gaspee Point: A Type of Cuspate Foreland." Jour. Geog., I, 343–352, 1902.
4. JOHNSON, DOUGLAS. "Shore Processes and Shoreline Development," 94–103, New York, 1917.
5. GULLIVER, F. P. "Island Tying." Rept. 8th Int. Geog. Cong., 146–149, 1905.
6. SHALER, N. S. "Geology of the Island of Nantucket." U. S. Geol. Surv., Bull. 53, 13, 1889.
7. GULLIVER, F. P. "Nantucket Shorelines, II." Bull. Geol. Soc. Amer., XV, 521, 1904.
8. JOHNSON, DOUGLAS. "Shore Processes and Shoreline Development," 287–290, New York, 1917.
9. McINTOSH, D. S. "A Study of the Cow Bay Beaches." Nova Scotian Inst. Sci., XIV, Pt. 2, 109–119, 1916.
10. ROORBACH, G. B. "Shoreline Changes in the Winthrop Area, Massachusetts." Phil. Geog. Soc., VIII, 172–190, 1910.
11. WHITING, H. L. "Report on Edgartown Harbor." Mass. Board of Harbor Comm., 6th Ann. Rept., 104–109, 1872.
12. MITCHELL, HENRY. "Report on Edgartown and Nantucket Harbors." Mass. Board of Harbor Comm., 6th Ann. Rept., 110–120, 1872.
13. WHITING, H. L. "Shorelines and Beaches of Marthas Vineyard." Mass. Harbor and Land Comm., Ann. Rept. for 1886, 47–52, 1887.
    WHITING, H. L. (Results of successive surveys on Marthas Vineyard.) U. S. Geol. Surv., 7th Ann. Rept., 361–363, 1888.
14. WHITING, H. L. "Recent Changes in the South Inlet into Edgartown Harbor, Marthas Vineyard." U. S. Coast and Geod. Surv., Rept. for 1889, 459–460, 1890.
15. DAVIS, C. H. "A Memoir upon the Geological Action of Tidal and other Currents of the Ocean." Amer. Acad. Arts and Sci., Mem., N. S. IV, Pt. I, 122, 1849.
16. JOHNSON, DOUGLAS. "Shore Processes and Shoreline Development," 486–489, New York, 1917.
17. MITCHELL, HENRY. "Report to Professor Benjamin Peirce, Superintendent United States Coast Survey, Concerning Nausett Beach and the

Peninsula of Monomoy." U. S. Coast Surv., Rept. for 1871, 134–143, 1874.

MITCHELL, HENRY. "Report Concerning Nauset Beach and the Peninsula of Monomoy." Mass. Board of Harbor Comm., 7th Ann. Rept., 94–108, 1873.

18. MITCHELL, HENRY. "Additional Report Concerning the Changes in the Neighborhood of Chatham and Monomoy." U. S. Coast Surv., Rept. for 1873, 103–107, 1875.

MITCHELL, HENRY. "Monomoy and Its Shoals." Mass. Harbor and Land Comm., Ann. Rept. for 1886, 37–46, 1887.

19. HITCHCOCK, EDWARD. "On Certain Causes of Geological Change Now in Operation in Massachusetts." Bost. Jour. Nat. Hist., I, 69–82, 1837.

20. WHITING, H. L. "Report on Haulover Beach, Nantucket." Mass. Board of Harbor Comm., 7th Ann. Rept., 109–111, 1873.

21. MITCHELL, HENRY. "Monomoy and Its Shoals." Mass. Harbor and Land Comm., Ann. Rept. for 1886, 42, 1887.

22. BARNARD, C. "Some Recent Changes in the Shoreline of Nantucket." Sci., N. S., X, 895, 1899.

23. GULLIVER, F. P. "Nantucket Shorelines, I." Bull. Geol. Soc. Amer., XIV, 555–556, 1904.

GULLIVER, F. P. "Nantucket Shorelines, II." Bull. Geol. Soc. Amer., XV, 507–522, 1904.

GULLIVER, F. P. "Island Tying." Rept. 8th Int. Geog. Cong., 146–149, 1905.

GULLIVER, F. P. "Wauwinet-Coscata Tombolo, Nantucket, Massachusetts." Brit. Assoc. Adv. Sci., Rept. of 79th Meeting (Winnipeg), 536, 1910.

GULLIVER, F. P. "Nantucket Shorelines, III and IV." Bull. Geol. Soc. Amer., XX, 670, 1910.

24. MARINDIN, H. L. "On the Changes in the Shorelines and Anchorage Areas of Cape Cod (or Provincetown) Harbor as Shown by a Comparison of Surveys Made Between 1835, 1867, and 1890." U. S. Coast and Geod. Surv., Rept. for 1891, Pt. II, 283–288, 1892.

25. GULLIVER, F. P. "Shoreline Topography." Amer. Acad. Arts and Sci., Proc., XXXIV, 191, 1899.

26. MCDONALD, S. D. "Notes on Sable Island." Nova Scotian Inst. Nat. Sci., Proc. and Trans., VI, 12–33, 1886.

MCDONALD, S. D. "Sable Island, (Continued)." Nova Scotian Inst. Nat. Sci., Proc. and Trans., VI, 110–119, 1886.

MCDONALD, S. D. "Sable Island, No. 3 — Its Probable Origin and Submergence." Nova Scotian Inst. Nat. Sci., Proc. and Trans., VI, 265–280, 1886.

27. PATTERSON, GEORGE. "Sable Island: Its History and Phenomena." Roy. Soc. Can., Proc. and Trans., XII, Sec. II, 3–49, 1894.

28. MACOUN, J. "Report on Natural History." Geol. Surv. Can., Ann. Rept., N. Ser., XII, 212A–219A, 1902.

29. GOLDTHWAIT, J. W. "The Physiography of Nova Scotia." Manuscript copy of a volume to be issued by the Geological Survey of Canada.

30. DAVIS, W. M. "The Outline of Cape Cod." Amer. Acad. Arts and Sci., Proc., XXXI, 303–332, 1896.
31. JOHNSON, D. W., and REED, W. G. "The Form of Nantasket Beach." Jour. Geol., XVIII, 162–189, 1910.
32. DAVIS, W. M. "Die Erklärende Beschreibung der Landformen," 532–539, Leipzig and Berlin, 1912.
33. STONE, G. H. "The Glacial Gravels of Maine and their Associated Deposits." U. S. Geol. Surv., Mon. XXXIV, 54–58, 1899.
34. DAVIS, W. M. "Coastal Plain of Maine." Amer. Assoc. Adv. Sci., 5th Anniversary Meeting; Guide to Localities Illustrating the Geology, Marine Zoölogy, and Botany of the Vicinity of Boston, 4–5, 1898.
    DAVIS, W. M. "Un Exemple de Plaine Côtière: la Plaine du Maine." Annales de Géographie, VIII, 1–5, 1899.
    DAVIS, W. M. "Die Erklärende Beschreibung der Landformen," 565 pp., Leipzig and Berlin, 1912.
35. KATZ, F. J., and KEITH, A. "The Newington Moraine, Maine, New Hampshire and Massachusetts." U. S. Geol. Surv., Prof. Paper 108, 11–29, 1918.

# CHAPTER XIV

## SUBMARINE FORMS BORDERING UNCON-
## SOLIDATED DEPOSITS

**Advance Summary.** — In earlier chapters we found that off the hard-rock coasts the waves had made little or no progress in reducing the initially irregular seabottom to a smooth slope nicely adjusted to wave action; and that even off the weak-rock coasts the progress toward the establishment of the marine profile of equilibrium was slight, except where the initial form of the seafloor left but little work for the waves to do before such a profile would result. It would seem reasonable to expect that off coasts composed of unconsolidated débris the progress of marine action in grading the seabottom might be farther advanced than off the more resistant coasts. In the present chapter we shall examine some submarine profiles bordering unconsolidated deposits, to discover whether or not the facts meet our expectations.

**Southern Coast of Marthas Vineyard.** — Where conditions were favorable, as for example where the waves worked upon fairly fine homogeneous débris, and the initial form of the seafloor did not show extensive or abrupt departures from a form well adjusted to the action of the waves, the marine profile of equilibrium appears to have been established with a degree of perfection seldom observed elsewhere. Thus off the south coast of Marthas Vineyard the waves had a minimum amount of work to do upon the submerged southward slope of the slightly dissected glacial outwash plain; and here we find excellent profiles of equilibrium (Fig. 243, A and Fig. 242).

**Scituate Region, Massachusetts.** — In the Scituate region of Massachusetts the bedrock is well mantled with glacial débris, and a profile offshore (Fig. 243, B) is far simpler than many we have examined. Nevertheless equilibrium is far from being established here, apparently because the waves have not yet removed projections of the crystalline floor which make rocky shoals. The suggestion of a terrace at a depth of 22 fathoms reminds us of somewhat similar forms found farther north (Fig. 146),

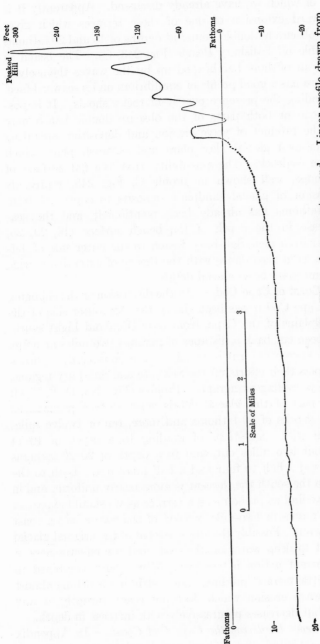

FIG. 242. Profile of equilibrium off the south coast of Marthas Vineyard near western end. Linear profile drawn from Nashaquitsa Cliffs (near contact of moraine and underlying coastal plain deposits with outwash plain) southward across submerged outwash plain. Vertical exaggeration approximately × 50. Based on photographic copy of original hydrographic sheet No. 1843 (scale 1 : 40,000) in archives of U. S. C. & G. S., which shows additional soundings not printed on published charts.

the origin of which we have already discussed.  Apparently it is the southward extension of one of these terraces which gives the bench, obscurely double, found at depths of 16 and 20 fathoms on the profile off Salisbury Beach (Fig. 243, C).  The beach in question is an offshore bar heaped up by the waves themselves, and therefore has a good profile of equilibrium on its seaward face, notwithstanding the presence nearby of rocky shoals.  It is possible that one or both parts of the obscure double bench may represent the product of wave erosion and deposition operating on the combined glacial clay plain and outwash plain which mantles the bedrock.  The possibility that the flat surface of Jeffreys Ledge, well shown in profile C, Fig. 243, represents marine erosion of glacial sandplain deposits to depths of from 25 to 30 fathoms has already been mentioned; and the seaward increase in the depth of the bench surface (16, 20, 25, 30 fathoms) from near Salisbury Beach to the outer side of Jeffreys Ledge, is in accordance with the theory of extensive marine erosion of unconsolidated glacial débris.

**Eastern Coast of Cape Cod.** — In the discussion of the changing outline of Cape Cod it has been shown that the outer side of the glacial sandplains of the Cape, from near Highland Light southward, has been cut back a distance of perhaps two miles or more. So far as is known the waves do not here encounter the bedrock which hampers their efforts off the Scituate and Salisbury regions, cited in the preceding paragraph.  Profiles (Fig. 243, D, E, F) off the central part of this glacial débris coast show a pronounced declivity to depths of 60 fathoms and more, ten or twelve miles offshore, but with suggestions of grading to a depth of 10–14 fathoms about two miles out, and to a depth of 20–26 fathoms some three and a half to four and a half miles out.  Both to the north and to the south the descent is more nearly uniform, and in no case do we find as pronounced a terrace as we should expect on the basis of a one- or two-mile incision of the waves into a coast of this character.  Possibly the steep descent of the original glacial embankment to deep water on the east, and the effectiveness of longshore current action in removing débris, have combined to permit but little terrace building, thus restricting benching almost entirely to wave erosion which does not cease abruptly at any given level, but decreases progressively with increase in depth.

*Detailed Forms Bordering the Cape Cod Coast.* — In Appendix No. 13 of the United States Coast and Geodetic Survey Report

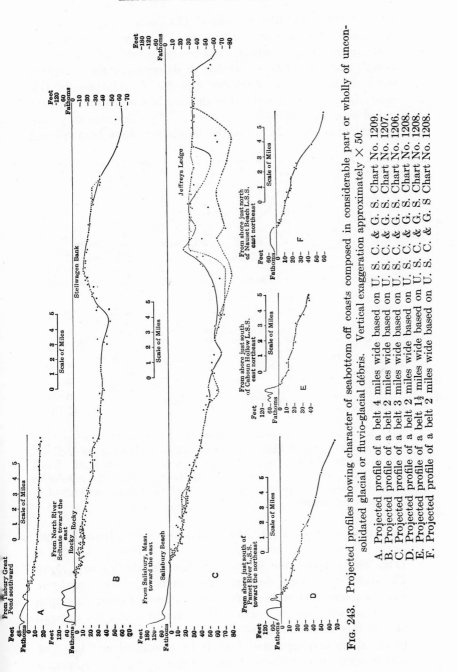

FIG. 243. Projected profiles showing character of seabottom off coasts composed in considerable part or wholly of unconsolidated glacial or fluvio-glacial débris.  Vertical exaggeration approximately × 50.

A. Projected profile of a belt 4 miles wide based on U. S. C. & G. S. Chart No. 1209.
B. Projected profile of a belt 2 miles wide based on U. S. C. & G. S. Chart No. 1207.
C. Projected profile of a belt 3 miles wide based on U. S. C. & G. S. Chart No. 1206.
D. Projected profile of a belt 2 miles wide based on U. S. C. & G. S. Chart No. 1208.
E. Projected profile of a belt 1½ miles wide based on U. S. C. & G. S. Chart No. 1208.
F. Projected profile of a belt 2 miles wide based on U. S. C. & G. S Chart No. 1208.

for 1889 Marindin[1] gives a series of 143 linear profiles across the outer shore of Cape Cod in the form of tabulated measurements of distances and elevations. These profiles do not extend far enough seaward to be of service in determining the extent to which the waves have established a profile of equilibrium off this coast; but they are of interest in showing how much the landward end of a profile undoubtedly determined by the waves may vary in short distances. Many of the tabulations have been reduced

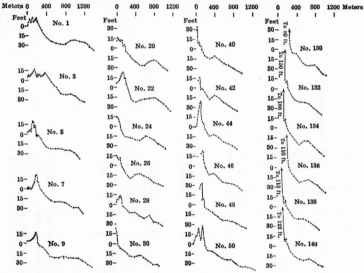

FIG. 244.   Linear profiles across the outer shore of Cape Cod between Chatham and Highland Light, showing transition of submarine bar or "ball" to shoreface terrace. Vertical exaggeration approximately × 50. Based on tabulated results of surveys by H. L. Marindin. The number of each profile corresponds to the number of the tabulation as given in Marindin's report.[1]

to graphic form by E. A. Moon, and four series, from different parts of the coast, are here reproduced. Profiles 1–3–5–7–9 (Fig. 244) traverse the sandspit or bay bar which nearly closes Pleasant Bay toward the southern end of this shore, and are located about 600 meters apart along a stretch of coast something less than two miles in length. They show that on the seaward face of this wave-built form a submarine bar or "ball" parallel to the shore and separated from it by a channel or "low" of deeper water, may within a short distance change to a shoreface terrace with a faint seaward slope.   Profiles 40–42–44–46–48–50, similarly spaced along a similar stretch of the shore where Nauset Harbor is nearly closed by a bay bar, show a ball flattening out to an obscure terrace, below which a second terrace or ball is developing.   In profiles 20–22–24–26–28–30, along a two-mile stretch of a low portion of the mainland coast, one well developed ball gives place to two smaller and more obscure examples, one of which quickly changes to a vaguely formed terrace.   Where the mainland is high, near Highland Light, profiles 130–132–134–136–138–140 show similar variations in the bottom contours.   It is well known that low and ball, like the shoreface terrace, experience rapid changes of form at the same place in short periods of time, as well as such changes in short distances as are here illustrated by observations made in the same general time period.[2]

**Submarine Profiles Bordering Morainal Coasts.** — Large scale linear profiles off the south shores of Cuttyhunk and Nashawena Islands (Fig. 245, A and B) show that wave attack on these more protected shores has not wholly succeeded in reducing the original irregularities of the morainal topography to a graded marine profile.   Just opposite, at Gay Head on Marthas Vineyard, the waves work on weak coastal plain deposits overlain by terminal moraine. Here the large scale profiles show a closer approach to a graded bottom, although minor irregularities persist and the normal curve, concave upward, seems to be marred by convexities which are not due to the presence of balls or other wave-built features (Fig. 245, C and D).   None of the profiles shows clearly the wave-cut bench described by Shaler as extending a mile seaward from Gay Head to plunge abruptly into deep water beyond,[3] nor does such a feature appear on the original large scale hydrographic sheets where soundings are extremely numerous and closely spaced. The only forms corresponding to such a description are a terrace east of Gay Head (profile E) which is only a third of a mile across, is the seaward extension of a wave-built beach, and has the form of a wave-built shoreface terrace with its seaward edge raised to produce a " ball "; and the very imperfect suggestion of benches off the coast south of Gay Head (profile C), briefly referred to in a later paragraph.   The Devils Bridge extends a mile seaward, but profile D along its crest shows a gradual descent by a convex curve full of minor irregularities which wholly lacks the characteristics of a cut-and-built terrace profile.

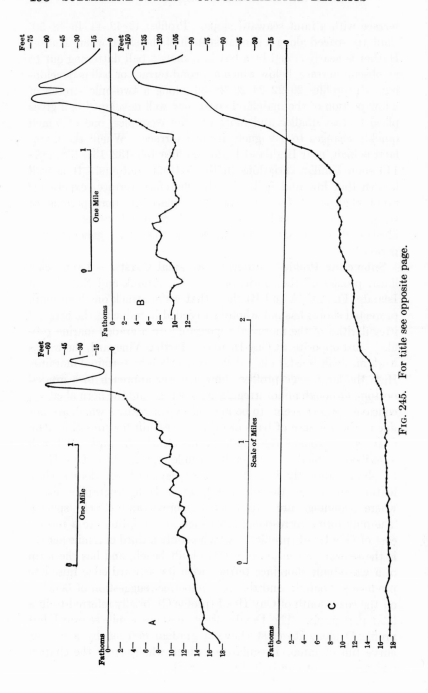

FIG. 245.   For title see opposite page.

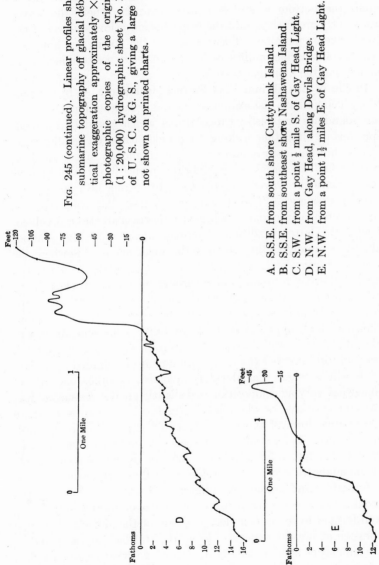

FIG. 245 (continued). Linear profiles showing details of submarine topography off glacial débris coasts. Vertical exaggeration approximately × 50. Based on photographic copies of the original large scale (1 : 20,000) hydrographic sheet No. 1802 in archives of U. S. C. & G. S., giving a large amount of data not shown on printed charts.

A. S.S.E. from south shore Cuttyhunk Island.
B. S.S.E. from southeast shore Nashawena Island.
C. S.W. from a point ½ mile S. of Gay Head Light.
D. N.W. from Gay Head, along Devils Bridge.
E. N.W. from a point 1½ miles E. of Gay Head Light.

Similar profiles based on photographic copies of large scale original hydrographic sheets for the Block Island region show some irregularities, yet a closer approach to a graded condition even near shore; but here the waves are probably cutting into older glacial sands, gravels and clays beneath the morainal deposits, if not in the coastal plain beds underlying both. Off Montauk Point the bottom is still somewhat irregular where the waves apparently are cutting into the continuation below sealevel of the Ronkonkoma moraine. There is always the possibility, however, that the submarine profiles are located in the deposits immediately underlying the morainal covering.

**Profile of Equilibrium Less Perfect near Shore.** — In the profiles which we have last examined the larger scale and more numerous soundings emphasize irregularities which would be less conspicuous or altogether lacking on profiles based on smaller scale charts showing fewer soundings. Nor should we in any case expect to find the profile of equilibrium perfectly established near shore where the waves are still actively cutting into material of varying resistance. Time is required to grade the seabottom, except where unconsolidated débris of uniform character is involved. Under the latter condition alone can waves grade the seafloor almost as rapidly as they cut into the weak mass. Elsewhere the work of erosion keeps somewhat ahead of gradation; hence the landward end of a profile, which throughout most of its length has attained approximate equilibrium, may show moderate irregularities. In the profiles just discussed the normal curve of equilibrium is best approximated where fairly homogeneous fluvioglacial débris is well exposed to vigorous wave attack, and the original form favored the rapid attainment of a graded condition. In localities where glacial till is involved, or other material of somewhat varying composition and slightly greater resistance than the sands or clays, or where wave attack is less vigorous, or where the original form of the land submerged imposed a heavier task on the waves before equilibrium could be obtained, the work of gradation is not so far advanced; and the difference is noticeable in the landward ends of the profiles as well as farther out.

**Imperfect Indications of Submarine Benches.** — None of the profiles examined gives a wave-cut bench or terrace sufficiently well formed to serve as a clear measure of the amount of marine abrasion at present sealevel. From the cliff base at the shoreline the submarine surface usually descends somewhat irregularly, but more or less gradually, into deeper water, without any sudden drop over a clearly marked terrace scarp. Where the terrace form is simulated, it is usually under conditions which point strongly to an origin under different conditions and at a different time from the present. Where glacial deposits or other unconsolidated materials alone are believed to be involved, the absence of a well-defined submarine terrace is notable. Crude suggestions of benches, each less than a mile broad, are found off the coast south of Gay Head (Fig. 245, C), with their outer edges at depths of 52 and 75 feet; or the whole might constitute a single rough terrace a mile and a half broad. In the profile along the Devils Bridge at Gay Head (Fig. 245, D) one may imagine a terrace two-thirds of a mile broad with its outer edge at a depth of 24 feet. Off the eastern end of the south coast of Marthas Vineyard there are very uncertain suggestions of a poorly defined terrace a mile or more broad with its outer edge 45 to 50 feet deep, with others equally doubtful still lower (Fig. 243, A); while a larger scale profile off the western part of this same shore (Fig. 242) suggests the possible existence of three separate and distinct benches, at distances of $1\frac{1}{2}$ miles, 3 miles, and 6 miles from shore, at depths of 63 feet, 74 feet, and 88 feet, respectively. More doubtful indications of benching were observed off the south side of Montauk Point at a depth of from 25 to 35 feet; off the southern shore of Nashawena Island at a depth of about 50 feet; off the southeast point of this same island at depths of 12 and 34 feet; off the southwest corner of Block Island at a depth of 37 to 40 feet. In all these cases the possible benches were narrow, from two-thirds of a mile to less than half that breadth.

**Significance of the Supposed Benches.** — The poorly developed form of the supposed benches, the variability of their depths, the frequent irregularity of both their top and frontal surfaces, the gentleness of the frontal slope in many cases and the lack of a sharply defined transition from gentle top slope to steep frontal pitch in others, together with the fact that a majority of the great number of profiles drawn show no evidence of benching, make one hesitate to attempt to measure the erosion of the coast on the basis of the breadth of benches cut by the waves. Apparently the products of erosion of the unconsolidated débris coasts have been widely distributed over the initially irregular seabottom, partially filling the depressions and in most places giving a gradual but somewhat irregular slope from shore to deeper water, without the development of a pronounced submarine terrace. The most we can say is that if the crude benches described are the product of marine erosion, they do not indicate that the waves have cut very deeply into the land at the present or any other level. Such a result would be the consequence of a gradual progressive submergence in post-glacial time, without any long halts in the movement. It must be remembered, however, that this negative evidence of the profiles is not conclusive; for waves may cut far into a mass of loose débris, much of it fine grained, without producing a sharply defined bench; and benches cut at lower levels may be obscured by such débris widely distributed from the present shores. Nothing in the profiles is opposed to the conception that in exposed localities the glacial débris coasts have been cut back from one to a few miles during the stand of the sea at its present level; although the roughness of the bottom in protected localities, and the rarity of good profiles of equilibrium on exposed shores, suggests that even off these very weak coasts the extent of marine abrasion has been strictly limited.

**General Résumé.** — We have now completed our survey of the New England-Acadian shoreline as affected by wave action. It has appeared that in general the initial shoreline of submergence has not been greatly altered. On the resistant crystalline coasts the attack of the waves has produced little effect, even upon the most exposed headlands. Weak-rock coasts have been cut back at the rate of a few inches a year in favorable localities, but the total changes effected are usually of moderate extent. Coasts of unconsolidated glacial débris are eroded at a much more rapid rate where exposed to the open sea, a loss of several feet a year being not unusual. Even here the total work accomplished seems moderate, and the loss of a strip of loose sand and clay a mile or so broad seems the most that can ordinarily be credited to marine erosion on the outer parts of these coasts, while more protected areas have suffered comparatively little. The weak clays and sands of the narrow and irregular post-glacial coastal plain strip have usually been trimmed back only a short distance before waves encountered the more resistant floor on which they rest; but where a typical coastal plain topography is developed, the shoreline is in its youthful " marsh and bar " stage. The impression remaining with one, after such a survey as we have made, is that the waves have been at work at the present level for an extremely short period. A few thousand years, perhaps only a small fraction of post-glacial time, have the present relations of land and sea endured along this coast. That the time has not been shorter than a few thousand years, is indicated by the physiographic evidence at critical points like Cape Cod and Nantasket.

BIBLIOGRAPHY

1. MARINDIN, H. L.  "Cross-sections of the Shore of Cape Cod between Chatham and the Highland Light-House."  U. S. Coast and Geod. Surv., Rept. for 1889, 409–457, 1890.
2. JOHNSON, DOUGLAS. "Shore Processes and Shoreline Development," 217, 486, New York, 1917.
3. SHALER, N. S.  "Report on the Geology of Marthas Vineyard."  U. S. Geol. Surv., 7th Ann. Rept., 350, 1888.

# CHAPTER XV

# RÔLE OF THE TIDES IN SHORELINE
# DEVELOPMENT

**Advance Summary.** — Throughout the previous discussions it has generally been assumed that wave action, and not tidal or other current action, is primarily responsible for such modifications of the shoreline as we have observed. Only incidentally have we touched on the much debated question as to the relative importance of "waves" and "currents" (or "longshore currents"), as the two types of forces are generally phrased, in marine erosion and deposition. In a volume on "Shore Processes and Shoreline Development" I have discussed this important question at some length,[1] and it does not seem desirable to repeat such a discussion here. The reader will find set forth in the volume cited reasons for the opinion that the rôle of tides and other forces classed as "currents" has been greatly exaggerated by many students of shore problems, and that the importance of waves as moulders of shore forms has too often been imperfectly appreciated. In the present chapter it is proposed to consider briefly the subordinate rôle of the tides, and to describe such modifications of shoreline or offshore bottom as appear to be wholly or mainly the product of tidal action. Special attention will be given to the supposed unusually vigorous erosive action of tides in the Bay of Fundy.

**"Waves" versus "Currents."** — It is unfortunate that "waves" should so often be contrasted with "currents" or "longshore currents," for this is to obscure the vital fact that wave action inevitably involves current movements of enormous potency, and that these wave currents generally compel a longshore movement of débris, a process to which I have applied the term "beach drifting." If it were possible to stop every tidal, planetary, wind-drift, and other current which affects the ocean waters, save only the orbital movement of water particles which constitutes wave motion; and then to project against a shore, at ever so faint an obliquity, a series of large waves, there would be found to develop along the shore, under the short but continually repeated and violent impact of the wave currents, all the phenomena of beaches, bars, spits, and forelands with which we are familiar. And so predominant, in my opinion, is the action of beach drifting, due to oblique wave impact, in fashioning shore forms, that I am convinced the absence of the other currents would affect the final result only to a subordinate degree. Not that tidal and other currents do not often aid wave action in the manner described by Gilbert,[2] or may not, under favorable conditions, independently excavate seabottom or shores and even build bars or forelands. But recognition of these possibilities should not obscure what seem to be the major facts, — that waves can, and often do, erode shores, transport débris, and construct beaches, bars, and forelands of all types, without the aid of tidal or planetary currents, and apparently with but limited and incidental assistance from the wind-drift, hydraulic, and other currents usually associated with wave motion; and that where tidal or other currents do operate, their rôle is generally subordinate to that of true wave currents.

**Tidal Scour in Narrow Passages.** — There are localities on the New England-Acadian coast where tidal currents have marked strength, and appear to exercise a modifying effect upon seabottom or shores; and we may now briefly consider some of these. We can dismiss at once the obsolete theory that tides have played an important part in excavating the deep embayments of the rocky coasts of Maine, Nova Scotia, and other parts of the New England-Acadian province. This is a theory which antedates our better understanding of embayed coasts as the product of a submergence drowning former land valleys, and for the most part persists only in revisions of older textbooks[3] and other ultra-conservative quarters. But that tidal currents through narrow passageways originally formed by other agencies may exert a scouring action cannot be doubted. When during a storm in 1886 a new inlet was broken through the bar closing the mouth of Katama Bay (Fig. 224), the fishermen found that the scour of the tidal currents which then could pass through the inlet, through the bay, and on through Edgartown Harbor into the Sound beyond, injured clam and quahaug grounds of much local value.[4] Here the scouring action was apparently removing silts deposited in slack water after an earlier inlet near the same point had silted up.[5]

Bailey[6] emphasizes the great strength of tidal currents through Petit Passage, one of the narrow straits through the North Mountain-Digby Neck trap ridge (Fig. 13), where a velocity of " not less than 8 knots " an hour is attained; while Daly[7] refers to a " 6-knot flood and ebb " at Grand Passage and past the southwestern end of Brier Island.   These are apparently the " passes on the southwest " where Daly states that " excavation by tidal scour is now going on apace," as well as at Minas Channel and Digby Gut; and in his opinion " all these gates are every day opening wider."[8] The evidence on which this last conclusion rests is not given. Charts of Digby Gut show that in the middle portion there is a hole more than 80 feet deeper than the seafloor outside.   Goldthwait[9] calculates that at every tide over 21,000,000,000 cubic feet of water pass through this gateway with a maximum velocity higher than five miles per hour, or sufficient to move stones several inches in diameter; and he attributes the hole in question to overdeepening by tidal scour on the bottom, but makes no reference to evidence of tidal erosion of the hard-rock shores.   This same authority ascribes to tidal action similar local scour holes in the narrow tidal passage over the bar of Hadley Beach at the entrance to Guysborough Harbor, Nova Scotia, where the overdeepening amounts to about 25 feet only; at the entrance to the Basin of Minas, where the tidal currents attain a velocity of 7 to 9 miles an hour, and three holes, in places nearly 200 feet deep below the level just outside, exist in spite of the movement of vast quantities of mud and sand across them; and at the narrow entrance to the Great Bras d'Or on Cape Breton Island, where a tidal current of 7 miles an hour maintains a hole about 40 feet deeper than the sea or lake bottom at either end.   Matthew[10] long ago attributed to tidal scour the deeps at the entrance to the Basin of Minas and other similar depressions, including one above and one below the tidal " falls " at St. John, New Brunswick, which, respectively, measure over 100 and over 150 feet deeper than the intervening reef which causes the falls.   In a paper entitled " Über Erosion durch Gezeitenströme " Krümmel[11] adopted the interpretation that the Basin of Minas deeps are due to tidal erosion.

It need not be supposed that the depths cited above represent any scouring of the rock bottom; not even in the St. John case, since the " falls " reef does not represent the normal outlet of the St. John River, but a ridge separating two pre-glacial valleys.

In the Guysborough Harbor case Goldthwait makes clear his belief that the depression is merely a subordinate detail on the surface of a bar consisting wholly of unconsolidated sediments.  It may also be pointed out that in this last locality successive recurving of the Hadley Beach spit, with the submarine extension of each recurved point more or less nearly blocking the passage, would leave between them depressions similar to the one shown on the chart.  In most of the cases cited the depressions may represent merely lack of deposition while adjacent parts of the seafloor were aggraded, and not real erosion in the sense in which that term is ordinarily employed.  The same may be said of the rocky, gravelly, and sandy areas, free from silt, on the floor of the Bay of Fundy, cited by Matthew[10] as evidence of tidal erosion. On the other hand, there is no reason to doubt the ability of such currents to erode bottom deposits where narrow constriction gives them high velocities, and there are recorded cases of changes in the form and depth of scour holes which seem to show such action.[12]  The only shore changes attributed " almost wholly to tidal currents " by Goldthwait are the formation of three triangular cuspate forelands in Petit Passage, Digby Gut, and the Strait of Canso, — narrow strips of water in which it would seem that conditions are exceptionally favorable to the development of cuspate forms by wave action alone.  Goldthwait thinks " it is probable that wave-driven shore currents have aided in their construction," and recognizes that similar forms " are common in the Bras d'Or lakes where tides are weak or wholly absent, and where wave action alone can be appealed to."

**Tidal Action on the Submerged Banks Cuesta.** — Where the crest of the Banks Cuesta comes close to the surface, and the movement of waters across it into and out of the Gulf of Maine are restricted to a narrow vertical zone, the tidal currents may in places have sufficient energy to shift the shoals on the Banks; but it is not always easy in case of such movements to distinguish between the work of tidal currents and the work of wave currents. This is true on the shoals about Nantucket, where tidal currents are strong[13] but wave action must also affect the bottom.   Crosby[14] has shown that in Boston Harbor, where wave action is weak but tidal currents are fairly strong, the amount of scouring action is surprisingly slight.

**Tides of the Bay of Fundy.** — It is quite natural that the possible importance of tidal erosion should receive most attention in connection with the Bay of Fundy, where we find associated with a broad and deep embayment a phenomenal vertical range of the tides and the peculiar form of tidal wave known as the bore. Both the range of the Fundy tides and the importance of the bore are exaggerated in certain of our textbooks and other published accounts. Instead of the normal tidal range of 30 to 40 feet, or in some places spring ranges up to 50 feet, these works often cite only exceptional " storm tides," with supposed ranges of 70 feet or more, in which the rise of the water was only in part due to tidal action. Similarly the bore, which is usually but from 1 to 2 feet high, and only rarely as much as 5 or 6 feet at Moncton,[9] is more often credited with the maximum figures. While an interesting and novel sight to the visitors on this coast, the bore (Fig. 246) is not particularly impressive to the student of shore processes, nor is it suggestive of tremendous erosive power. In general the velocity of the tides close to the land along the open shore is not great, although it may on occasion rise to more than 11 miles an hour in a narrow passage like the entrance to the Basin of Minas, where according to Hamilton[15] a stranger floating up with the flood first begins to appreciate the tides of the Bay of Fundy, and " in the calmest of weather the waters seethe and boil and whirl along, as if they were in a gigantic cauldron." Where the bay narrows to drowned valleys of small width, currents of 6 or 7 miles an hour may develop, and may maintain a fairly high velocity close to the bordering shores.

Nearly half a century ago Shaler[16] cited the Bay of Fundy tides as providing " the most striking example of tidal wear on this coast," and propounded seven fundamental principles which he believed to control tidal erosion. He was still influenced by the early theory that the deep embayments of our coasts are caused by the gnawing action of the tides, and believed that in the Fundy region tidal erosion at the head of the Bay would eat a passage through into the Gulf of St. Lawrence. It is significant of the great advance made in physiographic science during the short space of fifty years, that probably not one of the seven principles of tidal erosion propounded by this fertile thinker in 1875 would command his acceptance, were he living today. The evidence is clear that so far from eroding the head of the Bay of Fundy the tides have long been, and still are, filling the bay head by extensive deposition.

Matthew's belief in the efficiency of tidal erosion in the Bay of

Fig. 246. Tidal bore in the Petitcodiac River near Moncton, New Brunswick. Photo by Percy R. Crandall.

Fundy, where he thought the tides had " cut deeply into the substance " of the seabottom,[10] has already been cited.   Chalmers[17] is another who credits extensive erosion to the Fundy tides. " The bold cliffs, headlands, and rock-bound shores evidence intense erosion " by the " wonderful tides and currents," while " the scour on the bottom must be enormous."   Yet he notes that the Bay is comparatively shallow, and "must have a great thickness of detritus spread over it;" and elsewhere[18] he says: " The action of the tidal wave in the northeastern extremities of the Bay of Fundy is therefore accumulative and not destructive; that is, it deposits material where it is thrown back on itself; but further down the bay, where it receives no check to its onward progress, its erosive power, especially on the shores, is very great."

In his excellent account of " The Physiography of Acadia," Daly[19] leans strongly to the idea of extensive tidal erosion in the Bay of Fundy, and even considers the possibility of a " tidal cycle " to account for the production of the Triassic Lowland occupied by the Bay.   But after a somewhat elaborate analysis of the tidal conditions which theoretically should have existed in the Fundy region in earlier times, based on the assumption that tides are effective denuding agents under proper conditions, he concludes that the Triassic Lowland is essentially subaërial in origin, although " we are sure that tidal work cannot be ruled out."   He thinks tidal action in the past was weaker than today, but apparently favors the conception of vigorous tidal erosion at the present time.

It is not necessary to review in detail the many opinions which have been expressed in favor of strong tidal erosion in the Bay of Fundy and its branches.   Those cited above are typical of many others which will confront the reader who studies the literature descriptive of this interesting locality.   For the most part the opinions are unaccompanied by any specific evidence to support them, and are apparently based on the assumption that tides of such extraordinary range must be vigorous eroding agents, or that tidal currents with such velocities as have been observed in parts of the Bay cannot fail to accomplish a large measure of denudation.

**Conditions Affecting Tidal Erosive Power.** — In many of the discussions of past tidal conditions the assumption that erosive power varies directly with tidal range is particularly noticeable; and there is lost from view the additional fact that the course the tidal waters must take through broad or narrow channels, or over shoals, may have much to do with tidal erosive power.  Thus it has been said that when the tides " eat through " the narrow isthmus at the head of the Bay of Fundy, erosion will be decreased owing to a decrease in tidal range; and that before the tides ate through (sic) the Straits of Dover their erosive power in that vicinity must have been far greater than now, because the tidal range must have been greater when the waters were held in check by and piled up against the barrier then connecting England with France.  Similarly, it has been argued that submergence of the

FIG. 246a.   Large current ripples in sand near Boat Island, Nova Scotia. Photo by J. W. Goldthwait, Geol. Surv. Canada.

Isthmus of Chignecto, between the Bay of Fundy and Northumberland Strait, would give weak tidal currents in the Bay, because the tidal range would be much less than now.

The matter is less simple than these statements would imply. In the lower, open parts of the embayments the current velocities are not high under the most favorable conditions, especially near the bordering shores; and the difference in current velocity and erosive power to be expected there as a result of opening or closing a barrier at the narrow head of such an embayment must be negligible.  In the upper parts of the embayments, where alone the changes suggested could produce significant consequences, it would appear that the results might well be just the reverse of those indicated above.  The opening of a channel at the head of the Bay of Fundy, by permitting free passage of the waters now piled up and held in check there, might change the present depositing action, by which the channels are being silted up and the marshes formed, to a scouring action such as has been noted at other narrow channels through which tidal currents pass with increased velocities.  Conversely, if we could block the Straits of Dover, the tidal range would doubtless be increased; but the checked waters might then deposit extensively where today erosion is in progress, and so bring about conditions like those now found in the upper part of the Bay of Fundy.  Chalmers[20] recognized that when the Isthmus of Chignecto was submerged there may have been erosion at the head of the Bay of Fundy, and that deposition to form the present marshes must have begun when the creation of that barrier blocked the tidal waters and increased their vertical range.

The second assumption, that high current velocity necessarily means extensive erosive action, likewise seems subject to qualification.  Whether or not a rapid current erodes, depends on the nature of its load.  If the current consists of pure water flowing over resistant bedrock, the amount of erosive work accomplished may be negligible.  If it carries a heavy burden of sediment, it may deposit instead of eroding.  In the more open parts of the Bay of Fundy, where the currents are comparatively weak, there is evidence[10] that they are shifting back and forth on the bottom large quantities of débris, probably delivered to them by waves and streams; and Chalmers' statement that the bottom of the Bay " must have a great thickness of detritus spread over it "[21] is quite likely true.  Where revealed at low water the shifting bottom deposits are often fashioned by overburdened tidal currents into giant ripples of the asymmetric or current type (Fig. 246a).  Along the margins of the open Bay the currents are still weaker, and there seems to be no evidence of appreciable tidal erosion there.

In the narrow branches into which the Bay divides at its head the tidal currents reach velocities of 5 to 7 miles an hour; and in the Petitcodiac River near Moncton the foaming wave of the " bore " (Fig. 246), discussed briefly and figured by Chalmers[22] and Davis,[23] and described more dramatically by Hamilton[24] and Murphy,[25] advances at similar speeds.  Yet it is precisely in these upper branches where velocities are high that the tidal currents have long been, and apparently still are, depositing their burden of sand and silt to build up the remarkable Fundy marshes. Instead of eroding and thus widening their channels, they are perhaps narrowing and shortening them by continued deposition. In 1867 Hamilton[26] declared that all the channels at the head of the Bay of Fundy were filling up. " For instance, not more than twenty-five years since, vessels of from fifty to one hundred and fifty tons used, almost daily, to sail up this Cobequid Bay to receive and discharge cargo at the place where it is now bridged, a short distance below the village of Truro. Now nobody ever attempts to take any sort of a craft above the class of an open boat, further up the bay than Yuill's Island, which is about six miles below the bridge. The channel is obviously narrowing and becoming more shallow every year." Murphy,[25] a government engineer, says " the flood tide carries with it the silt and mud, and deposits its load chiefly in the creeks and on the flats at the head of the bays "; and describes an example of rapid deposition of sediment in a large steel cylinder at the bridge crossing Avon estuary. Chalmers[27] does not see any evidence that the marsh areas have extended seaward in the last two centuries, but apparently credits the general belief that the estuaries are filling up and becoming narrower. He states that it is not uncommon for a single tide to deposit an inch of sediment in certain spots along the banks, and cites a tradition among the old settlers that Missaguash River was navigable for canoes nearly to its source when Fort Beausejour (now Fort Cumberland) was captured by the English in 1755, which he points out is no longer the case. Monro[28] gives similar testimony with regard to the loss of this navigable route. In his account of the vegetation of the Fundy marshes Ganong[29] states that the process of marsh building still continues. Locally erosion of the soft deposits may take place, as where the shifting of a tidal channel has uncovered a buried forest at Fort Lawrence (Fig. 272). But there is little room to doubt that the rapid tidal currents at the head of the Bay of Fundy carry too heavy a load to be effective agents of erosion; and while they stir up the silt, and shift the débris by scouring here and depositing there, the net result of their operation is more and more perfectly to protect the estuaries from erosion. As has well been said, the effect of these currents is not destructive, but constructive.

Only where constriction of the tidal currents to a narrow passage gives them an excessive velocity, is there evidence that deposition is restricted or prevented; and it remains to be shown that in these places any appreciable erosion of bottom or sides of the Fundy basin has been accomplished by tidal action. One is constrained to believe that while the tidal currents may indirectly aid wave attack by helping to remove the products of wave erosion, the rôle of the tides in the classic Fundy region is a very minor one so far as erosion is concerned, although through marsh building they have much modified the upper shores of the Bay. In like manner it is believed that elsewhere the tides have usually played but a subordinate part in shoreline development; although it is not doubted that locally, under specially favorable conditions, they may exert a more pronounced influence upon shoreline topography.

**Résumé.** — There appears to be reliable evidence of tidal scouring where currents compressed in narrow passages or over shallows attain exceptional velocities, although part of the results commonly attributed to " erosion " at such points may represent mere failure of the currents to deposit sediments there. As a rule tidal currents are comparatively weak near the shore, and one is in general impressed with the limited extent to which shoreline topography is affected by tidal action. Wave action, including the currents involved in the movement of water particles in waves, appears to be responsible for most of the modifications of shores frequently attributed to tidal phenomena. The forces generated by tides in the Bay of Fundy in particular are popularly exaggerated, and the conception that the remarkable tidal phenomena of this region must of necessity give rise to profound erosion of the floor and margins of the tidal basin, is not supported by a careful analysis of the problem. Neither great tidal range nor high current velocity necessarily implies vigorous erosive power; and in the Bay of Fundy region deposition has exceeded erosion in the upper parts of the basin where current velocities are high and the tidal range is at its maximum. Apparently the tides exert their greatest influence upon shoreline topography by transporting and depositing the fine débris worn from the lands largely through the action of other agencies, especially streams and waves.

BIBLIOGRAPHY

1. JOHNSON, DOUGLAS. "Shore Processes and Shoreline Development," 143–145, 333–339, New York, 1917.
2. GILBERT, G. K. "The Topographic Features of Lake Shores." U. S. Geol. Surv., 5th Ann. Rept., 85, 1885.
3. LE CONTE, JOSEPH. "Elements of Geology," 5th Ed., 32a, 36, New York, 1910.
4. WHITING, H. L. "Shorelines and Beaches of Marthas Vineyard." Mass. Harbor and Land Comm., Ann. Rept. for 1886, 50, 1887.
5. WHITING, H. L. "Cotamy Beach and Skiff's Island." Mass. Harbor and Land Comm., Ann. Rept. for 1886, 54, 1887.
6. BAILEY, L. W. "Report on the Geology of Southwest Nova Scotia." Geol. Surv. Can., Ann. Rept. (1896), N. Ser., IX, Rept. M, 23, 1898.
   BAILEY, L. W. "Notes on the Geology and Botany of Digby Neck." Nova Scotian Inst. Sci., Proc. and Trans., 2nd Ser., II, 73, 1898.
7. DALY, R. A. "The Physiography of Acadia." Bull. Mus. Comp. Zoölogy, XXXVIII, 91, 1901.
8. DALY, R. A. "The Physiography of Acadia." Bull. Mus. Comp. Zoölogy, XXXVIII, 96, 1901.
9. GOLDTHWAIT, J. W. "The Physiography of Nova Scotia." Manuscript copy of a volume to be issued by the Geological Survey of Canada.
10. MATTHEW, G. F. "Tidal Erosion in the Bay of Fundy." Can. Nat., N. Ser., IX, 368–373, 1881.
11. KRÜMMEL, OTTO. "Ueber Erosion durch Gezeitenströme." Pet. Geog. Mit., XXXV, 129–138, 1889.
12. HALLETT, H. S. (On tidal scour.) Min. Proc. Inst. Civil Eng., LXVI, 54–55, 1881.
13. MITCHELL, HENRY. "Report on Edgartown and Nantucket Harbors." Mass. Board of Harbor Comm., 6th Ann. Rept., 114, 1872.
14. CROSBY, W. O. "A Study of the Geology of the Charles River Estuary and the Formation of Boston Harbor." Rept. Comm. on Charles River Dam, Appendix 7, 345–369, Boston, 1903.
15. HAMILTON, P. S. "On the Tides of the Bay of Fundy." Nova Scotian Inst. Nat. Sci., Proc. and Trans., II, Pt. I, 39, 1867.
16. SHALER, N. S. "Notes on Some Points Connected with Tidal Erosion." Bost. Soc. Nat. Hist., Proc., XVII, 465–466, 1875.
17. CHALMERS, ROBERT. "Report on the Surface Geology of Southern New Brunswick." Geol. Surv. Can., Ann. Rept., N. Ser., IV, 16N, 17N, 1890.
18. CHALMERS, ROBERT. "Report on the Surface Geology of New Brunswick, Northwestern Nova Scotia, and a Portion of Prince Edward Island." Geol. Surv. Can., Ann. Rept., N. Ser., VII, 20M, 1895.
19. DALY, R. A. "The Physiography of Acadia." Bull. Mus. Comp. Zoölogy, XXXVIII, 88–92, 1901.
20. CHALMERS, ROBERT. "Report on the Surface Geology of New Brunswick, Northwestern Nova Scotia, and a Portion of Prince Edward Island." Geol. Surv. Can., Ann. Rept., N. Ser., VII, 19M–20M, 1895.

# 516 RÔLE OF TIDES IN SHORELINE DEVELOPMENT

21. CHALMERS, ROBERT. "Report on the Surface Geology of Southern New Brunswick." Geol. Surv. Can., Ann. Rept., N. Ser., IV, 16N, 1890.
22. CHALMERS, ROBERT. "Report on the Surface Geology of New Brunswick, Northwestern Nova Scotia, and a Portion of Prince Edward Island." Geol. Surv. Can., Ann. Rept., N. Ser., VII, 11M, 1895.
23. DAVIS, W. M. "Tides in the Bay of Fundy." Nat. Geog. Mag., XVI, 71–76, 1905.
24. HAMILTON, P. S. "On the Tides of the Bay of Fundy." Nova Scotian Inst. Nat. Sci., Proc and Trans., II, Pt. I, 35–48, 1867.
25. MURPHY, M. "The Tides of the Bay of Fundy." Nova Scotian Inst. Nat. Sci., Proc. and Trans., VII, Pt. I, 48–62, 1888.
26. HAMILTON, P. S. "On the Tides of the Bay of Fundy." Nova Scotian Inst. Nat. Sci., Proc. and Trans., II, Pt. I, 43, 1867.
27. CHALMERS, ROBERT. "Report on the Surface Geology of New Brunswick, Northwestern Nova Scotia and a Portion of Prince Edward Island." Geol. Surv. Can., Ann. Rept., N. Ser., VII, 126M, 1895.
28. MONRO, ALEX. "On the Physical Features and Geology of Chignecto Isthmus." Nat. Hist. Soc. New Brunswick, Bull., I, No. V, 23, 1886. Also a series of 9 newspaper articles in the Chignecto Post, May-July, 1883 (not seen).
29. GANONG, W. F. "The Vegetation of the Bay of Fundy Salt and Dyked Marshes: An Ecological Study." Bot. Gazette, XXXVI, 167, 168, 1903.

# CHAPTER XVI

## TIDAL MARSHES OF THE NEW ENGLAND TYPE

**Advance Summary.** — The marshes of the Atlantic coast deserve some attention as the chief contribution made by the tides to the phenomena of shoreline development. In the present chapter we shall first review briefly the literature relating to our tidal marshes, and the principal theories regarding their origin and development. Three fairly distinct types of tidal marshes will be discriminated and one of these, the New England type, will particularly command our attention throughout the remaining pages of the chapter. The surface zones of the New England type of marsh will be described, the effect of progressive subsidence on such marshes will be considered, and marsh phenomena which often give rise to fictitious indications of subsidence will be explained. A number of marshes of the New England type will then be described more at length, and the results of detailed studies of these marshes will be set forth, in order that we may better establish the essential characteristics and the range of variation of this group of marshes, and determine the physical history of the group as recorded in its surface forms and internal structures.

**Literature of Tidal Marshes.** — Dawson[1] for the Acadian region, and Shaler[2] for the shores of the United States, early gave us systematic if brief accounts of the nature and origin of tidal marshes. The two accounts differ widely, in part because of a marked difference in the nature of the marshes upon which each based his descriptions, in part because the substructure of American marshes was not well known when Shaler propounded his theory of their origin, and in part because Dawson recognized to some extent the rôle played by progressive submergence in marsh formation, a factor which does not figure in Shaler's theory. We will return to Dawson's and Shaler's accounts in later paragraphs. Other contributions to the literature of tidal marshes in Acadia include Lyell's earlier reference to the subject in his " Travels in North America;"[3] papers by Monro,[4] an experienced surveyor of the Fundy marshes, on the features of Chignecto Isthmus at the head of the Bay of Fundy; a paper by Boardman[5] on the tidal lands and dyked marshes of Nova Scotia and New Brunswick; a brief general account of the Fundy tides and marshes by Eaton;[6] the more technical discussion of the Northumberland Strait and Fundy marshes by Chalmers[7] in which two sections through the Fundy marsh deposits are described and their significance considered; a paper by Trueman[8] on the marshes at the head of Chignecto Bay which seems to exaggerate the thickness of the deposits and the depth to which stumps in place are known to exist, but gives a good idea of certain features of the district; and the valuable essay by Ganong[9] on the vegetation of the salt and dyked marshes of the Bay of Fundy region, in which the nature and origin of the marsh deposits are fully discussed.

Among the accounts of salt marshes of the Atlantic coast of the United States first place must be given to a practically unknown but highly important early paper by Mudge[10] in which for the first time the true origin of the type of marsh deposits found on our New England coast was clearly pointed out. Had Mudge's contribution been better known, the erroneous conceptions of salt marsh formation which prevailed in this country for half a century after his time, might early have been corrected. It remained for C. A. Davis[11] by more extended studies and publications to establish the truth of Mudge's theory, which apparently Davis had himself independently rediscovered.

Other additions to the literature of American salt marshes include the valuable detailed study of the relation of plants to tide levels in Cold Spring Harbor by Johnson and York;[12] a series of papers by Harshberger[13] on the marshes of New Jersey in which the salt marsh vegetation zones are considered, as well as the strand flora; another paper on the same region by J. B. Smith;[14] an account of the plant-covering of Ocracoke Island, North Carolina, by Kearney,[15] which includes a treatment of adjacent salt marshes; a report on Connecticut salt marshes by Nichols;[16] and a discussion of the origin and development of some of the New England marshes by Penhallow.[17] A description of tide marshes of the United States and of attempts at their reclamation will be found in an early report by Nesbit,[18] while a beautifully illustrated popular account of sand dunes and salt marshes, with special emphasis on the Ipswich section of the Massachusetts coast, has been published by Townsend.[19] Additional references to works on tidal marshes will be found at the end of Ganong's essay,[9] cited above, and in the present writer's volume on " Shore Processes and Shoreline Development."

It should be appreciated that many tidal marshes are not salt marshes, although the terms are often used interchangeably. Tidal and marsh conditions often extend up rivers and bays beyond the reach of salt water, and the dyked marshes of New Jersey, Pennsylvania and Delaware, as well as those of the rice lands of the southern Atlantic coast, were largely fresh marshes in their wild state. Our attention will be directed chiefly to the salt marshes, although we shall have occasion later to refer incidentally to some of the fresh tidal marshes first mentioned.

**Dawson's Theory.** — Dawson's theory for the origin of the Fundy marshes may be stated very briefly. The rising tide sweeps away the fine material from every exposed bank and cliff, becoming loaded with mud and extremely fine sand, which, as it stagnates at high water, is deposited in a thin layer on the surface of the flats. During this process the land gradually subsides, carrying the earlier formed parts of the marsh deposit deeper and deeper, while the tides continue to build the marsh surface upward to the new high tide level. Thus the marsh deposit consists largely of silt which progressively encroaches upon the subsiding upland, killing and burying the forests clothing its slopes. The preserved stumps of the forest trees are frequently encountered where excavation removes the silt and reveals the old land surface below.

**Mudge's Theory.** — In 1857 Mudge found that the salt marshes of Lynn, instead of consisting mainly of silt as in the Bay of Fundy region, were composed in large part of the roots of high tide grasses found undisturbed *in situ*, and extending down to the bottom of the marsh, far below the present high tide level, and indeed well below the limits of the lowest tides of today. From this he correctly argued that the marsh must record a progressive subsidence of the land during the time of its formation; for, he said: " The saline grasses grow only above ordinary high water mark, and as the roots in the lowest part of the soil, even eight or more feet below the surface, are in their natural position, showing no distortion, we must conclude that their *situs* was above the high water line, and that the subsidence has been so gradual that the growth of the plants has never been interrupted." Mudge was not so happy in explaining the cause of the subsidence, for he

attributed it to local settling due to special conditions, not realizing that he had to do with a phenomenon of wide occurrence.

**Shaler's Theory.** — Twenty-seven years after Mudge published
his acute observations on the nature and origin of the Lynn
marshes, Shaler propounded a theory of tide marsh development,
apparently anticipated in part by Mather[20] in 1843, which is of
considerable historical interest because of its influence on the conceptions as to the origin of these marshes held by two generations
of geologists and geographers, and which may have practical value
in explaining the formation of marsh in areas of open water not
filled during progressive submergence, as well as the regeneration
of local areas of marshland where shifting tidal creeks or other
causes completely remove the original marsh deposits formed after
the manner described by Mudge. According to Shaler, when
silting has shallowed quiet lagoons or other protected areas to

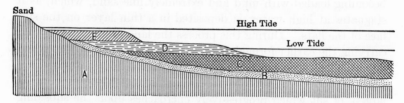

Fig. 247.  Diagrammatic section through a growing salt marsh, according
to Shaler's theory of salt marsh formation.  A, bedrock or soil; B, silt;
C, eel grass remains with much silt; D, silt deposits giving mud flats
at low tide; E, salt-marsh grasses and turf.

depths of ten feet or a little more, eel grass (*Zostera marina*) takes
root, and by checking currents laden with silt, and by providing a
favorable habitat for marine animals whose remains are added to
the growing deposit, aids materially in raising the seabottom
nearly to the level of low tide.  Now the eel grass ceases to
flourish, and for a time sedimentation must operate without its
aid until the deposit rises high enough to expose bare mud flats
when the tide is out.  Meantime other grasses begin to grow
outward from the shore over the mud flats, their tops dying down
each winter but their roots remaining to raise the accumulation
higher and higher, until the marsh surface is built up nearly, but
not quite, to the limit of the high tides (Fig. 247).

**Criteria for Testing the Mudge and Shaler Theories.** — It is
easy to test the two theories of salt marsh formation propounded
by Mudge and Shaler.  According to Mudge's explanation the

marshes have in general been built vertically upward under fairly constant conditions which should give a more or less homogeneous vegetable deposit from top to bottom; although the theory does not exclude local variations in composition, due to silting or to growth of eel grass and other types of vegetation where for any reason grass did not grow originally or was later removed. According to Shaler's theory the marshes have been built vertically upward in their lower parts by the accumulation of silt, aided at the end by eel grass growth, and horizontally outward in their upper parts by the growth of high tide grasses; and sections through the marsh should show a regular vertical succession of beds of very different composition (Fig. 247). If Mudge be right, remains of high tide vegetation should commonly be found from the top of the marsh downward to considerable depths; if Shaler be right, remains of high tide grasses should be found near the top, remains of intermediate and low tide grasses at lower levels, and silt without vegetation after one passes below the eel grass zone.

The extended investigations of our salt marsh deposits made by C. A. Davis have demonstrated beyond any doubt that Mudge's theory is correct. In no case did he find a marsh deposit showing the succession of beds demanded by the Shaler theory. Instead he commonly found the roots of high tide grasses, especially *Spartina patens*, from the present sealevel down to depths far below the lowest ranges of the tides. My own studies and those of my assistants, involving the making of many hundreds of sections through our coastal marshes from Prince Edward Island to Florida, amply confirm the essential points in the conclusions of Mudge and Davis. Marsh sections showing the theoretical sequence of deposits described by Shaler do exist, however, but they seem clearly to represent local departures from the normal sequence of marsh development, due to recent regeneration of limited areas of our marshes from which the original deposit had been removed, or to the filling of new areas not previously occupied. In an extended examination I have found no example of any large marsh area which I could be sure had developed in the manner described by Shaler. On the other hand, I have found abundant illustrations of the fact that the roots of high tide vegetation *in situ* extend to considerable depths below the limits both of high and low tide. And while my observations indicate a greater variation in character of the marsh deposits than Davis' descriptions imply, and I am unable, for reasons to be discussed fully in a later volume, to accept his deductions as to the date of the subsidence indicated by the deposits, we are in complete agreement as regards the fundamental proposition that the marshes of the Atlantic Coast have been formed during a slow, progressive submergence, due either to a sinking of the land or to a rise of sealevel in post-glacial time. Inasmuch as Dawson early argued that the Fundy marshes were deposited during a subsidence of the coast, we are in substantial agreement in confirming the theories of Dawson and Mudge with respect to the Acadian and New England coastal marshes.

## The New England Type of Tidal Marsh

**Three Types of Tidal Marshes.** — There are three distinct types of tidal marsh deposits bordering the Atlantic coast. The first is typically developed along the shores of New England and may for convenience be called the " New England type." The second finds its best expression at the head of the Bay of Fundy, and for this reason I have called it the " Fundy Type." The third is characteristic of the shores of the Atlantic Coastal Plain of the southeastern United States, and may therefore be denominated the " Coastal Plain Type." In subsequent pages the internal composition and the surface characters of these three types of marsh deposits will duly appear.

**Composition of the New England Marshes.** — Sections through the New England type of marsh (made with the ingenious peat sampler (Fig. 248) devised by C. A. Davis and by means of which a cylindrical core of the deposit may be brought up from any desired depth, or continuous cores through the whole deposit may be taken) show that characteristically it consists of a horizontally bedded deposit of greyish or brownish salt peat with variable amounts of silt, often underlain by deep brown or black brackish to fresh water peat, sometimes of very considerable thickness. Below this, sand, glacial till, or bedrock is usually encountered and stops the operation of the peat sampler.

**Surface Aspect: Juncus Zone.** — The present surface aspect of the New England type of tidal marshes is familiar to every careful observer of our coastal topography. In the higher marginal areas, bordering the upland, grow those forms which can live with only an occasional wetting by the exceptional, extremely high tides. This is the " Juncus zone," or " Black grass zone " (Fig.

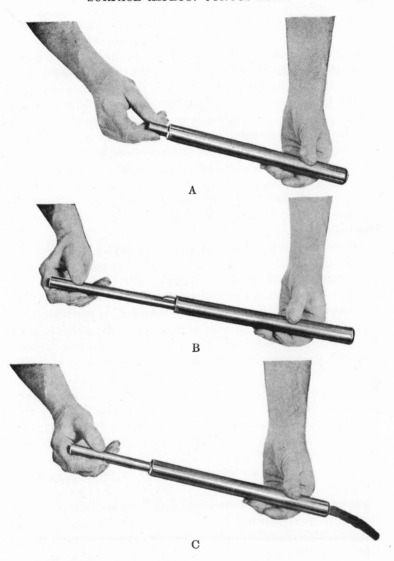

A

B

C

FIG. 248.   Sampling device designed by C. A. Davis to take cores from peat
bogs or salt marsh deposits at any desired depth.   A. Sampler closed,
and in position to be forced down into the deposit.   B. When at the
desired depth the rod handle is raised, thus withdrawing the plunger
and locking it in the position here indicated, leaving the hollow cylinder
ready to receive the core when the sampler is again pushed downward.
C. The sampler is then withdrawn, the plunger unlocked and pushed
back into the cylinder, thereby expelling the core of peat.

197), typified by *Juncus gerardi*, with which, however, are associated the salt marsh golden rod (*Solidago sempervirens*) and other species somewhat salt-tolerant but unable to endure long or frequent submergence by salt water.  The vertical range of this zone is usually small, perhaps one foot.  Dr. Barton of our party, on the basis of careful measurements on the marshes near Port Jefferson, Long Island, found it to be approximately .75 foot in that locality.  Horizontally it does not normally cover a breadth of more than a few yards, but in some cases may extend much farther.  It should be noted that *Juncus gerardi* and other species of this zone grow not only upon the marsh proper, but are found rising a few inches (vertically) on the sandy slopes of bordering beaches, dunes, or upland, where the highest tides occasionally wet the soil.

Where the salt marsh grades into a fresh water swamp, instead of coming more abruptly into contact with the relatively dry upland, very different conditions prevail.  The Juncus zone is normally absent, and the Patens zone (described below) merges into a somewhat variable association of plants.  On the basis of an extended examination of salt marshes along the Atlantic coast, Dr. G. B. Reed of our party concluded that in this variable association *Scirpus americana* and *Eleocharis rostellata* form one of the most frequent combinations; but that these are frequently replaced by or have mixed with them other species, including *Cyperus nuttallii*, *Hypericum virginicum*, *Pluchea camphorata*, *Aspidium thelypteris* and *Scirpus olnei;* these grading imperceptibly into *Sphagnum*, *Chamæcyparis*, *Acer rubrum* and their associates.  Where swampy conditions prevail, the cattails, *Typha latifolia* and *Typha angustifolia*, fairly tolerant of salt water, are sometimes very abundant.

**Patens Zone.** — The next lower zone includes that portion of the marsh vegetation which thrives from a little above to a little below the level of ordinary high tides, and is known as the " Patens zone " or " Marsh hay zone " (Fig. 249).  The salt grass *Spartina patens*, sometimes called fox grass, is the type form for this zone; but the spike grass *Distichlis spicata* is also abundant, and other forms which will endure wetting by the tides a brief period only each day, and require such wetting a few times each month only, although by capillarity they may secure salt water much more frequently.  The vertical range of this zone varies with the tidal range, but on the New England coast is approximately two feet.

FIG. 249. Mystic River marshes near Boston, showing surface largely in the *Spartina patens* zone, but with a narrow zone of *Spartina glabra* bordering the tidal channel in foreground.

On the Port Jefferson marshes, Long Island, Dr. Barton's measurements gave an average of 1.55 feet.  In breadth it is the most extensive of the zones, and on a maturely developed marsh covers the greater part of the surface, although frequently interrupted by narrow, meandering tidal channels, on the walls of which other zones are represented.  Except during spring tides one may walk with ease where the *Spartina patens* association thrives, for this part of the marsh is not only comparatively dry during much of the month, but the compacted roots of the plant, which together with silt constitute most of the substructure, make a relatively firm and wholly safe footing.  It is true that this part of the marsh is " springy," and one can distinctly feel the surface shake when he stamps upon it.  In trying to run levels across certain apparently firm marshes our party found it difficult, and in places impossible, to get even approximately correct results, because the ground with the instrument always tilted toward the side on which the observer was standing.  Sections through the marsh commonly show wet peat and silt a foot or two below the surface, and Townsend[21] describes the manner in which horses are trained to wear broad, wooden marsh shoes in order that they may draw mowing machines over the marsh without danger of sinking in and becoming mired.  When the tide is low the areas nearest the tidal creeks are drained most perfectly, with the result that they settle more and often give a perceptible slope of the surface toward the channels.  An interesting account of the methods of harvesting the marsh hay from the Patens zone will be found in Townsend's popular account of the marshes, cited above.  Both the Juncus zone and the Patens zone often merge into each other in a manner which makes it difficult to draw a sharp boundary between them; and the type forms of each frequently occur in abundance in the other.  Thus *Juncus gerardi* becomes an abundant constituent of the salt marsh hay.

**Glabra Zone.** — The " Glabra zone," or " Salt thatch zone " (Fig. 249), extends from near the level of ordinary high tides down to slightly below half-tide level.  The common salt thatch, *Spartina glabra*,* which requires daily submergence by the tides, is the one conspicuous species of this zone, the vertical range of

* Under the American Code of Botanical Nomenclature the name of this grass is *Spartina stricta* (Ait.) Roth., but geologists and geographers have used *Spartina glabra* for so long that I am retaining this name throughout the present work.

which on the New England coast is from four to six feet.   On
portions of Hampton Marsh, New Hampshire, a number of
measurements west of Great Boars Head showed the surface of
the Glabra zone to average only five inches lower than the Patens
zone, whereas in other localities differences of one to several feet
have been noted.  Characteristically the tall, coarse, broad-
bladed glabra forms a conspicuous but narrow fringe along the
tidal creeks, or broader zones along the outer edges of the marsh
where it faces the open water of lagoons or bays.   In one exceptional case I found it covering practically all of a broad marsh
surface, where a break in a baymouth bar near Scituate, Massachusetts (Fig. 260), had recently admitted a higher range of tides
to the North River marshes, destroying the patens association
which doubtless covered the marsh surface under former conditions, and permitting the spread of the glabra which alone could
endure the daily submergence of the new tidal régime (Fig. 262).
In time the marsh will build up to the new high tide level, and
glabra give place to patens and its associates; a process which will
be hastened if the break in the bar is closed, and the tidal range in
the North River embayment is again decreased.   Needless to say,
the Glabra zone of tidal marshes is wet and passable with difficulty, particularly as one may sink deep into the soft mud deposited when tidal currents are checked in the thick tangle of
stalks and blades.

**Mud Flat Zone and Zostera Zone.** — Below the Glabra zone is
a zone of mud flats exposed at low water, and having a vertical
range of from one to several feet.   Horizontally the barren flats
may have a great extent under favorable conditions;  and they
continue under water before the lowest zone of all, the " Eel grass "
or " Zostera zone " is encountered.   The most important plant of
this latter zone is the so-called eel grass, *Zostera marina*, the long,
narrow, ribbon-like green leaves of which may be seen bent over
in the direction of the moving tide in the bottom of tidal channels
or on continuously submerged shoals in protected bays or lagoons.
This plant grows best on a muddy bottom, requires continuous
submergence by salt water, and ceases to thrive when the bottom
is built up nearly to low tide level.   I have made no observations
on the vertical range of this zone, but according to Shaler,[22] the
eel grass begins to grow about 12 feet below low tide level.   In
Casco Bay, Maine, and Great South Bay, New York, it is found
at depths of 10 feet below low water mark.[23]   As it continues to

thrive until near the low tide level, we may estimate the usual vertical range of the Zostera zone at 10 to 12 feet, although the occurrence of eel grass at a depth of 75 feet has been reported.[24]

**Effect of Progressive Submergence.** — From the foregoing considerations relating to the present surface features of tidal marshes of the New England type, it is obvious that if similar conditions existed in the past, and a progressive submergence of the land was taking place, the substructure of the marshes should consist principally of the remains, especially roots, of vegetation belonging to the *Spartina patens* association (Figs. 252 and 253), the group which occupies the most extensive zone on the marshes, with greater or less admixtures of silt deposited by the highest tides. Occasional thicker layers of silt or sand left by the shifting of meandering tidal channels, or representing mud flats, should be encountered; but only exceptionally should one find large quantities of vegetable remains (Fig. 254) characteristic of the more limited salt thatch and eel grass zones. Traces of the black grass zone, if found at all in sections through the marsh deposit, should be at the bo⌄om of the sections where used to be the marsh margin next to the upland. The initial stage of marsh formation, showing the succession of beds figured by Shaler, would be preserved, if at all, at the very bottom of the seaward portion of the marsh. But it is obvious that if the submergence has been extensive, and the seaward portion of the deposit has been removed *pari passu* with the landward encroachment of the inner edge, all the initial portion of the marsh might long ago have been destroyed.

We have already seen that the observations of Mudge and Davis accord with the expectations outlined above; and the sections made through the Atlantic coast marshes by our party, some of which are described on later pages, add further confirmatory data.

**Effect of Dyking and Draining Tidal Marshes.** — Certain physical peculiarities of tidal marshes which are apt to escape casual observation, but which will prove important in connection with our discussion of the problem of coastal subsidence in a later volume, deserve notice. Attention has already been directed to the fact that the marsh surface, especially in the Patens zone, often bends downward toward the tidal creeks due to better subsurface drainage and greater compacting of the marsh deposits in the vicinity of such channels. This suggests the obvious conclusion that the dyking and draining of salt marshes should be followed by an appreciable lowering of the marsh surface; and consequently that one must hesitate to accept the oft-quoted argument that the relatively low level of marshes long dyked proves a recent subsidence of the coast. How compressible is the marsh peat may be judged from the fact that the retreat of the baymouth bar of gravel and cobbles near Scituate (Fig. 260) over the North River marshes in its rear, reduced 14 feet of ordinary peat and silt through which one could drive a sampler with ease, to a compact, leathery mass only 4 feet thick in which the operation of the sampler at times required the strength of two men. The density

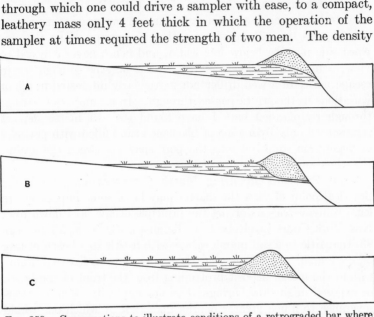

FIG. 250. Cross-sections to illustrate conditions of a retrograded bar where: (A) the weight of the bar does not of itself greatly compress the marsh deposits; (B) the weight is so great that the marsh deposit is nearly eliminated by compression and squeezing out; (C) a migrating inlet has removed the underlying marsh deposit and reconstituted the bar.

of the compressed product and the nature of the adjacent marsh indicated that true compression rather than displacement was the major factor in bringing about the change observed; and while draining alone could never cause any such reduction of thickness as was effected under the weight of the superincumbent bar, the degree of compressibility indicated is so great as to render easily understandable a lowering of a marsh surface by from one to a few feet following dyking and draining (Fig. 259).

**Consequences of Marsh Compression.** — That a thick deposit of salt marsh peat may be enormously reduced through compression and displacement due to the weight of a superincumbent sand or gravel bar retreating over the marsh on a retrograding shoreline is a matter of both theoretical and practical importance. Theoretically it is interesting to note that failure to find salt marsh sod outcropping on the seaward side of a bar or recorded in well records has sometimes been accepted as evidence of the extreme youthfulness of a shoreline and of a supposed absence of any appreciable landward migration of the bar. But a bar may retreat for miles across a salt meadow and at any stage of its retreat so compress the salt marsh peat that its outcrop along the seaward side may be below low water, and hence never exposed to view; while the thickness of the deposit may be so slight as to escape notice of a well driller not particularly interested in minor variations in the strata passed through. In a number of borings through retrograded bars I have found the salt marsh deposit represented only by a zone of blackened sand filled with particles of vegetation squeezed into the pore spaces between the grains, the whole smelling strongly of $H_2S$.

**Legal Problems Involving Marsh Compression.** — From the practical point of view the matter may be of some importance in legal controversies involving the principle of law, laid down by a New York Court (McRoberts vs Bergman, 132 N. Y. 73, at page 83) that title to a salt marsh carries with it title to a beach resting on the marsh. In such a case it is important to realize that failure to find the marsh deposit protruding from the front of the beach or exposed in shallow borings, does not imply its absence. Perseverance to much greater depths than that at which one would at first expect to find the marsh layer has been rewarded by its discovery, enormously reduced in thickness, but often preserving its characteristic appearance. It is worth while noting in this connection that the form of the cross-section of the bar under these circumstances is very unlike that usually represented in the textbook diagrams of retrograding bars, due to the fact that the rear of the bar sinks almost as effectively as its central and seaward portions. A series of more than two dozen borings through a retrograding bar (Fig. 196) involved in litigation near Oak Neck, Long Island, showed it to have the general form indicated in Fig. 250 B and Fig. 251 C. If the weight of the bar is not great, and repeated draining at low tide causes compression of the seaward edge of the marsh deposit, it may show the form represented in Fig. 250 A. Such relations have been observed shortly after a great storm has caused rapid encroachment of a small bar upon the marsh in its rear.  If there has been no retreat of the bar, or equally if the bar has retreated over the marsh but a tidal inlet has recently migrated past the position where the borings are made, the conditions shown in Fig. 250 C will be encountered. Where prograding of the bar has occurred following either condition outlined in the last sentence, the relations will be those diagrammatically portrayed in Fig. 251 B.

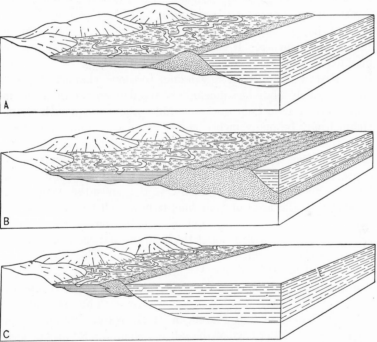

FIG. 251.  A. Initial stage of bar and marsh formation.  B. Conditions observed where the bar has been prograded.  C. Conditions observed where retrograding has carried the bar back upon the marsh.

**Natural Levees Bordering Tidal Creeks.** — If the tidal waters carry a heavy load of sediment, the banks of tidal creeks may be built higher than the adjacent marsh, after the manner of natural levee formation along an ordinary river.  The waters drop a larger proportion of their load where first checked as they begin to spread from the creek channel out over the marsh surface. This is the reverse of the condition described above, and should most often be observed in those marshes built in the presence of much sediment.  No doubt this is the reason this phenomenon is more frequently reported in connection with the second type of salt marsh, to be described below.

**Natural Levees Bordering the Sea.** — It sometimes happens that the portion of a salt marsh nearest open water is higher than that bordering the upland.  This is due in part to more abundant deposition of sediment where the marine waters have easier and more direct access to the marsh, and where fine material is blown upon the marsh from sandy beaches.  But I believe another factor is often of equal or greater importance.  Much emphasis is laid on the fact that the tide often rises higher near the head of an estuary than in the open sea.  It is less widely recognized that the reverse may likewise be true.  Where the tides are " damped down " in a long, narrow channel, in a winding, tortuous channel, or in a channel which subdivides indefinitely and delivers the tidal waters over a broad area, high tide some miles above the mouth of the channel may be many inches, sometimes even a number of feet, *lower* than high tide in the ocean.  This phenomenon, which has an importance in connection with the problem of coastal subsidence not generally realized, will be discussed more fully in a later volume.  Here we should observe that since the tidal marsh builds up to the level of high tide, it may well happen that the marsh nearest the upland, controlled in its development by a relatively low high tide level at the head of tidal channels, will be lower than the marsh surface nearer the sea.  This condition is encountered in some of our Atlantic coast marshes, and I have seen farmers mowing grass from the outer portions of a marsh, the inner portions of which were too wet for such an operation.

**Encroachment of Salt Marsh on Fresh Water Swamps.** — In some cases the inner edge of the salt marsh grades into a brackish water or fresh swamp or bog, and this whether the inner edge be low or high; for a fresh water swamp may rise gradually inland to an elevation a number ·of feet above the neighboring marsh level.

If, as there is every reason to believe, the salt marshes were in times past frequently bordered by fresh water swamps along their inner margins, progressive submergence due to a subsidence of the land or to a rise of sealevel must cause the fresh swamp deposits to encroach upon the upland, and the salt marsh deposits in turn to encroach upon those of fresh water origin.  Sections through the salt marshes should then show salt marsh peat overlying fresh peat, beneath which the upland surface would be encountered, possibly mantled by clay or sand early accumulated in the swamp area.

Where swamps or ponds occupy depressions near the upland border, and waves remove the seaward portion of the salt marsh, it is obvious that salt marsh conditions may be shifted landward, and that salt marsh deposits may come to rest upon low-lying swamp or bog deposits near the upland, without any relative change in the general level of land or sea. Such conditions would give rise to a fictitious appearance of recent coastal subsidence.

## Descriptions of Tidal Marshes of the New England Type

The following account of some tidal marshes of the New England type, based in part on the work of Dr. G. B. Reed, the member of our party especially charged with investigating the salt marshes, will give the reader a fair idea of the range of variability in the character of the marsh deposits. Dr. Reed was at the time in the service of the United States Bureau of Mines, working under the direction of Dr. C. A. Davis by virtue of a coöperative arrangement between that Bureau and the Second Shaler Memorial Investigation. The identifications of the salt marsh and other plant remains are mainly those made in the field, but are believed to be substantially correct. During part of the field work Dr. Reed was accompanied by Dr. Davis, and in addition to his own botanical training was able to profit by that expert's special knowledge of salt and fresh marsh peat deposits. Dr. Reed's report on his studies was awarded a Walker Memorial Prize by the Boston Society of Natural History in 1912.

**Marshes of Southern Long Island.** — On the southern side of Long Island, where physiographic conditions cause the shoreline to be classed and treated with the coastal plain shoreline to the south, the marshes fringing the lagoons back of the offshore bar appear to belong to the New England type. The encroachment of the salt marsh upon the fresh marsh is shown by a section at Swan Island, back of the bar separating Moriches Bay from the ocean, where 3 feet of *Spartina patens* peat is found overlying peat of brackish to fresh water origin. At the inner edge of the bay are marshes in which the salt vegetation gives place gradually to brackish and fresh water forms, with much broad-leaved cattail, especially in drowned valleys like that just east of Patchogue.

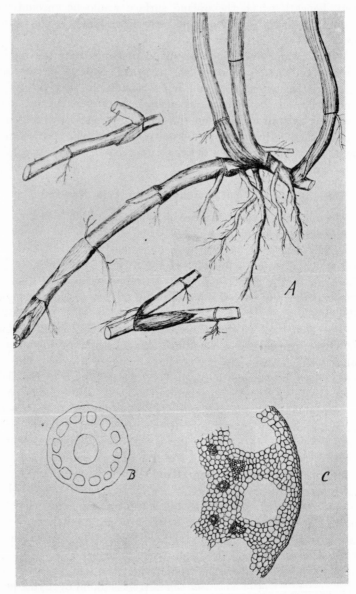

FIG. 252. *Spartina patens* remains, showing characters useful in identifying salt marsh deposits. *A*. Culm bases, rhizomes and roots, × 2½. *B*. Diagram cross-section of rhizome, × 14. *C*. Cross-section of rhizome, × 40. Drawn by G. B. Reed.

About Shinnecock Bay are good examples of submerged stumps of upland trees, especially in Tiana Bay where the covering of salt marsh peat is but a few inches thick, and overlies a layer of fresh peat filled with root stocks of sedges, woody bits of shrubs, and fragments of wood.

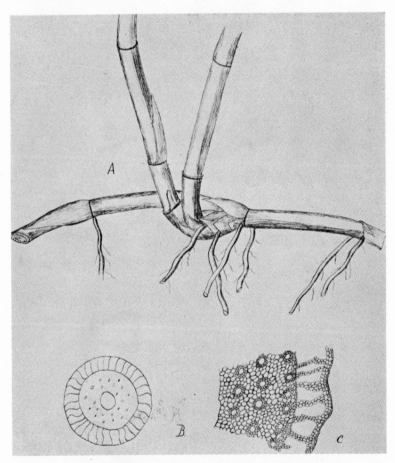

FIG. 253.   *Distichlis spicata* remains.   *A*. Culm bases, rhizomes and roots, × 2½.   *B*. Diagram cross-section of rhizome, × 14.   *C*. Cross-section of rhizome, × 40.   Drawn by G. B. Reed.

**Peconic Bay Region, Long Island.** — At the head of Peconic Bay the Flanders marshes are more closely akin to the typical New England marshes in their physiographic relationships, occupying the lower parts of submerged valleys unassociated with

an offshore bar. Near Flanders, on Reeves Bay, the seaward
edge of the marsh shows 3½ to 4 feet of peat composed for the

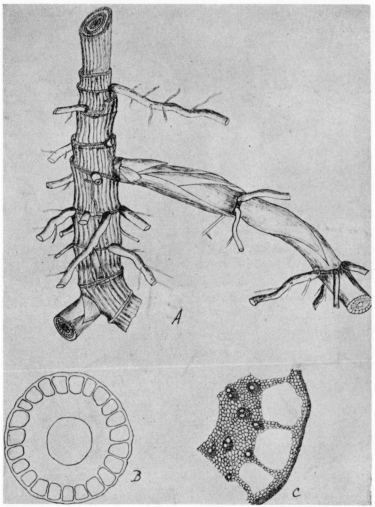

Fig. 254. *Spartina glabra* remains. *A.* Culm bases, rhizomes and roots,
× 1½. *B.* Diagram cross-section of rhizome as seen with a hand lens,
× 7. *C.* Cross-section of rhizome, × 14. Drawn by G. B. Reed.

most part of *Spartina patens* and *Distichlis spicata* remains (Figs.
252 and 253) resting upon a fresh water peat bed 10 to 12 feet
in thickness. Toward the upland the stratum of salt peat grad-

ually thins out, and the fresh peat reaches and forms the surface in places along the inner border of the marsh (Fig. 255 A). Just outside of Flanders Bay, east of Red Cedar Point, where a small bar between retreating headlands has been driven back over marsh deposits, a section reveals 3 feet of *Spartina patens* peat overlying 2 feet of clay with *Spartina glabra* remains (Fig. 254). This suggests local marsh development according to the Shaler theory; but the thickness of the *patens* peat and the fact that, farther in, the salt marsh deposits are found to rest upon a layer of brackish or fresh water peat one foot thick, shows that the deposit was in large part formed during progressive submergence. Stumps of upland trees are found in the landward portions both of this marsh and of those bordering the northern side of Flanders Bay, where dead trees still standing indicate a recent encroachment of the salt water upon the upland. In this latter locality salt peat, consisting in part at least of *Spartina patens* roots and varying in thickness from 1 or 2 feet up to 7 feet, overlies sandy bottom in some places, but in others a deposit of brackish to fresh water peat having a maximum measured thickness of 9 feet.

**Marshes of Nantucket Island and Marthas Vineyard.** — On Nantucket Island the marshes of Polpis Harbor, on the east side opposite Quaise Point, show on their outer margin, in the Glabra zone, 3 feet of *Spartina glabra* remains with some *patens* remains in the lower foot, overlying a layer of brackish to fresh water peat 1 foot thick. Such a succession may record a normal advance of salt marsh upon a progressively submerged coast, the fresh swamp encroaching higher and higher upon the upland, the Patens zone in its turn encroaching upon the fresh swamp deposit, and finally the Glabra zone encroaching upon the patens deposit. Or it may record a local pronounced rise of the high tide surface due to shoreline changes, the flooding causing a patens marsh overlying a fresh swamp to change to a glabra marsh, as in the case of the North River marshes cited below. Nearer the upland border 8 inches of patens peat overlies 3 feet of fresh peat, while farther inland the salt marsh grades into brackish and fresh swamp on the surface, with cattails, *Scirpus robustus*, and other forms in the transition zone. The conditions appear to be those indicated diagrammatically in Fig. 255 B. In the western branch of the harbor a section in the midst of the salt marsh showed 2 feet of *Spartina patens* peat, followed by 2 feet of the same mixed with *Scirpus* root stocks, below which came 6 feet of black fresh

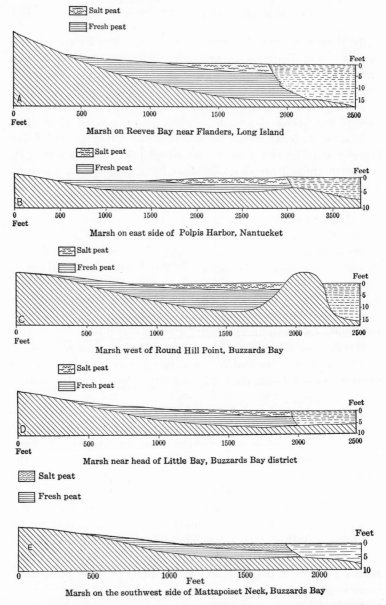

Fig. 255. Diagrammatic cross-sections showing structure of New England salt marshes as indicated by peat-sampler sections through the deposits. Coastal subsidence accompanied by progressive upbuilding of fresh swamp and salt marsh deposits permitted fresh peat to encroach upon the upland, and salt peat in turn to encroach upon the fresh peat. Typically each deposit is a landward thinning wedge, but locally there are important exceptions, especially where the fresh peat fills depressions in the upland surface. (538)

peat with roots of shrubs, pieces of wood and other fresh water material.  On Marthas Vineyard the marsh border of Sengekontacket Pond usually showed 6 to 8 inches of *Spartina patens* peat above 2 to 3 feet of brackish or fresh water peat; but near the outer border Dr. Reed reports 2 to 4 inches of *Spartina glabra* remains overlying 6 to 8 inches of *Spartina patens* peat, with fresh peat below in most cases.

**Marshes Bordering Buzzards Bay.** — The shores of Buzzards Bay show many small marshes of the New England type.  Just west of Round Hill Point, a few miles south of New Bedford, one of these, separated from the sea by a bar (Fig. 255 C), showed 2 feet of *Spartina patens* peat over 1 foot of black fresh peat not far from the inner edge of the salt marsh, while out in the central area the salt peat had increased to 3 feet, and the underlying fresh peat to 5 feet in thickness.  Landward the salt marsh deposits thin out and the salt marsh surface grasses give place to a fresh swamp.  About the head of Apponagansett River a thickness of 2 feet of *Spartina patens* peat was found over 1 to 2 feet of fresh peat, with a few inches of *Spartina glabra* above the *patens* peat in places.  Recent encroachment of salt water upon the forest is shown by the presence of stumps in the marsh, and dead and dying trees along its inner border.  Similar encroachment is shown along the inner border of a marsh east of Fort Point, Fairhaven, while at the outer edge *glabra* and *patens* peat have a combined thickness of 3 feet, with 4 feet of black fresh peat below.  The seaward edge of the marsh about the head of Little Bay shows 3 feet of *Spartina patens* and *Distichlis spicata* peat above 2 feet of fresh plant remains; but the salt peat thins out toward the upland, and in places along the inner border the fresh peat shows at the surface (Fig. 255 D).  Similar conditions were found on the southwest side of Mattapoiset Neck (Fig. 255 E), where recent encroachment of salt marsh on fresh swamp was attested by a dead tree fringe at the contact.  About Pine Neck Cove the border of the forest is fringed with dead trees, while out in the marsh 2 feet of *Spartina patens* peat overlie 1 to 2 feet of brackish or fresh peat.  In the Sippican Harbor region the outer edge of the marsh shows 3 feet of salt peat, most of it *glabra* with much blue clay, over a few inches of *patens* and brackish water plant remains, with 1 foot of black fresh peat below; while landward the salt peat was thinner, and at the head of the harbor many stumps were observed surrounded by grasses of the Patens and Juncus zones.

As an example of what is believed to be a fresh water bog deposit encroached upon by salt marsh we may cite the following section near the head of Johnsons Creek, a tributary of Wareham River: 3 feet of *Spartina glabra* peat at the surface, followed in descending order by 1 foot of brackish water plant remains including *Eleocharis rostellata*, 8 feet of reddish to black fresh peat, 4 feet of brown peaty soil, and 4 feet of blue silty clay. Near the mouth of the creek 1 to 2 feet of *Spartina patens* peat overlies 4 to 6 feet of black, peaty soil containing brackish water plant remains, below which a thin layer of sand covers an old soil bed containing roots of trees. Sections through the marshes at the head of Back River and at North Pocasset show fresh water pond deposits at the base, a typical section near the outer edge of the marsh at the first locality being as follows, from above downward: 5 feet of *Spartina patens* peat, 9 feet of black fresh peat, 7 feet of distinctive pond-formed material. As much as 6 feet of salt peat overlies fresh peat in the marsh back of the bar just east of Nyes Neck. On the shore of Quamquisset Harbor, near Woods Hole, the sea has cut into and the salt marsh encroached upon a depression in which had accumulated 12 to 14 feet of fresh peat containing logs and branches of trees, and the upper part of which at least contains stumps *in situ*. This deposit has been described by Bartlett[25] in an interesting paper which will engage our attention when we come to discuss the problem of coastal subsidence.

**Green Harbor Marsh, Massachusetts.** — Northward along the eastern coast of New England the evidence of a gradual encroachment of salt marsh upon the upland with its peat bogs and its bordering fresh swamps is equally impressive. The region of Green Harbor marsh (Figs. 256 and 257), Massachusetts, is particularly interesting both because of the fact that the inlet connecting the marsh with the sea has been opened and closed repeatedly in the past, both by artificial and natural means; and because of the work done in reclaiming the marsh from the domain of salt water. On the northeast the marsh (Fig. 257) is separated from the ocean by a continuous, low, narrow baymouth bar (not shown on the topographic quadrangle covering the region), while the opening southeastward into the Duxbury Harbor region is blocked by an artificial dyke.

As the Green Harbor marsh was long regarded as the best case of improved salt meadow in New England, it received much attention from engineers, geologists, and others interested in marsh reclamation. The Harbor Commissioners and Board of Health of Massachusetts investigated it, while Shaler[26] in reporting on the " Seacoast Swamps of the Eastern United States," and Mitchell[27] in discussing the " Reclamation of Tide Lands," devoted some space to the locality. From old records cited in a joint report by the Harbor Commissioners and the Board of Health it would appear that the opening toward the southeast

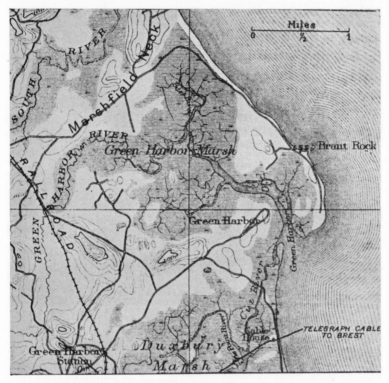

Fig. 256. Green Harbor marsh, Massachusetts. From U. S. G. S. Topographic Atlas, Duxbury quadrangle (slightly modified).

was nearly or quite closed in the early part of the 17th century, for there is evidence that the marsh was not wholly salt then, and about 1633 it was ordered that a cut should be made through to Duxbury Harbor. During the next two centuries the marshes were now salt, now fresh, with shifting inlets opening and closing alternately, the connection with Duxbury Harbor for part of the time being more than half a mile south of the main opening shown on the map.

*Fictitious Indications of Coastal Subsidence.* — Early in the nineteenth century the inlets were closed and the marshes laked for considerable periods, despite efforts to open a canal through to Duxbury; and it is reported that in 1811 during a storm the fishermen cut a new opening in order that they might get their boats into Green Harbor.   This opening widened to a broad inlet, the location being approximately that shown on the map today; and the tidal range increased on the marshes to such an extent that the bordering forests were invaded by salt water and the trees killed.   Thus originated the " stump meadow " of this locality, where we have a typical example of submerged stumps

FIG. 257.   Green Harbor salt marsh, Massachusetts, showing houses on bar which separates marsh from the ocean.

in the marsh, a phenomenon confidently attributed to modern coastal subsidence by many observers.   The killing of trees by a local rise of the high tide surface, induced in this case artificially, and the similar phenomenon produced around the North River marshes a few miles distant by a local rise of the high tide surface in that embayment following a breach in the barrier beach effected naturally by the Portland Storm of 1898, illustrate one of the commonest causes of fictitious indications of modern coastal subsidence.   Here we need only note that, pending a fuller discussion of the problem of coastal subsidence to be presented in a companion volume to the present work, the reader who peruses the brief descriptions of tidal marshes on these pages should not fall into the too common error of confusing evidence which clearly demonstrates a general subsidence of the land or rise of sealevel at some unknown time in the past, with evidence which merely indicates a local encroachment of salt water or salt marsh in modern time.

The building of a dyke across the opening into Green Harbor marsh in 1872 permitted reclamation of the area.    At the time of my visit the contrast between the wild salt marsh and the reclaimed land was very striking (Figs. 257 and 258).    I made two borings through the deposits, one outside and the other inside the dyke, and these are here presented in tabular form for comparison

Fig. 258.    Reclaimed portion of Green Harbor salt marsh, showing fresh water vegetation.

(Fig. 259).    As is usual in such cases, the surface within the dyked land is somewhat lower than outside, from 1 to 3 feet in the present instance.    That the discrepancy is due to settling of the reclaimed land following dyking and draining, rather than to continued building up of the marsh outside of the dyke while the inner, protected land was carried downward by continued coastal subsidence in modern times, as some would believe, is indicated by a correlation of the successive layers of deposits in the two sections.    As shown in Fig. 259, such a correlation demonstrates pretty clearly that the difference does not consist in the presence of an extra layer of deposits at the top of the outside section, but in a proportional reduction of the whole series from top to bottom

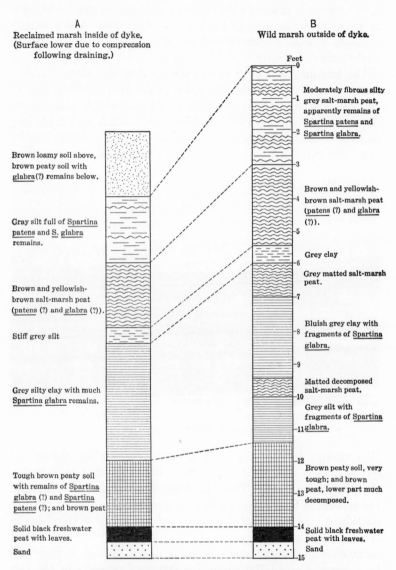

FIG. 259.   Sections through Green Harbor marsh, Massachusetts.
A. Reclaimed marsh.   B. Wild marsh.

within the dyked area.   If the brown loamy soil at the top of the
inner section (A) represents stream or tidal silts deposited on the
reclaimed marsh at times of flooding, the latter rather than the wild
marsh has received an additional layer of material, and the total
compression of the former salt marsh deposits amounts to nearly
4 feet.   The thin layer of fresh peat at the bottom of the sections
near the dyke, is represented in one place near the western upland by
a much thicker deposit containing prostrate logs but no stumps in
place, according to the testimony of one of the residents who made
an excavation 15 feet deep through the marsh muck and mud.

**North River Marshes, Massachusetts.** — The North River
marshes, a few miles farther up the coast, are separated from the
sea by a long, narrow baymouth bar which prior to 1898 connected the drumloidal hills of till resting on older deposits at
Third Cliff (Fig. 260 A), with the similar hill of Trouant Island,
and extended far south toward the next headland from which it
was separated by a narrow inlet.   Like the Green Harbor marshes,
those of North River have had a checkered history, due to repeated fluctuations of the tidal range consequent upon changes
in the protecting bar and inlets.   Some of these changes have
been described by Mitchell;[28]  but since his time they have apparently been even more striking.

*Fictitious Indications of Coastal Subsidence.* — The Portland
Storm of 1898 opened a wide breach through the bar north of
Trouant Island (Fig. 261), and subsequently the remaining part of
the bar, consisting largely of gravel, cobblestones and large boulders,
was driven some distance in over the marsh.   The weight of the
great mass of boulders, and the removal of fine material from the
marsh deposits due to draining of the exposed seaward margin at
low tide, caused a remarkable compression of the original strata, 14
feet of typical marsh material with *Spartina patens* remains abundant in the upper portion, being reduced to less than one-third
that thickness where it protruded at low water from under the seaward edge of the retrograding bar, thus reproducing another
fictitious appearance of coastal subsidence.   The increased range of
the tides resulting from freer connection with the ocean (Fig. 260 B)
favored the growth of *Spartina glabra*, where grasses of the Patens
and Juncus zones had formerly grown, and caused a salt water
invasion into the bordering forest; and at the time of my visit
the area was almost wholly a *glabra* marsh, bordered by a fringe
of dead trees (Fig. 262).

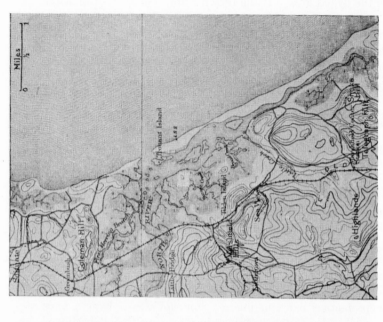

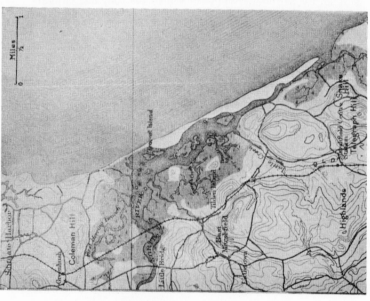

Fig. 260.   The North River embayment near Scituate, Massachusetts, before and after the breach in the baymouth bar during the "Portland Storm" in 1898 which permitted an increased range of tides in the bay, killing the marginal forests, overflowing dykes, transforming the marsh vegetation, and producing other phenomena commonly attributed to coastal subsidence. From successive editions of the Duxbury quadrangle, U. S. G. S. Topographic Atlas.

FIG. 261.   In the foreground, Third Cliff near Scituate, Massachusetts, undergoing rapid marine erosion.   In centre distance the low hill of Trouant Island, and just this side of it the breach in the bar effected by the Portland Storm of 1898.

FIG. 262. Trees bordering the North River marshes, Massachusetts, killed by a local rise of the high tide level due to shoreline changes effected by the Portland Storm of 1898. The surface of the marsh is chiefly covered by *Spartina glabra*, another indication of the recency of the new tidal régime.

**Mill Cove Marsh, Massachusetts.** — In the Boston Harbor region numerous marshes offer valuable opportunities for study. One of my former students, Mr. N. J. Bond, made detailed cross-sections of some of these; and Fig. 263 reproduces in graphic form the results of 9 of his borings (with the peat sampler), for the most part at intervals of 20 to 30 paces, beginning at the upland on the north side of the Mill Cove marsh, Weymouth Fore River, and extending southward to the deep central portion of the marsh. Typical specimens from a number of the borings were submitted to Dr. C. A. Davis, and the plant and other remains identified by him. In general the sections show from 6 to 9 feet of *Spartina patens* peat, grading downward into a mixture of clay and remains of salt marsh grasses, with pure clay below, thickest in the deeper sections. At the bottom there is usually found a thin layer of black, fresh water peat, or black peaty clay or sand, resting on sand, gravel or bedrock, and quite surely representing brackish or fresh swamp deposits next to the upland, or upland forest soil, encroached upon by the rising marsh deposit. In the section 30 paces out from the marsh border a thin layer of clayey peat at a depth of 9 feet is followed by several feet of dark brown peat, partly soft, partly compact, containing some roots of *Spartina patens* associated with foraminifera and diatoms, the whole possibly representing a transition from fresh or brackish water swamp to salt marsh. An east-west series of borings by the writer gave similar results, from 7 to 8 feet of typical *Spartina patens* peat being found overlying a layer, usually thin, of brackish or fresh water peat, sometimes containing fragments of wood and resting on sandy or gravelly bottom. As these borings were all nearer the upland, and the greatest depth reached was 9 feet, the silty clay appeared to a small extent only in one of them.

**Neponset River Marshes, Massachusetts.** — The Neponset River marshes, developed on a larger scale than those at Mill Cove, seemed to the writer well suited to a more thorough examination than had seemed necessary in the case of the marshes previously mentioned, and a series of cross-sections of the deposit was accordingly planned in such manner as best to develop the facts of its internal structure (Fig. 264). The borings were executed by Mr. Bond under my general direction, and I am much indebted to him for the care and ability with which he performed the task and recorded his findings. Dr. C. A. Davis, who throughout this whole investigation spared no pains to aid in

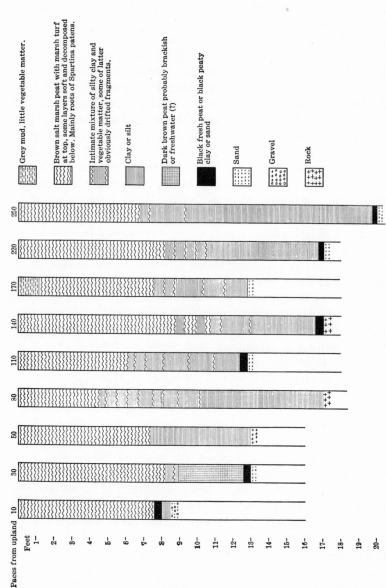

FIG. 263. Successive sections from north to south across small salt marsh on east side of Mill Cove, Weymouth Fore River, Massachusetts. Numbers at tops of sections show distance of each (in paces) from north side of marsh, where it borders southwest side of Mill Cove Neck.

every possible way, generously examined more than two hundred
samples from Mr. Bond's borings, and reported at length upon
them.   The results of the work were thus effectively checked by
the most competent authority on salt marsh peat deposits, and
the comments appended to the graphic sections are largely from
Dr. Davis' notes; while the sections themselves are based on
Mr. Bond's excellent report.

Near the head of the marsh a short section (Fig. 264, AB) across
a small tributary valley shows from 3 to 6 feet of *Spartina patens*

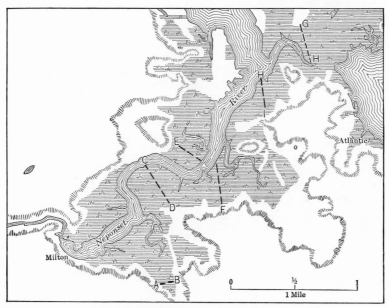

Fig. 264.   The Neponset River marshes, Boston Harbor, showing location
of cross-sections described in the text.

remains, overlying 2 to 4 feet of brown to black brackish or fresh
water peat resting on a sandy bottom.   Just above the bottom a
variable amount of silt or clay is found associated with the peat.
Eighteen borings here showed such similarity of structure in the
deposit that no detailed section is presented.   The maximum
depth recorded was 9 feet.

Farther down the river, where it impinges on the northern wall
of the valley and the whole breadth of the marsh is on the south
side of the stream, a section (CD, Figs. 264 and 265) shows somewhat greater variation in the character of the deposit.   Over the

FIG. 265. Sections through the Neponset River marshes, Boston Harbor region, based on peat-sampler cores. Locations of sections are shown on Fig. 264.

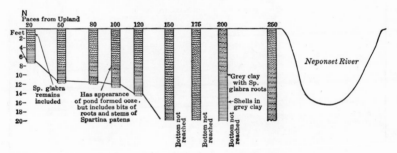

Section EF. (Continued on opposite page.)

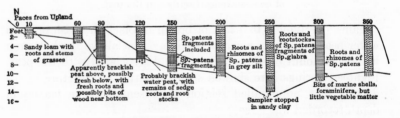

Section GH. (Continued in HI.)

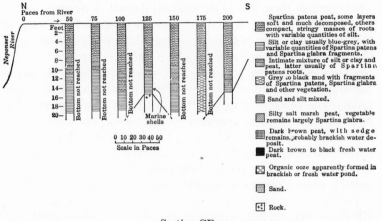

Section CD.

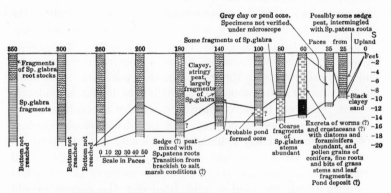

Section EF.    (Continued from opposite page.)

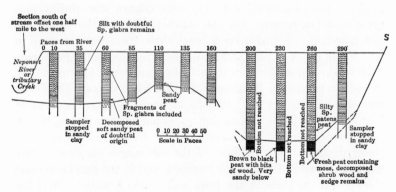

Section HI.    (Continued from GH.)

whole surface there is a fairly uniform deposit of *Spartina patens* peat from 8 to 10 feet thick; but near the river the succeeding 10 feet in depth consist of fairly pure greyish blue silt or clay, quite plastic, with scattered remains of salt grasses, while nearer the southern upland grey to black mud, chiefly organic, is found in the lower 8 feet, and next to the upland a somewhat plastic silty sand. The marsh is deep, only two out of seven borings reaching bottom. One of these appeared to be bedrock, but might represent a boulder of the glacial drift. In any case it is clear that the depression occupied by the marsh is subdivided, and that the mud and silty sand occupy the landward side of the hollow nearest the upland, while a purer silt came in from the river side.

Downstream to the east, near the middle of the marsh, Section EF (Figs. 264 and 265) runs from the northern upland southeastward to the river, thence nearly southward to the southern upland. The marsh here occupies a somewhat unsymmetrical valley, the deeper portion of which lies nearer the northern wall, and more than 20 feet below high tide level. In general the *Spartina patens* deposit is wedge shaped, thinnest toward the valley walls, and deepening toward the main channel until the remarkable thickness of 20 feet or more of this high tide deposit is evidently present. Nearest the river, however, a large proportion of the total thickness consists of grey clay or silt in which *Spartina glabra* remains are fairly abundant. This may in part record the erosion of a previous *patens* deposit by the meandering tidal stream with concurrent deposition (on the inside of the meander) of silt to which the Glabra zone bordering the channel would naturally contribute no little vegetable material; and in part the normal upward growth of a very silty Glabra zone during progressive submergence. On the southern side of the valley the salt marsh encroached upon a brackish to fresh water swamp in which 4 to 6 feet of peat had locally accumulated, and also apparently upon a pond-formed deposit of organic ooze approximately 10 feet in maximum thickness. In this latter deposit Dr. Davis records the presence of " excreta of worms and crustaceans in large amount, diatoms, foraminifera, conifer pollen grains, bits of tree leaves, etc." The transition zone from fresh or brackish water deposits below to those of the salt marsh above is clearly marked in two or three of the borings; and in the graphic section the general thickness of the fresh and brackish water material is included between lines drawn through the top and bottom of these

deposits in the several sections.   There is some suggestion of a
pond-formed deposit at one point on the north side of the valley;
but the evidence here was more doubtful, and in general the salt
marsh deposits seem to rest directly upon the sandy valley wall,
the lower layers of the marsh silt having incorporated some of the
sand.   *Spartina glabra* fragments and roots are often abundant
in the silt, and are found in the *Spartina patens* peat; but only in
one case did the deposit seem to justify the name *Spartina glabra*
peat.   This was a deposit one or two feet thick found about 8 feet
down in the boring located 140 paces out from the southern upland, the sample being described by Dr. Davis as consisting
" chiefly of fragments of *Spartina glabra* loosely held together and
not much decomposed."

Near the seaward end of the marsh is located the section GHI
(Figs. 264 and 265), which is a combination of two sections, one
of which, GH, extends from the northern upland (here rising as an
island out of the marsh) southward to a tidal stream tributary
to the Neponset River, while the second, HI, begins on the south
bank of the river half a mile farther west, and continues southward to the southern upland.   In both cases the stream is found
to be located over a shallow portion of the submerged valley, and
the marsh is much deeper some distance back from the stream
bank.   The wedge-like form of the encroaching *Spartina patens*
deposit is best shown on the north, where it thickens from practically nothing near the upland to 11 feet in the deepest channel,
the full depth of which was not determined.   Beneath the wedge
is a deposit of dark brown to black brackish or fresh water peat
containing remains of sedge roots and root stocks, and possibly
bits of wood, having a maximum measured thickness of nearly
7 feet and resting on sandy or rock bottom.   The fact that next to
the stream the deposit consists of *Spartina patens* peat from top
to bottom, whereas fifty paces back light grey silt is found from
top to bottom, may simply indicate that in its meanderings the
stream cut into the *patens* deposit at the latter point and not at
the former; for here the section parallels one of the stream mean-
ders.   South of the Neponset the marsh shallows to a depth of
only 7 feet at a distance of 110 paces back from the river bank,
then drops down to a depth of more than 20 feet, three soundings
failing to reach bottom at 21 feet.   In all three *Spartina patens*
peat is present to a depth of 19 feet, mixed with much silt in the
lower part in two cases, but fairly pure throughout in the third.

At the bottom, as shown by these deepest borings, the depression contained an unknown thickness of black fresh water peat containing moss, remains of shrubs and sedges, and decayed wood.

*Evolution of the Neponset Marshes.* — With these sections before us it is not difficult to picture the history of the marsh growth. When the sealevel was 20 feet or more lower than now, and the salt marsh of that time lay not only lower but farther to the east where now is the floor of Boston Harbor, the Neponset River and its tributaries flowed through small valleys cut mainly in glacial débris to enter the marshes somewhere northeast of the present mouth of the river. Bordering the streams there were often brackish water swamps near the sea, and fresh swamps farther in, while elsewhere forested uplands came down to the water. Here and there ponds, possibly occupying blocked valleys or kettleholes in glacial débris, lay close to the stream channels. In other words, conditions then were much as today, except that the similar topography was then lower and farther seaward because of the lower position of sealevel.

Gradually the land sank or the sealevel rose, perhaps the latter as a result of deglaciation's returning to the sea the water long locked up in land ice. Slowly the salt marsh built upward to the ever-rising high tide level, and reached farther and farther up the river valleys. The landward encroachment of the salt marsh caused a similar migration inland of brackish and fresh water swamps; for salt water now began to reach swamps formerly fresh, and the fresh water farther in became stagnant where formerly there was effective drainage. Thus progressively the fresh swamps so common in the lower parts of stream valleys migrated upstream, and encroached more and more on the flanks of the bordering uplands; brackish water swamps in turn encroached upon the fresh, until brackish peat came to overlie fresh water peat; and finally came the salt marsh, depositing its layers of silt and salt peat upon the brackish water remains. Not finally, either; for let us not forget that back of all came the relentless ocean, driving beaches in upon the marshes, cutting away the exposed margin of the deposit, and slowly but surely destroying the older, deeper, seaward portion of the record.

Along the deeper axes of the valleys the salt marsh must arrive first, and there accordingly we find the greatest thickness of the gradually upbuilt salt marsh peat. There too is most frequently encountered a bottom layer of fresh or brackish water peat, for swamps are more common in valley bottoms than along upland slopes. Higher up on the valley walls and at the valley head the salt marsh deposit thins out, only the last part of the formation being represented where the salt marsh level last arrived. Where salt marsh encroached upon dry upland, no fresh or brackish peat is discovered at the bottom of the borings. Where it invaded a pond, the pond deposits remain to tell the story, whether it be the history of a kettlehole pond in the initial glacial débris surface, or of a pond formed by blocked drainage as swamp or marsh deposits built upward to new levels.

That the progressive submergence was gradual is shown by the fact, first noted by Mudge[10] for the Lynn marshes, that *Spartina patens* peat formed largely of roots *in situ*, is found in some of the sections from top to bottom. No matter how variable the deposits may be elsewhere, due to various events in the history of deposition, some of which we have already discussed, the fact that the high-tide grass, *Spartina patens*, could anywhere form a continuous deposit of its roots in place from the bottom upward, is sufficient proof that at no period was the general submergence rapid enough to destroy the growth and initiate a new and different cycle of marsh formation. One is tempted to say that the submergence was continuous: but here one begins to tread on ground less solid than that of the marshes themselves.

The abundance of submerged stumps and the fringes of dead trees urge one to the seemingly logical conclusion that the progressive submergence is still in progress. But here again the critical student will test the ground carefully before he takes his stand upon it. Not until all the elements of the problem are clearly before us will it be safe to draw far reaching conclusions as to the nature and duration of the submergence which gave to our salt marshes their present structure. This task awaits us in a later volume.

**Other New England Marshes.** — Borings made by the writer in the Mystic River marshes (Fig. 249) and the marshes near Lynn, show for these areas a history of development similar to that sketched above. The Mystic marshes provide excellent examples of stumps submerged in the marsh deposits, while those near Lynn are especially noteworthy as the scene of the observations which led Mudge to his discovery of the method of salt marsh formation which seems best to account for all of the observed facts.[10] West of the Plum Island bar (Fig. 241) borings across the Plum Island marshes, executed by Mr. Bond, usually showed from 1 to 5 feet of *Spartina patens* peat resting on a few feet of sandy clay; but in one boring 9 feet of sandy peat and peaty sand of marine origin was passed through. The deepest boring showed 5 feet of sandy *patens* peat, 3 feet of silty *patens* peat, and 3 feet of mud containing organic matter, resting on a sandy bottom. A number of the borings near a small knoll rising from the marsh surface, or near the gently sloping upland at the west, showed at the bottom black peaty sand, sometimes containing wood fragments. The effect of sand blown from the dunes upon the marsh deposit was shown in the extremely sandy nature of the material encountered in those soundings nearest the dune-covered bar. Near Portland, Maine, are several small marshes discussed at some length by Penhallow,[17] of which the Brave Boat Harbor marsh and the one next south are described as bogs occupying basins in the rocky upland invaded by the sea when coastal subsidence brought them low enough. I was unable to verify the depth of 30 or 40 feet reported by Penhallow for the fresh peat deposit, borings at the localities specified by him being in every case stopped at a depth of 10 to 14 feet by what appeared to be firm, sandy bottom. Pilings for the trolley track crossing the bog are driven deeply into the peat and underlying sand, and while some of the local residents calculated the depth of the bog from the length of the pilings, others informed me that these were driven for the most part in sand. Good examples of submerged stumps surrounded by salt marsh are found on the surface of the Brave Boat Harbor marsh. Studies of the salt marsh peat deposits of Maine by Bastin and Davis[29] show that the New England type of deposit is well represented along that part of the coast. Soundings by the writer in other marshes near Marblehead, Magnolia, Rye, Ragged Neck, Nahant, Barnstable, Truro, Centreville, and at many other points on the New England coast developed no points essentially novel, but served to give added confirmation of the correctness of that theory of salt marsh development which has as its most vital element a gradual submergence of the coast at some period in post-glacial time.

**Résumé.** — It has appeared in the course of the present chapter that the literature of tidal marshes presents three theories of origin for these marshes which deserve special consideration. The theories of Mudge and Dawson involve a subsidence of the marsh deposit *pari passu* with its development, whereas the theory of Shaler is applicable to a stationary coast. One may distinguish three types of tidal marshes along the Atlantic coast: the New England type, the Fundy type, and the Coastal Plain type. The first of these alone has received our attention thus far. The zonal surface arrangement of the marsh vegetation has been described, and the effects of progressive submergence of such a zonal marsh explained. It has been shown that the dyking and draining of tidal marshes, the compression of marsh deposits under encroaching beaches or bars, the invasion of marsh or swamp areas occupying low belts back of natural levees bordering tidal creeks or the open sea, increase of the tidal range following changes in the form of the coast, and other causes, frequently give rise to fictitious appearances of modern coastal subsidence. A detailed examination of marshes of the New England type from Long Island to Maine shows that such fictitious indications of changes of level are associated with reliable evidences of a progressive submergence of the coast at an epoch which was more remote, although certainly post-glacial. It appears that Mudge's theory of marsh formation best explains the development of the New England type of marsh, although the element of submergence is equally involved in Dawson's theory for the origin of a different type found in the region of the Bay of Fundy. Failure to discriminate carefully between fictitious appearances of modern subsidence, and real evidence of a more ancient submergence, has led to a widespread misapprehension as to recent changes of level along the Atlantic coast, which it will be our purpose to study more fully in a later volume.

## BIBLIOGRAPHY

1. DAWSON, J. W. "Acadian Geology," 2nd Ed., 687 pp., London, 1868.
2. SHALER, N. S. "Preliminary Report on Sea-Coast Swamps of the Eastern United States." U. S. Geol. Surv., 6th Ann. Rept., 364, 1886.
   SHALER, N. S. "The Geological History of Harbors." U. S. Geol. Surv., 13th Ann. Rept., Pt. 2, 148–152, 1893.
   SHALER, N. S. "The Origin and Nature of Soils." U. S. Geol. Surv., 12th Ann. Rept., Pt. 1, 317–320, 1891.
   SHALER, N. S. "Beaches and Tidal Marshes of the Atlantic Coast." Nat. Geog. Mon. I, 157–159, 1896.
3. LYELL, CHARLES. "Travels in North America," II, 166, London, 1855.
4. MONRO, ALEX. "On the Physical Features and Geology of Chignecto Isthmus." Nat. Hist. Soc. New Brunswick, Bull., I, No. V, 20–24,

1886. Also a series of 9 newspaper articles in the Chignecto Post, May-July, 1883 (not seen).

5. NESBIT, D. M., et al. "Tide Marshes of the United States." U. S. Dept. Agric., Misc. Spec. Rept. No. 7, 33–61, 1885.

6. EATON, F. H. "The Bay of Fundy Tides and Marshes." Pop. Sci. Mo., XLIII, 250–256, 1893.

7. CHALMERS, ROBERT. "Report on the Surface Geology of New Brunswick, Northwestern Nova Scotia, and a Portion of Prince Edward Island." Geol. Surv. Can., Ann. Rept., N. Ser., VII, 125M–133M, 1895.

8. TRUEMAN, G. J. "The Marsh and Lake Region at the Head of Chignecto Bay." Nat. Hist. Soc. New Brunswick, Bull., IV, 93–104, 1899.

9. GANONG, W. F. "The Vegetation of the Bay of Fundy Salt and Dyked Marshes: an Ecological Study." Bot. Gazette, XXXVI, 161–186, 280–302, 349–367, 429–455, 1903.

10. MUDGE, B. F. "The Salt Marsh Formations of Lynn." Essex Inst., Proc., II, 117–119, 1858.

11. DAVIS, C. A. "Peat Deposits as Geological Records." Mich. Acad. Sci., 10th Rept., 107–112, 1908.

    BASTIN, E. S., and DAVIS, C. A. "Peat Deposits of Maine." U. S. Geol. Surv., Bull. 376, 127 pp., 1909.

    DAVIS, C. A. "Some Evidences of Recent Subsidence on the New England Coast." Sci., N. Ser., XXXII, 63, 1910.

    DAVIS, C. A. "Salt Marshes, a Study in Correlation." Assoc. Amer. Geog., I, 139–143, 1911.

    DAVIS, C. A. "Origin and Formation of Peat." U. S. Bur. of Mines, Bull. 38, 165–186, 1913.

    DAVIS, C. A. "Salt Marsh Formation near Boston and its Geological Significance." Econ. Geol., V, 623–639, 1910.

12. JOHNSON, D. S., and YORK, H. H. "The Relation of Plants to Tide Levels." Carnegie Institution of Washington, Pub. No. 206, 162 pp., Washington, 1915.

13. HARSHBERGER, J. W. "An Ecological Study of the New Jersey Strand Flora." Phil. Acad. Nat. Sci., Proc. for 1900, 623–671, 1901.

    HARSHBERGER, J. W. "Additional Observations on the Strand Flora of New Jersey." Phil. Acad. Nat. Sci., Proc., LIV, 642–669, 1902.

    HARSHBERGER, J. W. "The Vegetation of the Salt Marshes and of the Salt and Fresh Water Ponds of Northern Coastal New Jersey." Phil. Acad. Nat. Sci., Proc., LXI, 373–400, 1909.

14. SMITH, J. B. "The New Jersey Salt Marsh and its Improvement." N. J. Agric. Exp. Sta., Bull. 207, 24 pp., 1907.

15. KEARNEY, T. H. "The Plant Covering of Ocracoke Island: A Study in the Ecology of the North Carolina Strand Vegetation." U. S. Nat. Herb., V, 263–319, 1900.

16. NICHOLS, G. E. "The Vegetation of Connecticut: The Associations of Depositing Areas along the Seacoast." Torrey Bot. Club, Bull., XLVII, 511–548, 1920.

17. PENHALLOW, D. P. "A Contribution to our Knowledge of the Origin and Development of Certain Marsh Lands on the Coast of New England." Roy. Soc. Can., Proc. and Trans., 3rd Ser., I, Sec. 4, 13–56, 1907.

18. NESBIT, D. M., et al. "Tide Marshes of the United States." U. S. Dept. Agric., Misc. Spec. Rept. No. 7, 259 pp., 1885.
19. TOWNSEND, C. W. "Sand Dunes and Salt Marshes," 311 pp., Boston, 1913.
20. MATHER, W. W. "Geology of the First Geological District of New York," 17, Albany, 1843.
21. TOWNSEND, C. W. "Sand Dunes and Salt Marshes," 193, Boston, 1913.
22. SHALER, N. S. "Beaches and Tidal Marshes of the Atlantic Coast." Nat. Geog. Mon. I, 158, 1896.
23. JOHNSON, D. S., and YORK, H. H. "The Relations of Plants to Tide Levels." Carnegie Institution of Washington, Pub. No. 206, 24, Washington, 1915.
24. NICHOLS, G. E. "The Vegetation of Connecticut: The Associations of Depositing Areas along the Seacoast." Torrey Bot. Club, Bull., XLVII, 523, 1920.
25. BARTLETT, H. H. "The Submarine Chamæcyparis Bog at Woods Hole, Massachusetts." Rhodora, XI, 221–235, 1909.
26. SHALER, N. S. "Preliminary Report on Sea-Coast Swamps of the Eastern United States." U. S. Geol. Surv., 6th Ann. Rept., 385, 1886.
27. MITCHELL, HENRY. "On the Reclamation of Tide Lands and its Relation to Navigation." U. S. Coast Surv., Rept. for 1869, Appendix 5, 89, 1872.
28. MITCHELL, HENRY. "On the Reclamation of Tide Lands and its Relation to Navigation." U. S. Coast Surv., Rept. for 1869, Appendix 5, 74–104, 1872.
29. BASTIN, E. S., and DAVIS, C. A. "Peat Deposits of Maine." U. S. Geol. Surv., Bull. 376, 127 pp., 1909.

# CHAPTER XVII

## TIDAL MARSHES OF THE FUNDY TYPE

**Advance Summary.** — The preceding chapter was devoted primarily to the consideration of tidal marshes of the New England type. It now becomes our duty to discuss somewhat fully the second or Fundy type of marsh. After an account of the surface characters of both the wild and dyked Fundy marshes, and an examination of their internal composition and structure, we shall enquire into the source of the silts which constitute most of their bulk, and the reason for the concentration of such large quantities of this material in the head of the Fundy basin. Detailed sections through various marshes will then be presented, to establish more fully the range of variation in composition and depth, and to enable us to develop with greater precision the physical history of the marshes. We shall then indicate briefly the nature of the third or Coastal Plain type of tidal marsh, the further treatment of which must be deferred to a later volume dealing with the Coastal Plain shoreline. The significance of the distribution of the three types of tidal marshes will next be discussed, and certain conclusions derived from tidal marsh studies will then be applied to the problem of progressive coastal subsidence.

**Relation of the Fundy and New England Marsh Types.** — The second type of tidal marsh deposit has its most remarkable development about the head of the Bay of Fundy, and may for convenience be called the " Fundy type." Like the New England type, it is not necessarily confined to the locality from which it derives its name, but may occur wherever the conditions essential for its development are found. Sections through the Fundy type of marsh deposit show it to consist mainly of silt, with only scattered bits of vegetable remains or occasional rare layers of peat. The submergence history is the same for the Fundy as for the New England type of tidal marsh. Upland soils, stumps of trees *in situ*, fresh and brackish water peat beds are found below the salt marsh deposits in the one case as in the other.

The chief difference between the two consists in the fact that the New England type is essentially a deposit of salt marsh peat with variable amounts of silt, whereas the Fundy type is essentially a deposit of silt with variable, but usually small, quantities of vegetable remains.

**Surface Aspect of the Fundy Type of Marsh.** — Turning to a consideration of the present surface aspect of the Fundy marshes, we must distinguish clearly the wild salt marshes unaltered by man's activities, and the reclaimed lands from which " dykes that the hands of the farmer had raised with labor incessant shut out the turbulent tides." The wild marsh is of very limited extent, and usually consists of narrow strips bordering the tidal channels outside the dyked lands. It is distinctly different in appearance from the unreclaimed New England type of marsh, for instead of a close-set growth of salt grasses springing from a dense mat of roots, we find a surface of soft red mud, or dry hard-caked silt, much of it showing bare, with a sparser growth of the marsh vegetation (Fig. 266). These narrow strips show, above the sloping mud flats of the channels exposed at low tide, (according to Chalmers[1] the force of the tides prevents the growth of eel grass), a Glabra zone (" Spartinetum " of Ganong) of very limited breadth, extending from a number of feet below ordinary high water up to that level or slightly above. In the lower part of this zone the *Spartina glabra* occurs in scattered clumps a few square feet in area, called " sedge bogs," while higher up it may give somewhat more extended fringes along the tidal channels. From the vicinity of ordinary high tide nearly to the upper limit of spring tides the Patens zone is represented by what Ganong has called the Staticetum, or Statice-Spartina juncea (patens) association, in which *Spartina patens*, the most abundant grass, is associated with other high-level marsh forms. Where new marsh is forming, an intermediate " Salicornia zone " exists for a time, only to be crowded out by the extension of the Glabra and Patens zones. *Salicornia herbacea* and *Suaeda linearis* here occur in a loose, open formation showing much bare silt between them. For the best account of the characteristic vegetation of these zones on the Fundy marshes the reader should consult Ganong's essay on " The Vegetation of the Bay of Fundy Salt and Dyked Marshes."[2]

**Dyked Marshes of the Fundy Region.** — The dyked marshes include most of the 70,000 to 80,000 acres of marsh and bog land

FIG. 266.   Tidal channel emptying into the Avon estuary near Hantsport, Nova Scotia, seen at low tide.   Photo by J. W. Goldthwait, Geol. Surv. Canada.

which it has been estimated exist about the head of the Bay of
Fundy (Fig. 267).   If a traveller crosses from Sackville on the
northwestern side of the Cumberland region, to Amherst on the
southeast, he will first descend the gentle slope of the western
upland and pass out over the Great Tantramar Marsh.   To the
north, east and south stretches the wonderfully level surface of
the marsh, green with meadow grasses if his visit be made in

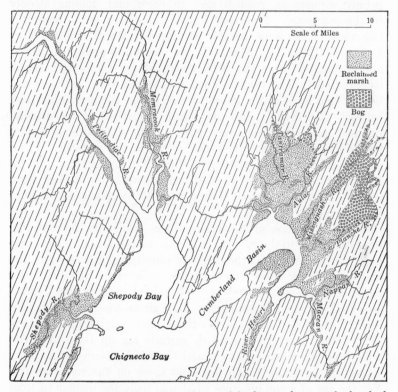

FIG. 267.   Salt marshes, dyked marshes, and freshwater bogs at the head of
the Bay of Fundy.   (After Ganong.)

early summer, and dotted with the great barns (Fig. 270) which
bear witness to the wealth of the plain.   Three miles or more to
the eastward rises the low Fort Cumberland Ridge, here dark
with evergreen forests, there bright with the green of cultivated
fields.   Around the northern end of the marsh the uplands send
smaller spurs out into the plain, the largest of which is the Joli-
cure Ridge.   Flowing southwest to the Cumberland Basin, the

Tantramar and Aulac Rivers drain the marsh at low tide; but when the tide is high in the Basin, the muddy waters pour inland along the deep-cut channels of these streams, unless held in check by a dam, like the " aboideau " on the Aulac.

Crossing the Aulac River, our imaginary traveller reaches the southern end of the Fort Cumberland Ridge. Here he may observe that the ridge-maker consists in part at least of resistant pebbly sandstones, reddish grey in color and dipping steeply to the southeast. From the Fort Cumberland crest there is a fine view of the long, narrow Missaguash Marsh and the Fort Lawrence Ridge (Fig. 269). On the marsh are occasional barns; and through it runs the Missaguash Marsh Company's canal, constructed to lead the silt-laden tide waters into the lakes and bogs at the head of the marsh in order that silt deposition may convert that district into dry land; a method of reclamation pursued successfully in other parts of the Cumberland region, but which has not proven so satisfactory in this instance. From the crest of the Fort Lawrence Ridge the marshes of the La Planche River are in view; and nearly two miles of their level surface must be traversed before the eastern upland at Amherst is reached.

Standing on one of the rocky ridges which jut far out like promontories into the vast sea of green, one cannot but realize that here has been repeated the essential physiographic history of the Narragansett or Bras d'Or lowlands. The same parallel rocky ridges are present, eroded on beds folded in the same general sense. The same submergence has given an irregular rocky coast, with projecting linear headlands and outlying linear islands (Fig. 269). But the sea which spreads far up the submerged valleys is here a sea of green, and the wind sets in motion only waves in the grass, which leave no trace on the rocky shores. Yet the sea of green occupies what was truly the domain of tidal waters, and the submergence was as real here as in the Narragansett or Bras d'Or embayments. The great difference is that here, *pari passu* with the submergence, the encroaching waters deposited silts up to the high tide level, and man later dyked out the sea from the bays of red mud and turned them into vast fresh grass meadows.

Over the great expanse of green the eye may scan the horizon without encountering any prominent obstacle save the great barns (Fig. 270) which are so characteristic a feature in the land-

scape of the dyked lands.   No trees interrupt the view, and no
human habitations.   At infrequent intervals a road or a railway
stretches a narrow ribbon straight across the grassy plain; but
for the most part, only the grass-covered dykes (Fig. 268), the
numerous drainage ditches, and an occasional river, winding clear
and green-bordered where the tides are shut out, but red between
muddy banks when open to the sea, vary the pleasing monotony
of the level surface of waving grass.   In this region one may see
ten times as much dyked salt marsh as is found along the entire
Atlantic coast of the United States.

FIG. 268.   Reclaimed marshland at head of Bay of Fundy, near Sackville,
showing dyke bordering tidal channel, and barns on the dyked marsh.

**Solidity of the Fundy Marsh Deposits.** — The solidity of the
Fundy type of marsh is in striking contrast with the " springy "
character of the New England type.   With only subordinate
quantities of vegetable remains incorporated in it, the silt becomes very compact.   Even the low, wet flats near the sea,
covered much of every day by the tides, offer no serious impedi-
ments to one equipped with boots and not opposed to lifting a
goodly quantity of mud at every step.   Under these conditions
one may safely examine the submerged forests (Fig. 272) at the
head of the bay, thirty feet or more below the high tide level.
The wild salt marshes at high tide level, just outside the dykes,
are firmer still, and except during the periods of spring tides, may
be baked dry and cracked open by the sun.   Here with much

difficulty one forces a peat sampler into the deposit to secure a section illustrating its composition.

Most solid of all are the dyked areas. No ordinary upland soil could seem firmer, and one can understand the objection raised locally against applying the term " marsh " to lands so hard and dry.[3] Only at the expense of patient labor, extracting with difficulty one small core after another, could I sound the marsh deposits with the sampling device, so solidly do they become compacted when allowed to dry and settle. Doubtless this settling accounts for the fact that the Fundy marshes, instead of being slightly above the level of mean high water as is normally the case for undyked marshes along the Atlantic coast, are from one to three feet below that level as determined by the engineers of the Baie Verte Canal.[4] Both dykes and marshes are submerged by exceptional storm tides, the waters during the great Saxby storm of October, 1869, rising from 9 to 10 feet above the plane of mean high water, and covering the dykes by several feet, with a depth of 10 to 13 feet on the marshes.

**Natural Levees and Bog Lands.** — As should be expected where tidal currents deposit much sediment, the Fundy marshes are higher near the tidal rivers and creeks, and lower between them or along the inner edge of the plain bordering the upland. In these low areas are lakes, fresh water swamps, and bogs, which correspond to the back-swamps found along the inner edge of a mature river's floodplain next to the upland; or between the distributaries of a river on its delta. In both cases the more rapid deposition of somewhat coarser material where the waters first spread outward from the stream channel during flood time, operates to build that portion of the tidal deposit or river floodplain highest, forming natural levees having slopes too faint to attract the eye, but quite sufficient to check flowing water. The drainage from the adjacent upland, and that resulting from rainfall on the aggrading plain, unable to flow up the levees and reach the streams to which they are naturally tributary, accumulate in the lowland between two levees or between levees and upland. Similarly, the tidal sediments are apt to attain their maximum thickness some distance downstream (although not at the mouth of a narrowing channel which causes tides to rise higher upstream) rather than near the heads of tidal rivers; with the result that lakes, swamps, and bogs will form in the broad valley heads as well as along their sides. Such seem to be the ways in which

FIG. 269. Looking eastward over the Missaguash Marsh (light strip just beyond trees), from the Fort Cumberland Ridge. Beyond the belt of marshland the Fort Lawrence Ridge is visible.

were created the bog lands estimated by Monro in 1883 to cover 8700 acres on the inner borders of the marshes at the head of the Cumberland Basin alone.

**Reclamation of Bog Lands.** — These bog lands were formerly much more extensive than now, for their reclamation has long been in process by the method of admitting sediment-laden tidal waters along canals and ditches to overflow the low areas and thus bury the bog under a thick layer of fertile red silt. At the time of my examination great areas of bog still existed along the upper portions of the La Planche and Missaguash embayments (Fig. 267), and a view from the neighboring upland showed here and there the typical scenery of the bog land with its trees and shrubs, quite different from the grassy dyked lands of the true tidal marsh deposit. Much of the bog is of the floating type, while ponds and lakes are numerous, especially along the northeastern margins next to the upland (Fig. 267), a relation which Ganong[5] explains as the result of prevalent southwest winds creating on the northeast shores of the lake a surf unfavorable to the development of bog vegetation.

*Fictitious Indications of Coastal Subsidence.* — When for purposes of reclamation tidal waters are turned upon the bog, the vegetation is killed, the bog deposit is compressed and sinks, and the marine silts are deposited upon it. It is not difficult to see that this same process would be repeated if bog or swamp were flooded naturally by a break in the levees or by overflow of storm tides; and that it would give a deposit of fresh water peat under marine silts without the intervention of any relative change in the level of land and sea.

**Buried Peat Bogs and Stumps due to Veritable Progressive Submergence.** — On the other hand, where there has been a real progressive submergence causing the tidal marshes to encroach gradually upon the upland, as is clearly the case in the Fundy region, we must not be surprised to find beds of fresh water peat below the marsh silts to depths nearly equivalent to the amount of the submergence; for during all stages of the submergence bogs may have persisted near the upland border; and their burial under the encroaching marsh to give a peat bed mantling over the irregular rocky floor is just as normal as the burial of the upland forest. Indeed, the bogs, rising on the flanks of the upland as submergence progresses, invade the forest, kill the trees, and bury the stumps; and in turn are encroached upon and buried by the rising tidal silts. Both stumps and peat beds have repeatedly been found in excavations through the Fundy marshes, as have also beds of sand and clay presumably deposited, in part at least, in the ponds and lakes of the bog zone.

**Character of the Marsh Silts.** — As a rule the fresh silt of the Fundy marshes shows red or buff tints, because the iron which determines its color is present in an oxidized form; but layers of blue or grey silt are formed locally near the surface, especially in poorly drained areas, and are present in considerable thickness in the depth of the marshes. Dawson[6] thus describes the manner in which the blue or grey silt is formed in the marsh deposits at the head of the Bay of Fundy: " The chemical composition of this singular soil, so unlike the red mud from which it is produced, involves some changes which are of interest both in agriculture and geology. The red marsh derives its color from the peroxide of iron. In the grey or blue marsh the iron exists in the form of a sulphuret, as may easily be proved by exposing a piece of it to a red heat, when a strong sulphurous odor is exhaled, and the red color is restored. The change is produced by the action of the animal and vegetable matters present in the mud. These in their decay have a strong affinity for oxygen, by virtue of which they decompose the sulphuric acid present in the sea water in the forms of sulphate of magnesia and sulphate of lime. The sulphur thus liberated enters into combination with hydrogen obtained from the organic matter or from water, and the product is sulphuretted hydrogen, the gas which gives to the mud its unpleasant smell. This gas dissolved in the water which permeates the mud enters into combination with the oxide of iron, producing a sulphuret of iron, which with the remains of the organic matter, serves to color the marsh blue or grey. The sulphuret of iron remains unchanged while submerged or water soaked, but when exposed to the atmosphere the oxygen of the air acts upon it, and it passes into sulphate of iron or green vitriol — a substance poisonous to most cultivated crops, and which when dried or exposed to the action of alkaline substances deposits the hydrated brown oxide of iron. Hence the bad effects of disturbing blue marsh, and hence also the rusty color of the water flowing from it. The remedies for this condition of the soil are draining and liming. Draining admits air and removes the saline water; lime decomposes the sulphate of iron and produces sulphate of lime and oxide of iron, both of which are useful substances to the farmer."

Analyses of red and blue silts from the Bay of Fundy marshes will be found in Dawson's " Acadian Geology,"[7] in the essays by Trueman[8] and Ganong[2] previously cited, and in papers by Shutt,[9] quoted in part by Ganong. The physical properties of the marsh silts especially as affecting their fertility, are discussed by Ganong,[10] who emphasizes their remarkable uniformity of composition and fineness of grain. According to his investigations the silts consist chiefly of fine siliceous sand (too fine for the naked eye to distinguish individual grains), with an average of about 10 per cent of clay, and very little organic matter. Despite the dryness and compactness of the silts underlying reclaimed marshes of this type in the Bay of Fundy region, along the Delaware Bay shores, and elsewhere, I found it possible, because of the fineness of the silts, to operate in them to some depth with a sampler (Fig. 248) designed for use in soft deposits of peat.

**Source of the Silts.** — The source of the silts in the Bay of Fundy region is doubtless to be found in the relatively weak red sandstones and shales (Carboniferous, Permian and Triassic) which border and presumably underlie the Fundy lowland, and to the ready removal of which by subaërial agencies the lowland owes its existence. When the land was submerged the encroaching sea must have found ready to hand on the floor of the lowland a large amount of red detritus, partly in the form of glacial débris representing pre-glacial soils and alluvium scraped from the lowland areas, and partly more recent alluvial deposits along the stream courses. As the sea worked over this material, part of it was doubtless carried out to deep water; but a large part was always shifted towards the head of the embayment by tidal currents, and there deposited during slack water.

**Reason for the Great Volume of the Silts.** — Continued subsidence caused the sea to rework and shift northward the tidal deposits as well as the subaërial deposits, with the result that we find at the present head of the Bay of Fundy, particularly in its two major branches known as the Basin of Minas and Chignecto Bay (Fig. 267), material from the entire lowland repeatedly shifted northward from successive heads of the Bay as the land sank. Thus may we reasonably account for the enormous quantity of silts represented in these extensive marsh deposits. The waves eroding the rocky shores about the present margins of the embayment add their contributions to the silts today, just as they did

FIG. 270.  Dyked marshes at head of Bay of Fundy, near Sackville.    Drainage ditch in foreground, barns in distance.

at all lower levels during the past; tidal scour of bottom deposits must also be effective, whether or not the bedrock bottom be affected by this agency; and to the present rivers we may credit a small contribution. But to look to present conditions alone for an explanation of the great silt deposits of the Fundy marshes is to ignore the most effective factor in their formation, — progressive submergence of a comparatively narrow lowland under circumstances favoring constant accumulation of tidal deposits in the headward portion of the advancing embayment.

**Quantity of Silt Carried in Suspension by Tidal Waters.** — The red, silt-laden tidal waters of the Bay of Fundy afford an impressive illustration of this agent of transportation and deposition; while the red tidal creeks with their red muddy banks, add a striking element to Acadian scenery. The amount of sediment in the water is less than appears, Ganong[11] finding from 2 per cent to 4 per cent as the maximum figures for different stages of tides in the rivers at the head of the Bay; yet this is enough to produce a rapid silting up of the bay heads. In 1887, when the old wooden bridge across the Avon River at Windsor was being replaced by a steel structure, Murphy[12] found that a thickness .of 30 inches of silt was deposited in one of the steel cylinders of the substructure in a period of 122 days, while Chalmers[1] reports that it is not uncommon for a single tide to lay down an inch or more at certain spots along the river banks. Advantage is taken of this fact by the farmers, who renew the fertility of long dyked areas, and reclaim for agriculture lakes, fresh water swamps, and bogs near the inner borders of the salt marsh, by admitting the tides and allowing them to deposit a thickness of from a few inches to several feet of the fertile red silt. According to Ganong[11] the deposit from a single tide may amount to several inches on the bottom of a lake thus connected with the sea.

**Depth and Composition of the Marsh Deposits.** — The depth of the Fundy marsh deposits and their general composition can best be illustrated by a few type sections. At Aulac Station on the Great Tantramar Marsh (Fig. 267) the maximum depth of 80 feet of marsh mud underlain by 20 feet of fresh water peat was encountered in a well boring made by the engineers of the Intercolonial Railway. According to Chalmers[13] the exceptionally great depth at this point is due to extensive faulting of the rock floor in post-glacial time; but the facts presented to substantiate such faulting seem open to a different interpretation.

*Tantramar Marsh.* — Our party secured the following section of the Tantramar marsh deposit in a boring through the Dixon Island reclaimed marsh near Sackville, (Fig. 270), the boring being made about 200 feet from the upland and 100 feet from the river:

*Feet*

Hard, dry red silt with few vegetable remains except grass roots
at top, partly *Spartina glabra*............................... 2
Reddish grey silt with some roots of *Spartina patens* (?) and
*Spartina glabra*....................................... 2
Blue clayey silt with roots and fragments of *Spartina glabra*...... 1
Red silt nearly free from vegetable remains.................. 2
Dark blue to black silt, with few remains of vegetation.......... 4
Tenaceous blue-black clay with more abundant vegetable re-
mains.................................................. 1
Dark brown fresh water peat............................. 1

This marsh had been dyked for over 100 years, and its surface was about $2\frac{1}{2}$ feet lower than the level of the wild marsh outside the dyke.

*Missaguash Marsh.* — A section through the Missaguash Marsh (Fig. 269), about 1 mile northeast of the village of Pt. de Bute, gave the following sequence:

*Feet*

Ploughed surface soil containing moss fragments.............. .5
Reddish silt with roots and fragments of grasses, quite dry...... 3.5
Reddish silt with little vegetable matter, usually wet........... 3
Reddish-black silt free from vegetable remains............... 1.5
Black silt, some layers firm and sandy, others soft, especially
the bottom layer...................................... 5

What appeared to be solid bottom was encountered at a depth of $13\frac{1}{2}$ feet. The marshes were fresh here at the time of our visit, and fresh grasses grew well down the inner sides of the canal which contained fresh water.

*Fort Lawrence Locality.* — Near the southern end of the Fort Lawrence Ridge, where a shifting tidal stream has stripped away the marsh silts to reveal the old submerged forest of the classic locality (Fig. 272) first described by Dawson,[14] we found the following section exposed in the sloping bank (Fig. 271):

*Feet*

Red silt with marsh grasses at surface...................... 4–8
Blue clayey silt with few vegetable remains................. 12–20
Old forest soil with hundreds of stumps, some prostrate logs
and branches, leaf mold, and fern roots.................. 1–2
Thin layers of white sand............................... 1
Red sandstones............................ Rock bottom (?)

Thicknesses in this section are estimated, and may omit other strata concealed under the coating of wet clayey red silt.

Two sections at the Fort Lawrence dock, near the site of this submerged forest, are reported by Chalmers. The first was located close to the upland of the Fort Lawrence Ridge (Fig. 269), near the thinning inner edge of this particular portion of the marsh, and showed in descending order:

|  | *Feet* | *Inches* |  |
|---|---|---|---|
| Marsh mud, reddish............... | 2 | 11 | |
| Marsh mud, bluish-grey............ | | 9 | |
| Marsh mud, greyish............... | 1 | 8 | full of roots. |
| Marsh mud, bluish................ | 2 | 10 | with roots. |
| Marsh mud, dark grey and bluish..... | 1 | 8 | full of roots and stems. |
| Gravel, sand, and clay............. | 1 | 11 | partially stratified, with roots. |
| Boulder clay..................... | 40+ | | with striated boulders. |

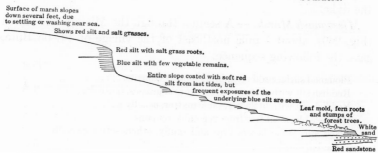

FIG. 271.   Section of Fundy marshes at the Fort Lawrence "submerged forest" locality.

The second section from the same region was located farther out in the marsh, where it was deeper, and showed the following:

|  | *Feet* |  |
|---|---|---|
| Marsh mud................ | 12–15 | with roots and stems. |
| Marsh mud, grey......... | 5–10 | stratified, with marine shells. |
| Clay (stratified) blue........ | 5–6 | with abundant molluscan fauna. |
| Fresh water peat........... | 1–2 | with stumps of forest trees. |
| Clay, reddish-blue.......... | 1 or less, | partially stratified above, changing to boulder clay below. |
| Boulder clay ............. | unknown, | with large glaciated boulders. |

The color of the marsh mud at the top of the second section is not stated, but is doubtless red, in part at least. Chalmers points out that the Fort Lawrence forest bed, represented in his first section by the dark grey and bluish marsh mud full of roots and stems, and in the second by the peat layers with stumps of forest trees, slopes downward from the upland ridge toward the Cumberland Basin at the rate of 20 feet in 300 feet, so as to lie 30 feet below the marsh surface in the vicinity of the second section. In both these cases the forest bed rests on a thin layer of clay or sand passing below into the glacial boulder clay which mantles the bedrock formation.

*Sunken Island Bog.* — To test the internal structure of one of the bog areas, Dr. Barton of our party made a series of twelve borings from west to east across Sunken Island. This is a large mossy bog covered with small trees (usually 15 to 20 feet high) and shrubs, and showed quite uniformly, beneath the surface covering of vegetation, 8 to 10 feet of peat, so very soft that no cores could be secured. Beneath this soft peat or muck, probably largely of fresh water origin, was usually found a deposit of red silt 2 to 4 feet thick, sometimes containing black particles of decaying vegetation which gave to some specimens a blackish hue; but toward the eastern side of the bog the peat rested directly on sandy bottom. That marine conditions prevailed from time to time in parts at least of the bog area, is shown not only by the presence of the silts, but also by the fact that remains of *Spartina patens* and *Spartina glabra* were encountered in various borings, usually at depths of 8 to 11 feet. Doubtful remains of *Juncus gerardi* were also observed 8 to 10 feet deep in two sections. The greatest depth attained in the bog area was 14 feet, near the western side. East of the bog a boring showed 9 feet of red and blue silt in alternating layers, with one compact peat layer in the midst and a decayed log at the bottom resting on sand.

**Physical Evolution of the Fundy Marshes.** — It is obvious from the foregoing sections that the Fundy marshes, like those of the New England type, were deposited during a progressive submergence of the coast in post-glacial time. The red silts encroached upon the forested upland to kill the trees and entomb their stumps; but not rapidly enough to bury standing trees. In valleys partly silted up there was occasionally opportunity for marsh or swamp peat to form before freer access of the silt-laden waters again continued the silting-up process. Other areas remained under the rule of fresh water to the present period, showing nothing but fresh peat above, with the red or blue marine silt below. Into some of these latter areas man has recently re-introduced the silty waters by means of canals, killing and burying the bog under a modern layer of the red sediment. That the silt-filled valleys of this region were never occupied by the open waters of the sea, as some observers have believed, is evidenced not only by the general history of the marsh development already traced, but locally by the fact that the slopes of the ridges show no indications of geologically recent cliffing due to wave action, and by the presence of submerged forests and forest soil in exposed positions like that at the southern end of the Fort Lawrence Ridge, where wave action would have destroyed both had they been subjected to the attack of the sea.

**Fort Lawrence Submerged Forest.** — The submerged forest at Fort Lawrence is a most impressive spectacle. Dropping over the cliffed upper edge of the marsh deposit (Fig. 271), our party ploughed through the tenaceous red mud and the sticky blue clay, down the long slope toward low tide level. Below the clay zone, in a belt of scattered boulders, gravel, and sand, we found the object of our muddy trip, numberless stumps of a once imposing forest (Fig. 272). The Atlantic coast furnishes no finer example of submerged stumps than this. Looking back to the upper edge of the marsh above us, we obtained a realizing sense of how far were we below the level of the ocean at high tide; yet here we were in the midst of a forest of young saplings and sturdy trees, under our feet was the old forest soil, and about us were prostrate logs and clumps of ferns. So vivid was the impression, it required an effort to realize that the forest was only a forest of stumps, and the ferns mere blackened masses of root stocks embedded in the decayed leaf mold of a woodland so ancient that its age must be computed in thousands of years.

There could be no doubt that the stumps were in their original position on the lower slopes of the Fort Lawrence Ridge. Here, as throughout this whole region, forests of spruce, hemlock, birch, alder, ash, elm and other trees, covering the ridges and valleys of the maturely dissected and glaciated Carboniferous Lowland, were gradually killed and buried, during post-glacial time, by the encroaching silt of the Fundy marshes as the land sank or the sealevel rose. Numerous engineering enterprises throughout the region, including well borings, excavations for docks, the digging

FIG. 272. Submerged forest of the Fort Lawrence locality at the head of the Bay of Fundy, photographed at low tide. When the tide is high the stumps, rooted in place, are covered by 30 feet of salt water.

of canals, and various operations of marsh reclamation, have abundantly proven the presence of upland forest remains resting on solid bottom at various depths below the marsh silts.

**Depths of Submerged Stumps.** — The photograph of the submerged forest just described was taken some 30 feet below the surface of the adjacent marsh, beneath which the buried stumps undoubtedly continue. They were encountered in the Fort Lawrence dock excavations 30 feet below marsh level; and 35 feet below at the mouth of the Petitcodiac estuary.[15] Thus reliable observations confirm the submergence of upland forest covering a very irregular land area to depths as great as 35 feet or more below high tide; while the Aulac boring, if correctly reported and not related to post-glacial faulting, gives us one record of 80 feet. Trueman's[16] figure of 150 feet for the depth of the marsh mud is apparently based on an inaccurate report of the depth of the Aulac boring.[17] As the tidal range may have increased as progressive subsidence brought the ocean waters farther and farther into the Fundy embayment, the figures given above do not necessarily imply so great a change in the relative level of land and sea; but the difference cannot have been appreciable, since the tides must have had a great range when they first reached these forests, located as they are well up in the head of the embayment.

**Other Marshes of the Acadian Region.** — Tidal marsh deposits believed to be of the Fundy type, some dyked and some not, occur in other branches of the Bay of Fundy than those indicated in Fig. 267, as for example the Annapolis Basin. But their most perfect development is found about the two principal bayhead branches, the Basin of Minas and Chignecto Bay; and more particularly at the head of that subdivision of the latter known as the Cumberland Basin. Northward I have not made sufficient study of the marshes to speak with assurance, but Ganong[18] reports that " the ordinary marshes " are abundant about the Gulf of St. Lawrence.

In the Shemogue marshes north of Baie Verte, several sections revealed six inches to a foot of the present salt marsh grass roots and soft muck, underlain by an unknown depth of red clayey silt, somewhat like that of the Fundy region, but so sandy that I could penetrate it to a depth of but four feet, with a defective sampler which refused to work in the presence of so much grit. Submerged stumps are a prominent feature in these marshes, and are well exposed in the banks of tidal creeks. The marshes bordering

Kouchibouguet River, farther west, gave very different sections. Under the surface layer of present salt marsh grasses were found four feet of a dark brown peat containing decayed wood and resembling fresh water peat, but showing also remains of the grass *Spartina patens* in the midst of the deposit. Below the peat the sampler stopped in a fine, light grey sand. It remains to be shown to just what extent the soft sandstones bordering Northumberland Strait yield enough sediment to make silts transported by tidal currents the dominant element in marsh building. According to Chalmers[19] the rivers here bring in so much sediment that the harbors are silting up; and this same observer[20] describes the marshes as consisting of silt covered by a thick mat of roots of grasses.

At the head of the southeast arm of St. Simons Inlet, Shippegan Harbor, Goldthwait found the following section near the inner edge of a marsh surrounding stumps of trees apparently just within reach of high tides:

|  | *Inches* |
|---|---|
| Black, woody peat surrounding dead stumps | 6 |
| Brown salt marsh peat with roots and root stocks of *Spartina* | 6 |
| Greenish-grey silt, more sandy below | 6 |
| Red sand | 12 |

This section is interpreted by Goldthwait to indicate that a salt marsh was for a time encroached upon by an advancing fresh water bog, which in turn was recently killed by a local rise of the high tide surface.

On the western side of this same Inlet head, where a " typical *glabra* marsh " borders a meandering tidal creek, Goldthwait found this succession of deposits:

|  | *Inches* |
|---|---|
| Brown salt marsh peat with *Spartina glabra* root stocks | 10 |
| Blue sandy silt containing shells | 18 |
| Brown salt marsh (?) peat | 2 |
| Blue sandy silt | 3 |
| Dark brown to black earthy fresh water peat containing fragment of birch bark | 21 |
| Coarse red sand | 6 |

This section is quite reminiscent of the usual New England type deposit. About the margins of the marsh dead trees and many stumps testified to a recent encroachment of the salt water. As in the New England marshes previously described, such encroachment is no proof of a veritable subsidence of the coast or general rise of sealevel, but may result from local fluctuations of tide level.   So also the reported occurrence of marsh turf exposed at low tide is easily explained as a local phenomenon where heavy beaches driven back upon salt marshes (Fig. 273) compress the yielding marsh deposits and force them to a low level.   These and other fictitious evidences of subsidence in Acadia have been analyzed by Goldthwait.[23]

It will be seen that while the foregoing examples of marsh sections north of the Fundy region present no novel relations, they do not indicate a marked predominance of either the New

Fig. 273.  Thrum Cap Beach, near Yarmouth, Nova Scotia, showing advance of cobblestone bar over salt marsh.  Photo by J. W. Goldthwait, Geol. Surv. Canada.

England or Fundy type of deposit.   Further study of the internal structure of these northern marshes might yield more decisive results.

## The Coastal Plain Type of Tidal Marsh

The third type of tidal marsh deposit is abundantly developed along the Atlantic Coastal Plain from Virginia to Georgia, and may conveniently be called the Coastal Plain type.   It is largely covered with *Spartina glabra* instead of *Spartina patens*, and glabra remains predominate in the salt marsh deposits. These consist of bluish-grey silt or clay 10 to 20 feet deep, while true salt peat is found only locally. Thus the Coastal Plain type differs markedly from the New England type. It is closely related to the Fundy type; but the relative abundance of vegetable remains in the deposits, the different character of the silt, and the strikingly different surface aspect of the Coastal Plain marshes perhaps justify us in placing them in a separate class. Like the two more northern types, the southern type of deposit is sometimes found overlying layers of fresh peat; while up the rivers fresh tidal marshes replace the salt, and 10 to 20 feet of fresh peat, clay, and clayey fresh peat appear in the sections.

The detailed study of these southern marshes will engage our attention when we come to consider the physiographic development of the Coastal Plain shoreline in a later volume.

### Significance of the Distribution of Tidal Marsh Types

The distribution of the different types of tidal marshes appears to be significant of differing conditions on the mainland. From Georgia to New Jersey the Coastal Plain type of silt deposit is the rule, although exceptions occur, as near Beaufort where a *Spartina patens-Juncus gerardi* marsh shows 7 feet of salt peat below the surface. New Jersey is a debatable ground where the Coastal Plain and New England types of deposit are more or less intimately associated. But from New York to the Bay of Fundy the New England type of salt peat deposit prevails, to be replaced by the Fundy type of silt deposit about the shores of the great embayment from which the type takes its name.

South of New Jersey the rivers gather much sediment from the weak coastal plain beds, and as a rule are not compelled to drop this load in lakes such as characterize the glaciated regions farther north. Consequently they reach the sea with a heavy burden of silt. The silt-laden waters seem less favorable to the dense, matted growth of salt grasses than do the clearer waters farther north; in any case they prevent the formation of salt peat, by building upward to high tide level a deposit consisting largely of silt.

North of New Jersey the rivers traverse for the most part regions of more resistant rock, from which they gather a less abundant load; and much of what they do gather is dropped in the lakes and swamps of the glaciated regions. Crosby's studies[21] of the Charles River, Massachusetts, are significant in this connection. Rivers of the glaciated region, therefore, generally reach the sea comparatively clear, do not contribute enough sediment to interfere with the most luxurious growth of the salt marsh grasses, and add comparatively little to the bulk of the upbuilding salt marsh deposits, which accordingly consist to an unusual extent of the roots and other remains of marsh grasses. Some silt is brought from the outer shores by incoming tides, enough to give a heavy percentage of silt in parts of the deposits, but not enough to destroy their special nature except locally.

The Bay of Fundy region lies in the glaciated belt; but it occupies a lowland of weak red sandstones and shales. And while today the relatively small drainage from the lowland rocks does not contribute greatly to the silt accumulation in the Bay, the tides appear to have worked over and pushed headward up the Bay the joint contributions of rivers, glaciers and waves of earlier times. Hence we find in this embayed weak-rock lowland, silt-laden tidal waters which operate much as do those far south along the Atlantic Coastal Plain. The salt grass growths are not luxurious, or are even wholly lacking over areas where the tidal muds are constantly shifting; and before the vegetation can add greatly to the deposit, the silts have built up the surface to the high tide limit.

In the physical conditions of the bordering lands, therefore, we seem to find a reasonable explanation for the fact that on the Atlantic coast we have two regions of silt marsh deposits separated by a region of salt peat deposits.

## Tidal Marshes and the Problem of Submergence

**Maximum Depth of Marshes does not Indicate Total Amount of Submergence.** — It must fully be appreciated that even the maximum depth of the marshes as observed today does not necessarily record more than a small part of the submergence which made possible their development. Only the inner, shallower parts of the marsh belt are preserved. The waves have largely destroyed their seaward, deeper portions as progressive submergence gradually brought the exposed margins more and more effectively within their reach. Here and there stumps dredged from harbor bottoms, or peat preserved under sediments on the seabottom, give evidence of the former continuation, outward and downward, of the formerly forested upland and the marshes which encroached upon it. But for the most part we can only speculate on the depth to which these features were once developed. We know it exceeded 20 feet along the New England shore, and perhaps 30 feet in the Bay of Fundy region; with every possibility that the excess may be very great.

**Progressive Submergence the Last Important Movement Along the North Atlantic Coast.** — The tidal marshes seem to indicate submergence as the last important movement along the New England-Acadian coast. Had there been a recent emergence, it should be recorded by uplifted salt marsh deposits, by a general encroachment of fresh marsh upon salt marsh, and by other phenomena which seem to be absent from this coast. The wedge of *Spartina patens* peat encroaching on fresh marsh and upland, shows that for a long time past whatever movement of the strand line occurred has been in the opposite direction. If the data assembled by Daly[22] constitute valid evidence of a general downward movement of the sealevel, such movement must have antedated the formation of the marshes. As these reached their present level several thousand years ago, according to evidence which we shall critically analyze in a later volume, and as their formation doubtless required some thousands of years, it would seem that any negative eustatic shift of sealevel affecting the Atlantic coast must have taken place a number of thousands of years ago. It would also appear that the shift must have been at least more than double the 20 feet which mark the present elevation of the supposed abandoned strand; for since the negative movement, a positive movement of more than 20 feet has occurred, as recorded in the marshes, leaving out of account the less conclusive evidence in favor of a still more extensive submergence during the marsh period. Thus the supposed negative shift would approximately double, perhaps much more than double, the volume of displaced water to be accounted for in Daly's hypothesis.

**Résumé.** — Our study of the Fundy type of tidal marsh has shown us that superficially it differs from the New England type, previously considered, in the greater extent of mud flats, the sparser growths of marsh vegetation, and in certain aspects of the plant associations; while in depth the Fundy type reveals a great thickness of red and blue silts with comparatively small amounts of vegetable remains, instead of the salt marsh peat so characteristic of the New England marsh deposits. The vast extent of the dyked and reclaimed marshes of the Fundy region has been noted, and the curious aspect of the upland islands and peninsulas, half buried in the grass-covered marsh silts, has been described. We have seen that the reclaimed " marshes " are as firm and dry as upland soils; that natural levees raise the marshes highest nearest the tidal streams, while fresh water swamps and bogs accumulate in the lower areas between the streams and along the inner edge of the marshes bordering the uplands; and that these fresh water deposits have been encroached upon and buried under the salt marsh silts during a progressive subsidence of the land or rise of sealevel, although the same encroachment on a smaller scale results when artificially or naturally the silt-laden tidal waters are admitted to the low bog areas to transform them into tidal mud flats. The fresh silts of the Fundy region are usually red, due to the presence of iron in the oxidized form, while the reducing action of decaying organic matter gives the blue or grey silts found in depth and in certain poorly drained parts of the marsh surface. As progressive submergence caused the sea to advance farther and farther into the Bay of Fundy depression, the waves found at their disposal large quantities of red débris previously detached from weak sandstones and shales by the action of streams and glaciers. Constant reworking of this material by the waves, and the continual shifting of its finer portions northward to the head of the embayment, there to be deposited when the tidal currents were checked, has given us a great volume of silts in the upper reaches of the present Bay which apparently represents a concentration from the floor of the whole lowland effected during a long period of rising sealevel. The quantity of silt at present carried by the tidal waters, while less in terms of percentage than one might suppose, is shown to be sufficient to cause a deposit from one to a few inches thick in favored localities during a single tide. A study of sections through different parts of the marshes and bogs shows that a total depth of from 15 to 30 feet of silt is not uncommon, while one record of 80 feet has been reported. Remnants of upland forest, sometimes beautifully preserved, are encountered at the base of the silts, as are likewise buried fresh water swamps and bog deposits, both resting on glacial débris. These record in unmistakable manner the gradual submergence of the upland due to a sinking of the land or a rise of the sealevel in post-glacial time. While the maximum depth of the marshes probably does not indicate the maximum amount of submergence, a study of the marshes shows that submergence rather than emergence was the last important change of level along the Atlantic coast of Acadia and the United States.

The Coastal Plain type of tidal marsh differs from the New England type in that it is characteristically covered with *Spartina glabra* rather than with *Spartina patens*, while silts are much more abundant in depth than are beds of salt marsh peat. It differs from the Fundy type in surface vegetation, and in the much greater quantity of vegetation mingled with the silts in depth. Full consideration will be given to these marshes in a later volume, when we come to study the Coastal Plain shoreline. But we have anticipated the further discussion sufficiently to point out that the geographical distribution of the three types of tidal marshes seems to depend in part upon the physiographic character of the adjacent mainland, a glaciated hard-rock upland giving conditions favorable to the development of the New England type of marsh, while a non-glaciated coastal plain or a weak-rock lowland favors the silt marshes of the Coastal Plain and Fundy types.

## BIBLIOGRAPHY

1. CHALMERS, ROBERT. "Report on the Surface Geology of New Brunswick, Northwestern Nova Scotia, and a Portion of Prince Edward Island." Geol. Surv. Can., Ann. Rept., N. Ser., VII, 126M, 1895.
2. GANONG, W. F. "The Vegetation of the Bay of Fundy Salt and Dyked Marshes: An Ecological Study." Bot. Gazette, XXXVI, 161–186, 280–302, 349–367, 429–455, 1903.
3. GANONG, W. F. "The Vegetation of the Bay of Fundy Salt and Dyked Marshes: An Ecological Study." Bot. Gazette, XXXVI, 177, 1903.
4. HIND, H. Y. "The Ice Phenomena and the Tides of the Bay of Fundy." Can. Mo., VIII, 191, 1875.
5. GANONG, W. F. "The Vegetation of the Bay of Fundy Salt and Dyked Marshes: An Ecological Study." Bot. Gazette, XXXVI, 175, 1903.
6. DAWSON, J. W. "Acadian Geology," 2nd Ed., 24, London, 1868.
7. DAWSON, J. W. "Acadian Geology," 2nd Ed., 23, London, 1868.
8. TRUEMAN, G. J. "The Marsh and Lake Region at the Head of Chignecto Bay." Nat. Hist. Soc. New Brunswick, Bull., IV, 93–104, 1899.
9. SHUTT, F. T. "Soil Investigations." Can. Exper. Farms, Rept. of Chemist for 1901, 142–146, 1902.
   SHUTT, F. T. "Marsh, Creek, and Tidal Deposits." Can. Exper. Farms, Rept. of Chemist for 1897, 171–174, 1898.
10. GANONG, W. F. "The Vegetation of the Bay of Fundy Salt and Dyked Marshes: An Ecological Study." Bot. Gazette, XXXVI, 280–285, 1903.

11. GANONG, W. F. "The Vegetation of the Bay of Fundy Salt and Dyked Marshes: An Ecological Study." Bot. Gazette, XXXVI, 170, 1903.
12. MURPHY, M. "The Tides of the Bay of Fundy." Nova Scotian Inst. Nat. Sci., Proc. and Trans., VII, Pt. I, 50, 1888.
13. CHALMERS, ROBERT. "Report on the Surface Geology of New Brunswick, Northwestern Nova Scotia, and a Portion of Prince Edward Island." Geol. Surv. Can., Ann. Rept., N. Ser., VII, 41M, 1895.
14. DAWSON, J. W. "On a Modern Submerged Forest at Fort Lawrence, Nova Scotia." Quart. Jour. Geol. Soc. London, XI, 119–122, 1855. Amer. Jour. Sci., 2nd Ser., XXI, 440–442, 1856.
    DAWSON, J. W. "Acadian Geology," 2nd Ed., 28–30, London, 1868.
15. CHALMERS, ROBERT. "Report on the Surface Geology of New Brunswick, Northwestern Nova Scotia, and a Portion of Prince Edward Island." Geol. Surv. Can., Ann. Rept., N. Ser., VII, 126M–128M, 1895.
16. TRUEMAN, G. J. "The Marsh and Lake Region at the Head of Chignecto Bay." Nat. Hist. Soc. New Brunswick, Bull., IV, 95, 1899.
17. GANONG, W. F. "The Vegetation of the Bay of Fundy Salt and Dyked Marshes: An Ecological Study." Bot. Gazette, XXXVI, 168, 1903.
18. GANONG, W. F. "The Vegetation of the Bay of Fundy Salt and Dyked Marshes: An Ecological Study." Bot. Gazette, XXXVI, 163, 1903.
19. CHALMERS, ROBERT. "Report on the Surface Geology of New Brunswick, Northwestern Nova Scotia, and a Portion of Prince Edward Island." Geol. Surv. Can., Ann. Rept., N. Ser., VII, 124M, 1895.
20. CHALMERS, ROBERT. "Report on the Surface Geology of New Brunswick, Northwestern Nova Scotia, and a Portion of Prince Edward Island." Geol. Surv. Can., Ann. Rept., N. Ser., VII, 125M, 1895.
21. CROSBY, W. O. "A Study of the Geology of the Charles River Estuary and the Formation of Boston Harbor." Rept. Comm. on Charles River Dam, Appendix 7, 345–369, Boston, 1903.
22. DALY, R. A. "A Recent Worldwide Sinking of Ocean-level." Geol. Mag., LVII, 246–261, 1920.
    DALY, R. A. "A General Sinking of Sealevel in Recent Time." Proc. Nat. Acad. Sci., VI, 246–250, 1920.
23. GOLDTHWAIT, J. W. "The Physiography of Nova Scotia." Manuscript copy of a volume to be issued by the Geological Survey of Canada.

# CHAPTER XVIII

## RÔLE OF SHORE ICE IN SHORELINE DEVELOPMENT

**Minor Rôle of Shore Ice.** — In far northern latitudes shore ice may prove to be an important agent of erosion, especially when storm winds drive ice fields against the coast, or storm waves armed with ice blocks attack the margins of the lands. The quantity of rock débris often observed encased in shore ice shows that the latter is likewise by no means a negligible agent of transportation. On the Acadian shores, and still less on the shores of New England, where the great ice fields of the north are lacking, the indications of shore ice erosion are not particularly striking, although one is in danger of underestimating the increased efficiency of wave erosion on these coasts due to the presence of floating ice during part of each year. Nevertheless, it seems to be true in general that along the shores in question the rôle of shore ice is a minor one, and that its contribution to shoreline topography is largely restricted to the heaping up of shore ridges through ice shove, and the incorporation of shore débris in ice masses which may then be floated to more or less distant points, there to deposit their burden on melting.

**Ice Rafting as a Factor of Marsh Development.** — When studying the physiography of New England shores my attention was early directed to the rôle which ice may play in the formation of tidal marsh deposits in northern latitudes. The surfaces of salt marshes in the region in question were sometimes found covered in the spring with thickly scattered patches of sand and gravel. As a rule the patches were small, but their aggregate volume on the surface of a marsh was sometimes large. The oft-observed fact that ice freezes to gravel and even large boulders, and later rafts them upon the shore, suggested ice rafting as the most plausible explanation for the deposits on the marsh. At extraordinarily high tides ice, which along the beaches or on sandy and gravelly shallows had secured a load of this coarse débris, might easily be carried up the tidal creeks and left stranded on the marsh surface, there to contribute, upon melting, a new element to the marsh deposits.

589

Ice rafting is an important means of transporting boulders upon the shores of the St. Lawrence embayment, and has recently been briefly described by Coleman,[1] who does not, however, deal with its effect on marshes.  Chalmers[2] reports the finding of crystalline boulders lying upon the surface of marshes back of the bay bars fringing the north side of Prince Edward Island, a fact which may be explained as the result of recent ice rafting of glacial erratics.  He also describes natural dykes due to ice-shove on the marshes bordering Northumberland Strait.  In the Basin of Minas the amount of débris borne by ice at one time may amount to over three million tons, according to Bancroft;[3] and while this author believes that most of this débris is dropped on the floor of the Basin or carried out into the Bay of Fundy, he thus describes the deposition of ice-borne sediment on the marshes: " The amount of sediment carried by this floating ice is greatly emphasized to one if he watches the melting of some of the ice clumps stranded upon the marsh by an exceptionally high tide.  In one case, the layer of sediment left after the melting of such a stranded cake was six inches thick, and in the midst of the detritus was a boulder of trap rock which weighed over twenty pounds.  Early in the spring the marsh has the appearance of being covered with ant hills, this effect being produced by the melting of these isolated ice cakes, and the deposition of their burden of débris."

In his interesting account of ice phenomena in the Bay of Fundy, Hind[4] estimated that a small ice field in the Avon estuary alone carried 93,750 tons of mud.  This author regards the erosive work of the ice blocks as more important than their constructive effect on the marshes, and even goes so far as to attribute the large size of estuaries of small streams to the removal of vast quantities of material by the floating ice blocks. As there is no necessary relation between the size of a stream and the size of its valley, and very large drowned valleys or estuaries are commonly found at the mouths of insignificant streams in regions where floating ice is not an important factor, as for example in the Chesapeake Bay region, it does not appear that the large size of an estuary can safely be attributed to the agency in question; but we should not lose sight of the fact that the process so graphically described by Hind may locally operate to accomplish more destructive than constructive work.

The preceding observations indicate that ice-rafted sediments may under favorable circumstances contribute materially to tidal marsh deposits. It is possible that sand, gravel, and boulders deposited in this manner may explain the obstacles encountered from time to time when sounding in the marshes with an iron rod or with a peat sampler. That this source of sediment is not of major importance in the New England-Acadian region is evident from the usual surface appearance of our marshes, and from the ease with which most marsh deposits may be penetrated by a rod or by the sampling instrument.

## BIBLIOGRAPHY

1. COLEMAN, A. P. "Physiography and Glacial Geology of Gaspé Peninsula, Quebec." Geol. Surv. Can., Bull. 34, 11, 1922.
2. CHALMERS, ROBERT. "Report on the Surface Geology of New Brunswick, Northwestern Nova Scotia, and a Portion of Prince Edward Island." Geol. Surv. Can., Ann. Rept., N. Ser., VII, 124M, 133M, 1895.
3. BANCROFT, J. AUSTEN. "Ice-Borne Sediments in Minas Basin, N. S." Nova Scotian Inst. Sci., Proc. and Trans., XI, 158–162, 1908.
4. HIND, H. Y. "The Ice Phenomena and the Tides of the Bay of Fundy." Can. Mo., VIII, 189–203, 1875.

# INDEX OF AUTHORS

# INDEX OF AUTHORS

This part of the INDEX includes the names of all authorities mentioned throughout the book.

In some cases, the name of the authority will not be found upon the page noted, — only the number of that authority in the table of *References* at the end of the chapter.

# INDEX OF SUBJECTS

# INDEX OF SUBJECTS